1963

This book m͏ͅ ͏ ͏ k͏

THE DIGNITY OF SCIENCE

THE
DIGNITY OF SCIENCE

Studies in the Philosophy of Science

presented to

WILLIAM HUMBERT KANE, O.P.

EDITED WITH INTRODUCTION

BY

JAMES A. WEISHEIPL, O.P.

in collaboration with

THE THOMIST

AND

THE ALBERTUS MAGNUS LYCEUM

PREFACE BY MICHAEL BROWNE, O.P., S.T.M.

THE THOMIST PRESS

1961

Originally published as a

SPECIAL ISSUE OF

THE THOMIST
Volume XXIV, Nos. 2, 3, & 4
April, July, October
1961

THE DIGNITY OF SCIENCE

WITH

Introduction by JAMES A. WEISHEIPL, O. P.

THE THOMIST PRESS
Printed in U. S. A.

WILLIAM HUMBERT KANE, O. P.

CONTENTS

vii

PART THREE

PHILOSOPHY OF SCIENCE

PART FOUR

SPECIAL PROBLEMS OF SCIENCE

PART FIVE

SOCIOLOGICAL ASPECTS

LETTER OF THE MASTER GENERAL

∽

Roma, (8-48) . . . .

Convento S. Sabina (Aventino)

CASA GENERALIZIA
DELL'ORDINE
DEI FRATI PREDICATORI

It was with great pleasure that we learned of this special occasion to honor the Very Reverend William Humbert Kane, O. P., founder of The Albertus Magnus Lyceum at River Forest, Illinois. We were particularly pleased to hear that this homage on the part of brethren and Sisters of our Order as well as religious of various other Orders and a host of eminent laymen transcended nationalities and provincial boundaries. It is only by cooperative effort among learned men that the sublime ideal of St. Albert the Great can be realized in a troubled world.

No one can view recent developments in atomic physics without grave concern not only for the future of humanity, but also for the very scientists who have merited the respect of their peers and the admiration of the masses and withal have come to feel a certain uneasiness of their own consciences.

Scientists have become accustomed to the adulation of the general public. This adulation, growing with every new discovery, led them to spurn the traditional channels of wisdom, and to close their eyes ever more to the legitimate claims of supernatural religion, moral principles, perennial philosophy, and other elements of culture which contribute to a truly human life. In the nineteenth century certain specialists in a particular branch of physics, chemistry, biology or psychology

xi

were willing to be considered the oracles of all human wisdom. The narrow confines of a specialized branch of natural science, as we know, provided no vantage point. Consequently, whatever could not be comprehended by the specialized principles was misinterpreted, ridiculed or rejected. However, recent developments within many branches of science have shaken these imprudent positions. From the turn of the century to the present day an ever increasing number of scientists have found themselves asking questions which formerly were looked upon by them as purely " philosophical."

Pope Leo XIII saw clearly that all social errors, and consequently a large part of social evils, are ultimately traceable to false philosophical principles. These are as erroneous today as they were in the nineteenth century. Throughout his encyclicals he used the principles of St. Thomas Aquinas, that " prince and master " of all Scholastic doctors, to analyze prevailing thought and to outline the rehabilitation of Christian society. In his immortal encyclical *Aeterni Patris* he observed: " If anyone will but turn his attention to the sad condition of our times, and contemplate thoughtfully the state of things which exists publicly and privately, he will surely perceive that the fertile cause of the evils which actually surround us, or of which we fear the coming, consists in this, that the wicked maxims on divine and human things which have recently sprung from the schools of the philosophers have invaded all classes of society, and are approved by a very great number." [1] Consequently, he urged all Bishops, teachers and students " to restore the illustrious system of St. Thomas Aquinas to its former glory " that the coming generations may nourish themselves " abundantly from those purest streams of wisdom that flow from the Angelic Doctor, as from an inexhaustible and precious fountain." [2] That same pontiff in the year 1880, by his Apostolic Letter *Cum hoc sit*,[3] made and declared Thomas Aquinas, " who ever shone as the sun in his doctrine and virtue," the heavenly patron of all Catholic schools, commending him

[1] AAS, XII (1879), 98.   [2] *Ibid.*, p. 112.   [3] AAS, XIII (1880), 56-59.

especially as the guardian, leader and master of philosophical and theological studies.[4] The call of Pope Pius XI, *Ite ad Thomam*, rings as clear today as it did in 1923 when he addressed *Studiorum Ducem* to the whole Catholic Church.[5]

In more recent times, a deep need was felt by many for a heavenly patron in the natural sciences. In the solemn Decree *Ad Deum* of December 16, 1941, the late Pope Pius XII wrote: " It is no wonder, then, that the universities and the more important Catholic colleges, not only in Italy, but in Germany, France, Hungary, Belgium, Holland, as well as in Spain, America and the Philippine Islands, besides numbers of professors of physics and other natural sciences, at the present time look upon Albert the Great as a beacon shining in a world engulfed in gloom. To make sure of the help of Almighty God in their exacting researches into the world of nature, they eagerly desire to have for their guide and heavenly intercessor him who, even in his own day, when many, puffed up with a hollow science of words, were turning their eyes away from the things of the spirit, has taught us by his example how we should rather mount from the things of earth to the things above." [6] Speaking of the important role played by Our own predecessor, Father Martin S. Gillet, the late Holy Father continues: " It is, therefore, with sentiments of deepest pleasure that we accede to the wish expressed by the Catholic Academicians at their recent convention in Trier, by universities and by other international gatherings of scientists, and brought to Our notice by the Master General of the Order of Friars Preachers, who, on behalf of himself and of the Order over which he presides, adds a fervent plea that We may deign to constitute Saint Albert the Great the heavenly Patron of students of the natural sciences." [7] The Decree *Ad Deum*, constituting Albert the heavenly Patron of those who cultivate the natural sciences, was issued on the

[4] Cf. Letter of Pius XII to Martin Stanislaus Gillet, March 7, 1942. AAS, XXXIV (1942), 89.

[5] AAS, XV (1923), 323.

[6] AAS, XXXIV (1942), 90.

[7] *Ibid.*

tenth anniversary of the Decree *In thesauris sapientiae* by which Pope Pius XI enjoined upon the universal Church the veneration of Saint Albert the Great, Bishop and Confessor, with the additional title of Doctor.[8]

We have watched with paternal concern the growth of The Albertus Magnus Lyceum at the Pontifical Faculty of Philosophy in River Forest, Illinois. Since its small beginnings in the Autumn of 1950 under the inspiration of Father Kane and the support of the Very Reverend Edward L. Hughes, at that time Provincial of the Province of St. Albert the Great, it has grown in wisdom and prestige. This growth has taken place to a great extent under the care of the Very Reverend Edmund J. Marr, Provincial of the Province of St. Albert the Great. We have been particularly pleased to observe the devotion of its members to the solid principles of St. Thomas and St. Albert, and at the same time the concern of its members with vital problems of modern science. Problems such as the relation of Thomistic philosophy to modern science, the foundations and nature of modern science, the true constitution of matter, the biological problem of evolution as distinct from evolutionism, the validity of depth psychology, the influence of physiological and biochemical factors on mental diseases and many other problems, cannot be solved without the mutual cooperation of well trained minds. The Albertus Magnus Lyceum has gradually enlisted the cooperation of Our sons in other Provinces, the cooperation of Our Sisters of various communities, and most important, perhaps, it has enlisted the cooperation of eminent laymen.

We are aware that the inspiration for the Lyceum was due in large measure to the vision and zeal of its founder, Father Humbert Kane. Despite many difficulties and obstacles, he saw the need of cooperation within a specially recognized institute, and he did not falter. It is indeed a happy coincidence that the tenth anniversary of The Albertus Magnus

[8] AAS, XXIV (1932), 5-17.

Lyceum should coincide with the sixtieth anniversary of the birth of its founder.

We take this opportunity to impart our paternal blessing to Father Humbert Kane, on the occasion of his sixtieth birthday, and to The Albertus Magnus Lyceum, founded by him ten years ago. We ask the blessing of St. Thomas Aquinas and of St. Albert the Great for all his associates concerned with problems of philosophy and science.

Given at Rome, from the Convent of Santa Sabina, on the Feast of St. Margaret of Hungary, V. O. P., January 19, 1961.

FR. MICHAEL BROWNE, O. P.
Master General

INTRODUCTION

The Dignity of Science

WHEN the first atomic bomb struck the populous seaport capital of Hiroshima on August 6, 1945, the entire civilized world was profoundly shocked at the horror unleashed by science. Ordinary citizens and international leaders recoiled at the awful potential of the atomic bomb. Science no longer meant the production of useful gadgets, discovery of effective drugs, or development of quicker and better means of communication. It meant something much more, something that affects human consciences and destiny. The moral issues involved in the Hiroshima bombing and in nuclear warfare in general have been widely discussed, sometimes with considerable vehemence. But even apart from the moral issues, it is clear to many today that scientific progress has reached a precarious ledge in its lofty climb. Careful maneuvering along the ledge can indeed lead to still further heights. It is the sight of some new height still to be conquered that urges the scientist, as well as the mountain climber, forward with confident step. But a single misstep at such heights could bring on a landslide or a plunge to final doom. The alternatives are clear, and have been clear since Hiroshima: the possibility of further progress or the annihilation of civilization. Henceforth mankind has to work out its salvation in the shadow of the mushroom cloud.

The successful launching of Sputnik I in October of 1957 threw government departments, military officers, scientists, educators and journalists into panic. Incredible as it seemed, the Soviet Union had overtaken the United States in missile thrust and guidance systems. American prestige dropped, particularly in uncommitted countries; investigations were begun into the so-called " missile lag," and educators hastened to build up the science program in schools of all sizes. Despite the fact that Soviet students of science are thoroughly indoctrinated with the philosophy of Dialectical Materialism, some American educators urged diminishing, and eliminating if possible, courses in the humanities in a frantic effort to produce more trained scientists. The panic instilled by Sputnik I almost obliterated the vision and hope of wiser educators: the molding of a human being, whether he be a theoretician or a technician. Before Sputnik I many educators realized the inherent danger to society and to the individual of excessive specialization, which neglects history, literature, culture, sound philosophy, religion and even ordinary grammar. These educators tried to give potential scientists an appreciation of the real dignity of science through the history of science, the philosophy of science, or a study of the Great Books of mankind. Because of Sputnik I this movement has suffered a temporary set-back. Perhaps after the fear and panic have subsided, there may still be the possibility of educating human beings intelligently devoted to science, rather than technicians unaware of the dignity of their pursuit.

Long before the atom bomb came to the attention of the ordinary man, an important revolution had been taking place within science itself, a theoretical revolution which, in fact, made the atom bomb possible. The story of this transition from the mechanical age of physics to the age of relativity and quantum mechanics has been written many times in this generation. The path which leads from Clerk Maxwell's hypothesis identifying magnetic and luminiferous media to the theories of relativity and quantum was constructed by many experimental and theoretical physicists. It is a path which leaves far behind the assurances of Newtonian solids in a void, the fallacy, as Whitehead called it, of " misplaced concreteness." The transition from classical mechanics to the two principal theories of modern physics, relativity and quantum, had an unsettling effect on philosophers of physical theory. Before the end of the nineteenth century Carl Neumann, Ernst Mach and Karl Pearson had already perceived some of the weaknesses of Newtonian axioms and some of the ambiguities in Newtonian concepts. But they were not willing to reject the basic theory of Newtonian science. Even after Planck's paper of 1900 and Einstein's theory of 1905, theoreticians of science, such as Henri Poincaré and Pierre Duhem, were unwilling to reject Newtonian principles as erroneous. Instead they conceived all scientific theories as conventional constructs and approximations of the truth. A scientific theory may be induced from experimental data; its predictions may be verified in every detail. But, for Poincaré and Duhem, the theory was only one way out of many for interpreting the data; it was an hypothetical approximation. The same data could be interpreted with equal verification by other hypotheses. The irreconcilability of relativity theory and quantum mechanics, as well as the wave and particle theories of light, gave much weight to this interpretation of scientific theory.

Later authors, it is true, have considered Poincaré's interpretation of science and hypothesis to be somewhat naïve and oversimplified, and they have rejected certain details of his conventionalism (*commodisme*). Nevertheless, the fundamental elements of his view have been incorporated into the generally accepted theory of science today. His insistence on the hypothetical character of scientific theory has, in fact, been extended by modern theoreticians beyond the limits intended by Poincaré himself. He was willing to grant certainty at least to the first principles of scientific investigation and to other types of knowledge. Obviously, he did not reduce his own philosophical speculations to the status of mere convention and hypothesis. In the currently accepted view of scientific knowledge, expounded in philosophies of science, there are three fundamental points which ought to give us pause. (1) It insists that no scientific knowledge can be taken as absolutely certain, that is, without an intrinsic doubt concerning its alterability. The hypothetical character of all scientific knowledge, it is said, requires that we accept current scientific knowledge on a tentative basis only. (2) It insists that all true knowledge must be 'scientific,' and therefore hypothetical. This means that even the first principles of scientific investigation must be regarded as hypothetical and tentative. (3) It restricts 'scientific knowledge' to investigations modeled on, and employing the scientific method of modern physics. This means that the various branches of speculative and practical philosophy, theology, history and so forth are not at all scientific, while biology, psychology, anthropology and sociology deserve the name of 'science' only insofar as they employ the unique 'scientific method' of physics.

Here is not the place to controvert these fundamental points. However, a brief comparison of modern scientific theory with the scientific optimism of Aristotle and the ancients is most revealing. Modern theoreticians apparently have abandoned hope in the power of man's speculative reason; they seem to be content with universal uncertainty and a solitary path to knowledge. Whatever may be said of Aristotle's science, he was, at least, much more confident in the powers of human reason and more appreciative of the dignity of scientific knowledge. (1) The tentative status of hypotheses and theories proposed by modern theoreticians falls far short of Aristotle's ideal of scientific knowledge. Science, for Aristotle, is the attainment of true and certain causes within reality. Such causes are, of course, discovered only after careful research and analysis. Whatever hypotheses, theories or suspicions one may have during the investigation, they are not to be confused with genuine science. Such hypotheses are indispensable and inevitable, but they are only means to the ultimate goal of scientific explanation. (2) Aristotle's lofty, and perhaps unattainable, ideal of scientific knowledge did not blind him into thinking that all true knowledge must be of this type. Defending the dignity of science against the skeptics of the Academy on the one hand, and protesting the universality of science on the other, Aristotle saw that not all knowledge can be 'scientific,' that is, demonstrable, for then there would be no beginning. He insisted that the starting point of scientific investigation must be prior and more certain than the torturous path leading to a true solution. This starting point is the light of absolutely first principles, known with certainty before all scientific demonstration. The complex process of investigating nature was recognized as extremely difficult, but Aristotle did not think it hopeless. There is the security of an immoveable starting point. (3) For Aristotle the investigation of nature occupied a preeminent place in the pursuit of knowledge; he himself devoted most of his life to it. But he did not claim this as the only pursuit of mankind. Even in the study of the world and man Aristotle recognized various approaches, each of which is legitimately called ' science.' In other words, 'science' is an analogical term, and its dignity requires that it be recognized in its diversity and complementarity. The pluralist approach to reality respects the principles, method and limitations of each legitimate endeavor. No one branch can be erected into a monolithic idol without destroying the integrity of truth and the dignity of science.

The warfare between scientists and religion cannot be subdued for long. This is not because of any intrinsic incompatibility between science and true religion, but because of the third point mentioned above. If the scientist refuses to acknowledge any theories other than those proposed by his own method, conflicts are bound to break out periodically. Today the conflict is most evident in the conception some neo-biologists have of evolution on the one hand, and the testimony of sound philosophy and revelation on the other. This was evident in the Darwin Centennial held at the University of Chicago in 1959. Some biologists claimed the triumph of science over revelation, since evolutionary theory now proves that man is no more than a form of evolved matter, and religion a superstition. Even apart from the embarrassing fact that the methodology of prehistory is far removed from that of modern physics, we might pause to marvel at this strange note of triumph. Man is no more than the beast, the weed, the puff of air! Rejoice! Man is not very much after all! Dialectical Materialism has been saying this for over a century. Will there be no voice to defend the nobility of man and the dignity of science?

II

We have every right to expect Catholic philosophers and scientists to enter the arena in defence of human dignity, because they know from revelation and the perennial philosophy that man's soul is spiritual, made to the image and likeness of God. We also expect Catholic philosophers and scientists to make positive contributions to science and its theoretical foundations. In other words, we expect Catholic philosophers and scientists to appreciate the true dignity of scientific knowledge and research—not because they might be more gifted, but because they have the advantage of the true faith and the resources of a *philosophia perennis*. This does not mean that Catholics are in a position to judge scientific details *a priori*, or without careful study. Scientific research and analysis are laborious occupations for everyone, Catholic and non-Catholic; and progress in scientific knowledge is a result of cooperative effort, utilizing every means at one's disposal. Nevertheless, Catholics start out with the assurance that the truths revealed by God are absolutely certain and that no truth discoverable by science can contradict them. These revealed truths include both supernatural realities beyond the scope of reason and certain natural realities within the competence of reason and science, such as the existence of God and the immortality of the human soul. Further, the Catholic starts with the assurance that all truth is from God and can lead back to Him if the whole pattern of reality is considered. Finally, the Catholic has at his disposal a font of ancient wisdom which Leo XIII called the *philosophia perennis*. This perennial philosophy, of course, is not a matter of divine revelation; nor does it pretend to contain all the answers. But it does propose true answers to some of the more basic questions of science and human life, answers which can be evaluated by natural reason, and which can be accepted as a starting point for further serious investigation. Even the method whereby fruitful investigation can be continued today is to be found in the perennial philosophy of the ancients. Only an unreasonable or prejudiced thinker would dismiss this wisdom of the ancients without fair study. An ancient truth does not cease to be true just because it is ancient. Nor does the perennial philosophy cease to be philosophy just because someone else thought of it first.

When Leo XIII called for the restoration of the *philosophia perennis* in Catholic schools, he explicitly desired this to be the light by which modern problems of natural science, social ethics and metaphysics are to be worked out. "Even physics, the study which is now held in such high esteem, and which by its many wonderful discoveries has secured to itself everywhere special admiration, will not only receive no detriment but a powerful help from the restoration of the ancient philosophy." Leo XIII pointed out that the consideration of facts and the observation of nature are alone not sufficient for the fruitful appreciation and advancement of natural science. One needs discussion of more fundamental questions of science, reflection on the data obtained, synthesis of various aspects, analysis of scientific theory itself and epistemological evaluation in the light of human knowledge as a whole. "To these investigations it is wonderful what light and powerful aid is afforded by scholastic philosophy, if it be wisely handled." The examples of St. Thomas Aquinas and Blessed Albertus Magnus were proposed to modern investigators of nature by Pope Leo. Over half a century later Pope Pius XII gave modern scientists St. Albert the Great for their heavenly patron, "in order that students of the natural sciences, bearing in mind that he had been given them as their guide, might follow in his footsteps and not cling too tightly to the investigation of the fragile things of this life, nor forget that their souls are meant for immortality, but use created things as rungs in a ladder that will elevate them to understand heavenly things and take supreme delight in them."

Leo XIII had ordered the restoration of scholastic philosophy, particularly that of St. Thomas Aquinas, in all centers of Catholic learning—seminaries, colleges, institutes and universities—that Catholic intellectuals might contribute to the solution of modern problems. The carrying out of this directive was a difficult task. There are some observers today who claim, with considerable justification, that the Leonine directive has never been carried out fully even to this day. However, there were special difficulties in the 1880's. Scholastic philosophy was a philosophy, and ' philosophy ' since the time of Leibniz and Wolff meant metaphysics and ethics. Metaphysics, for Wolff and his innumerable disciples, was divided into general ontology and special ontology, embracing cosmology, psychology and theodicy. Consequently some Catholics fancied that Thomistic philosophy had to be truncated to fit the Procrustean bed of Wolffian metaphysics. Furthermore, the acquisition of scientific knowledge is a difficult task, requiring special training and devotion. Professional philosophers in seminaries and universities could hardly be expected to acquire detailed knowledge of highly developed sciences. Consequently it seemed more expedient to let science alone and concentrate on a metaphysical type of cosmology and rational psychology.

The first university to attempt to fulfill the wishes of Leo XIII was the Catholic University of Louvain. In a papal brief of December 25, 1880, the bishops of Belgium were directed to establish a chair of Thomistic philosophy. By July, 1882, arrangements had been made with the University, and Canon Désiré Mercier, professor of philosophy at the Seminary of Malines, was appointed to the chair. To prepare himself for this new and unique post, Dr. Mercier (with beard and without clerical garb) undertook formal training in psychology under the famous Charcot in Paris. At Louvain he followed the formal courses and laboratory work in physiology, neurology, chemistry, mathematics and linguistics. He was convinced that no domain of modern science can be considered foreign to Thomistic philosophy. In 1888 Msgr. Mercier founded, with the enthusiastic approval of the pontiff, the *Institut Supérieur*

de Philosophie, or *Ecole saint Thomas d'Aquin.* Outlining the
program of the *Institut,* Msgr. Mercier said, " The science of
today is above all a science of the most exact individual research. . . . Let us train, in greater numbers, men who will
devote themselves to science for itself, without any aim that is
professional or directly apologetic, men who will work at first
hand in fashioning the materials for the edifice of science." The
new *Institut* was to be a center of study and research where
work would be done on " science in the making." Msgr. Mercier
accepted the tripartite division of speculative knowledge explained by St. Thomas: natural philosophy, mathematics and
metaphysics. Natural philosophy and experimental science
constituted a unified discipline of mind, quite distinct from
metaphysics. But, as Mercier expressed it, Thomistic natural
philosophy seeks ' ultimate ' causes *(propter quid)*, while experimental science seeks ' proximate ' causes *(quia)*. Mercier's
distinction, which was accepted by his distinguished associates,
Michotte and Nys, is still found in many modern manuals of
scholastic philosophy.

The influence of Mercier was very great, both at Louvain and
elsewhere. The example of Louvain was soon followed by the
Catholic institutes and universities of Munich, Milan, Paris,
Cologne, Münster, Fribourg, Nijmegen, the " Gregorian," the
" Angelicum " and the Catholic University of America.

After the death of Cardinal Mercier in 1926, a number of
Louvain professors under the inspiration of Fernand Renoirte
have come to see a sharp distinction between the non-causal
explanations of modern science and the causal explanations of
Thomistic philosophy. For them St. Thomas' natural philosophy seems to be of the metaphysical order and different from
the technique of modern science. In effect, this was a return
to the Wolffian conception of philosophy, although today it is
presented as the authentic teaching of St. Thomas. Alumni of
Louvain have made this view widely known in the Netherlands
and in the United States. According to this view the philosophy
of nature is a metaphysical study, differing essentially from the

experimental sciences, because it reaches " a level of thought in which no sense-perceptible element is retained and therefore no verification by the senses is possible." In " support " of this view, proponents invariably quote, out of context, a passage from St. Thomas' *In Boethium De trinitate*, q. 5, a. 1 ad 6. However, apart from the impossibility of justifying this view in the writings of St. Thomas, St. Albert or any of the schoolmen, it seems to be unsatisfactory for many reasons. It is based on what seems to be a misconception of metaphysics; it apparently ignores the genesis of analogical concepts; and it widens the chasm between philosophy and science, returning to the insoluble situation of Wolffian Idealism. It denies the dignity of natural science by giving it too little intellectual content, and it denies the dignity of natural philosophy by rarefying it beyond sense contact. There is no doubt that the physical universe can be studied ' metaphysically,' but only at the expense of those very details of interest to the natural philosopher. The universe which interests the natural philosopher is full-blooded, and quite un-metaphysical.

A more realistic approach to the relation of philosophy to science was made by Jacques Maritain in his monumental *Distinguer pour Unir: ou Les Degrés du Savoir* (1932) and in his detailed *La Philosophie de la Nature* of 1935. This distinguished Thomist learned contemporary philosophy from Henri Bergson and biology from Hans Driesch before finding his home in Thomism. First, Maritain accepts the traditional division of speculative philosophy into natural philosophy, mathematics and metaphysics. Second, he realizes that the experimental sciences have developed greatly since the time of Aristotle and St. Thomas Aquinas. Third, he examines modern ' science ' and sees that it is not a homogeneous whole; in fact, it includes two specifically different types of knowledge. One type is formally mathematical, even though empirical. This type Maritain calls *empiriométrique*, because it is concerned solely with the measurable aspect of empirical observation. This concern is characteristic of all parts of modern physics and a great part of modern chemistry. However, for Maritain, this type of knowledge was familiar to Aristotle and St. Thomas as *scientiae mediae* between pure mathematics and natural philosophy. The second type of knowledge found in modern science is essentially empirical, descriptive of phenomena, ' perinoetic ' and somewhat hypothetical in character. This type Maritain calls *empirioschématique*, because it is concerned solely with ordering empirical observation by means of non-mathematical constructs. This concern is characteristic of such experimental sciences as biology, botany, anthropology, physiology, neurology and psychology. Finally, Maritain comes to reconciling his analysis of modern science with the traditional division of speculative knowledge. The empiriometric sciences present no difficulty, since they are *scientiae mediae* between mathematics and the first degree of abstraction. The empirioschematic sciences, however, present a problem. They do not attain the essential natures of material things; they are rather descriptive, hypothetical and superficial (perinoetic). Aristotle's natural philosophy, on the other hand, intuitively attains the essential, ontological natures of changeable being; it is ' dianoetic,' profound and certain. Therefore Maritain suggests that Aristotelian natural philosophy and modern empirioschematic science belong to two different levels of intelligibility within the traditional first degree of abstraction, the former resolving its definitions to ' being,' the latter to sense and ' mobility.' The view of Jacques Maritain, therefore, is similar to that of Cardinal Mercier, except that Maritain alone accounts for the unique position of physics in modern science.

There is no denying the acumen of M. Maritain's analysis and the astuteness of his solution. There is only one difficulty: if the empirioschematic sciences are as superficial and hypothetical as Maritain believes, then they are not sciences at all, but only dialectical preparations for science. Scientific knowledge, as understood by Aristotle and St. Thomas, consists in true demonstration, that is, a causal explanation of essential properties. But this is impossible without dianoetic knowledge of essential natures. In other words, without knowledge of the essential nature of the subject and the property, there can be no demonstration; there can be no scientific knowledge properly so called. The anomaly of M. Maritain's position is that he reconciles modern empirioschematic science with Thomistic philosophy of nature by depreciating modern science. Undoubtedly there are many areas of modern ' science ' which are superficially descriptive, tentative and dialectical in content. If, on the other hand, there are areas of modern science which truly attain essential natures and through them demonstrate characteristic attributes, as often seems to be the case in the biological sciences, then the situation is very different from that presented by M. Maritain.

A better solution was recognized by Fr. Aniceto Fernandez-Alonso, O. P. In 1936 he published a remarkable paper entitled " Scientiae et Philosophia secundum S. Albertum Magnum." Examining the scholastic scene of the 1930's, Fr. Fernandez saw that all scholastics wished to recognize a real distinction between modern science and Aristotelian philosophy. This distinction was variously described as one of content (accidental relations vs. substantial essences, phenomena vs. noumena, sensible vs. intelligible) or one of method (inductive vs. deductive, proximate causes vs. ultimate causes, *quia* demonstrations vs. *propter quid* demonstrations). Fr. Fernandez then went on to show that none of these can differentiate the speculative sciences, for every science, whether it be called empirical or philosophical, must deal with substance and accidents, must be intelligible and sensible; further, every science must be inductive and deductive, must demonstrate through immediate (*propter quid*) and remote (*quia*) causes. Fr. Fernandez's own view can be summarized briefly in three propositions, each of which he proves at great length. (1) All modern science and all natural philosophy are specifically distinct from metaphysics. (2) All sciences formally illuminated by mathematical principles are specifically distinct from sciences of nature, although materially they all study the same physical universe. (3) Aristotelian natural philosophy and the so-called empirical, or experimental sciences constitute one specific discipline, both materially and formally: they are two parts of one and the same science concerning *ens mobile*, and each part has need of the other. These propositions are all justifiable according to the principles of Albertus Magnus. Fr. Fernandez concludes his study by saying, " The division of human knowledge into philosophic and scientific as into two species necessarily and always distinct by the very nature of the objects and the formal independence of one from the other is an assertion which can be made in Platonic, Cartesian, Hegelian and Bergsonian philosophy, but cannot be made in Aristotelian or Albertine philosophy, nor according to the truth of the matter."

Today the view of Fr. Fernandez is defended by the Very Reverend William Humbert Kane, O.P., and the Albertus Magnus Lyceum. On reading the paper in 1936, Fr. Kane immediately recognized the merits of this view, and his own quest for a solution fell into place. Through his stimulating classes and informal discussions he developed a group of disciples and friends who were equally convinced of the importance of a unified view of Thomistic natural philosophy and modern investigations. By 1950 sufficient unified interest was shown in the study of natural philosophy and modern problems to warrant suggesting a special institute directed by Fr. Kane for serious work in this area. The idea of such an institute was, indeed, unique in the Dominican Order; on the other hand, nowhere in the Order were there so many men convinced of the importance of Thomistic natural philosophy for the solution of modern problems. The idea of an institute devoted to special research was also unique among Dominicans in the United States; on the other hand, the time was ripe for such a venture in this country. Consequently the idea was formally presented to the Provincial of the Dominican Province of St. Albert the Great, the Very Reverend Edward L. Hughes, O.P., by the Regent of Studies and President of the Pontifical Faculty of Philosophy at River Forest, Illinois, the Very Reverend Sebastian E. Carlson. By special decree of the Provincial, the Albertus Magnus Lyceum was established at River Forest in 1951, its official date of inception being celebrated on November 15, the feast of St. Albert.

On this tenth anniversary of its establishment the Lyceum takes great pleasure in presenting this volume of studies to its founder and former director on his sixtieth birthday. The volume reflects the wide interest of its members and friends. From small beginnings the Lyceum has grown to include Dominicans of other Provinces and many non-Dominicans. It has developed a serious interest in scientific methodology, the history and philosophy of science, various technical problems of physics, biology, evolution and psychology; and it has had a decided influence on the teaching of natural science in the schools. Of course, much remains to be done in these vast areas of natural science and more specialists are needed even now. Here one can apply the phrase of St. Thomas: *Fiat aliqualiter per plura, quod non potest fieri per unum.*

The Lyceum's view of natural philosophy and the modern sciences has been presented in innumerable writings, lectures, symposia and discussions. Nevertheless, its view has been frequently misunderstood and misrepresented by those who, presumably, disagree with its position. Presumably they have read at least some of the writings which they attack. But it is unreasonable to expect fruitful discussion and disagreement without mutual understanding. By far the most commonly misunderstood point is the Lyceum's (and Maritain's) distinction of modern sciences. Neither Maritain nor the Lyceum considers 'modern science' to be a single, homogeneous body of knowledge. They make a careful distinction between those sciences which are formerly mathematical and those which are not. Formally mathematical sciences (*empiriométrique, scientiae mediae*, mathematical-physical sciences) are acknowledged to be really distinct from the philosophy and science of *nature.* Although extrinsic, the mathematical-physical sciences are of utmost importance to the naturalist in the examination of problems and in the quest for proper solutions, demonstrative or tentative. Conversely, the natural sciences are of importance to the mathematical physicist in giving him the extrinsic foundation for his own science. Further, the Lyceum considers the non-mathematical parts of modern science to belong to a single science concerning *ens mobile ut mobile*. In practice, courses in natural philosophy rarely get beyond general considerations, and courses in experimental science rarely get beyond particular considerations and experiments. However, the Lyceum considers that in both the general and particular parts of this unique discipline there are to be found diverse types of certainty: demonstrative, most probable, tentative, hypothetical, factual and even historical. Finally, the Lyceum maintains that the single science of nature is autonomous in its own field, and in the order of learning prior to and independent of metaphysics.

There are many advantages to this view. First, it recognizes the dignity of a scientific study of the natural world which includes man, animals, plants and inanimate realities. Second, it recognizes the importance of this science for moral, metaphysical and theological concepts. Third, it offers a real possibility of cooperation between the professional philosopher and the experimental scientist. Fourth, it is consistent with the teaching of St. Thomas and St. Albert, for whom natural science is incomplete unless after studying the general theory found in the *Physics*, one proceeds to more and more particular species and varieties of living and non-living natures. Fifth, it is consistent with the actual practice of modern scientists, who begin with very particular varieties and gradually ascend to a more embracing unity, usually in old age. Here the statement of Heraclitus would be applicable: "The way up and the way down is one and the same."

III

It is not very often that an institution can celebrate its own anniversary and that of its founder at the same time. Hence it is a privilege for the Lyceum to celebrate its tenth anniversary by presenting these special studies to Fr. William

Humbert Kane on his sixtieth birthday, July 12, 1961. His inspiring devotion to study, to teaching and to the Dominican way of life deserve some recognition from his brethren and friends besides the normal courtesies of academic and religious life. This *Festschrift* is presented to him with warm affection, deep respect and eternal gratitude. It is a token, indeed a very small token, of our great esteem. Those who esteem Fr. Kane's life-long work recognize his influence on the intellectual life in the United States, both within and without the Dominican Order. Those who have not had the privilege of knowing him will find in this volume the fruits of much of his labor.

William (Dean) Kane was born in La Grange, a suburb of Chicago, on July 12, 1901. After completing Lyons Township High School and attending Aquinas College in Columbus, he entered the Order of Preachers in Somerset, Ohio, in 1920, and took the religious name of Humbert. After the normal course of studies he was ordained to the priesthood in Washington on June 9, 1927. But while he was studying theology at the Dominican House of Studies in Washington, he studied pre-medicine at the Catholic University of America (1923-26) and medicine at Georgetown University School of Medicine (1926-28) in preparation for the Chinese missions. Successfully completing his Lectorate dissertation, "The Criterion of Philosophical Truth," in 1928, he was sent to the Collegio Angelico in Rome for two years graduate study in philosophy. His examination and dissertation on " Finality in Nature " obtained for him the Doctorate of Philosophy *summa cum laude* in June of 1930. His life thereafter was completely devoted to teaching, and it is for this that he is best known. In thirty years of teaching—biology, logic, natural philosophy, metaphysics and theology—he has given much serious thought to the text of St. Thomas and to modern problems. From 1933 until 1940 Fr. Kane was *Lector Primarius* in the House of Philosophy at River Forest, and from 1940 until 1948 he was Pro-Regent of Studies for the newly created Province of St. Albert the Great. On December 17, 1944, the River Forest *studium* was established as a Pontifical Faculty of Philosophy, and Fr. Kane became its first President. On that day, too, he received the ring and biretta of a Master in Sacred Theology, a degree which he had rightfully earned through his teaching. Returning to Rome as Professor of Natural Philosophy in 1948, he created such an impression on the students that he was thought to be more European than American in his devotion to study. In 1951 when the Albertus Magnus Lyceum was established, he returned to the United States to be its director. The bulk of his writings date from this return to River Forest. Now at sixty, the Very Rev. William Humbert Kane feels that his work is just beginning, but he has the assurance that his ideals have taken root in the minds and hearts of his disciples. We extend to him our gratitude, prayers and best wishes AD MULTOS ANNOS.

For the preparation of this volume special gratitude is due not only to the eminent contributors, who enthusiastically endorsed the project from the start, but also to those members of the Albertus Magnus Lyceum who are not represented here. Particular acknowledgement must be made to the President, the Very Rev. Sebastian E. Carlson, and to the Secretary of the Lyceum, the Rev. William B. Mahoney, whose tireless efforts supported the whole project. The Lyceum gratefully acknowledges the encouragement and contribution of the Master General of the Order of Preachers, the Most Rev. Michael Browne, and his Socius for the North American Provinces, the Very Rev. John A. Driscoll. Our sincere gratitude is offered to the Very Reverend John E. Marr, O.P., Provincial of the Province of St. Albert, who has given his encouragement and support to this volume. Since the effort has reached beyond provincial boundaries, we extend this same gratitude to the Very Reverend W. D. Marrin, O.P., Provincial of the Province of St. Joseph. Above all, we are grateful to The Thomist Press and the editorial staff of The Thomist who have joined with the Albertus Magnus Lyceum in honoring our Father William Humbert Kane, O.P., S.T.M.

JAMES A. WEISHEIPL, O.P.
D. Phil. (Oxon.)

PART ONE
SCIENTIFIC METHODOLOGY

DEMONSTRATION AND SELF-EVIDENCE

∽

I. Scientific Methodology

IT can be forcefully argued that there is no place in philosophy for an " epistemological critique " of knowledge, as though the integrity of the intellect stood in doubt till it was somehow philosophically " cleared." [1] Surely, for reason to attempt to establish the trustworthiness of reason is for it to try to pull itself up by its own epistemological boot straps. The history of thought gives ample evidence that critical attempts to justify the philosophical effort are in vain. No matter how honest the epistemological critique in intention, it results characteristically in an unnatural imposition of artificial limits placed upon our capacities to know. Witness the divergent streams of extreme rationalism and extreme empiricism which find their source in the critique of Descartes.[2] Significantly, St. Thomas did not find it necessary to initiate his philosophical effort with a critique of knowledge. A Thomist speaks meaningfully of epistemology best in reference to a metaphysical inquiry into the character of intentional being. He takes epistemology as an attempt to understand what it is to know, not an attempt to defend the radical integrity of our

[1] Cf., Gilson, Étienne, *Realisme Thomiste et Critique de la Connaissance* (Paris: J. Vrin, 1947); *Realisme Méthodique* (Paris: P. Téque, 1935).

[2] Gilson's frequently quoted remark on Berkeley and the Cartesian critique bears repetition here: " Everyone is free to decide whether he shall begin to philosophize as a pure mind; if he should elect to do so the difficulty will not be how to get into the mind, but how to get out of it. Four great men have tried it and failed. Berkeley's own achievement was to realize at last, that it was a useless and foolish thing even to try it. In this sense at least, it is true to say that Berkeley brought Descartes' ' noble experiment ' to a close, and for that reason his work should always remain as a landmark in the history of philosophy." *The Unity of Philosophical Experience* (New York: Chas. Scribner's Sons, 1937), pp. 196-197.

3

capacities for knowledge. That we can know is evident. It is both futile and unnecessary to attempt to prove this.[3]

Although St. Thomas did not hamper his capacities for knowledge by imposing *a priori* restrictions upon them, he saw that, in a sense, they imposed restrictions upon him. There is no question, from the very start, as to the radical integrity of sense and intellect. Despite the fact that we are sometimes in error, it is evident that we can, and adequately, know what is. But our capacities for knowing are in no sense unlimited. Honest reflection upon the epistemological facts reveals that the human intellect is that lesser type of intellect which is at once a reason. For us all doctrine and discipline is from pre-existing knowledge.[4] We learn by moving from what is already known to what follows from this. The fact is clear that, as far as learning is concerned, the human intellect is naturally discursive. Moreover, the price of discursive advance in knowledge is the construction within the intellect of logical artifices such as definitions and argumentations. The method of construction which is called for by the demands of discourse is in no sense arbitrary. As always, the final cause is the cause of the causality of the other causes. The end of the logical construct requires certain determinate rules according to which the objects known are to be ordered in knowledge in reference to one another. Thus, there are definite rules of procedure which constrain the intellect in its discursive progress.[5] These

[3] Cf., Smith, Gerard, S. J., "A Date in the History of Epistemology," in *The Maritain Volume of The Thomist* (New York: Sheed and Ward, 1943), pp. 246-255.

[4] *In I Post. Anal.*, lect. 1, n. 9: "Omnis autem disciplinae acceptio ex praeexistenti cognitione fit." (The quotations from St. Thomas will be taken from the Leonine for the *Summa*, the Decker for the *De Trinitate*, the Lethielleux for the *Sentences*, and from the respective Marietti editions for each of the other works cited.)

[5] The general rules of discursive procedure, we shall note, are one with the laws of logic. Logic is simultaneously an art and a science. As an art it is directive of a productive activity—precisely, for logic, the construction within the reason of the instruments of discourse, such as definition and argumentation. The character of any work-to-be-produced sets the standard according to which the artistic effort is to be effected. Thus every art has its own determinate rules of procedure. In the case of logic, of course, these are the rules of sound discourse. And in the case of

can be said to constitute a method, and the reflexive investigation of them can be spoken of as methodology. It should be clear that this is not *method* in the manner of Cartesian method, nor is it *methodology* in the manner of epistemological critique.

There is for man but one reason. Hence, there is generally but one method, that is, the discursive method which measures up to the demands of that one reason. But there are many different things to be known, on radically different scientifically relevant levels. As a consequent, the general method of the reason must be proportioned *to* each scientifically different object *for* each formally different scientific effort. The general method of the reason is logic. Logic is at best analogously common to every scientific inquiry. By itself it is inadequate to any particular scientific subject matter. Logic must be contracted, and in analogously different ways, to the needs of every scientifically different subject. This contraction of logic is realized in the particular scientific methods proper to each formally different scientific subject.[6] Note that while logic by itself is inadequate to any given scientific inquiry because of the special demands of the proper subject of that inquiry, there can, because of the demands of the reason itself, be no particular

logic, because discourse is aimed ultimately at a fully defended scientific knowledge of things, the rules of the art must themselves be evident in themselves or demonstratively defended. Since only the most fundamental rules of logic are evident in themselves the majority of them must be demonstrated. Thus, in order for logic to be the art that it is, it must be at once the demonstrative science of the rules of discourse. As a matter of fact, the rules of discourse are the canons which express the demands of the second intentions which accrue to objects as known and in virtue of which these objects are to be ordered in discourse. Thus logic is simultaneously the art of sound discourse and the demonstrative science of second intentions or rules of discourse. For a more complete exposition and defense of this position, cf., Simmons, Edward, " The Nature and Limits of Logic," *The Thomist,* XXIV (January, 1961), pp. 47-71.

[6] In *In Boeth. de Trin.*, q. 6, a. 1, St. Thomas distinguishes between the demonstrative method characteristic of natural science (*rationabiliter*), the method of mathematics (*disciplinabiliter*), and the method of metaphysics (*intellectualiter*). These represent different contractions of the general logic of demonstration in favor of formal differences in diverse scientific subjects.

scientific method which is not generally logical. Clearly, the investigation into general logical method is methodology in one sense, while the investigation into the precise method of any given scientific inquiry is methodology in another (related) sense. We can refer to the former as general methodology and the latter as particular or special methodology.[7]

In this paper we shall concern ourselves with the role of the self-evident proposition in the theory of demonstration. This is a study in general methodology. The point made will be of a common character, and the methodological principles uncovered will be only generally relevant for scientific inquiry. In every case an appropriate contraction of the doctrine presented will be necessary before it is proximately adequate to any given scientific effort. Before proceeding, however, there remains one more distinction to be made, the better to locate the discussion of this paper. General methodology is identical with logical theory, and, as such, admits of the distinction between formal and material logic. This is a distinction which is both legitimate and significant, but it is a distinction which is frequently misunderstood. Although it is a distinction which should be made within the limits of general logical theory, it is not infrequently understood in such a way that formal logic is identified with general methodology while material logic is associated intrinsically with particular scientific methodology. This mistaken view makes logic less than adequate to the demands of reason even in abstraction from the particular demands of any given scientific subject. And, while it may not positively vitiate the investigation into particular scientific method, it places an unreasonable burden upon it. Just as there are general rules of logical procedure to be followed if discourse is to be consistent or valid, so there are general rules of procedure to be followed if discourse is to be of some determinate scientific force. Categorical syllogism is defined in terms of validity. The rules which must be followed to make the syllogism precisely a syllogism (e. g., the middle term must be fully

[7] Cf., *In II Met.*, lect. 5, n. 335; *In II De Anima*, lect. 3, n. 245.

distributed at least once) are canons of valid or consistent discourse. Demonstration, on the other hand, while pre-supposing validity, is defined in terms of scientific force. And there are general rules, able to be determined apart from any particular scientific subject, which must be followed if a syllo-gism is to be demonstration (e. g., the premises must be necessarily true), and even more determinate general rules which must be followed if the demonstration is to be of a certain type (e. g., explanatory demonstration must have a middle term which is related to the scientific subject as its real definition). These rules, while quite clearly remaining of a general logical character (i. e., open to contraction in the face of special scientific subject matter, but not yet con-tracted) are canons of properly scientific, and not simply con-sistent, discourse. Rules such as these are proper to material logic, while the rules of merely consistent discourse are rules of formal logic. There are reasons which explain why formal logic is sometimes confused with the whole of logic and why material logic is sometimes confused with particular scientific methodology.[8] But these reasons only help to excuse the man

---

[8] The formal subject of the science of logic is the second intention. Second inten-tions are logical forms or relations of the reason which accrue to objects (first intentions) precisely as known. Some second intentions accrue to an object properly in virtue of its mode of signifying (e. g., predicate, middle term, and syllogism). Others accrue directly in virtue of the intelligible content of the object (e. g., species, immediate, and demonstration). The former are second intentions in *formal* logic, and they set the demands for *valid* discourse. The latter are second intentions in *material* logic. and these set the demands for *scientific* discourse. Although St. Thomas explicitly distinguishes between formal and material logic only on the level of the logic of the third operaton (cf., *In I Post. Anal.*, prooem., nn. 5-6), the distinction makes sense also on the levels of the first and second operations, as the examples above illustrate. [Cf., Simon, Yves, " Foreword," *The Material Logic of John of St. Thomas*, translated by Yves Simon, John Glanville, and G. Donald Hollenhorst (Chicago: Chicago University Press, 1955), pp. ix-xxiii.] The subject matter for logical theory is always the second intention, and never directly the first intention to which the second intention accrues. Thus, there is a sense in which logic is only formal (investigating logical *forms*) and never material (discussing the intelligible content of first intentions, which is the *matter* of dis-course). And even apart from this, it is clear that second intentions in material logic are more proximately connected with the intelligible content of first intentions

who is confused. They do not defend the confusion as a noetic fact. The theory of demonstration in general remains, as much as the theory simply of syllogism, the concern properly of the logician. It must be assumed and contracted to the needs of the special subject matter for any given scientific inquiry. Thus the concern of this paper is within the limits of logic, but it belongs to that branch of logic which is material logic rather than formal logic. This brings us significantly closer to the area of particular methodology than a paper in formal logic would, but we remain in logic without trespassing beyond.

II. Self-evident Proposition—The Basic Truths of Demonstration

Early in the *Posterior Analytics*, after determining the nature of scientific knowledge (in brief, *certa cognitio per causas* [9]),

than are those in formal logic. The connection is so intimate that Simon and his fellow translators suggest that the *habitus* of material logic is reduced in actual use to the science which employs it (*ibid.*, note 39, pp. 594-595). Whether this is the case or not, it remains true that the formal subject of material logic as well as the formal subject of formal logic is no more nor less than a logical form or second intention. This means, of course, that material logic is integrally a part of logic proper and is not, as a science, to be confused with any (and every) particular sicence of the real. (Cf., Simmons, E., *op. cit.*)

[9] *The Posterior Analytics*, Book I, Ch. 2, 71b9-12: "We suppose ourselves to possess unqualified scientific knowledge of a thing . . . when we think we know the cause on which the fact depends, as the cause of that fact and of no other, and, further, that the fact could not be other than it is." [Translation from *The Basic Works of Aristotle*, edited by Richard McKeon (New York: Random House, 1941), p. 111] There should be no need to insist that, in the face of current usage, this gives a highly restricted (and exceedingly strict) meaning to "science." As we begin to speak of this kind of science as demonstrated knowledge there is, of course, a proportionately strict understanding of the meaning of "demonstration." Still, the terms "science" and "demonstration" admit of analogous impositions, even as used by us in this paper. For example, demonstrations differ analogously from one genus of speculative science to another—so that mathematical demonstration is only proportionally like metaphysical demonstration (cf. *In Boeth. de Trin.*, q. 6, a. 1; *In I Post. Anal.*, lect. 41), and even within a given science—so that a *propter quid* demonstration in one science is only proportionally like a *quia* demonstration in that same science (cf., *ibid.*, lect. 23). Having introduced this strict meaning of science in the second chapter of *The Posterior Analytics*, Aristotle has set the stage to demand of the scientific syllogism that its premises be necessarily true and

Aristotle defines demonstration in terms of its final cause as a syllogism productive of science. Then, using this definition of demonstration itself as a principle of demonstration, he proceeds to demonstrate the definition of demonstration in terms of its matter. He argues that if a syllogism is to produce the kind of conclusion which is properly scientific it must proceed from premises which are true, primary, immediate, better known than, prior to, and cause of the conclusion. This is to say that it must proceed from necessarily true, absolutely first propositions, which look to no prior proposition for their evidence but are calculated to supply evidence for other propositions. We speak of these propositions as self-evident. Scientific knowledge is proven in a demonstration whose premises manifest the truth of the scientific conclusion. As principles of the conclusion these premises are properly premises. In any given case, however, they may also be conclusions from other premises. But it is impossible, of course, that every premise be itself a conclusion from a prior premise. We must arrive ultimately at premises which are only premises, at propositions which are not shown to be evident by way of prior propositions but whose evidence is found within themselves. These absolute premises are ultimately the complex principles [10] of scientific knowledge, themselves not properly scientific, but rather prescientific. They are self-evident propositions, the propositions spoken of in the *Posterior Analytics* as " the immediate basic truths of syllogism " or, more determinately, of demonstration.

immediately so (Ch. 3). It is important to note that, for the most part, the subsequent discussion of the requirements for demonstration is centered upon the strictest type of *propter quid* demonstration and is only proportionally relevant to other types.

[10] The absolute premises of demonstration are significant principles of demonstrative discourse. So too is the middle term of the demonstration (which is not identical with any premise, though it is built into each). The former are complex principles of demonstration. The latter is an incomplex principle. We are concerned primarily with the complex principles of demonstration in this paper, although, as we shall note, the definition itself plays a significant role in the discussion of these complex principles. As a matter of fact Aristotle lists the definition as a type of demonstrative principle in the very context of the discussion of immediate premises (cf., St. Thomas' explanation for this, *op. cit.*, lect. 5, n. 9).

St. Thomas speaks of these " basic truths " as *per se nota* propositions. Although this is an apt expression, there is some danger of confusion here. First of all, St. Thomas may sometimes use the term *per se nota* of a proposition which is not evident in the way in which the basic truths of demonstration are self-evident.[11] Secondly, St. Thomas frequently speaks of the modes of perseity (the *modi dicendi per se*),[12] and, despite the terminological suggestion to the contrary, it is not true that whenever we have a proposition which involves a mode of perseity we have a *per se nota* or self-evident proposition. These points will have to be clarified before we are through.

For the premises of demonstration to be at all they must be *true*, for the *esse* of a proposition is an *esse verum*. For them to be principles of manifestation for the *scientific* conclusion they must be *necessarily* true, for necessity is of the essence of science. And for them to be *basic* truths, that is *absolute* premises, the premises of demonstration must be, at least reductively, *immediate* propositions. Here is precisely where the scientific proposition differs from its pre-scientific principle. The scientific proposition is necessarily true, and it is a conclusion. The scientific principle is necessarily true, but it can be (ultimately) in no sense a conclusion. The conclusion of a syllogism is characteristically mediate, for the connection between its extremes is manifested in a syllogism by way of a term commonly identified with both extremes, thus functioning as a middle. The basic truths of syllogism or the absolute premises must themselves be evident without a middle. The predicate must belong immediately to the subject lest we admit the infinite regress which would make deduction totally ineffective. Two things, at least, should be pointed out here. First of all, there is a significant and not unrelated use of the term " immediate " which is not intended at this point. For example, *having three angles equal to two right angles* is necessarily

---

[11] *In II Phys.*, lect. 1, n. 8: " Naturam autem esse, est per se notum, in quantum naturalia sunt manifesta sensui."

[12] Cf., *In I Post. Anal.*, lect. 10; *In II De Anima*, lect. 14, n. 401; *In V Met.*, lect. 19, nn. 1054-1057.

true of both *triangle* and *isosceles triangle*. But it is true of *isosceles triangle* only insofar as *isosceles triangle* is *triangle*. Thus we might well say that this property belongs immediately to *triangle* and mediately (through *triangle*) to *isosceles triangle*. However, the proposition *Every triangle has three angles equal to two right angles* can be demonstrated as the conclusion of a syllogism employing the essential definition of *triangle* as its middle term. Insofar as it is able to be proven through a middle, it is clearly not immediate in the sense in which self-evident propositions are immediate. " Immediate " here means, rather, commensurately universal or convertible (*primo* or possessed of the intention spoken of as *dici ut universale*). As a matter of fact, not every proposition which is commensurately universal is self-evident and not every self-evident proposition is commensurately universal.[13] Secondly, even though we understand the self-evident proposition to be immediate in such wise as to lack a demonstrative middle, it is not the case that every proposition which is immediate in this sense is self-evident. A self-evident proposition is a proposition with a subject and a predicate in necessary matter, and with a subject and predicate so proximately connected with one another that the necessary truth of the proposition can escape no one who understands this subject and predicate. Hence, propositions are said to be self-evident precisely insofar as they can be seen necessarily to be true once their terms are known.[14] These

[13] For St. Thomas' position on the *dici ut universale*, cf., *In I Post. Anal.*, lect. 11. We shall see that the prime instance of the self-evident proposition has a predicate which is of the definition of the subject. If the predicate is the whole of the definition of the subject it is, of course, convertible with the subject, and we have a commensurately universal proposition. *Every man is capable of speech* is commensurately universal without being self-evident, and *Every man is animal* is self-evident without being commensurately universal.

[14] Only this type of proposition is so necessarily true, while being at the same time immediate, that it can ground the necessity of a scientific conclusion. *In IV Met.*, lect. 5, n. 595: "Ad huius autem evidentiam sciendum, quod propositiones per se notae sunt, quae statim notis terminis cognoscuntur. . . ." *De Malo*, q. 3, a. 3, c.: " Unde intellectus ex necessitate assentit principiis primis naturaliter notis. . . . Unde in intellectu contingit quod ea quae necessariam cohaerentiam habent cum primis principiis naturaliter cognitis, ex necessitate moveant intellectum,

propositions are not totally non-empirical, for, as we shall note, they are known by way of an immediate induction from sensible data. Yet they do not depend directly upon empirical data for verification. Assent to them is founded upon an intelligibility built into them such that it is impossible to think the opposite. Thus, if one understands the meanings of the terms in the proposition *The whole is greater than any of its parts* one immediately assents to this proposition quite apart from the existence of this or that sensibly existing whole or part. The motive for assent is, in a sense, built into the proposition itself. The self-evident proposition is immediate because it looks to no prior proposition for its evidence, but there are propositions which are evident in this way without being *self* evident. These are the factually evident propositions which are true, because they report accurately on the way things happen in fact to be, whether they could be otherwise or not. Examples of propositions like this are *This pencil is yellow*, *The weather is pleasant today*, and *I feel great*. These propositions are immediate since they do not depend on prior propositions to manifest their truth. The evidence for them is found immediately in the factual situation. Insofar as a factually evident proposition is formally characterized by its commitment to what happens to be the case, the factually evident proposition cannot intend the necessity needed for an absolute premise of demonstration. Thus, though each is immediate, the factually evident proposition differs radically from the self-evident proposition.[15] In the *Commentary on the Physics* St.

sicut conclusiones demonstratae, quando apparent; quae si negentur, oportet negari prima principia, ex quibus ex necessitate consequuntur." Cf., among other texts of this type, *In I Post. Anal.*, lect. 5; lect. 19; *De Ver.*, q. 11, a. 1; *Summa*, I, q. 17, a. 3 ad 2; q. 82, a. 2; q. 85, a. 6; *De Malo*, q. 16, a. 7 ad 18; *Quodl.*, VIII, a. 4.

[15] What I refer to as the "factually evident" proposition is usually spoken of simply as "evident," but since the self-evident is (at least) evident it seems better to use a more determinate expression. There is nothing highly sophisticated intended by my use of "factually," despite the *fact* that the word "fact" does frequently take on a very specialized meaning in philosophical discussion. Note that none of my examples involves necessary matter in any sense. This helps to make the notion of the factually evident quite clear. Nonetheless it seems to me that *This whole*

Thomas says that it is *per se notum* that nature exists because natural things are manifest to the sense.[16] *Natural things exist* is an immediate proposition. But it is not self-evident—for, since natural things are existentially contingent and need not be, we cannot assent to the proposition *Natural things exist* simply because we understand the meaning of its terms. It is immediately evident only on the basis of the empirical fact unmistakably given in our sensory-intellectual grasp of the existence of sensible existents immediately present to the external sense. This is clearly a factually evident proposition. It is of significant relevance for the philosophy of nature, but it is not relevant in the way in which a self-evident proposition is relevant,[17] despite the fact that St. Thomas describes it as *per se nota*. One more clarification at this point. The immediacy of the self-evident proposition makes it indemonstrable. But not all indemonstrable propositions are immediate (consider conclusions of dialectical or probable argumentation). Nor even, of course, are all immediate and indemonstrable proposi-

is greater than its parts can be taken as a proposition which intends simply a report on a concrete situation. As such this is factually evident, and it is not the same as the proposition *Every whole is such that it must be greater than any of its parts*. This second proposition is, of course, self-evident, and it is certainly known by anyone who can express the former proposition (because the terms which must be known in order that the former be expressed immediately make evident the latter). Although the most perfect instance of *propter quid* demonstration involves two premises each of which is self-evident, there is no reason why less strict demonstration cannot include one factually evident premise. The necessity needed in the antecedent of a demonstration would be lacking if every premise were factually evident, but it can be supplied by one self-evident proposition coupled with a factually evident premise. As a matter of fact, demonstration makes sense only in reference to scientific subjects known to exist. Where both premises are self-evident it is a requirement that the existence of the scientific subject be known prior to demonstration and *presumed* within demonstration. The existence of the scientific subject can be *expressed* within a demonstration when one of its premises is factually evident.

[16] Cf., *supra*, note 11.

[17] There would be no reason for a philosophy of nature if natural things did not exist; but since they need not exist, the proposition which reports on the fact of their existence cannot be used as a necessary premise manifesting the scientific necessity of any conclusion.

tions self-evident (consider the examples given above for the factually evident proposition). Certainly true propositions in contingent matter are indemonstrable because of a deficiency in matter. Self-evident propositions are always in necessary matter, and their indemonstrability springs from their excellence rather than from some deficiency in matter. Demonstration makes evident something which is not already evident. To be demonstrable entails a privation. Because they are evident in themselves, self-evident propositions do not have this privation.[18]

Self-evident propositions are necessarily true and immediate. This makes them at once primary: they have no propositions prior to them (upon which they depend for evidence), and they are presupposed to the mediate propositions which look to them for evidence. Insofar as they supply evidence for these mediate propositions they cause them to be conclusions. And they can be related to the conclusion as cause to effect only insofar as they are prior to and better known than the conclusion. The " basic truths of syllogism " are *basic* insofar as they admit of no prior propositions necessary to make them evident. They are truths *of the syllogism* insofar as they are principles from which conclusions can be generated.

III. THE TYPES OF SELF-EVIDENT PROPOSITION

We have noted that a self-evident proposition is one which is known to be necessarily true once its terms are understood. The most perfect instance of this is found in the proposition in which the predicate is of the definition of the subject.[19] Once

---

[18] Though scientific or demonstrated knowledge is spoken of as *perfect* knowledge (cf., *In I Post. Anal.*, lect. 4, n. 5), it is clear that it is *inferior* to the pre-scientific absolute premises of demonstration.

[19] *Summa*, I, q. 17, a. 3 ad 2: " Nam principia per se nota sunt illa quae statim intellectis terminis cognoscuntur ex eo quod praedicatum ponitur in definitione subiecti." As Cajetan points out in his *Commentary on the Posterior Analytics* (Book I, Ch. 19), St. Thomas does not intend in texts such as this one strictly to define the self-evident proposition but to manifest the principal case. An example of a self-evident proposition which does not have its predicate within the definition of its subject is *Every rational animal is capable of speech.*

the subject is understood in its definition the identity of subject and predicate is grasped, and the intellect is moved to commit itself irrevocably to the truth of the proposition. If a proposition has a predicate within the definition of its subject, but this subject defies definition by any man, then this proposition can be described as self-evident in itself, but not self-evident to us. If, on the other hand, its subject can be defined by us, it is self-evident both in itself and to us. If the subject is able to be defined only by those who are habituated to operate within a given scientific field, the proposition is said to be self-evident only to the learned. But if is is a common concept understood by every one, it is, of course, self-evident to all. Thus, it is rather easy to see, at least apropos of the prime type of self-evident proposition, the rationale of the traditional division of the *per se nota* proposition into the *per se nota in se* and the *per se nota quoad nos,* and the subdivision of the latter into the *per se nota quoad sapientes* and the *per se nota quoad omnes.*[20]

St. Thomas appeals to the fact that the proposition *God is* is not self-evident *quoad nos* even though it is self-evident in itself.[21] Were we to know the essence of God we could not— nor would we need to—demonstrate His existence, for His essence is His existence. Yet, since we do not know His essence we are able from His effects, which are known to us, to prove His existence. Aristotle and St. Thomas supply several examples of *per se nota* propositions which are known to all because their terms are common conceptions easily and surely grasped by all men. These examples include: *The same thing cannot be and not be; The same proposition does not admit simultaneously of affirmation and denial; The whole is greater than any of its parts; Things equal to one and the same thing are equal to one another; Equals taken away from equals leave*

---

[20] This traditional division of the self-evident proposition is explained by St. Thomas in several texts, including: *De Ver.,* q. 10, a. 12; *In IV Met.,* lect. 5, n. 595; *In I Post. Anal.,* lect. 5, nn. 6-7; *In Boeth. de Hebd.,* lect. 1. Cf., also Cajetan, *op. cit.,* Ch. 3.

[21] *Summa,* I, q. 2, a. 1; *De Ver.,* q. 10, a. 12.

equals.[22] These propositions are called *dignitates* or axioms because they are the absolutely ultimate and common prin-ciples which guarantee the integrity of all discourse and into which all discourse is resolved. Discourse would be impossible for anyone ignorant of these axioms. Propositions *per se nota quoad sapientes* are related to the axioms as the proper is related to the common. They can be known only by the learned because the terms involved are more determinate than the common notions which alone are able to be understood by the academically unskilled. St. Thomas illustrates this by suggesting the proposition *All right angles are equal.* This is a proposition which is immediately evident only to one who knows that *equality* enters into the definition of *right angle*; and this is a definition, of course, which escapes the knowledge of many. Another example which is traditionally offered is the proposition *Incorporeal substances are not situated in place.* We can add to these any proposition in which the essential definition or some part of it is predicated of a specific subject, such as *Every man is a rational animal.* A proposition of this type is known as a *positio* or thesis.[23] The axioms are necessary if we are to demonstrate in any scientific area, but the theses proper to a given area are necessary only for demonstrations properly within this area. Axioms may or may not be used explicitly as premises in demonstration, but theses are principles of demonstration only if they appear explicity as premises. Axioms can be distinguished generally into those which are ontological in character (e. g., the principle of identity) and those which are logical in character (e. g., the principle of contradiction). Those which are ontological in character are

---

[22] *In I Post. Anal.*, lect. 5, n. 7; *In IV Met.*, lect. 5, n. 595.

[23] St. Thomas considers the division of the immediate principles of demonstration especially in lessons 5, 18, and 19 in the first book of his *Commentary on the Posterior Analytics.* We have already noted the inclusion of definition as a principle (although incomplex) of demonstration. St. Thomas also speaks of a proposition taken as though it were immediate in one science, but proved in another (lect. 5, n. 7). This proposition is called a *suppositio* or hypothesis. We are not concerned properly with this proposition in this paper.

presupposed to any demonstration, even when they are not explicitly expressed as premises, precisely because the knowledge of proper concepts which is required for theses presupposes and in a sense depends upon a prior grasp of common concepts.[24] Those which are logical in character function necessarily as methodological principles which guarantee the integrity of discourse without being built into it as doctrinal principles. For example, the principle of contradiction is an absolutely common methodological principle without which there could be no discourse at all. No proposition can function properly as a principle of demonstration except that it be firmly accepted that the affirmation of its opposite is excluded in the face of its own affirmation.[25] Of course axioms of an ontological character (when illumined by the light of metaphysical abstraction) can be used as premises in metaphysical discourse, just as axioms of a logical character must be built into proofs in logical theory as explicit premises. The reason for this is that metaphysics and logic are common sciences, so that the principles common to the other sciences are proper to them. As a matter of fact, these common propositions can even be used as explicit premises in the particular sciences, though here they become principles of dialectical rather than demonstrative discourse.[26]

[24] Consider the relation of *being* to all other concepts. *De Ver.*, q. 1, a. 1, resp.: "Illud autem quod primo intellectus concipit quasi notissimum, et in quo omnes conceptiones resolvit, est ens;" *In III Met.*, lect. 5. Cf. Cajetan, *Comm. In De Ente et Essentia*, q. 1.

[25] *In IV Met.*, lect. 6, n. 603: "Si igitur quis opinetur simul duo contradictoria esse vera, opinando simul idem esse et non esse, habebit simul contrarias opiniones: et ita contraria simul inerunt eidem, quod est impossibile. Non igitur contingit aliquem circa haec interius mentiri et quod opinetur simul idem esse et non esse. Et propter hoc omnes demonstrationes reducunt suas propositiones in hanc propositionem, sicut in ultimam opinionem omnibus communem: ipsa enim est naturaliter principium et dignitas omnium dignitatum." Cf., also *In I Post. Anal.*, lect. 6, n. 7.

[26] Though the direct use of logic is methodological, supplying either the rules of demonstrative or dialectical discourse, logic can, along with metaphysics, because of the correlatively common character of the formal subjects of each, supply premises for argumentation in the particular sciences. Since demonstration requires premises appropriate to the conclusion, the argumentation in some particular science with a premise from metaphysics or logic will be dialectical at best.

IV. The Genesis of the Self-evident Proposition

As St. Thomas teaches, the self-evident absolute premises from which scientific conclusions are generated are natural to the human intellect.[27] However, this does not mean, on the one hand, that they are possessed from the very start as fully formed conceptions dependent in no sense upon experience or, on the other, that they are no more than mental constructs fabricated by the intellect totally out of its own " stuff." In the final lesson of his *Commentary on the Posterior Analytics* St. Thomas finds fault with those who suggest that we already possess the principles but do not know this from the beginning. This is absurd since the principles of demonstration must be better known than the conclusions they generate, and it is impossible to know demonstratively and not be aware of this. St. Thomas also disputes with those who say that self-evident propositions arise in us from nothing. Experience indicates and reason demands that they come from something. But they cannot come from prior intellectual knowledge, for then they would not be immediate. They are generated from previous sense knowledge by way of an immediate induction.[28] However, to say this is not to imply that they are easily achieved.[29] This is simply not the case for the large majority of self-evident

[27] *Summa*, I, q. 117, a. 1: " Inest enim unicuique homini quoddam principium scientiae, scilicet lumen intellectus agentis, per quod cognoscuntur statim a principio naturaliter quaedam universalia principia omnium scientiarum."

[28] I say *immediate* induction to distinguish this from the mediate induction of a conclusion whose evidence is supplied by a sufficient enumeration of singulars.

[29] Our students seem to be easily misled into identifying the self-evident with the easily understood. This may be because in our classroom approach to them our examples of the self-evident proposition are almost exclusively axioms which are self-evident to all (e. g., *The whole is greater than any one of its parts.*), or it may be because of a tendency on the part of a student to give a psychologically sub-jective reading to what must be understood objectively (i. e., to think " self-evident" means evident *to myself* rather than *in itself*). This confusion is not limited to our students. For example, Joseph Brennan, in *The Meaning of Philosophy* (New York: Harper and Bros., 1953), p. 94, suggests two meanings to " self-evident," namely, *indemonstrable* or *completely clear to me*. That the type-writer I am using is gray is both indemonstrable and completely clear to me. But it is in no sense self-evident.

propositions. It takes a sufficient experience (spoken of by St. Thomas as an *experimentum* which comes about from many memories)[30] of the singular manifestations of a universally necessary truth before we are ready to penetrate beyond the accidentals of these singulars to the underlying necessity. This *experimentum* is not always easily achieved. And the intuitive insight (into the necessity potentially in the *experimentum*) effected by the possible intellect through the light of the agent intellect is difficult as a matter of course. More often than not, it seems, propositions which are self-evident in themselves are not seen to be self-evident by us; and when they are, it is only by way of a tremendously difficult dialectical procedure.[31]

To grasp the truth of a self-evident proposition one must first grasp the meaning of the terms involved. Hence, the search for

[30] *In II Post. Anal.*, lect. 20, n. 11; *In IV Met.*, lect. 6, n. 599.

[31] Thus far I have used the expression "dialectical" to refer to probable argumentation. This type of dialectical discourse is supplementary to demonstration. We can also speak of a pre-demonstrative dialectic—which prepares the way for demonstration by manifesting the absolute premises of demonstration. This is the way the term is used here. There is no question of a proof, in any strict sense of the word, for a self-evident proposition. Assent to the self-evident proposition depends upon and comes with an insight into the intrinsic intelligibility of the proposition itself. The assent is automatic with the insight, but the insight may be difficult to achieve. The way to insight may require long and complicated discourse involving division, definition, and even argumentation. For example, one typical dialectical device for manifesting the truth of a self-evident proposition is the reduction of its contradiction to absurdity. (Cf. *In III Met.*, lect. 5, n. 392.) The important point is that once the threshhold of insight is achieved the assent is made in virtue of the intrinsic intelligibility of the proposition itself. The dialectic is a scaffolding which can now be torn down, for it is not needed as a defense of the self-evident proposition once seen (no matter how instrumental it might in fact have been prior to insight). Here precisely is where the immediate induction of the principles of demonstration differs from the mediate induction of a conclusion from a sufficient enumeration of singulars. The induced conclusion is assented to precisely in virtue of the enumeration of singulars and cannot be known without pointing to them for evidence. This is not the case for the induced principle. No matter how many singular wholes and parts have to be observed before a man sees into the meaning of whole and part so that he knows the whole must be greater than its parts, the proposition is seen to be true independently of each and all of these singular wholes and parts. (*In III Sent.*, d. 24, q. 1, a. 2, q. 1 ad 2: "Termini principiorum naturaliter notorum sunt comprehensibles nostro intellectui: ideo cognitio quae consurgit de illis principiis, est visio. . . .")

self-evident propositions is at least as difficult as the search for definitions. Cajetan suggests that it is more difficult than this. At the end of his *Commentary on the Posterior Analytics* he discusses the induction of the *per se nota* proposition. He contends that induction is necessary, not only as the source of the incomplex terms of the complex principles, but that it is necessary as well for the composition of these terms in the proposition. He argues that we would not know that equals taken from equals leave equals if we knew only the meaning of "equal," "to be taken from" and "to leave." For this reason he holds that for the genesis of this self-evident proposition there must be induction, not only of the meanings of the terms, but even of their conjunction in this proposition. In some texts at least, as we have seen, St. Thomas indicates that the induction of the terms is sufficient for the intellectual grasp of first principles. Appeal to personal experience, after the suggestion of Cajetan, seems to indicate that sometimes the induction of the terms alone suffices (as, for example, with the self-evident proposition *Every man is a rational animal*), and that sometimes more is required (as in the example cited by Cajetan).

The self-evident proposition is not simply a report on a factual situation. Yet it is not *a priori*, and it does have an empirical reference. If it were not the case that some things happen to be such and such precisely because they cannot be and not be such and such, we would never grasp the self-evident proposition. It is only through sufficient contact with the things in question that an insight into the necessity which dictates the facts (that is, the way in which these things are) is achieved.[32] It is true that we can be sure that the whole is greater than any of its parts even though we are not presently confronted by a concrete whole and its parts. The truth of this proposition is guaranteed by the very meanings of whole

---

[32] There is no intention here to suggest that all facts are necessitated. I refer simply to the necessity that belongs to those facts which are necessary (e. g., that this whole is greater than its parts).

and part. Still I would never know the meaning of whole and part if I never knew any concrete whole and its parts. And, what is more important, there is no intelligibility at all to whole or part except that there are (at least possibly) concretely existing wholes and parts. The whole *is* greater than any of its parts precisely because that's the way wholes and parts *are*. For every whole and its parts there is the fact that this whole happens to be greater than each of its parts—and behind this fact is the necessity which demands it, a necessity which is one with the intelligible structure of whole and part. The fact and the necessity which dictates it are equally real. Yet they differ. The fact is incommunicable, and it alone can be expressed in a factually evident proposition. The necessity behind the fact is impervious to sense. Yet it is potentially in what is sensed (and in what is reported on in a factually evident proposition), and it is, of course, fundamentally universal. It can be known only by an intuitive insight which is the result of an abstractive induction, and when known it is expressed in a formally universal proposition. The self-evident proposition comes into being only when it is inductively achieved from an experience of singulars—and it is meaningful only insofar as it bears finally upon singulars. However, the self-evident proposition is only materially dependent on experience for its verification. It is directly verified in its own intrinsic intelligibility, which precludes the possibility even of conceiving the opposite.

V. *Per Se Nota* AND *Modi Dicendi Per Se*

There is a temptation to identify *per se nota* or self-evident propositions with propositions involving a *modus dicendi per se* or a mode of perseity. However, such an identification can be seen to be erroneous once it is noted that the conclusion of a strict *propter quid* demonstration involves the second mode of perseity. As conclusion, and not premise, the proposition in the second mode of perseity is obviously not a self-evident proposition. Hence, not every *per se* proposition is *per se nota* or self-evident. The modes of perseity of concern to us here are the first, second, and fourth. A proposition involves the first mode of perseity when its predicate falls in the definition of its subject, the second when its subject falls in the definition of its predicate, and the fourth when the subject is related to the predicate as a necessary and proper cause.[33] In a strict *propter quid* demonstration the major premise has the fourth mode of perseity (e. g., *Every rational animal is capable of speech*), the minor premise the first mode of perseity (e. g., *Every man is a rational animal*), and the conclusion the second mode of perseity (e. g., *Every man is capable of speech*).[34] "*Per se*" here indicates an essential rather than accidental connection between subject and predicate, and it refers exclusively to the objective structure of the propositions. *Per se nota*, on the other hand, refers rather to intelligible structure apropos of our knowledge of it, i. e., with or without a middle term, on the basis of intrinsic intelligibility or empirical data). A *per se nota proposition* is one known immediately on the basis of its intrinsic intelligibility. Every proposition (including the conclusion) in a strict *propter quid* demonstration must be *per se*, but only the premises must (and can) be *per se nota*.

Yet the case of the proposition in the second mode of perseity cannot be easily disposed of. True enough, as conclusion this proposition cannot be self-evident—at least not to us. But why isn't it self-evident to us? And is it, while not self-evident to us, self-evident in itself? It is necessary prior to demonstration that we know something about the subject and predicate of our conclusion and about the premises from which the conclusion is generated—that they are and/or what they are. Concerning the predicate of the conclusion, namely, the proper

---

[33] Cf., *supra*, note 12.

[34] *In I Post. Anal.*, lect. 13, n. 3: "Sciendum autem est quod cum in demonstratione probetur passio de subiecto per *medium*, quod est definitio, oportet quod prima propositio, cuius praedicatum est passio et subiectum est definitio, quae continet principia passionis, sit *per se* in *quarto modo*; secunda autem, cuius subiectum est ipsum subiectum et predicatum ipsa definitio in *primo modo*. Conclusio vero, in qua praedicatur passio de subiecto, est *per se* in *secundo modo*."

passion to be proven of the scientific subject, we must know only its nominal definition. In fact we cannot, prior to demonstration, know its essential definition, for this is what is to be proved. To know, prior to demonstration, the essential definition of the proper passion in the demonstration, is to know its inherence in its proper subject (i. e., the scientific subject of this demonstration), for the proper subject is included in the essential definition of the passion.[35] It would seem that a proposition *per se* in the second mode, with a proper passion predicated of its subject, is self-evident in itself, since the subject itself is in the definition of the predicate, but not self-evident to us, precisely because we fail to understand the essential definition of the passion short of demonstration. Cajetan seems to agree with this position, for when he points out that the *per se nota* proposition whose predicate falls into the definition of its subject is only the principal type of *per se nota* proposition, he adds a second type in which a passion is said of its proper subject.[36] If this type of proposition is self-evident it cannot be self-evident *secundum nos*, since it can be demonstrated, but *in se tantum*. Suppose this is the case, why should it be that this is *per se nota* only *in se*? The reason may be found in the type of causality exercised by the proper subject in reference to its proper passion. This is at least material causality, and in the case of the second mode of perseity it is precisely material causality which is actually involved.[37] But matter as such is not proportioned to manifest. The connection between the subject and its property is manifested to us only by way of the form which is implied by the subject and which is the active cause of this property. The conclusion can be said to be virtually in the fourth mode of perseity because its subject implies this form. It is only in explicating this in the *propter quid* demonstration that we see

[35] *Ibid.*, lect. 2.
[36] Catejan, *In I Post. Anal.*, Ch. 19.
[37] *In I Post. Anal.*, lect. 10, n. 4.

the necessary (but not, to us at least, immediate) connection between the subject and its property.[38]

IV. In Conclusion

At the very beginning of the *Posterior Analytics* Aristotle faces up to the famous dilemma of Meno. How can one ever be said to learn anything? Either he already knows what he learns—and this is not learning. Or he is ignorant of what he seeks to learn and thus cannot recognize it when he does come upon it—so that learning is impossible.[39] The difficulty reminds us of the Parmenidean dilemma apropos of motion. Aristotle, of course, defends the possibility of motion by introducing the

[38] There is, of course, no difference between the major premise in the strict type of *propter quid* demonstration and its conclusion unless there is a difference between the fourth mode of perseity and the second mode of perseity. And there is no difference here unless there is a difference between a real definition and the thing it defines. There can be, of course, no difference *in re* between the definition and the thing defined, so that the distinction between them must be a distinction of the reason rather than a real distinction. There is not even a foundation in the real for this distinction, so that it cannot be said to be a virtual logical distinction. Yet it must be more than the distinction exemplified between subject and predicate in the proposition *John is John*, for this is sheer tautology. If the definition and what it defines do not differ somehow as objects so that a proposition in the first mode of perseity is more than a tautology, then the prime instance of the *per se nota* proposition loses its significance and ceases to function meaningfully as an absolute premise at the same time that the major premise and conclusion of the strict type of *propter quid* demonstration became formally identical. This is, quite clearly, the death of demonstration. There is, however, a legitimate distinction to be made between the definition and what it defines. True, there is no advance in knowledge from thing to thing in defining. But there is in the definition a more perfect (clear and distinct) grasp of something known obscurely and confusedly prior to definition. This is enough to make the definition, from the point of view of the manner in which it is conceived, an object different from the defined; though, in itself, it remains identically the defined. This in turn is enough to make the *per se nota* proposition whose predicate is of the definition of the subject something more than tautologous. It is enough to guarantee a difference between the major and conclusion in the strict *propter quid* demonstration, and thus to guarantee the advance in knowledge without which demonstration would be meaningless. Cf. Simon et al, *op. cit.*, note 14, p. 618; McArthur, Ronald, "A Note on Demonstration," *The New Scholasticism*, XXXIV (1960), pp. 43-61; and especially Cajetan, *In I Post. Anal.*, ch. 3.

[39] Plato, *Meno*, 80D-86D.

notion of potential being (which in a sense represents a middle ground between being *simpliciter* and non-being *simpliciter*). In a similar fashion he defends the integrity of discourse by introducing the notion of the self-evident proposition. Self-evident propositions are the basic truths of demonstration, and in them scientific conclusions exist in potency. The demonstrative movement represents a true advance in knowledge from the potentiality of the scientific conclusion to its actuality. Prior to discourse the conclusion is not known *simpliciter*; but at the same time it is not unknown *simpliciter*. It is potentially known in its principles. The actual grasp of the self-evident proposition is the potential grasp of the scientific conclusions virtually contained therein. The premises of demonstration— taken as premises, that is, seen together to involve a middle term—function after the fashion of efficient causes which actuate the potentiality of the conclusion and make it be.[40] The whole of the *Posterior Analytics* is concerned to investigate the logical vehicle (namely, demonstraton) which brings us from the self-evident principles to our scientific conclusions. In the first book demonstration and its types and properties are investigated. The second book concentrates on definition precisely as the medium of demonstration. Quite significantly the last chapter of this second book—which completes the *Posterior Analytics*—comes full round to the topic of the very first chapter. Meno's dilemma is absolved in terms of the universally necessary and immediate basic principles of discourse. Scientific conclusions are truly *conclusions* insofar as they are different from these basic truths but are generated from them. They are truly *scientific* insofar as the basic truths of discourse into which they are resolved are primary and incontrovertible affirmations of the real. Upon the integrity of these basic truths or principles of demonstration depend the integrity of demon-

---

[40] *Quodl.*, VIII, a. 4; " Insunt enim nobis naturaliter quaedam principia primo complexa omnibus nota, ex quibus ratio procedit ad cognoscendum in actu conclusiones quae in praedictis principiis potentialiter continentur. . . ." Cf., also *De Ver.*, q. 11, a. 1; *Summa*, I, q. 117, a. 1.

stration and the worth of its conclusions. Thus, in this final chapter, Aristotle defends the integrity of the principles themselves in terms of an intuitive induction from the incontrovertible data of sense experience. St. Thomas points out that the difference between dialectical discourse and demonstration is the difference between unterminated and terminated discourse.[41] The dialectician falls short of being a scientist precisely because dialectical conclusions are not finally grounded in the real. The dialectical method can be referred to as a " rational method " precisely insofar as its conclusions remain within the reason. The demonstrative method is the method of science because it grounds its conclusions necessarily in the real—and it does this insofar as it resolves them into self-evident propositions. There is no science save that there be a rational progression from principles to scientific conclusions. Thus the scientific intellect is of necessity a *ratio*. But, at the same time, there is no science save that there be an intuition of basic principles—so that the scientific intellect is also an *intellectus*.[42] Demonstration may be an instrument of the intellect as reason, but there can be no meaningful theory of demonstration save that the *per se nota* proposition, itself properly the object of intellect as intellect, be significantly a part of that theory.

EDWARD D. SIMMONS

Marquette University,
Milwaukee, Wisconsin.

---

[41] *In Boeth. de Trin.*, q. 6, a. 1 ad 1: "Alio modo dicitur processus rationalis ex termino, in quo sistitur procedendo. Ultimus enim terminus, ad quem rationis inquisitio perducere debet, est intellectus principiorum, in quae resolvendo iudicamus; quod quidem quando fit, non dicitur processus vel probatio rationabilis, sed demonstratio. Quandoque autem inquisitio rationis non potest usque ad ultimum terminum perduci, sed sistitur in ipsa inquisitione, quando per probabiles rationes proceditur, quae natae sunt facere opinionem vel fidem, non scientiam, et sic rationabilis processus dividitur contra demonstrativum."

[42] *Summa*, I-II, q. 57, a. 2: " Verum autem est dupliciter considerabile; uno modo, sicut per se notum; alio modo, sicut per aliud notum. Quod autem est per se notum, se habet ut principium, et percipitur statim ab intellectu; et ideo habitus perficiens intellectum ad huiusmodi veri considerationem vocatur *intellectus* qui est habitus principiorum." *In Boeth. de Trin.*, q. 6, a. 1 ad 1: " Ultimus enim terminus, ad quem rationis inquisitio perducere debet, est intellectus principiorum, in quae resolvendo iudicamus. . . ."

THE SIGNIFICANCE OF THE UNIVERSAL
UT NUNC

∽

IN his commentary on the *Posterior Analytics* of Aristotle, St. Thomas notes that *dici de omni*, sometimes translated as " true in every instance," is treated differently in the *Posterior Analytics* from the way it is in the *Prior Analytics*. In the latter work, which is concerned with the form of the syllogism and therefore with what is common to any syllogism, *dici de omni* is treated only commonly, disregarding the differences attaching to a demonstrative or dialectical use. In this context, it is enough to say that *dici de omni* is realized whenever the predicate is found to be in each of those things which are contained under the subject. Once, however, we begin to consider the syllogism on the part of matter, we must say more about *dici de omni*. Hence, immediately after saying that the predicate is found in each of those things which are contained under the subject, St. Thomas adds: " This can happen either *ut nunc*, and in this way the dialectician sometimes uses *dici de omni*, or *absolutely* and for all time, and in this way only the demonstrator uses it." [1]

In discussing the ancient and medieval theory of universals, we are apt to overlook this distinction between the verified *dici de omni* and the provisional one called universal *ut nunc*, and we tend to ignore the importance the latter has as a tool particularly for the investigation of nature. An example of the verified *dici de omni* was the common property of every parabolic triangle, ' to have its three angles equal to two right angles.' An instance of the universal *ut nunc* was ' white ' predicated as a common property of swans. The former property was based upon a *propter quid* demonstration; the latter was based upon, or rather derived from, an incomplete

---

[1] " Hoc autem contingit vel *ut nunc*, et sic utitur quandoque *dici de omni* dialecticus; vel *simpliciter* et secundum omne tempus, et sic solum utitur eo demonstrator." *In I Post. Anal.*, lect. 9, n. 4.

induction: no one reporting about swans had ever seen a black one.

We come therefore at once to the following question. Since "white," as a common property, was not certain, why is it that we could use the universally distributive 'all' and say that all swans are white? Why not use a roundabout expression and state: "It appears that some, if not all, swans are white." Or why not say, even more simply, "swan is white," as we say "man is white." In this more simple way of putting the matter we would be plainly predicating something of a universal ("swan") by reason of something found in one or some individuals. The point then is whether this would be regarded as a universal *ut nunc*, a universal "for the time being." Presumably not, for what we are aiming at is an enunciation like "man is an animal," an essential predication. But why use this mode of enunciation before it is warranted?

What we are in fact faced with is two distinct modes of essential predication: a true one and a hypothetical one. What is the foundation for this distinction? Why are hypothetically essential predications required? Why not use unambiguous circumlocutions that show the essential predication to be only hypothetical? After all, many essential predications are in fact no more than hypothetical.

To answer such questions—which in effect are one question—about the distinction between true and hypothetical essential predications, it will be opportune, first of all, to make a further distinction by comparing the notion of "triangle" with what we intend by "swan." We can define the first as to what it is, namely a three straight-sided figure whose exterior angle is equal to the two opposite interior angles. But what about "swan"? We define, not the swan, but the name by pointing to individual instances, or by describing the figure and habits that set swans apart from chickens, turkeys, geese, and so on. Now surely there must be in nature something that accounts for these differences. But what is this exactly? As St. Thomas says: " That nature is, is *per se* known, insofar as natural things are manifest to sense. But what the nature of any thing is, or what its principle of motion, is not manifest." [2]

Meanwhile, we have the name " swan " and whoever knows this name, using it with the meaning agreed upon, does not confuse swans with chickens or geese. Still, there may exist somewhere, or there may have existed, some types of fowl between swans and geese which could make us hesitate about using the name to stand for what is assumed to be a definable nature. The opposition of contradiction between " swan " and " non-swan " is plain enough, but where and how it actually applies may be uncertain. Such is the case whenever the positive term referred to is imperfectly known. Lacking definitive knowledge, we have agreed to use the word in a way that is at least in practice meaningful. In the measure that certain sensible signs set swans apart from other feathered creatures, we are confident that our naming has some determinate basis in nature, that swans do in fact have a nature. Just what this is, however, we have to acknowledge that we do not know.

Let us recognize, however, that even if we knew exactly what a swan is as we know what a plane triangle is, the term " swan " by itself, apart from an enunciation, would be neither true nor false. The same applies to the nominal definition of the name, whether obtained by designation or by description of what it stands for: " a large-bodied, web-footed water bird of the genus *Cygnus*, having a long neck and sort legs placed far back," etc. We can, of course, go further and state that there are such animals. However, the truth of this statement does not imply that we know exactly what a swan is. Accordingly, we are forced to acknowledge a hiatus (a) between the truth of the statement and the relative indetermination as to what a swan is; (b) between the name itself, used to stand for

---

[2] " Naturam autem esse, est per se notum, inquantum naturalia sunt manifesta sensui. Sed quid sit uniuscujusque rei natura, vel quod principium motus, hoc non est manifestum." *In II Phys.*, lect. 1, n. 8.

a universal that is predicable of certain individuals, and the way
it would signify if we knew, once and for all, just what a swan
is as we know what a plane triangle is. In other words, we can
name things before we know precisely what the thing is that
we name. The history of biology proves that what we had
long considered to be a species turns out to be a genus.

That simple naming, as distinguished from enunciation, does
not presume that we know exactly what it is that we name is
strikingly plain in the instance of the word " atom." It is taken
from the Greek " indivisible," in common usage. Democritus
imposed a further meaning upon it to signify what he believed
to be the indivisible elements of all things, differing from
one another by their geometrical figure. Dalton, for quite
different reasons, was led to an analogous conception, but his
minute spheres still retained the meaning of " indivisible."
Rutherford finally broke down these indivisibles, and they are
becoming unceasingly the opposite of what the name was first
intended to mean. The word " atom " continues to make
history, a history reflecting progress in our knowledge of the
basal entities of the physical world. But the original meaning
has dropped from sight, and the physicist will no longer refer
us to nature except most indirectly. He will explain what he
means when using this word by relating certain observations,
such as the Brownian movement, and operations of measurement which led to interrelated measure-numbers permitting
him to establish equations, etc., which he then goes on to
explain in terms of hypotheses and theory that lead to further
experiments, etc. This elaborated understanding becomes very
atomic in one sense, if you will, but Democritus might well be
puzzled about his word " atom."

Of course, someone might say of Democritus that he did not
know what he was talking about, and the same of Dalton.
But of course they knew. What they were ignorant of was the
real import of what they said, which could be no more than
vague, as the history of science has proved. What we must
recognize is that there can be uncertainty, not only as to

whether B belongs to A, or whether B is common to A and C, or a commensurate property of B, but that there can also be uncertainty concerning what the term A exactly stands for. If A and B are known exactly, then their relationship can be known exactly too. But if they are not known exactly for what they are, their relationship will be proportionally vague and provisional.

There is a difference, then, between a universal *ut nunc* as a simple term, viz., A, and as a subject or a property in an enunciation, such as "All A is B." The following questions remain open: " *Is* A? " " *Is* B? " "Is AB? " The first two concern the bearing of the names: do these definite names refer to something we know definitely? The answer to the other question is obvious: the relation of A to B is either definitely known or it is provisionally posited. Yet why should we posit names and relations provisionally? Why not wait until we know the named exactly and, in the case of enunciation, until we know the exact relation?

This brings us to the very heart of scientific method and to the relevance of the theory of positing a universal " for the time being " in the practice of science. We must, for the time being, posit such universals and wait to see what happens for having posited them. But let us not suppose that " to see what happens " is merely a passive attitude. The very positing must suggest an activity, a further induction or experimentation, with attendant hypotheses and theory which give further meaning to the original positing. To posit a universal *ut nunc* is to advance something that not only requires further testing but also suggests it.

Now had we confined ourselves to predicating something of a universal nature (or of a quasi-universal nature) by reason of what is verified in its inferior singulars, the matter would be immediately closed and settled. For, if Socrates walks, we are quite justified in saying that " man walks," and that's the end of it. But if we say " man is an animal," this must be true of every man, not just of this man. However, this mode of predication, as we have suggested, need not be reserved to cases that are certain. Mere likeliness may suffice to posit propositions in that mode, such as "man came about by mutations that occurred in lower living beings," but they will be *posited* and require further proof. In other words, the universal *ut nunc* appears both in the order of simple apprehension and in the order of composition and division, with all that this entails in the order of argumentation.

Now there is a further aspect to this type of universality. It is, in a sense, pragmatic: we may have to do something about it. This "doing" can mean a speculative operation, as when we are inclined to believe that there is no last prime number: the statement is a challenge that sets us on to attempt a proof. But the doing may also be more strictly a practical operation, such as experimentation, or careful isolation for further induction. And this brings us face to face with an important distinction. Suppose that we have laid down a thermodynamic theory, which is a coordinated ensemble of posits, and construct on the basis of it a machine that works. Does this prove that the theory is true? Pragmatically, it does. It is in this sense that as to truth, scientific theories are in the main pragmatic. But so far as sheer knowledge is concerned, pragmatic proof can do no more than indicate that as to speculative truth the theories are on the right track, that we are moving in the direction of the truth, not that we possess it. The whole point is, then, that we would not be moving on toward the truth if we did not take the liberty of constructing posits in the mode of universal terms and universal propositions for the immediate purpose of seeing what happens when we do this.

If our mind had to confine itself to terms and propositions that we know well and could only use these for further argument, there is very little that we could ever come to know.[3]

___
[3] This would not only preclude advances in scientific knowing, but also in vast areas of what we now regard as philosophy, for the "eternal truths" of philosophy occupy a relatively small position in relation to the whole. Indeed, it might be said

Tentatively we must go beyond what we know, starting from hints, as it were, and then proceeding from what we have posited as if it were true. It is as if, to move on, our mind must come to rest, provisionally, in a myth, a verisimilitude, and even in strictly logical fictions. But it must do so *wittingly*, which is what it does in fact by recognizing the type of universality we are concerned with here as being no more than *ut nunc*.

As we get closer to things in their concretion, the universals

that a defect of much scholastic philosophy, especially in the manual form, has consisted in treating so many things as falling under *dici de omni* absolutely and as though subject to rigorous demonstration. The great scholastics, however, were never under such illusion. St. Albert, for instance, especially with respect to the sort of knowledge we have in the investigation of nature, says the following:

" It is plain, then, from what has been pointedly considered in natural things, that every definition or notion of natural forms is conceived with matter, which is subject to motion or change or to both; and it must therefore be conceived with time inasmuch as time is in the temporal thing. Because of this, much opinion is involved in this sort of knowing, so that it cannot attain to the firm, constant and necessary habit of science, as Ptolemy says." After contrasting the " doctrinal sciences (mathematics) with such knowledge, St. Albert adds: ". . . the habits acquired by the speculative intellect have been given the name of true science, and are called doctrinal and teachable; and the reason is that they are taught from unchanging principles, which the disciple receives from the teacher by sheer notification of the terms, without need of experience, as Aristotle says in Book IV, but by the teacher's simple demonstration the intellect of the disciple comes to rest; hence it is that adolescents, without experience, can so often excel in these matters— something which is in no way possible in the natural sciences, where experience is of far greater account than doctrine by demonstration." *In I Metaph.*, Tract. I, cap. 1, (Borgnet, VI) pp. 1-2.

(Constat autem ex his quae subtiliter in naturis considerata sunt, omnem diffinitionem aut rationem formarum physicarum conceptam esse cum materia, quae motui subjacet, aut mutationi, aut utrique; et ideo concipi oportet eam cum tempore secundum quod tempus est in re temporali. Propter quod etiam id quod scitur de hujusmodi, multum miscetur opinioni, et pertingere non potest ad confirmatum constantem et necessarium scientiae habitum, sicut dicit Ptolemaeus. . . . habitus per speculativum intellectum adepti verae scientiae nomen acceperunt, et doctrinales et disciplinales vocantur, ideo quia ex principiis non mutantibus quae discipulus a magistro non accepit nisi per terminorum notitias, docentur, experientia non indigentes, ut dicit Aristoteles libro quarto, sed simplici demonstratione doctoris constante intellectu discipuli: propter quod etiam juvenes inexperti ut plurimum magis excellunt in ipsis: quod nullo modo possible fuit in physicis speculabilibus, in quibus experientia multo plus confert quam doctrina per demonstrationem).

are more and more provisional in the sense that we deliberately posit terms, vague and uncertain, which our mind is free to invest with intentions of universality, and thereupon seek to establish relations between those terms. Our mind has this power because it can bring together things which in nature are not *per se* connected, e. g., " man walks " or " man is white." In these examples we do attain a truth, however, since we do not mean that every man is walking or that every man is white. But what we learn from such examples is that what is accidentally one in nature can be brought together by the intellect to form a proposition that is *per se* one *as a proposition.* Moreover, the mind can go further than that, and in fact must do so, positing terms and bringing them together for the purpose of getting behind the appearances upon which our posits are based.[4]

Verisimilitude, either with respect to terms or with respect to composition or division, is the proper basis of universality *ut nunc.* By verisimilitude we mean that which may in fact have no more than a resemblance to truth, a mere appearance of it and recognized as being no more than that. This is enough for our mind to reach out beyond what we really know, beyond what is warranted. Actually, universality for the time being keeps us within the bounds of the mind, as any opinion does, so long as it is no more than opinion. But opinion, as dialectic in general, has the nature of a tool, an organon, with respect to truth. Constructed universals of the type we are concerned with (as distinguished from the relation of universality we may tentatively invest them with) are logical organa. For dialectics as *logica utens* does not go beyond the stage of instrumentality.

There is in all of this something of a paradox which we should notice. The mind goes beyond what it really knows, but in so doing it still remains within its own confines. How does this occur? A situation analogous to this is the one already noted, of the mind's composing a proposition that is one *per se* about

---

[4] Aristotle was certainly aware of this procedure. See, for example, *De Caelo*, III, chap. 7.

something that is one only *per accidens*. The *per se* one remains within the mind, yet the mind is thereby enabled to say something that is true, namely " man is white." However, at best this is only an analogy, or perhaps only an example, of the main point we have in mind. How does this main point differ from the instance of the mind's composing as *per se* one which is one only *per accidens?*

Let us try to bring out the difference by considering the status of opinion. Here we go beyond what is warranted, either by a proper reason (as in the case of an opinion concerning something in *logica docens*) or by what we know truly of reality (e. g., why ruminants need the type of digestive system they have; the reason assigned could be one that would apply to horses, who also eat and digest grass) . In thus going beyond reality, we do not do so in the way one real thing goes beyond another, as cows beyond cabbage. The " going beyond " is in the order of knowing. It is not as if our mind casts out a net. The mind does cast out nets (as, indeed, we do so well and frequently in logical divisions) but they remain within the mind and are ordered to knowledge, not to the actual handling of things. Of course, there is, nonetheless, a kind of reaching out physically toward reality and even a meddling in it when we perform an experiment. But why do we perform so many experiments? Not to improve things in any practical sense, at least primarily, but to improve our understanding of what things are so far as possible. And so we are back in the mind, which we have really never left. The external operation is performed with a view, not to altering a given order in reality, but to improving the knowledge in our mind. Hence the paradox remains, but is intelligible. We go beyond our mind in order for the mind to understand what it otherwise could not, but this " going beyond " is a dialectical extension, remaining an instrument for the mind's ever increasing grasp of an obscure physical reality. In this order, experience and experimenting contribute more to our knowledge than strict demonstration.

The evolution of scientific theories, based upon wider observations enhanced by physical instruments, suggesting new hypotheses that suggest further research and crucial experiments, shows that we may have to remain content with a knowledge that, ever progressive, remains nonetheless provisional. Now in the measure that this is true of most of our investigation of nature, it is clear that the domain of universality *ut nunc* has far greater dimensions than that of true universals, and this is the point of emphasis in this paper, a point which seems to have been somewhat ignored in the scholastic tradition. There are two complementary reasons for the greater dimension of the universal *ut nunc*. First, there is the very nature of our mind, which is an experimental one, seeing that our knowledge must be derived from things themselves. Second, there is the unexpected complexity of the things we seek to know, even of those which apparently are at close range, the sensible things. Even these are somehow fathomless in the experimental sense of the word. A simple example is enough to illustrate this point, our organs of external sensation. We agree that our skin is an organ of touch and that our eyes are organs of sight. This seems safe enough to say so long as we do not look too closely into the subject. We have initially recognized and understood these organs with reference to our sensations. But now we must delve into anatomy and physiology, and then into chemistry and physics. In this process we are wading toward a limit we shall never reach. Yet we know that the limit is somehow there though we have nothing more than an intimation of just what it is. And so it is that the whole interval between actual sensation along with the vaguely recognized organs, and the limit we are moving toward, is replete with provisionally contructed terms, with universals " for the time being," ever in need of reconstruction and implementation.

Even a true universal such as " what a man is " does not settle all that man is, once for all.[5] The example of sensation

---

[5] The definition of " man " as " rational animal " has often been criticized as inadequate and even ridiculed as being incomplete. But this definition, though an

and its organs shows that this true universal is quite incomplete and must be implemented with a world of universals *ut nunc*. Man is a good enough example, for in one sense he is the being which we know best, while in another sense we know least of him. We know him best because of our internal experience; but in terms of external experience we know the lower forms of life far better even though these, from the former point of view, are by far the more obscure. Now the situation is such that while we may be definitely certain about some things we come to know from internal experience, as soon as we try to narrow down our knowledge of living things in terms of external experience, then even our simplest terms, such as " protoplasm " or " genes," though their related conceptions have some basis in experience, are in the main " logical fictions " in even Lord Bertrand Russell's sense of this term.

Nevertheless, we should not wholly identify logical fictions with our universals *ut nunc*. The fictions are not intended to have that kind of resemblance to true universal natures. Logical fictions are symbolic constructions whereas the universals *ut nunc* are names and bear a real verisimilitude to natures.

When all is said and done, however, it still remains that the bulk of our knowledge remains provisional and in constant need of implementation. That such is the status of our knowledge is not itself mere theory. It is a well established fact. The history of science proves that we may be quite certain of our uncertainties, i. e., of the provisional nature of most of our knowing as regards things in their ultimate concretion, and therefore of the fact that most of our universals are *ut nunc*. We are definitely certain that two is an even number and even of what a circle is (no matter how little the calculator may care about this) ; and that if an even number is taken from an

---

essential one and a good one in precisely this sense, was never intended to be a complete definition. From the standpoint of completion, much remains to be said about what man is, and much of what we know in seeking to determine more fully what man is will remain provisional.

even number, the remainder will be an even number—all this being a matter of strict demonstration. But we have nothing like this kind of certitude about dogs and cats, not to mention the less familiar objects of even ordinary experience. Recognizing, therefore, how provisional most of our knowledge is, let us, for the time being, make all possible use of universals *ut nunc.*

JOHN A. OESTERLE

University of Notre Dame,
Notre Dame, Indiana.

WILLIAM HARVEY, M.D.: MODERN OR ANCIENT SCIENTIST?

∽

W ILLIAM HARVEY was born in England in 1578 and died in 1657. He received his grammar school education at the famous King's School in Canterbury. In 1593 he entered Caius College, Cambridge, and received his B.A. degree in 1597. In this period, it was not unusual for English Protestants interested in a scientific education to seek it in a continental Catholic university. Harvey chose the *Universitas Juristarum,* the more influential of the two universities which constituted the University of Padua in Italy and which had been attended by Thomas Linacre and John Caius, and where, incidently, the Dominican priests were associated with University functions.

Competency in the traditional studies of the day was characteristic of William Harvey's intellectual development. The degree of Doctor of Physic was awarded to Harvey in 1602 with the unusual testimonial that " he had conducted himself so wonderfully well in the examination, and had shown such skill, memory, and learning that he had far surpassed even the great hopes which his examiners had formed of him. They decided therefore that he was skilled, expert, and most efficiently qualified both in arts and medicine, and to this they put their hands, unanimously, willingly, with complete agreement, and unhesitatingly." [1]

In 1616 he gave his first Lumleian lectures in surgery at the Royal College of Physicians in London. The manuscript notes of his first course of lectures, the *Prelectiones,* are preserved and have been reproduced in facsimile and transcript.[2] In these lectures he first enunciates the circulation of the blood.

[1] D'Arcy Powers, *William Harvey* (London, 1897), pp. 26-27.
[2] William Harvey, *Prelectiones Anatomiae Universalis* (London: J. & A. Churchill, 1886).

He waited for 12 years, however, until 1628, before he published his great work entitled, *An Anatomical Exercise on the Motion of the Heart and Blood in Animals.* In this classic he formally demonstrated the true nature of the heart and that the motion of the blood was circular. This work is relatively short and takes up 86 pages in the standard English edition of his collected works.[3] In 1648 Harvey's demonstration was attacked in a treatise published by Dr. Jean Riolan of Paris. Harvey answered his critic in two lengthy letters published in Cambridge in 1649.

Harvey's second famous work, *Anatomical Exercises on the Generation of Animals,* which is over five times the length of the first, appeared in publication in 1651 through the solicitation and under the direction of Dr. George Ent, a well-known physician of the period.

In his personal life and professional career Harvey had a wide circle of acquaintances and friends. Though it is not certain whether he knew Galileo who was a fellow student at Padua, he knew most of the leading contemporaries of his day. This included Boyle, Hooke, Hobbes, Dryden, Cowley, Descartes, Gilbert, Wren, Bacon and others, in addition to prominent physicians and anatomists.

Harvey was extremely well-read and made reference in his lectures and writings to the Greek philosophers and scientists of the fourth through the seventh centuries, B. C., to many Greek writers of the Christian era, to numerous Latin writers including many of the poets, to Albert the Great, and to numerous Renaissance men of the fifteenth and sixteenth centuries. In all, he made reference to approximately 100 authors in his

---

[3] *The Works of William Harvey, M. D.* (London: Printed for the Sydenham Society, 1847): Translated from the Latin by Robert Willis, M. D. It includes *An Anatomical Exercise on the Motion of the Heart and Blood in Animals; The First Anatomical Exercise on the Circulation of the Blood to John Riolan; A Second Exercise to John Riolan, in Which Many Objections to the Circulation of the Blood are Refuted; Anatomical Exercises on the Generation of Animals, to Which are Added, Essays on Parturition, On the Membranes and Fluids of the Uterus, and on Conception;* and miscellaneous items (Harvey's will, autopsy of Thomas Parr and nine short letters).

writings. In particular, he had a comprehensive working knowledge of Aristotle, as well as Aristotle's commentators, Avicenna and Averroes. According to one Harvian lecturer, Harvey refers to Aristotle 269 times.[4] References are made to Aristotle's logical, physical, biological and metaphysical works. It is clear that Harvey's superior intellectual formation through ancient authors—the Great Books of his day—proved no block to his momentous contribution to the future.

Finally, it is pertinent to note his basic religious belief as it relates to his scientific work. On the title page of his *Prelectiones* he prefixes from his favorite poet, Virgil, the motto " Stat Jove principium, Musae, Jovis omnia plena." Over thirty years later he explicates this motto in Exercise 54 of the *Generation of Animals*:

. . . in the same way, as in the greater world, we are told that ' All things are full of Jove,' so in the slender body of the pullet, and in every one of its actions, does the finger of God or nature no less obviously appear . . . We acknowledge God, the supreme and omnipotent creator, to be present in the production of all animals, and to point, as it were, with a finger to his existence in his works, the parents being in every case but as instruments in his hand. In the generation of the pullet from the egg all things are indeed contrived and ordered with singular providence, divine wisdom, and most admirable and incomprehensible skill. And to none can these attributes be referred save to the Almighty, first cause of all things, by whatever name this has been designated,—the Divine Mind by Aristotle; the Soul of the Universe by Plato; the *Natura Naturans* by others; Saturn and Jove by the ancient Greeks and Romans; by ourselves, and as is seeming in these days, the Creator and Father of all that is in heaven and earth, on whom animals depend for their being, and at whose will and pleasure all things are and were engendered.[5]

In his last will and testament he states, " I doe most humbly render my soule to Him that gave it and to my blessed Lord

---

[4] D. F. Fraser-Harris, " William Harvey's Knowledge of Literature Classical, Mediaeval, Renaissance and Contemporary." *Proceedings of the Royal Society of Medicine*, XXVII (1934), 195-99.

[5] Harvey, *Works*, ed. cit., pp. 401-402.

and Savior Christ Jesus and my bodie to the Earth to be buried at the discretion of my executor . . ." [6]

Before we can determine whether Harvey was a modern or an ancient scientist, we must first know him as the great scientist he was. The twentieth century scientist, more narrowly educated for the most part, pays only lip service to Harvey's greatness. We can say about most contemporary scientists concerning Harvey, what Galen said about his contemporaries concerning Hippocrates: they admire him, but do not read him; when they read him, they do not understand him; when they understand him, they fail to put into practice what he has taught.[7]

Characterizing the lip service of contemporary biologists and physicians is the unexpressed and hidden belief—a reflection of our current pride and prejudice—that what Harvey enunciated was so obvious, so easily discoverable, so easily observable by all beginning students, that the uniqueness of his discovery was principally his ability to liberate himself from the yoke of ancient traditions, thought and terminology—from dark ages, sterile scholasticism, authoritarianism and philosophical encroachments—sufficiently to see what in itself was so patently observable. Even then, Harvey's liberation was incomplete according to many historians.

Part of the modern difficulty stems from not reading him. Typical of the difficulty is the belief that Harvey's discovery of the circulation of the blood was a sense observation rather than a conclusion resulting from reason utilizing inductions from sense observations, as principles or propositions in a demonstration.

Part of the modern difficulty also stems from those who have read him, but not well. Many such readers have failed to appreciate the complexity of obtaining a new and true conclusion within a context in which the old conclusion was a plausible part of an integrated body of knowledge. The modern reader,

---

[6] *Ibid.*, p. lxxxix.

[7] Galen, *Si quis optimus medicus est, eundem esse philosophum*, among *Isagogici libri*, in *Opera omnia*, 9th ed. (Venetiis, apud Juntas: 1625), fol. 6r-v.

by reading Harvey retrospectively as if his work were merely the beginning of what came afterwards, tends to miss what is more basic: that Harvey's discovery like most scientific discoveries results from a scientific methodology which is related to one's education, philosophy, habits, and experience as a scientist. Rather than relate Harvey's discovery to the past out of which it emerged, the modern reader acts as if it sprang *de novo* from a pair of eyes newly able to observe through the Renaissance liberation from the medieval blinders that enveloped this age.

The following comments are characteristic of those made by critics who dissociate Harvey's demonstration from the tradition of his predecessors. Harvey " with one blow demolished the structure, compounded of metaphysics, far-fetched analogy, and mysterious ' principles ' and ' spirits,' which constitute the method of medieval biology." Harvey's method was characterized " by the rigid exclusion of mysterious forces and agencies." [8] " Harvey . . . never entirely emerged from the mystifying language of his contemporaries, and even regarded himself as a loyal Aristotelian, but he builded better than he knew." [9]

The contemporary translator of the most widely read version of Harvey's classic on *The Motions of the Heart and the Blood* —an outstanding scientist in his own right—has this to say:

In his more scientific passages, Harvey is remarkably terse and ' snappy,' in the current style. In his philosophical discussions he becomes vague and his sentences grow beyond control . . . At the same time, he tried to complete his demonstrations by metaphysical arguments based on the traditional teleology. This was the antithesis of the method by which he had achieved such brilliant success in the preceding chapters . . . There is a good discussion of the comparative and embryological aspects of the subject, and then a peculiar use of the traditional authority of Galen as evidence. One may find almost all kinds of logic in Harvey.[10]

[8] Franklin Fearing, *Reflex Action* (Baltimore: William & Wilkins, 1930), p. 29.

[9] A. Wolf, *A History of Science, Technology and Philosophy in the 16th and 17th Centuries* (London, 1935), p. 415.

[10] Chauncey D. Leake, *An English Translation with Annotations of De Motu Cordis* (Springfield: Charles C. Thomas, 1931), Translator's Preface.

If these comments truly delineate Harvey's contribution, we are faced with the following paradox: Harvey, who was educated superbly in the traditional education of his time, who considered himself a loyal traditionalist in science and philosophy, and who utilized philosophical arguments based on the established teleology of the day, all of which are alleged to be antithetical to scientific advance, was also the same Harvey who produced a brilliant, original and revolutionary work of science which laid the groundwork for modern physiology and medicine.

To explicate this paradox, it seems incumbent upon us to keep open the possibility that the fruit of his labors bears a direct relationship to the tree that bore it and the intellectual soil that nourished it. That Harvey was well educated, and respected and utilized his learning heightens this possibility. Furthermore, Harvey was one of the few successful investigators in the history of science who actually thought about and wrote on scientific methodology, and whose thinking on this permits us to measure his reciprocal accomplishments.

It is ironic, in contrast, that the modern scientist looks upon Harvey's contemporary, Francis Bacon, as the father of modern science, despite history's testimony that no scientific discovery can be attributed to the Baconian method. It is particularly ironic since there is no indication that Bacon even recognized Harvey's striking contribution. A leading Bacon scholar writes, " The probability is that . . . he regarded the theory as hardly worthy of serious discussion." [11]   Contrariwise, Harvey, who was Bacon's personal physician, said of him derogatorily that, although he enjoyed his wit and style, Bacon " writes philosophy like a Lord Chancellor." [12]

The alternative of the hypothesis that Harvey's contribution flowed from his past is a dismal one. It forces one to conclude that Harvey was a schizophrenic, a duality—a sterile scholastic and a fertile scientist—rather than a unity; and that his " bril-

[11] Thomas Fowler, *Bacon's Novum Organum*, Edited with Introduction, Notes, etc., 2nd ed. (Oxford, 1889) p. 28.
[12] John Aubrey, *Lives of Eminent Men* (London, 1813), vol. 2, p. 381.

liant success " was accomplished by " almost all kinds of logic."
We can best seek to understand the paradox of Harvey by
seeing whether Harvey, in his turn, merely paid lip service to
Aristotle who dominated the medieval period or actually utilized him the way one scientist utilizes another.

To show that Harvey was a genuine disciple of Aristotle, four
illustrations of how Harvey utilizes and follows Aristotle are
presented below. The first summarizes Harvey's essay on scientific methodology and shows Harvey's adherence to Aristotle's *Organon*. The second illustration deals with the great
scientific controversy in embryology as to whether animals are
preformed or epigenetically unfold themselves in development.
It shows Harvey decisively siding with Aristotle. The third
reviews the actual references Harvey makes to Aristotle in
The Motion of the Heart and Blood and shows that Aristotle
abets rather than hinders Harvey's ultimate demonstration.
One of these references points up the need for a modern reader
to have a knowledge of Aristotle's works if he is to have an
adequate understanding of Aristotle's contribution to Harvey's
discovery and demonstration. The final analysis shows that
Harvey's demonstration of the true motion of the heart and
blood is a classic Aristotelian demonstration, and illustrates
that Harvey follows in practice what he adheres to in theory.

AN ESSAY ON THE SCIENTIFIC METHOD

Harvey's essay on the scientific method is the preface to his
work, *Anatomical Exercises on the Generation of Animals,*
which was published 23 years after the publication of his classic,
The Motion of the Heart and Blood, when Harvey was 73
years old. It is a product of his later years and reflects the
permanency of the position he held. It is not intended as a
complete exposition of the scientific method but only as a
preface to his work on generation. The preface [13] consists of 27
paragraphs and has three headings: ' Of the Mode and Order
of Acquiring Knowledge '; ' Of the Former, Calling to Mind

---

[13] Harvey, *Works, ed. cit.,* pp. 151-167.

Aristotle '; and ' Of the Method to be Turned to in the Knowledge of Generation.' The following is a paragraph analysis of
this essay.

PREFACE

Anatomical Exercises on the Generation of Animals

A. Introduction
　　1. Causes of writing (par. 1)
　　2. Present opinions concerning generation
　　　　a. Of Galen and physicians (par. 2)
　　　　b. Of Aristotle and philosophers (par. 3)
　　3. Concerning the falsity of these opinions (par. 4)
　　4. Further exposition of final causes of writing (par. 5)
　　5. Concerning the method employed
　　　　a. That it is difficult (par. 6)
　　　　b. That its difficulty should not be a deterrent (par. 7)

B. Of the Mode and Order of Acquiring Knowledge
　　　(*cognitio*)
　　1. That there can be only one road to science (*scientia*)
　　　　(par. 8)
　　2. Explication of the road
　　　　a. Relation of sense to universals (par. 9)
　　　　b. As expressed by Seneca and expounded by Harvey
　　　　　(par. 10)
　　3. The importance of sense for judgment (par. 11)
　　4. Why it was thought fit to present this by way of intro-
　　　　duction (par. 12)

C. Of the Former, Calling to Mind Aristotle
　　1. That knowledge (*cognitio*) is not innate but acquired
　　　　(par. 13)
　　2. Whence and how we come to know (par. 14)

3. Resolution by Aristotle of the difficulty involved (par. 15)

4. The order of knowledge in any art or science (par. 16)

5. Conclusions as to the relation of perfect knowledge to sense (par. 17)

6. Conclusions as restated by Aristotle (par. 18)

7. Explication of preceding passage from Aristotle (par. 19)

8. Concluding advice to the reader concerning testimony of the senses (par. 20)

D. Of the Method to be Turned to in the Knowledge (*cognitio*) of Generation

1. The method proposed (par. 21)

2. This method compared to that of Fabricius (par. 22)

3. What will be set forth according to the method
   a. in respect to formal content (par. 23)
   b. in respect to material content (par. 24 and 25)

4. What will be inferred from that set forth and the difficulties involved (par. 26)

5. Conclusion (par. 27)

Under 'Of the Mode and Order of Acquiring Knowledge' (Section B) Harvey rests his scientific method solidly on Aristotle.

Harvey juxtaposes two key Aristotelian texts which "at first blush may seem contradictory." The one text emphasizes that there is but one road to scientific knowledge, i. e., to the reasoned fact, namely, a syllogistic process by which we move from universals to particulars. He states that we "start from the things which are more knowable and clearer to us and proceed towards those which are clearer and more knowable by nature" (*Physics*, Bk. I, Ch. 1, 184 a 16-18). The second text stresses the inductive and prior knowledge obtained from sense data for "that is more perspicuous to us which is based on induction . . . whence it is advisable from singulars to pass to universals " (*Post. Anal.*, Bk. II, Ch. 13).

In the following section entitled "Of the same matters, according to Aristotle," Harvey elaborates Bk. I, Ch. 1, of the *Posterior Analytics*, which states that all doctrine and intellectual discipline, including the two forms of reasoning, the syllogistic and the inductive, is acquired from antecedent knowledge, none of which is innate. He then uses a passage from Aristotle to explicate this antecedent knowledge, which arises in sense, is retained by memory, and which, when repeated, results in experience, from which in turn is derived the beginnings of art and science. He again quotes a more "elegant" passage of Aristotle to the same effect (*Metaphysics*, Bk. I, Ch. 1).

Harvey goes on to say that "By this Aristotle plainly tells us that no one can truly be entitled prudent or truly knowledgeable (*scientem vere*), who does not of his own proper experience, i.e., from repeated memory, frequent perception by sense, and diligent observation, know that a thing is so in fact. Without these, indeed, we only imagine or believe, and such knowledge (*scientia*) is rather to be accounted as belonging to others than to us." Harvey concludes this section with a passage from one of Aristotle's research works:

That the generation of bees takes place in this way appears both from reason and from those things that are seen to occur in their kind. Still all the incidents have not yet been sufficiently examined. And when the investigation shall be complete, then will sense be rather to be trusted than reason; reason, however, will also deserve credit, if the things demonstrated accord with the things that are perceived by sense   (*Gen. An.*, Bk. III, Ch. 10, 760 b 28-33).

EPIGENESIS VS. PREFORMATION

A textbook in a required biological course in a leading university in the United States makes reference to the "preformationists" of approximately 300 years ago who thought that the "embryo was preformed in miniature in the microscopic spermatozoon and had but to unfold as the rosebud into the rose" and to the "ovicists," who "postulated a preformed embryo in the egg that needed only a slight stimulus to make it grow and develop." In contrast the authors cite the modern scientist who through " the employment of the scientific method of repeated and careful observations and deductions has made it clear to us that the embryo is not preformed in its final form. . ." but that " the various parts of the new individual are gradually formed and undergo a tremendous modification from their first appearance up to their final state." [14]

These same authors could have equally and more accurately written: Over 2300 years ago, Aristotle, by employing the scientific method of repeated careful observation as his basis for inference, made it clear to anybody and everybody who would read, that the preformationist account of embryological development was impossible and the epigenetic account necessary. He asked, " How, then, does it [the embryo] make the other parts? "; he answered, " Either all the parts, as heart, lung, liver, eyes and all the rest, come into being *together* or in *succession* . . ." " That the former is not the fact is plain even to the sense, for some of the parts are clearly visible as already existing in the embryo while others are not; that it is not because of their being too small that they are not visible is clear, for the lung is of greater size than the heart, and yet appears later than the heart in the original development " (734 a 17 ff.). William Harvey, 2000 years later, who did read, came out with experimental confirmation and enrichment of the same view. He states in his *Generation of Animals*:

Now it appears clearly from my research that the generation of the chick from the egg is the result of epigenesis (Exercise 45). And first, since it is certain that the chick is produced by epigenesis, i. e. the addition of parts successively, we shall investigate what part may be observed before any of the rest are erected, and what may be observed in this mode of generation. What Aristotle says of generation . . . is confirmed and made manifest by all that passes in the egg, viz. that all the parts are not made simultaneously, but

---

[14] *Syllabus, Introductory General Course in the Biological Sciences,* edited by Merle C. Coulter. Seventh edition. (University of Chicago, 1937), p. 104.

ordered one after the other, and that there first exists a genital particle, by the power of which as from a principle, all the other parts proceed   (Exercise 51).

Curiously enough, however, the preformationist theory came into prominence again—curiously, because it did so just following the discovery of the microscope and the aberrations that passed for facts that resulted thereof. But the epigenetic theory has since been restored and given great richness of detail in support.

It can be seen that Harvey in following Aristotle reaffirmed a truth that was lost during the late Renaissance, but rediscovered in modern times. That it was one of Harvey's prime objects in writing *The Generation of Animals* to defend and establish the opinion already held by Aristotle has been expressed by Thomas H. Huxley.[15]

REFERENCES TO ARISTOTLE

In *The Motion of the Heart and Blood*, which is more a demonstrative work than a descriptive one, 22 references to Aristotle are made. In only one instance does Harvey clearly disagree with Aristotle. In this instance Harvey writes, " Hence, since the veins are the conduits and vessels that transport the blood, they are of two kinds, the vasa and the aorta; and this not by reason of sides (as in Aristotle), but office (*officio*), and not, as is commonly said, by constitution, for in many animals, as I have said, the vein does not differ from the artery in the thickness of its tunic, but is distinct by duties (*munere*) and use (*usu*)." [16] It should be noted that the disagreement is not based on Aristotle's anatomical observations, which D'Arcy W. Thompson states to be " remarkable

[15] Thomas H. Huxley, " Evolution in Biology," in *Darwiniana Essays* (New York, 1898), p. 193.

[16] Harvey, *Works, ed. cit.*, ch. 8, p. 47. The English translations of Harvey appearing in this article are mostly adapted from the Willis translation following consultation with the original Latin. Where possible key Latin terms which have English equivalents are substituted. The Latin text consulted is the edition of Bernardus Albinus (Johannes van Kercjhem, 1737).

for its wealth of detail [and] for its great accuracy in many particulars . . . ," but rather on physiological considerations, viz. on its office, duty and use.[17]

In another reference Harvey discusses an anatomical observation which " probably led Aristotle to consider this ventricle double, divided transversely." [18] Other than these, the remaining references to Aristotle are utilized to help Harvey make or confirm a particular point.

Of particular interest is the reference to Aristotle where Harvey enunciates the possibility of " a motion, as it were, in a circle . . . which motion we may be allowed to call circular, in the same way as Aristotle says that the air and the rain emulate the circular motion of the superior bodies; for the moist earth, warmed by the sun, evaporates; the vapors drawn upwards are condensed, and descending in the form of rain, moisten the earth again; and by this arrangement are generations of living things produced; and in like manner too are tempests and meteors engendered by the circular motion, and by the approach and recession of the sun." [19]

In connection with this passage, a recent translator and a scientist of renown, who is now President of the American Association for the Advancement of Science, is able to observe only that " Harvey seems never to have heard of [the] studies [of] Copernicus, J. Kepler, and G. Galilei [which] had overthrown the Ptolemical theory of the circular motion of the stars in the heavenly spheres . . ." [20]

But to think of this reference as a poetic metaphor to which scientific error can be attached rather than as a striking evocation of Aristotle's analysis of locomotion misses the precision for the poetry in the analogy.

Here one has to know certain passages from Aristotle's works, *Post. Anal.*, Bk. II, Ch. 12, *Physics*, Bk. VIII, Ch. 8 & 9,

[17] Aristotle, *History of Animals*, Translated by D'Arcy W. Thompson (Oxford, 1910). 513 a 35, fn. 3.

[18] Harvey, *Works*, *ed. cit.*, ch. 17, p. 79.

[19] *Ibid.*, ch. 8, p. 46.

[20] Chauncey D. Leake, *op. cit.*, ch. 8, p. 70, fn. 1.

Gen. and Cor., Bk. II, Ch. 11, *Meteorology*, Bk. II, Ch. 4, among others. Aristotle divides natural locomotion into circular and rectilinear. Only circular motion can be single and continuous. When Harvey concludes in Ch. 14 that " it is absolutely necessary to conclude that the blood in the animal body is impelled in a circle, and is in a state of ceaseless (*perpetuo*) motion . . ." he is talking in a strict Aristotelian framework.

Harvey, in the development of this conclusion, had to combat in his own mind the prevailing physiological concept that blood was produced from nutriment in a central organ, and was moved peripherally to be totally consumed by the body. That Harvey refers to Aristotle's concept of circular motion in his exposition, which is in the order of demonstration, suggests the critical role that Aristotle's concept had in the order of discovery.

THE DEMONSTRATION OF THE MOTION OF THE HEART AND BLOOD

Harvey makes it clear throughout his work that his " new views of the motion and use of the heart and the circulation of the blood " [21] are the result of the application of both sense and reason. In his dedication to the learned physicians he states that " for nine years or more [he has] confirmed these views by ocular demonstrations [and] manifested them by reasons and arguments, freed from the objections of the most learned and skillful anatomists." In Ch. 14 entitled ' The Conclusion of the Demonstration of the Circulation of the Blood ' where he concludes that the blood is impelled to the whole body by the pulse of the ventricles, he states that this is " confirmed by reason and ocular experiment," and that one must " necessarily conclude " that the motion of the blood is circular. In the final words of the concluding chapter of his book, the chapter which confirms the motion and the circulation of the blood through an anatomical analysis of the heart,

[21] Harvey, *Works, ed. cit.*, Dedication to Learned Physicians, p. 5.

Harvey concludes that "All these phenomenon and many others observed in dissecting, if rightly weighed, seem clearly to illumine and fully confirm the truth contended throughout these pages . . . it would be difficult to explain in any other way for what cause all is constructed and arranged as we have seen it to be."

Notwithstanding, the modern scientist with his disproportionate worship of observation manages for the most part to ignore the role played by reason, thereby missing what is so magnificent in this classic work. The carefully organized nature of Harvey's demonstration can be detected by scrutinizing Harvey's table of contents, which, because it is a contraction, mirrors the logical structure of the masterpiece in bold outline. The following represents a structural analysis of the table:

ANALYSIS OF HARVEY'S TABLE OF CONTENTS [22] OF AN ANATOMICAL EXERCISE ON THE MOTION OF THE HEART AND BLOOD

Part 1. Prefatory

  A. Dedicatory: extrinsic to work,

    1. To the King: to civil authority,

    2. To Learned Physicians: to peers who respect truth.

  B. Introductory: intrinsic to work,

    1. 'Introduction': establishes the need for the work; dated to the belief of scientists of that period.

    2. 'The Causes Moving the Author to Write' (Ch. 1): establishes the difficulty of the work; timeless, as the truths obtained from nature are permanent and belong to posterity.

Part 2. Motion of the Cardiovascular System (Ch. 2-7)

  A. Motion of the Containing Parts

    1. 'Motion of the heart through dissection of living animals.' (Ch. 2)

[22] Words enclosed in single quotation marks are those used by Harvey as chapter headings. Other quotations have individual reference numbers.

    2. 'Motion of the arteries through dissection of living animals.' (Ch. 3)

    3. 'Motion of the heart and auricles through dissection of living animals.' (Ch. 4)

    4. 'Motion, action and function of the heart.' (Ch. 5)

B. Motion of the Contained Parts from Right to Left Ventricle

    1. 'Ways by which blood passes from right ventricle to left.' (Ch. 6)

    2. 'That the blood pass through the lung from right ventricle to left.' (Ch. 7)

Part 3. Circular Motion of the Contained Part (Ch. 8-17)

  A. The Thesis and Demonstration (Ch. 8-14)

    1. Preliminary statement of the thesis: "Of the abundance of blood passing through the heart out of the veins into the arteries and of the circular motion of the blood." (Ch. 8)

    2. The three suppositions necessary for the demonstration.

      a. 'The first supposition': "the blood is incessantly transmitted by the pulse of the heart out of the vena cava into the arteries in such abundance that it cannot be supplied from the ingesta, and in such wise that the whole mass must very quickly pass through the heart."[23]

        (1) 'circulation of blood confirmed from it.' (Ch. 9)

        (2) 'is freed from objections and further confirmed by experiments.' (Ch. 10)

      b. 'The second supposition': "the blood under the influence of the arterial pulse enters and is impelled in a continuous, equable, and incessant

---

[23] Harvey, *Works, ed. cit.*, ch. 9, p. 48.

stream through every part and member of the body, in much greater abundance than were sufficient for nutrition, or than the whole mass of ingesta could supply " [24]

(1) 'is confirmed.' (Ch. 11)

(2) 'circulation of blood confirmed from it.' (Ch. 12)

c. 'The third supposition': "the veins in like manner return this blood perpetually to the heart from all members of the body " [25]

(1) 'confirmed and that there is a circulation of blood from it.' (Ch. 13)

3. 'The conclusion of the demonstration concerning the circulation of the blood.' (Ch. 14)

B. Confirmation of Conclusion that the Blood Circulates (Ch. 15-17)

1. 'The circulation of the blood is confirmed by likely reasons.' (Ch. 15)

2. 'The circulation of the blood is proved from consequences.' (Ch. 16)

3. 'Motion and circulation of the blood is confirmed by those things that appear in the heart and which are clear from anatomical dissections.' (Ch. 17)

In the Introduction (Part 1, B, 1) Harvey paves the way for his new theory by showing that the existing theory is unsatisfactory. He states in the opening paragraph that " In discussing the motion, pulse, action, use and utility of the heart and arteries, we should first consider what others have said on these matters, and what the common and traditional viewpoint is. Then by anatomical dissection, multiplied experience, diligent and accurate observation, we may confirm what is rightly stated, but what is false make right." Harvey then carefully examines the beliefs of his contemporaries in a series of seven-

[24] *Ibid.*   [25] *Ibid.*

teen dialectical propositions and replies. He concludes, " From these and many other considerations it is plain that what has been said on the motion and use of the heart and arteries must seem obscure, inconsistent, or impossible to the thoughtful student. It will therefore be proper to investigate the matter more closely, to study the motion of the heart and arteries not only in man but in all animals possessing a heart, and to search out and find the truth by frequent vivisections and by constant ocular inspection."

This doxographic approach is distinctly Aristotelian,[26] and establishes that one should not lean on man as the final authority.[27] In Ch. 1, he indicates that nature, despite the difficulty of extracting answers from her, is the final authority.[28]

[26] It is part of Aristotle's methodology to examine dialectically existing opinion before proceeding to the scientific investigation of things. Examples of this procedure are found in *Physics*, Bk. 1, ch. 2; *Generation and Corruption*, Bk. 1, ch. 1; *The Soul*, Bk. 1, ch. 2, and elsewhere. The following passage from *On the Heavens* states some of the reasons for the procedure: " Let us start with a review of the theories of other thinkers; for the proofs of a theory are difficulties for the contrary theory. Besides, those who have first heard the pleas of our adversaries will be more likely to credit the assertions which we are going to make. We shall be less open to the charge of procuring judgment by default " (Bk. 1, ch. 10, 279 b 6-11). " We may convince ourselves not only by the arguments already set forth but also by a consideration of the views of those who differ from us . . . If our view is a possible one . . . and [what] they assert is impossible, this fact will be a great weight in convincing us . . ." (Bk. 2, ch. 1, 283 b 30-a). All translations from Aristotle are from the Oxford edition of his works.

[27] The true Aristotelian tradition may be gathered from the following statements: " We had perhaps better consider the universal good and discuss thoroughly what is meant by it, although such an inquiry is made an uphill one by the fact that the Forms have been introduced by friends of our own. Yet it would perhaps be thought to be better, indeed to be our duty, for the sake of maintaining the truth even to destroy what touches us closely, especially as we are philosophers or lovers of wisdom; for, while both are dear, piety requires us to honour truth above our friends." (Aristotle, *Nicomachean Ethics*, Bk. 1, ch. 6, 1096a 11-16).

" He who believes Aristotle to be a god ought to believe that he never made a mistake. But whoever thinks him to have been a man must admit that he was as liable to make mistakes as the rest of us." (St. Albert the Great, *Physicorum lib.* VIII, tr. I, cap. 14, ed. Borgnet, III, p. 553).

" Unless a man holds truth dearer than friends, he will be ready to pronounce false judgments and to bear false witness for the sake of friends. But that is immoral. All men ought to hold truth dearer than friends, because all men have the use of reason. But this duty is particularly binding on all philosophers, be-

In subsequent chapters Harvey begins to record his reading of the book of nature. In Chapters 2-5, he reports what she says about the heart and arteries. By obtaining the true attributes of these critical components of the cardiovascular system, their motion, pulse and action, he will be in a position subsequently to elucidate their use and utility. " For if none of the true attributes of things have been omitted in the historical survey " states Harvey's mentor Aristotle, " we should be able to discover the proof and demonstrate everything which admitted of proof, and to make that clear, whose nature does not admit of truth." Aristotle emphasizes in this same passage that " in each science the principles which are peculiar are the most numerous. Consequently it is the business of experience to give the principles which belong to each subject. I

cause they profess to teach wisdom, and wisdom is nothing else than the knowledge of truth . . . Truth is, indeed, divine for it is found fundamentally and primarily in God. That is why Aristotle insists on the sacredness of the duty of holding truth dearer than friends . . . Plato is of the same opinion. For, once, when setting aside a theory of his master, Socrates, he declares that truth must be our supreme concern. And elsewhere, he declares: Socrates is, indeed, a friend of mine, but truth is a greater friend. And in a third text, he declares that one may make little of Socrates, but one must make much of truth." (St. Thomas Aquinas, *In I Ethic.*, lect. 6, nn. 76, 78).

[28] This is another expression of the true Aristotelian position. " God, like a good teacher, has taken care to compose most excellent writings that we may be instructed in all perfection. ' All that is written,' says the Apostle, ' is written for our instruction.' And these writings are in two books: the book of the creation and the book of the Holy Scriptures. In the former are so many creatures, so many excellent writings that deliver the truth without falsehood. Wherefore Aristotle, when asked whence it was that he had his admirable learning, replied: ' From things, which do not know how to lie.' " (St. Thomas, *Sermo 5 in Dom. II de adventu*, ed. Vives, *Opera Omnia*, XXIX, p. 194).

William Harvey, who, on the one hand, makes clear that " the authority of Aristotle has always such weight with me that I never think of differing from him inconsiderately " (Harvey, *Anatomical Exercises on the Generation of Animals*, Ex. 11, *ed. cit.*, p. 207), also states that " Whoever, therefore, sets himself to opposition to the circulation, because [he] regards it as in some sort criminal to call in question disciplines that have descended through a long succession of ages, and carry the authority of the ancients; to all these I reply: that the facts manifest by the senses wait upon no opinions, and that the works of nature bow to no antiquity; for indeed there is nothing either more ancient or of higher authority than nature." (*Second Exercise to John Riolan, ed. cit.*, p. 123).

mean for example that astronomical experience supplies the principles of astronomical science: for once the phenomena were adequately apprehended, the demonstrations of astronomy were discovered. Similarly with any other art or science. Consequently, if the attributes of the things are apprehended, our business will then be to exhibit readily the demonstrations."[29]

Again Aristotle emphasizes that " each set of principles we must try to investigate in the natural way, and we must take pains to state them definitely, since they have a great influence on what follows. For the beginning is thought to be more than half of the whole, and many of the questions we ask are cleared up by it." [30]

Harvey, of course, as an Aristotelian, does not limit himself to man. To get at the heart of the matter and of man he must be interested in the hearts of other animals. His aim is to get at the true nature of the heart. His interest is not descriptive. He is not interested in this heart or that with the variations in numbers of chambers or differing associations with lung or gills, but in the heart universally considered, prescinding from the variations that are found in nature. He refers to cold blooded animals as well as to warm blooded: toads, snakes, frogs, snails, shellfish and fish. In all it has been estimated that he worked with about 80 species of animals.[31]

That this is a methodological approach and not simply the insatiable curiosity of a field biologist is made clear from the quote from Aristotle that appears on the title page of *Prelectiones*, from the fifth of the canons which Harvey lists for his own guidance at the beginning of his lectures, and from a passage from Harvey that appears in *De Motu*.

The Aristotle quotation states, " The fact is that the inner parts of man are to a very great extent uncertain and unknown, and the consequence is that we must have recourse to a con-

---

[29] *Prior Analytics*, Bk. 1, ch. 30, 46 a 18-27.

[30] *Nicomachean Ethics*, Bk. 1, ch. 7, 1098 b 4-9.

[31] William Harvey, *Prelectiones, ed. cit.*, Introduction by a Committee of the Royal College of Physicians of London, p. vi.

sideration of the inner parts of other animals which in any way resembles that of man." [32]

The fifth canon emphasizes that one should systematically study other animals " according to the Socratic rule " for this will permit one to refute and correct errors in natural philosophy, and to discover the use, action and dignity of things, and thereby obtain for anatomy knowledge of the causes of the parts, the ends, their necessity and use. The Harvey passage is as follows:

Since the intimate connection of the heart with the lungs, which is apparent in the human subject, has been the probable occasion of the errors that have been committed on this point, they plainly do amiss who speak and demonstrate the parts of animals generally (as all anatomists commonly do) from the dissections of man alone, and at that dead. They obviously act no otherwise than he, who, having studied the form of a single republic, should set about a general discipline of polity; or who, having taken cognizance of a single farm, should imagine that he has scientific knowledge of agriculture; or who, on one particular proposition attempts to syllogize the universal. Had anatomists only been as conversant with the dissection of the lower animals as they are with that of the human body, the matters that have hitherto kept them in a perplexity of doubt would in my opinion, have met them freed from every kind of difficulty.[33]

It should be seen here that in his dedication to comparative anatomy, to Socrates' and Aristotle's rule, Harvey differs from the modern scientist. The latter directs this branch of biology primarily to taxonomy or to the elucidation of evolutionary history. The Socratic rule, on the contrary, is directed at eliciting an essential definition through the use of the inductive method. Socrates, according to Aristotle, was interested in what a thing is, its essence, as the starting point for syllogizing. " Two things may be fairly ascribed to Socrates," says Aristotle, " inductive arguments and universal definitions, both of which are concerned with the starting point of science." [34]

[32] Aristotle, *The History of Animals*, Bk. 1, ch. 16, 494 b 21-24.
[33] Harvey, *Works, op. cit.*, ch. 6, p. 35.
[34] Aristotle, *Metaphysics*, Bk. M, ch. 4, 1078 b 18-30.

To understand the use and the goal of Grecian and Harvian comparative biology, two things should be understood. First, that one has to seek out and know the many. Secondly, that knowledge of the many which one has to seek out is the " one in the many "—that which is common to the many, that commonality which most fully accounts for why the thing is as it is.

To know the *many*, however, does not automatically result in an answer. Modern science suffers from a plethora of the *many*, because of the variety and the high output of sense observations from our laboratories. The modern scientist is in the position of Meno, who, in answer to Socrates' question, What is virtue?, responds that " Every age, every condition of life, young or old, male or female, bond or free, has a different virtue: there are virtues numberless, and no lack of definitions for them . . ." [35] The modern scientist in the absence of the Harvian answer would respond similarly to the question, What is a heart?, that every species of animal has a different heart: there are numberless hearts and numberless definitions. But Harvey, following Socrates, prescinds from the many and seeks what the heart is " in the universal . . . whole and sound, and not broken into a number of pieces." [36] Harvey also follows Aristotle, who formally discusses the method of obtaining definitions in his *Posterior Analytics* which, as part of the *Organon*, was part of Harvey's formal training in logic and scientific methodology.

Unlike the modern whose notion of causality is limited primarily to the material and efficient causes, Harvey further follows Socrates and Aristotle in seeking the fuller explanation that comes with the additional knowledge of the formal and final causes.

Socrates in his last days recollects his rejection of this ancient error of modern scientists when, as a young man, he, " with a prodigious desire to know that department of philosophy which

[35] Plato, *Meno*, 71 E-72 A (Jowett translation.)
[36] *Ibid.*, 77 A.

is called the investigation of nature: to know the causes of things, and why a thing is " [37] registers his disappointment after being directed to Anaxagoras who, forsaking any principle of order, tried to explain everything by " having recourse to air, ether, and water and other eccentricities." [38]

Aristotle as a scientist's scientist [39] and philosopher's philosopher fully and formally develops this Socratic position in Book I of the *Parts of Animals*. He, too, as if writing against the enthusiastic follower of Harvey, who reads but does not understand him, talks about " the ancient writers, who first philosophized about Nature as having busied themselves " with " the material principle and material cause." [40] Aristotle explains, on the contrary, that

if men and animals and their several parts are natural phenomena, then the natural philosopher must take into consideration not merely the ultimate substances of which they are made but also . . . the homogeneous and heterogeneous parts; and must examine how each of these comes to be what it is, and in virtue of what force. For to say what are the ultimate substances out of which an animal is formed, to state, for instance, that it is made of fire or earth, is no more sufficient than would be a similar account in the case of a couch or the like . . . For a couch is . . . such and such a matter with this or that form; so that its shape and structure must be included in our description. For the formal nature is of greater importance than the material nature.[41]

Aristotle finally concludes that

It is plain, then, that the teaching of the old physiologists is inadequate, and that the true method is to state what the definitive characters are that distinguish the animal as a whole; to explain what it is both in substance and in form, and to deal after the same

---

[37] Plato, *Phaedo*, 96 B.

[38] *Ibid.*, 98 C.

[39] Charles Darwin, *Life and Letters*, Letter to Ogle, 1882, vol. 3, p. 252: " From quotations I had seen I had a high notion of Aristotle's merits, but I had not the most remote notion what a wonderful man he was. Linnaeus and Cuvier have been my two gods, though in very different ways, but they were mere schoolboys to old Aristotle."

[40] Aristotle, *Parts of Animals*, Bk. I, ch. 1, 640 b 5.

[41] *Ibid.*, 640 b 15-29.

fashion with its several organs; in fact, to proceed in exactly the same way as we should do, were we giving a complete description of a couch.[42]

We can see then that Harvey as an Aristotelian is interested in function as well as action, in ends as well as means—the teleological as well as the mechanical. We shall also see that Harvey respects the differentiation as well as the interrelationship of what has to be known for a full understanding of the causes. Part of the modern difficulty in understanding Harvey stems from a failure to appreciate Harvey's sensitivity to language, and our insensitivity to the sharply delineated concepts which his terminology precisely communicates—concepts and terms which are the culmination of a long logical and biological tradition.

The conceptual difficulty can best be seen from the Leake translation. In the table of contents: the Latin words *dissectione*, in three instances, and *experimentis* are both translated into *experiment*; *dissectio*, in another instance, is translated into *investigation*; *confirmato* is translated into both *established* and *proved*; *probatur* is translated into *supported*; and *suppositio* is translated into *consideration* and *proposition*. The first sentence of the Introduction of this translation begins, " In discussing the movements and functions of the heart and arteries, we should first consider . . .". The original Latin, however, instead of *movement* and *functions*, has *motu, pulsu, actione, usu, utilitatibus.*

We can now return more specifically to the manner in which Harvey arrived at his revolutionary conclusions concerning the motion of the heart and blood. If one turns to the table of contents above, he will note that whereas the word *dissection* is characteristically found in the chapter headings on the motion of the heart and arteries (part 2 A), the word *supposition* is characteristically found in the section on the circulation of the blood (part 3 A). Dissection, of course, pertains to sense; supposition, to reason. One may correctly infer from this that,

---

[42] *Ibid.*, 641 a 14-18.

when it comes to the circulation of the blood, the demonstration is logical, not ocular. The absence of magnifying instruments of sufficient strength at the time made it impossible to observe either the circulation of the blood or the continuity of the cardiovascular system. It is not implied here, however, that the ocular, even if possible, could approach or match the certitude of the logical demonstration.[43]

Circulation, as such, is not mentioned in the body of the work until Chapter 8, where it is introduced in the form of a short review of the argument developed subsequently. Since the conclusion that the circulation of the blood is the end result of a long reasoning process, the chief function of Harvey's preceding chapters is to contribute premises which are true, primary, immediate, better known than, prior to, and the cause of the conclusions which follow from them.[44] In other words, it is necessary to establish the motion, pulse, and action of the heart and arteries, and the relationship of the lungs to the heart and the blood to the lungs first. This calls for the most exacting type of sense observations, their verification by collated findings, and care in the inferences drawn from them. It is through such knowledge that Harvey is in a position to ask questions leading to the initial idea and final demonstration that the blood circulates.

The first part of Harvey's treatise establishes, contrary to the beliefs at the time, that the heart and the arteries in the living animal always contain blood: that the proper motion of the heart is contraction, not expansion; that its action is pump-like, not bellow-like, and that it forcibly expels blood in one direction; that contraction, not expansion—systole, not diastole—corresponds to the pulse on the chest wall; that the arterial

[43] It should not be forgotten that the observations of Swammerdam of the perfectly formed butterfly in the cocoon in 1669, and those of Leeuwenhoek of the complete outline of both maternal and paternal individuals in the microscopic spermatozoa in 1677, led to the complete replacement of Harvey's theory of epigenesis by the preformation theory, which lent itself to a mechanical explanation of nature, and which was to dominate biological thinking through the first half of the eighteenth century.

[44] Aristotle, *Posterior Analytics*, Bk. 1, ch. 1, 71 b 16-22.

pulse, which in arterial diastole corresponds to carliac systole, not cardiac diastole; that cardiac systole is the cause of the arterial pulse via the motion it transmits through the blood; and that blood from the right ventricle gets to the left ventricle through the lungs.

Since " the one action of the heart is the transfusion and propulsion of the blood by mediation of the arteries to the extremities of the body," [45] the question arises as to where the heart gets the blood which is the subject of its action. The genesis of the belief and the hypothesis that blood circulates is as follows:

And sooth to say, when I surveyed in various disquisitions by how much abundance blood might be lost from cutting arteries, in dissections and induced experiments in the living; then the symmetry and magnitude of the vessels that enter and leave the ventricles of the heart (for nature doing nothing groundlessly, would never have given them such proportionate magnitudes groundlessly), then the ingenious and attentive fitting together of the valves and fibers, and the rest of the heart's fabric and many other things besides, I frequently and seriously bethought me, and long revolved in my mind, by how much abundance blood was transmitted, and the like, in how short a time its transmission might be effected, and not finding it possible that this could be supplied by the juices of the ingested aliment without the veins on the one hand becoming drained, and the arteries on the other hand getting ruptured through the excessive charge of blood, unless the blood should somehow find its way from the arteries into the veins, and so return to the right ventricle of the heart; I began to think whether there might not be a motion as it were, in a circle.[46]

Chapter 9 contains the principal demonstration of the circulation:

A fluid of limited quantity kept in
  perpetual motion in one direction   is   moved circularly.
And the blood   is   such a fluid.
Therefore the blood   is   moved circularly.

In this syllogism according to the Aristotelian logic em-

[45] Harvey, *Works, op. cit.*, ch. 5, p. 32.   [46] *Ibid.*, ch. 8, pp. 45-46.

ployed by Harvey the middle term is the material cause (i. e. limited quantity of fluid), and the demonstration is " one through the material cause." The major premise is a general physical theorem proved by Aristotle in Books VII and VIII of the *Physics*, where he shows that perpetual motion of any system must be circular in character. The minor premise is a definition of the blood derived from Harvey's careful studies recorded in his earlier chapters.

Harvey's conclusion is, as he admonishes a critic on a later occasion, " demonstrative and true, and follows of necessity, if the premises be true." [47] Therefore he adds that any criticism of his conclusion cannot be in the area of argument and logic, but in the area of observation and experiment which supplies the premises. Harvey insists here that " our senses ought to assure us whether such things be false or true and not our reason, ocular testimony and not contemplation." [48] That Harvey has learned well from Aristotle, who was the father both of biology and logic, is evident from Harvey's recognition of and respect for the proper spheres of sense and reason.

The degree to which Harvey's demonstration is Aristotelian should be noted further. First, it is an example of the relationship of a less general science, biology, to a more general and fundamental science, physics, to which it is subalternate: a particular biological fact is illuminated by a universal physical theorem to yield a new biological fact. Secondly, it is an example of the dictum that demonstrations in science are made through a definition expressing an essential characteristic. Thirdly, contrary to modern thinking, Harvey's demonstration does not depend on mathematical measurements but on physical proportions, i. e., the proportion of one quantity to another on the basis of physical comparison rather than on mathematical principles. In stating that Chapter 9 is " the first instance of the quantitative method in physiology " and that it " introduced the most important method of reasoning in

[47] Harvey, *Second Exercise to John Riolan*, ed. cit., p. 133.
[48] *Ibid.*

science," [49]   Leake misses Harvey's fidelity to Aristotle's method and its reward. Kilgour, in a recent and careful analysis of Harvey's use of the quantitative method, concludes that certainly " Harvey was not concerned with accurate measurement " and that his estimations were consciously indifferent to precision, the essence of the mathematical procedure. He adds, " Apparently, quantitative evidence was not important in leading Harvey to develop the idea of the circulation because there is no quantitation in his Lumleian Lecture notes of 1616." [50] The computations Harvey supplies, therefore, may be better viewed as communicating to the reader—in the manner in which a sensible model makes a theory vivid to the reader— the physical reality of the disproportion between the amount of ingesta and the flow of blood through the heart.[51]

Finally, it would be amiss not to recognize that the demonstration of the circulation of the blood is just an Aristotelian step in the elucidation of the nature of the heart, the prime component of the cardiovascular system. The ultimate purpose of Harvey's treatise is to define the heart upon which the motion of the blood is dependent.

One of the most remarkable chapters in this work of Harvey's is the 17th and final chapter. From all the fields opened up by the establishment of circulation—physiology, pathology, symptomatology and therapeutics—he selects his topic: to relate the various particulars that present themselves in the anatomical study of the fabric of the heart and arteries to their several uses and causes, " for I shall meet with many things

[49] Chauncey D. Leake, op. cit., ch. 9, p. 74, fn. 1.

[50] Frederick C. Kilgour, " William Harvey's Use of the Quantitative Method," Yale Journal of Biology and Medicine, XXVI (1954), 417-18.

[51] Some of the thoughts appearing in this article were first presented and in part developed at a summer institute for scientists and philosophers conducted by The Albert Magnus Lyceum for Natural Science at River Forest, Illinois, July 1952. A report of this institute is to be found in the publication, entitled, Science in Synthesis: A dialectical approach to the integration of the physical and natural sciences, by W. Kane, O. P.; J. D. Corcoran, O. P.; B. M. Ashley, O. P.; and R. H. Nogar, O. P. (The Aquinas Library, Dominican College of St. Thomas Aquinas: River Forest, Illinois. 1953). See pp. 93-108.

which receive light from the truth I have been contending for, and which, in turn, render it more obvious. And indeed I would have it confirmed (*firmatam*) and beautified (*exornatam*) by anatomical arguments above all others." [52]

This chapter is primarily an elaboration of the formal cause of the heart through the re-examination of the heart and the vessels—structurally, comparatively, embryologically and functionally—in the light of the final cause, viz. the circulation of the blood. His final statement which closes his treatise is: " it would be difficult to explain in any other way for what cause all is constructed and arranged as we have seen it to be."

He establishes what a heart is in his characterization of the heart *per se* as the left ventricle, viz. that ventricle " distinguished by use not position, the one namely that distributes blood to the body at large, not the lungs alone." In doing so he establishes the connection of the final and formal causes.

This chapter completes the definition of the heart for Harvey, which definition may be expressed in syllogistic form as follows:

An organ which must supply the body with a steady flow of a fluid whose quantity is proportionately small	is	an organ which is so constructed as to be able to produce a circular motion of that fluid.
And the heart	has	this very function.

Therefore the heart is:

1. An organ which has a pulsating " left " ventricle with a non-regurgitating valvular inlet and outlet and whatever additional cardiac parts that conform to the needs of the species (the *formal cause*: the anatomical structure described teleologically and in detail, i. e., in its relationship to its motion, pulse, action, use and utilities, e. g., the arrangement of the fibres in the walls, the valves, the braces of the heart; " the actions and uses of the heart may be understood from the con-

[52] Harvey, *Works*, *op. cit.*, ch. 16, p. 74.

stitution of its muscular fibers and the fabric of its moveable parts " [53]),

2. and is composed of muscular tissue and other tissue components necessary to the parts (the *material cause*),

3. for the sake of circulating the blood (the *final cause* or function)

4. by contraction (the *efficient cause* of circulation).[54]

[53] *Ibid.*, ch. 17, p. 82.

[54] That the last chapter is an integral and important part of Harvey's classic is not the common position. Leake presents a typical viewpoint when he states that " The last three chapters add little to the significance of the demonstration " (Chauncey D. Leake, *op. cit.*, Translator's Preface, p. x). But here it seems that Leake has a limited appreciation of the purpose of the work as explicitly stated by Harvey, and of the true scientific nature of the anatomical exercise employed by Harvey. As to the purpose of the work it should first be recalled that the title of this classic makes clear that it is an anatomical exercise, and that it concerns the motion of the heart as well as the motion of the blood. Secondly, that the opening statement of the *Introduction* states that Harvey is discussing " the motion, pulse, action, use and utility of the heart and arteries," and of Chapter 1 that his purpose is to discover " the motions, use and utility of the heart." That Leake does not appreciate the comprehensiveness of the anatomical exercise is reflected in his translation, in which he reduces *action, use and utility* to *function* in the Introduction, and *use and utility* to *function* in Chapter 1.

If we turn to the anatomical works of Fabricius, who was Harvey's teacher, we find the following exposition of the anatomical exercise: "to treat first the dissection or description of each organ, then its action, and finally its utilities, and in this way present our entire knowledge of the organs as comprised in these three divisions." He adds that he has followed " this path the more willingly because those distinguished pioneers, Aristotle and Galen, have blazed the trail and, so to speak, carried the torch before me on the way." (Fabricius, *De Visione, voce, auditu*, Preface, translated by Howard B. Adelmann, *The Embryological Treatises of Hieronymus Fabricius of Aquapendente*, Cornell University Press, 1942, p. 82). Fabricius classifies the biological works of Aristotle and Galen in these three divisions and states that " The third part, indeed, which discusses the utilities of the whole, as well as of the parts of an organ, corresponds to the four books of Aristotle's *De partibus animalium* [and] to that great work of Galen's, *De usu partium* . . ." (*ibid.*, p. 83).

When we turn to Aristotle's explication of the third part of the anatomical exercise he states that " In the first place we must look at the constituent parts of animals. For it is in a way relative to these parts, first and foremost, that animals in their entirety differ from one another: either in the fact that some have this or that, while they have not that or this; or by peculiarities of position or arrangement; or by the differences that have been previously mentioned, depending upon diversity of form, or excess or defect in this or that particular, or analogy, or

Naturally, the final and efficient causes are proximate causes and are not intended as complete in any sense. In this context Harvey's Aristotelian answer to his critic Riolan is pertinent: " To those who repudiate the circulation because they neither see the efficient nor final cause of it, and who exclaim, *Cui bono?* I have yet to reply, having hitherto taken no note of the ground of objection which they take up. And first I own I am of opinion that our first duty is to inquire whether the thing be or not, before asking wherefore it is (*propter quid*) ? for from the facts and circumstances which meet us in the

on contrasts of the accidental qualities." For, according to Aristotle " to do this [pass on to the discussion of the causes] when the investigation of the details is complete is the proper and natural method, and that whereby the subjects and the premises of our argument will afterwards be rendered plain." (Aristotle, *The History of Animals*, Bk. 1, ch. 6, 491 b 10-19).

Galen's position is quoted by Fabricius: "A practical knowledge of the nature of each of the members is gained from dissection together with a thorough understanding of its actions and utilities." Galen further adds, in the quotation from Fabricius: " Moreover, lest anyone unwisely neglects these aspects or be thoughtless enough to say that they are not of great consequence, I can truly say this: They are of so much importance, that whoever has learned them thoroughly must unhesitatingly confess that he has learned and comprehended the whole subject of anatomy, which, in my opinion, is nothing but the true and solid foundation of all medicine and the absolute and perfect end of natural philosophy." (Fabricius, *op. cit.*, p. 83).

Galen's statement is clearly in anticipation of criticisms such as Leake's. That Leake has this position is in great part explained by the fact that contemporary physicians and doctorates of anatomy have been raised on Gray's *Anatomy* which is entitled *Anatomy, Descriptive and Surgical* and which is intended for " Students of Surgery rather than for the Scientific Anatomist." (Henry Gray, *Anatomy, Descriptive and Surgical*, A New Edition Thoroughly Revised by American Authorities from the Thirteenth English Edition (Lea Brothers, 1896) Preface to the Thirteenth English Edition, p. 8). It can be seen that Gray's *Anatomy* is a practical work ordered to surgery and which only relates the first division of the traditional notion of anatomy, namely description, to surgery.

An understanding of Harvey's procedure then, may be summarized in the words of Fabricius: " Now in the second part of this treatise, I must discuss action, since, as Galen everywhere testifies, it is not permissible to arrive at the third section, which describes the usefulness (*utilitates*) of the parts, before the actions of the organs are understood. For the utilities of an organ always have reference to action, and depend upon the action which proceeds from the homogeneous parts of it. For this reason, in every organ there is always provided one part which is the principal instrument of its action, that is, a part from which the action proceeds, while the other parts of the organ are related to the action as useful assistants." Fabri-

circulation admitted, established, the use and utilities of its institution are especially to be sought." [55]

Notwithstanding, Harvey makes clear "the principal use and end of the circulation: it is that for which the blood is sent on its perpetual course, and to exert its influence continually in its circuit, to wit, that all parts dependent on the primary innate heat may be retained alive, in their state of vital and vegetative being, and apt to perform their duties; whilst to use the language of physiologists, they are sustained and actuated by the inflowing heat and vital spirits." [56]

The modern reader, of course, will have to understand that it would take some time, and the modern development of the science of chemistry, before this point could have been made in terms of oxygen instead of vital spirits, or amino acids, glucose, and fatty acids instead of natural spirits. In the meantime he can have the reassurance from Harvey that "There is, in fact, no occasion for searching after spirits foreign to, or

cius then exemplifies the above distinctions with the eye, in which the crystalline lens has the principal utility, and the other parts of the eye, the cornea, the iris and the rest, are structures useful for the eye's action through the secondary utilities they have for either improving or protecting vision, and concludes: "It is now clear from the foregoing that utility is always related to activity, whether the usefulness of the organ is sought from its action or from other things either consequential or accidental; nor can you inquire into the usefulness of any organ unless its action is first known." (Fabricius, *The Formed Fetus*, Part 2, The Action and Usefulness (*utilitas*) of the parts of the fetus, ch. 1, Adelmann translation, *ed. cit.*, p. 276).

Harvey's last chapter, which is entitled "The motion and circulation of the blood is confirmed by those things that appear in the heart and are clear from anatomical dissections," can now be seen as an integral part of the anatomical exercise. In the preceding chapters Harvey has established the proper action of the heart, as well as its use, the circulation of the blood. This now permits him to look at the heart so as to determine formally its utilities, i.e., its abilities to serve, in the light of its actions and use. By determining that the formal cause of the heart—its utilities—has a one to one correspondence with its action—the efficient cause of blood circulation—and with its use, the final cause, namely, the circulation of the blood, Harvey can now reflectively confirm the circulation. In this remarkable chapter Harvey identifies the principal utility with the muscular left ventricle and the secondary utilities with valves, braces, etc.

[55] Harvey, *Second Exercise to John Riolan, ed. cit.*, pp. 122-123.

[56] Harvey, *First Exercise to John Riolan, ed. cit.*, p. 98.

distinct from, the blood ": [57] for " the blood and spirits constitute one body (like—whey and butter in milk, or heat in hot water . . .) ." [58]

It should be stressed that Harvey in elucidating the formal cause of the heart, as well as the formal cause of the arteries and veins, has obtained the efficient cause of circulation and the basis for a *propter quid* demonstration. This is the import of his last chapter and his concluding statement quoted above.

CONCLUSION

Although Harvey's discovery of the circulation of the blood was truly revolutionary, its establishment was strictly traditional. Ironically, the greatest opposition to his work came from the traditionalists. What accounts for the paradox?

Most scholastics of the fifteenth and sixteenth centuries so admired Aristotle that they ended up slaves to his conclusions and caricaturists, rather than disciples, of the methods by which he arrived at them. As a result they were very unproductive in the natural sciences.

Modern biologists trace their lineage back to three seventeenth century scientists who revolted from these Aristotelians: Francis Bacon, René Descartes [59] and William Harvey. What

---

[57] Harvey, *Anatomical Exercises on the Generation of Animals*, Ex. 51, ed. cit., p. 502.

[58] Harvey, *The Motion of the Heart and Blood*, Introduction, ed. cit., p. 12.

[59] Descartes was one contemporary who had no difficulty accepting Harvey's conclusion. " I need only mention in reply what has been written by a physician in England, who has the honour of having broken the ice on the subject (that the blood's) course amounts precisely to a perpetual motion." (René Descartes, *A Discourse on Method of Rightly Conducting the Reason and Seeking Truth in the Sciences, Everyman's Library*, p. 41). He accepted Harvey's conclusion without difficulty because it fit in with his mechanistic and mathematized method. His method, however, did not protect him from misunderstanding Harvey's demonstration and almost everything that Descartes further said about the motions of the heart and blood was in error. (*Ibid.*, pp. 37-43).

Harvey, of course, was fully cognizant of Descarte's failure and makes this clear in the following passage: ". . . the ingenious and acute Descartes (whose honourable mention of my name demands acknowledgments,) and others . . . in my opinion do not observe correctly . . . Descartes does not perceive how much the relaxation and subsidence of the heart and arteries differ from their distention or

each of these three did was to free himself from the short-comings of his contemporaries by a daring innovation. The innovation of Descartes was philosophical. He allowed his philosophical genius to carry him to the extreme of founding a completely new philosophy. The innovation of Bacon was pseudo-philosophical. His lack of philosophical genius carried him to the extreme of founding a new methodology of investigation. Descartes paved the way for a whole series of modern errors; and Bacon caused the disappearance of methodology in those who became his followers. But the innovation of Harvey lay in the diligence of his investigation of the Aristotelian premises and the profundity of his penetration of Aristotle's method. From this novelty—fidelity to the tradition—has come his permanent contribution to modern science. It made him both an authentic representative of the past and an authentic representative for the future, and establishes him as a model for an age that slights sense, as well as for an age that slights reason.

HERBERT ALBERT RATNER, M. D.

Loyola University
Chicago, Illinois

---

diastole; and that the cause of the distention, relaxation, and constriction, is not one and the same; as contrary effects so they must have contrary causes; as different movements they must have different motors; just as all anatomists know that flexion and extension of an extremity are accomplished by opposite antagonistic muscles, and contrary or diverse motions are necessarily performed by contrary and diverse organs instituted by nature for the purpose " (Harvey, *Second Exercise to John Riolan, ed. cit.,* pp. 139-140).

PART TWO
HISTORY OF SCIENCE

MEDICINE AND PHILOSOPHY IN THE ELEV-
ENTH AND TWELFTH CENTURIES:
THE PROBLEM OF ELEMENTS

ᢙᣛᣜ

THE cultivation of the liberal arts and the sciences during the twelfth century developed new methods and investigated new subject-matters. What was achieved in theory and interpretation is obscured by the further transformation of problems and enlargement of data during the succeeding period, the hundred years between the middle of the twelfth and the middle of the thirteenth centuries, when the scientific and philosophical works of Aristotle and a vast body of accompanying commentary, elaboration, and speculation were translated for the first time. The problem of universals and the problem of elements are two highly ambiguous signs of the intellectual activity of a period of distinguished cultural and scientific renaissance.

The grammarian, rhetorician, and dialectician of the early twelfth century studied texts that had long been available more constructively and imaginatively—Latin grammars and rhetorics, translations of Aristotle's *Categories* and *On Interpretation*, Porphyry's *Introduction*, and Boethius' logical treatises and commentaries—and the twelfth century *Book of Six Principles* attributed to Gilbert de la Porrée was assimilated with Porphyry's *Introduction* to the canon of Aristotle's *Organon*. Even the problem of universals was familiar in the widely known three questions of Porphyry. After the translation of the last four books of Aristotle's *Organon* the work of twelfth century logicians like Abailard had little pertinence to the continuing problems; and, in general, the liberal arts of the trivium were turned from interpretative applications and constructive theories to demonstrative and speculative systematizations.

The encyclopaedist and the cosmologist of the twelfth century likewise worked on texts long available but neglected—Chalcidius' translation of Plato's *Timaeus* and his commentary on it, the works of the Platonists Apuleius and Macrobius or of Martianus Cappella who furnished bits of the theories of Hermes Trismegistus, and finally the eleventh century translations of works on medicine or on the nature of man, like those of Constantine the African or Alfanus of Salerno in which the problem of elements is stated. Thierry of Chartres, Peter Abailard, William of Conches (one of whose works is sometimes called *On the Elements of Philosophy*), and their critic William of St. Thierry as well as many other philosophers of the early twelfth century used the elements as beginning points and ordering principles in their expositions of composites as man, the universe, and the sciences; and elements were continued in that function in the encyclopaedias of the later twelfth and early thirteenth centuries, such as Alexander Neckham's *On the Natures of Things*, Thomas of Cantimpré's *On the Nature of Things*, and Bartholomew of Glanville's *On the Properties of Things*. After the translation of Aristotle's scientific work and of commentaries which put varying interpretations on his conception of things, neither the data nor the theories of these organizations of knowledge were useful in the continuing investigations; and, in general, encyclopaedic organizations of the sciences were turned from the classification of the nature and properties of things to the ordering of motions and functions according to principles.

The problem of elements is the counterpart of the problem of universals. (1) Science is of the universal; (2) it is derived from and applied to particulars; (3) examination of universal predicates is therefore involved in questions of existence and being, of experience and reason. Conversely, (1) wholes or complexes are composed of parts and ultimately parts are composed of simple parts; (2) the nature of parts depends on how the whole is conceived; (3) determination of simples is therefore involved in a complex of related questions concerning the indivisibility of the element, such as, whether the compound is divided actually or intellectually; whether the elements so produced are corporeal or incorporeal; whether they are individuals or classes; and whether they are infinite or finite; whether they are characterized only by properties like size, shape, weight, and motion or also by other qualities. Questions about universals arise from the opposition of different conceptions of logical and scientific method. Questions about elements arise in the opposition of different interpretations of data. The problem of universals and the problem of elements are important in periods like the twelfth and the fourteenth centuries and they are subject to similar resolutions, but the differences of disciplines and of information in two such periods change the implications of the problems and the considerations relevant to their treatment.

The history of the treatment of elements in the Middle Ages reflects the indirect influence of earlier theories of elements and repeats in ironic fashion the customary history of Greek philosophy. Aristotle taught us that the Ionian and Italian philosophers used the " elements " as principles in their philosophies in " lisping anticipations " of his own use of " causes " as principles. We fill in or modify this version of the development of thought by giving the elements interpretations suggested by the ways in which they are used in cosmological or medical accounts of the origin of the universe or the development and functions of organisms. Thales' conception of water as a principle is given meaning in application to the structure and origin of the universe, and Hippocrates' theory that all natural objects are characterized by four qualities—hot, cold, dry, and moist—has its obvious applications in physiology and therapy. The theories of elements propounded in the medical works of the eleventh century and the cosmologies of the twelfth century likewise provide the principles of the relevant sciences and prepare for the more diversified treatment, in the thirteenth century, of principles and sciences devised from the interpretation of Aristotle's works.

Aristotle's version of intellectual history depends on his distinction of principles, causes, and elements, yet his meaning of " elements " is seldom used even when his history is repeated. A principle is a " beginning "; all causes and all elements are principles, but not all principles are causes or elements, and not all causes are elements. Elements are one variety of one of the four causes, the material cause. Aristotle defines element as the first component part of a thing, indivisible in kind into other kinds. The Aristotelian conceptions of " matter " and of " kind " have prevented the wide acceptance of this definition, for incorporeal as well as corporeal things have matter and a thing indivisible " in kind " may be divisible in many ways. Aristotle gives three examples to clarify his definition; elements of speech, of bodies, and of geometrical or logical proof. The Greek word *stoicheion* means both " element " and " letter." The elements of speech or letters are the parts into which speech is ultimately divided and which cannot be divided into forms of speech different in kind from them: a syllable can be divided into parts different in kind, but if letters can be divided their parts are likewise letters. The elements of bodies are simple parts like water, whose parts in turn are water. The elements of geometrical and logical proof are the primary demonstrations and the primary syllogisms, which are each implied in many demonstrations and which have no parts different in kind from them. The elements of demonstrations are demonstrations, not propositions or terms. Some people use " element " in the broader transferred sense of the small and simple and indivisible; the most universal things and genera are then thought to be elements, and unity and the point to be first principles.[1] The first philosophers sought the principles of things among the material causes, including the four elements;[2] Leucippus and Democritus said the full and the empty, the atoms and the void, are elements;[3] the physicists

---

[1] *Metaphysics*, V, 3, 1014a26-b15.

[2] *Ibid.*, I, 3, 983b6-984b8.

[3] *Ibid.*, 985b3-19.

posited elements of bodies and neglected elements of incorporeal things, while the Pythagoreans treated the principles and elements even more strangely, for they derived their principles from non-sensible mathematical objects and applied them to perceptible bodies.[4]

Physical elements have an important place in Aristotle's organization of the physical sciences. The principles and causes of motion are treated in his *Physics*; elements become important in discriminating the kinds of bodies according to their motions in his *De Caelo*; elements are not fixed and changeless, and the effects of changes or transmutations of the elements are treated in his *On Generation and Corruption*; the remaining problems of phenomena caused by the operation of elements above the earth's surface and by the formation of mixtures, compounds, and functionally organized wholes are considered in his *Meteorology*.[5] The division of bodies in the *De Caelo* is into simples (*haplon*), which have simple motions, and compounds (*suntheton*) of those simples, which have composite motions. The circular motion of the first body, *aither*, and of the heavenly bodies, is treated in the first two books of the *De Caelo*;[6] the straight line motions of the simple bodies, fire and earth, which are respectively light and heavy, and of the bodies compounded of them, are investigated in the last two books.[7] The definition of a bodily element is that into which other bodies can be analyzed but which cannot itself be analyzed into parts differing in kind.[8] The *On Generation and Corruption* is concerned with substantial change rather than with local motion, and the transformation of the four elements or simple bodies, fire, air, water and earth, is explained by combinations of the primary qualities, hot, cold, dry and moist, rather than by the qualities light and heavy.

[4] *Ibid.*, I, 8, 988b23-990a18.

[5] Aristotle reviews this course of inquiry at the beginning of the *Meteorologica*, I, 1, 338a20-339a9.

[6] *De Caelo*, I, 2, 268b26-269b17.

[7] *Ibid.*, III, 1, 298a24-b12.

[8] *Ibid.*, III, 3, 302a15-19.

The *Meteorology* finally turns to phenomena less regular than the motions of the primary body, *aither,* below the region of the motion of the stars. These include, in addition to meteorological phenomena in the strict sense, the composition of elements into homogeneous bodies and of homogeneous bodies into structured or organic bodies. Two of the primary qualities, hot and cold, are active, and two, dry and moist, are passive. The combinations of elements may be mechanical mixtures (*sunthesis*) or chemical compounds (*mixis*). The latter are " homoeomerous " bodies, inorganic (gold, silver, stone), vegetable (bark, wood), or animal (bone, flesh, sinew). Homoeomerous bodies are distinguished by qualities which act on the senses (white, fragrant, resonant, sweet, hot or cold) and more intrinsic qualities which, like moist and dry, are passive, such as solubility, solidifiability, flexibility, frangibility, plasticity, ductility, malleability, combustibility, compressibility.[9] Homoeomerous bodies are composed of elements, and are in turn the material for more complex " non-homoeomerous " bodies. Aristotle's examples of inorganic structured complex bodies are artificial objects, like flutes and saws, which have specific functions, while his examples of organic complex bodies are leaf and root, hands, feet, and eyes.[10] The bodies composed, in turn, of non-homoeomerous bodies are men and plants and the like. In the course of discussing homoeomerous bodies Aristotle makes use of the distinction between masses or corpuscles (*onkos*) and pores (*poros*), which is used later in the history of elements and is thought to derive from Democritus' distinctions between atoms and void; it is to be observed, however, that these particles would have the status of molecules relative to simpler atoms or elements.

Philosophers continued to form theories concerning elements after Aristotle, and Aristotle's history of elements as the principles of the early philosophers was usually combined with a Stoic or Neoplatonic conception of elements. These were the

---

[9] *Meteorologica,* IV, 8, 384b24-385a18.
[10] *Ibid.,* IV, 10, 388a10-29; 12, 389b23-390b22.

versions in which the history influenced early Christian thought. The Stoics held that the universe, like other wholes, had two principles, an active and a passive principle, or an efficient and a material principle, and that the universe is ordered by reason and providence.[11] Plato distinguished and related the operation of reason and of necessity in the formation of the universe by placing reason in the composition of the world soul and necessity in the operation of elements. The pattern of later discussions of elements as the material parts of a universe brought into existence by the efficient or rational causality of God is established in pagan and Christian accounts of the history of philosophy during the early centuries of the Christian era. Almost the same doctrines are given in three related accounts— one by Sextus Empiricus, a physician and skeptical philosopher, the other two ascribed respectively to the physician Galen and to the Christian Clement the Roman—and they are adaptable to the Mosaic account of creation.[12] *The Recognitions* of the pseudo-Clement were translated into Latin, with modifications, by Rufinus and are well-known in various versions during the early Middle Ages; the *Historia Philosopha* of the pseudo-Galen is in accord with the treatment of elements in Galen's medical works which were translated in the eleventh century.

Sextus and the pseudo-Galen follow the Stoic division of philosophy into three parts, logic, physics, and ethics; and they organize their treatment of physics by distinguishing an efficient and a material principle.[13] The pseudo-Clement distinguishes simples from composites and argues that corporeal wholes cannot be accounted for by the elements of which they are composed without recourse to a simple cause, rational and providential, of the invisible universe which contains the visible

[11] Diogenes Laertius, VII, 134 and 138-139.

[12] Herman Diels (*Doxographi Graeci*, Berlin, 1889, pp. 251-2) argues that the three are so closely related that they must have been derived from a common Stoic source composed between the times of Seneca and the Antonines.

[13] Sextus Empiricus, *Pyrrhoneiai Hypotyposeis*, III, 1, *Adversus Mathematicos*, IX, 4; Galen, *Historia Philosopha*, 16 (Diels, pp. 608-9).

universe.[14] Sextus undertakes to show that dogmatic views of God and of elements are alike untenable; the pseudo-Galen enumerates the various philosophic views of elements and of God; the pseudo-Clement refutes Epicurus with the aid of Plato and sketches the various doctrines of elements before treating the problems of their use in explaining the phenomena of the universe. The enumerations of theories of elements in the three accounts have striking points of similarity.[15] Similar problems are treated—whether the " material " elements are " corporeal " or " incorporeal," perceptible by sense or by reason, or imperceptible, free of qualities or characterized by qualities, finite or infinite. The character of the elements reflects the mode of composition used as a model and is sometimes indicated by use of other terms instead of " element," such as " atom," " seed," " root," " minimum," or " molecule."

The place of elements in the discussion of problems of parts and wholes is apparent in each of these accounts. The author of *The Recognitions*, thus, presents himself as one who had frequented the schools of the philosophers before he became a Christian, and in the dialogue in which elements are discussed, the chief speaker, Niceta, acknowledges that he attended the Epicurean schools, while one of his brothers studied with the Pyrrhonians and the other with the Platonists and Aristotelians. He begins his treatment of the origin of the universe by differentiating all things (*omne quod est*) into the simple and the composite. The simple " lacks number, division, color, difference, roughness, smoothness, heaviness, lightness, quality, quantity, and, therefore, even limitation." The composite is made up of two, three, four, or more components. The simple is incomprehensible and immense, without beginning and end,

[14] *Recognitiones*, VIII, 9-12, Patrologia Graeca 1, 1375A-6C.

[15] Sextus Empiricus, *Pyrrhoneiai Hypotyposeis*, III, 30-32, *Adversus Mathematicos*, IX, 359-64; Galen, *Historia Philosopha*, 18, pp. 610-11; Clement, *Recognitiones*, VIII, 15, 1378. Sextus goes on to other problems of physical philosophy in *Adversus Mathematicos*, Book X—problems of place, motion, time, number, generation and corruption—which also involve elements, and a similar enumeration of theories is made in connection with generation and destruction, *ibid.*, IX, 310-18.

without cause, but himself father and creator. Man is able, however, to come to awareness of intellectual and invisible things from things seen and touched, as is apparent in arithmetic.

The problem of the origin of the world raises two questions: whether it was made or ungenerated; and, if it was made, whether it was made of itself or by another. Only the last position would provide a place for providence. Niceta argues that the world was made by God, and the argument turns therefore to the characteristics of the visible world. Bodies have two differentiae: either they are connected and solid or divided and separate. If the world was made from a solid body, it would have to be divided into parts; if it was made from diverse parts, they would have to be brought into relation and composition. He argues that the universe could not have been made from a single body or matter, and that a creator is necessary to compound it from two or more bodies. The Greek philosophers formed different theories of the principles of the universe. Pythagoras said the " elements of principles " are numbers; Strato qualities; Alcmaeon contrarieties; Anaximander immensity; Anaxagoras equalities of parts; Epicurus atoms; Diodorus the incomposite (*amere*) ; Asclepiades masses (*onkos*) which can be called tumors or swellings; the geometers limits; Democritus ideas; Thales water; Heraclitus fire; Diogenes air; Parmenides earth; Zeno, Empedocles, and Plato, fire, water, air, earth; Aristotle introduced a fifth element, called *akatonomaston* or the incompellable, no doubt to indicate him who made the universe one by conjoining the elements. The " machine of the universe " could not have been set up without a maker and director.[16] Niceta then refutes the position of

---

[16] *Recognitiones*, VIII, 15, PG 1, 1378A-9A. The enumerations of Sextus and Galen are somewhat longer and follow a different order from the pseudo-Clement's account, proceeding through the single elements, two, three, four, five, and finally other varieties of elements. The list in Sextus' *Pyrrhoneiai Hypotyposeis*, III, 30-32 runs: Pherecydes earth; Thales water; Anaximander the infinite; Anaximenes and Diogenes of Apollonia air; Hippasus of Metapontum fire; Xenophanes earth and water; Oenopides of Chios fire and air; Hippo of Rhegium fire and water; Onama-

Epicurus, reports the arguments of Plato, and finds support in the phenomena of the world—the courses of the stars, meteorological occurrences, vegetable, animal, and human structures and functions.

critus fire, water, and earth; the school of Empedocles and the Stoics fire, air, water, and earth; the school of Aristotle fire, air, water, earth, and the revolving (*kyklophoretikon*) body; Democritus and Epicurus atoms; Anaxagoras homeomeries; Diodorus Cronos minima (*elachista*) and incomposite (*amere*) bodies; Heracleides Ponticus and Asclepiades the Bithynian irregular masses or molecules (*anarmoi onkoi*); the school of Pythagoras numbers; Strato qualities. Some of the compexities of the problem of elements become apparent in the interpretation of these lists. Thus, Sextus elaborates the Pythagorean doctrine that numbers are the principles and elements of all things by observing that the Pythagoreans held that the method of philosophizing was the same as the method of linguistic analysis. Language is composed of words, words of syllables, syllables of letters or elements (*stoicheia*); in the same fashion the true physicist investigates the universe by seeking the elements (*stoicheia*) into which it can be resolved. The advocates of numbers (*arithmos*) as principles (*stoicheion*) of all things agree with the advocates of atoms (*atomos*), homoeomeries (*homoiomereia*), molecules (*onkos*), minima (*elachiston*), and incomposites (*amere*), recognizing that principles must be non-phenomenal, non-sensible, intelligible bodies. [*Adversus Mathematicos*, X, 248-57; cf. *Pyrr. Hyp.*, III, 151-55, where numbers in turn are generated from the monad (*monas*) and the indeterminate dyad (*aoristos duas*)]. In the same fashion, Galen emphasizes, in his medical writings, the affinity of the atoms of Democritus and Epicurus and the molecular masses (*onkos*) of Heracleides and Asclepiades, even to the extent of reducing the differences in the case of Asclepiades to a difference of terms, the substitution of *onkos* for *atomos* and of *poros* for *kenon*. (*De Theriaca ad Pisonem*, cap. 11, *Claudii Galeni Opera Omnia*, ed. C. G. Kühn [Leipzig, 1827], vol. XIV, p. 250.) Yet the molecules of Heracleides and Asclepiades were frangible or divisible, and possessed qualities, and the terms " molecules " and " pore " have an Aristotelian derivation which is clearer than their Democritean analogy, for they are terms used in the discussion of homogeneous bodies in the *Meteorology*. Or again, Strato of Lampsacus, the successor of Theophrastus as head of the Lyceum, is said to have shown tendencies to atomism, yet he is also said to have treated elements as " qualities "; this seems to be another case of the assimilation of a philosophy of of elements to a philosophy of atoms, for it is clear that in his opposition to Platonism, Strato based his analysis on " ultimate components " which he treated quantitatively and qualitatively. Doctrines of elements tended to be likened to atomism if the operations ascribed to the elements are naturalistic and mechanical; elements may be incorporeal and qualitative and still be presented as atomic; if they undergo qualitative changes and transmutations, exhibit purposive or teleological orderings, or show effects attributable to God or the world-soul, they are not atomic. It is relevant to this transformation of the characterization of elements that Galen claimed to have added a fifth instrumental cause (*di'hou*) to the formal, final, efficient and material causes of Aristotle.

The treatise *On the Nature of Man* by Nemesius, Bishop of Emesa, probably written toward the end of the fourth century A. D., was strongly influenced by the medical theories of Galen. Nemesius presents man as a conjunction of natures or functions, ranging from the inanimate and the irrational to the rational, combining the visible and the invisible, and giving evidence both of the elements of which he is composed and of the conjunctive union in man and in the universe, in both the lesser and the greater world, from which the Creator can be inferred. Man shares properties with inanimate things, life with animate beings, and knowledge with rational beings. He shares with inanimate things body and the conjunction of the four elements; he shares with plants the nutritive and generative powers; with irrational animals he shares, in addition to these powers, voluntary motion, appetite and anger, and the sensitive and respiratory powers; with intellectual natures he shares rationality, applying reason, understanding, and judgment, and following virtues. He is midway between intellectual and sensible essences, conjoined by body and corporeal powers with other animals and with inanimate things and by reason with incorporeal substances. The Creator conjoined step by step the diverse natures in order to make the universe one and of one kind, and this is the best proof that there is one creator of all existences.[17] God adapted and conjoined all things to all things harmoniously, and united into one, through the creation of man, invisible and visible things.[18] Nemesius finds the Mosaic account of creation bears out this analysis, and he organizes his treatment of the nature of man in accordance with it, presenting in turn the soul, the union of soul and body, and the faculties of man, ranging from imagination and sense through intellect, memory, thought, expression, passion, nutrition, pulse, respiration, voluntary action, free-will, and providence.

The body is presented as a conjunction of elements in humors,

[17] Nemesii, *Premnon Physicon* a N. Alfano Achiepiscopo Salerni in Latinum translatus, I, 8-11, ed. C. Burkhard (Leipzig, 1917), pp. 6-7.

[18] *Ibid.*, I, 23, pp. 9-10.

homogeneous parts, and members.[19] Nemesius defines the corporeal element (*elementum mundanum*) as the least part in the composition of bodies. The mundane elements are four: earth, water, air and fire. " They are the first and simple bodies relative to other bodies. For every element is of the same kind as the bodies of which it is an element. A principle is not of the same kind as the things of which it is a principle, but an element is wholly of one kind." [20] He analyzes the four elements by means of the four qualities hot and cold, wet and dry, but he argues that these qualities are not elements because bodies cannot be constituted of incorporeal things, and he treats the problem of the order of elements in the organization of the universe by interposition of elements to mediate between contrary qualities. He also expounds the Platonic analysis of elements, distinguishing two ways in which he classifies elements: (1) by the regular solids, (2) by assigning three qualities to each element—fire having sharpness, rarity, motion, and earth, at the other extreme, having dullness, density, rest. To these he added a third way used by some philosophers, who distinguish the heavy elements, earth and water, from the light elements, air and fire.[21] The elements and the body enter into the analysis of the functions of the soul, and Nemesius expounds the Galenic theory of the localization of functions: imagination in the anterior lobe of the brain,[22] understanding in the intermediate lobe,[23] and memory in the posterior lobe,[24] adding that evidence for the localization of these functions was derived from observation of brain lesions and diseases affecting the brain.[25]

Nemesius' *On the Nature of Man* was translated into Latin in the eleventh century by Archbishop Nicholaus Alfanus under the title *Premnon Physicon* or *Key to Natural Things* but without mention of the name of the author or of the title he gave

[19] *Ibid.*, IV, pp. 59-61.
[20] *Ibid.*, V, 1-2, p. 62.
[21] *Ibid.*, V, 24-25, pp. 67-69.
[22] *Ibid.*, VI, 4, p. 73.
[23] *Ibid.*, XII, 3, p. 87.
[24] *Ibid.*, XIII, 7, p. 89.
[25] *Ibid.*, 8-13, pp. 89-90.

his work. It was translated again in the twelfth century by Richard Burgundio of Pisa, who was under the impression that it was written by Gregory of Nyssa. Alfanus's version was used by Albertus Magnus, and Burgundio's is quoted by Peter Lombard and Thomas Aquinas.

Some remnants of these distinctions are transmitted to the Middle Ages by Isidore of Seville. Cassiodorus (490-583) had recommended the reading of Latin translations of Hippocrates and Galen,[26] but manuscripts of these early translations have not been found. He does not treat elements in his *Institutiones*, but a section on the four elements is added in a later interpolation.[27] It deals with the order of elements familiar in meteorology from the heavenly bodies to earth, and explains the sequence of fire, air, water, and earth, by combinations of the properties incorporeal, corporeal, immobile, mobile, sharp, blunt (fire is sharp, incorporeal, mobile, as well as hot and dry; earth is blunt, corporeal, immobile, as well as cold and dry) which are caused by the influence of proximate elements. The elements are also equated with regular solids and numbers: fire with the pyramid and 12; air with the sphere and 24; water with the icosahedron and 48; earth with the cube and 96. In a diagram, the four elements, the upper three and the lower three are connected by three sets of lines drawn in groups of four to points numbered 576 (12 × 48), 1152 (24 × 48), and 2304 (48 × 48). The text says that the lines indicate ways in which the elements by their obvious contacts with each other both prepare substances of different species from themselves and are combined because of the diversities in themselves. This is the bond binding the union of the world, the relation assembling the elements. The interpretation may be based on

---

[26] Cassiodorus, *Institutiones Divinarum et Humanarum Lectionum*, I, 31, PL 70, 1146. He also recommends the reading of Caelius Aurelianus' *On Medicine* which treats the problems of elements.

[27] *Cassiodori Senatoris Institutiones*, ed. R. A. B. Mynors (Oxford, 1937), pp. 167-8.

Plato or Macrobius or on St. Ambrose's statement that the Greek word *stoicheia* means joining with each other.[28]

Isidore of Seville (560-636) takes up the elements in his encyclopaedic *Etymologies*, briefly in his treatment of medicine, and more fully as ordering principles in his treatment of the universe. In medicine the four humors are explained by the four elements; blood refers to air, choler to fire, melancholy to earth, and phlegm to water.[29] Man is composed of soul and body; and his living flesh is compacted of the four elements.[30] The treatment of meteorology and geography opens with successive chapters on the world, on atoms, on elements, on heaven, and on the parts of heaven. Atoms are defined as " certain parts of the bodies in the world so extremely minute that they can neither be seen nor undergo *tome*, that is, cutting, for which reason they are called *atoms*." [31] Isidore adds that there are atoms in body, in time, in number, or in language. The list recalls Aristotle's list of kinds of elements, but Isidore's criterion for atoms is indivisibility: the atom of body is the indivisible particle, of time the point or indivisible moment of time, of number the unit, of language the letter. The chapter on elements begins with a definition of the Greek word *hyle* as a kind of first matter in no way formed but capable of all bodily forms. The Greek word for elements, *stoicheia*, means those things which agree with each other in a kind of concord of society and communion, since they are said to be joined to each other in a kind of natural proportion, and therefore the sequence from fire, through air and water, to earth, and the sequence back, are causal. All elements are present in all things, but a thing is named from the preponderant element. Animate beings are distributed among the elements by divine provi-

---

[28] Ambrose, *Hexaemeron*, III, 4. PL 14, 176: ". . . atque ita sibi per hunc circuitum et chorum quendam concordiae societatisque conveniunt. Unde et Graece *stoicheia* dicuntur, quae Latine *elementum* dicimus, quod sibi conveniant et concinnant."

[29] Isidore of Seville, *Etymologiae*, IV, 5.3; PL 82, 184C.

[30] *Etymologiae*, XI, 1; PL 82, 398-9.

[31] *Ibid.*, XIII, 2, 472D-3B.

dence: heaven filled with angels, air with birds, water with fish, and land with men and animals. Chapter 5 begins the treatment of the heavens with the element aether or fire; Chapter 7 proceeds to meteorology by way of air; Chapter 12 begins the treatment of waters with the element water; and Book XIV, which is devoted to the earth and its parts, has an opening chapter on the element earth.

The Venerable Bede (672-735) follows a similar order in his *On the Nature of Things*. A fourfold distinction concerning the divine creation is made in the first chapter; one phase of creation is that the elements of the world were made together in unformed matter. In the formation of the world it is specified, in the second chapter, that heaven, earth, angels, air, and water were made from nothing in the beginning, and the elements are used to differentiate the six days of creation. Elements enter into the definition of the world in the third chapter. The fourth chapter is on the elements and their influence on each other and the mixtures they form are stated in terms of the qualities heavy and light, hot and cold, moist and dry.[32] Astronomical questions are introduced by consideration of the element fire in Chapter 5; the transition to meteorological questions is made in Chapter 25, on air; waters are treated after Chapter 38 on the differentiation of salt and fresh waters; geographic questions are introduced by Chapter 45, on earth.

Bede makes use of the idea of atoms in his treatment of time. In Chapter 3 of the *De Temporum Ratione*, on " the most minute spaces of times," he calls the minimum indivisible part of time atoms. Days are divided into 12 hours, and hours into 12 points, 10 minutes, 15 parts, 40 moments—points and minutes being measured on clocks, parts on the circle of the Zodiac, moments by the swiftest motion of the stars. The least of all divisions of time which can in no way be divided further is called the *atom* in Greek, that is, the indivisible. Because of its smallness it is preceptible by grammarians rather than

[32] Venerable Bede, *De Natura Rerum*, I-IV, PL 90, 187-96.

calculators, for grammarians divide verses into words, words into syllables, syllables into feet, and feet into long and short, and since it is impossible to divide further, the short foot is the atom. Bede rejects the divisions of time proposed by the astrologer, and concludes his treatment of atoms by quoting Paul on the speed of resurrection: " We shall not all sleep, but we shall all be changed, in a moment, in the twinkling of an eye, at the last trumpet." [33] Bede's text, however, reads " atom " instead of " moment," and he therefore defines the atom of time by the flash of an eye which cannot be divided or cut, and which is sometimes called " moment," sometimes " point," and sometimes " atom." [34] Bede's interpretation of Paul could have been derived from Augustine, and one of the continuing sources of information concerning the meaning of atom during the Middle Ages was interpretations of the New Testament. [35] The elements of the world, the seasons of the year, and the humors of man are distinguished by the same qualities and for this reason man is a microcosm or lesser world. Air, spring, and blood which grows in spring, are damp and warm; fire, summer, and red choler, which develops in summer, are hot and dry; earth, winter, and black choler are dry and cold; water, autumn and phlegm are cold and damp. Moreover the successive ages of man and the different temperaments of men are determined by the predominance of one or another of the humors. [36]

Rhabanus Maurus (748-856) treats the world in Book IX of his *De Universo* in the manner of Isidore of Seville, even to the

[33] I *Corinthians*, 15: 51-52.

[34] *De Temporum Ratione*, iii. PL 90, 302-7A.

[35] St. Augustine, *Sermo*, CCCLXII, 16, 19-18, 20. PL. 29, 1623-25. Augustine explains the atom in time by the atom in body. He remarks that many do not know what an atom is, and then defines atom from *tome* or cutting, so that *atomos* means what cannot be cut. He uses the division of a stone into indivisible parts to clarify the division of a year into like parts. Moreover, he argues that the *ictus oculi* by which Paul explains *atomus*, does not mean the opening or shutting of the eye, but the emission of rays from the eye to what is to be seen, including distant objects, such as heavenly bodies.

[36] *De Temporum Ratione*, XXXV, 457C-9A.

extent of repeating in the first two chapters Isidore's treatment of atoms and of elements.[37] He follows Bede in his treatment of time, but his edition of the Epistle to the Corinthians has " momentum " instead of " atomum." He therefore adapts Bede's definition of " moment," and treats the moment as the minimum and smallest time measured by the motion of the stars. But he also remarks that another edition of the text of Paul has *in atomo et in ictu oculi*, gives the etymology of *atomos*, and explains that atoms of time are perceptible to grammarians rather than to calculators.[38]

The marks and remnants of older distinctions concerning elements are plentiful, but the medical writings which were translated during the eleventh century used elements more systematically to explain the phenomena of nature and provided greater precision of statement and more diversified data of application in the use of elements as principles. Constantine the African (c. 1015-1087) translated from the Arabic, or adapted, several books attributed to Galen, in which elements are treated in detail, as well as Isaac Israeli's *Book of Elements*, but the analysis of elements in the *Pantegni*, an adaptation of a portion of the *Royal Book of Medicine* of Haly Abbas, which is the tradition of Galen concerning elements, had a clearly marked influence.[39] The *Pantegni* begins, in medieval fashion, by reciting the six things which should be known about a book: the intention of the book, its utility, its title, what part of learning it deals with, the name of its author, the division of the book. The author's name is given as Constantine the African, who brought the materials together from writings of many authors. It was Constantine's ambition to write a book covering the whole of theoretical and practical medicine, which

[37] Rhabanus Maurus, *De Universo*, IX, 1 and 2, PL 111, 262A-3A.

[38] *Ibid.*, X, 2, 286A-B.

[39] Constantini Africani, *Opera*, Basel, 1536 and 1539. Several of Constantine's translations are published among the works of Isaac Israeli, *Opera Omnia Ysaac*, Lyons, 1515. Thus, only the portion of the *Pantegni* devoted to theory is published in the 1539 volume of Constantine's works; both parts, Theory and Practice, are in the edition of Isaac.

would make unnecessary the reading of any other book for preparation or supplementation. Medicine, he argues, is more necessary and of greater dignity than all the other arts, since without health of body rationality is impossible, and without rationality science is impossible. But to understand this art, dialectic and the arts of the quadrivium must first have been mastered. Moreover, medicine covers the whole scope of science, for science is divided into logic, ethics, and physics, and medicine deals with all three of these parts, but falls entirely under none.

The *Pantegni* is divided into two parts, Theory and Practice, and each in turn is divided into ten parts. Theory is perfect knowledge of things to be seized by intellect alone and stored in memory for the control of those things; practice is the manifestation of theory in things of sense and in manual operations in accordance with understanding of the preexisting theory. Theory is divided into three parts—the sciences of natural things, of non-natural things, and of things outside nature. Practice is the science of caring for the healthy and curing the sick with diet, potion, and surgery. Natural things are those necessary to the subsistence of bodies and pertaining to their contruction or destruction. Natural things have seven kinds of parts, three of which are common to sensible and insensible things, that is, elements, complexions, and actions, and four of which are proper to sensible things alone, that is, humors, members, virtues, and spirits. There are six non-natural causes—the air about the human body, motion and rest, food and drink, sleep and waking, inanition and continence, and the accidents of the soul. There are three things outside nature —disease, the causes and signs of disease, and the accidents of disease. The theoretic portion of the treatise proceeds systematically from elements to complexions of elements to members and virtues of members; then non-natural things and things beyond nature are treated.

The element, as philosophers define it, is a simple and minimum particle of composite bodies. The elements include fire, air, water, earth, but not rocks and metals which, though simple to sight are composite to understanding. The elements are themselves indestructible, and the destruction of all other things consists in their return to the elements of which they were composed. Constantine scouts the idea of a single element, whether atoms or any one of the ordinary four elements, with arguments, ascribed sometimes to Hippocrates, designed to show that it is impossible for a single thing to generate things diverse from itself without commixture with other things. The four elements are the hot, the cold, the dry, and the moist— not the qualities simply, rather heat actually perfect is fire; actual and perfect cold is water; naturally perfect moistness is air; and the perfectly dry is earth. Each element acquires a second quality from the element contiguous to it: from the motion of the circle of the moon which is next to it, fire acquires dryness; air acquires heat from its contiguity to fire; water has dampness from the propinquity of air, and earth coldness from water. The qualities light and heavy are likewise divided among the elements, fire being most light, earth most gross and heavy, air and water falling between the two.

The compounds of elements from which bodies are formed are called complexions. They may be of varying degrees, and the quality and function of the whole is determined by the preponderant element. Sensation is explained by the temperateness of the complexion of the organs. Thus, nothing would be perceived by touch if the organ were not changed into the quality perceived; if the organ of touch were not temperate it would not distinguish between hot and cold, soft and hard, smooth and rough. Man is the most temperate of all animals. Unlike the brute which is possessed of a single function, he can do all things, and he is rational and intellectual because he can understand and distinguish by reason whatever he does. The complexions are instruments of nature or of the soul or of both. Each animal has instruments of the body in agreement with the virtues of the soul, for the government of all bodies is either by the soul and nature or by nature alone, that is, nature rules in both animate and inanimate bodies, the soul only in animate bodies. Certain virtues must be present if the body is to complete its operations.

Constantine lists three general virtues: one pertains only to nature and is therefore called natural; a second, pertaining to the soul, only vivifies and is called spiritual; a third, also pertaining to the soul, gives understanding, sense, and voluntary motion, and is called animate. The action of natural virtue, which consists in generation, nutrition, and growth, is universal in animals and plants. Spiritual virtue is common to rational and irrational animals, but not to plants; it consists in the vivification which is accomplished by the action of the heart and the dilation and contraction of the arteries for the conservation of natural bodily heat. The animate virtue is partly common to rational and irrational animals, for both participate in sense and voluntary motion, and partly not, for only rational animals have fantasy, reason, and memory. This analysis permits the reduction of all actions to kinds of motion, and Constantine elaborates the enumeration of six kinds of motion, two simple and four complex, all depending ultimately on the simple contraries.

The details of medical theory and practice, for which this analytic structure was prepared, are organized relative to the means of recognizing and controlling the mixtures of these qualities. Constantine is credited with a translation of *The Book of Degrees* (*Liber de Gradibus*) ascribed to Isaac Israeli but of unknown origin, in which medicinal simples are considered in terms of their varying degrees of hot and cold, dry and moist. Constantine reports four principal grades: a food or medicine is in the first degree of heat if it is below that of the human body; in the second degree if it is of the same temperature; in the third degree if it is somewhat hotter; in the fourth if it is extremely hot. The consideration of the contraries is an analytical device for the unification of physiology, pathology, and therapy. The doctrines of the four elements and the four qualities, whose development can be traced from Hippocrates through Aristotle to Galen, were at times used for discovery or systematization of knowledge and at times as repetitive formulae for easy analogies or empty classifications. Their use in the twelfth century was as principles employed over a broadening scope in intellectual curiosity and on a diversifying body of empirical and rational data.

The framework within which the analysis of elements was fitted in the twelfth century was a Platonic conception of the universe derived from Plato's *Timaeus* and Latin Platonists, like Apuleius and Macrobius, with echoes of Hermes Trismegistus and the pseudo-Dionysius the Areopagite, a humanistic study of the liberal arts in which rhetoric and dialectic colored an Aristotelian scheme of categories, syllogisms, and topics, and a tradition of interpretation of the Mosaic account of creation which used Platonic conceptions and methods derived, by way of Augustine and Ambrose, from the Greek *Hexaemerons* and Philo. The medical conception of elements lent concreteness, specificity, and empirical detail to the consideration of the nature of things, but it also accentuated the tendency to use a variety of structures or organisms as models for the universe or to use the structure of the universe as a model for other lesser wholes, and therefore to analogize man and universe (microcosm and macrocosm), human soul and world-soul, deliberate action and physical motion, in the treatment of cosmology, psychology, physiology, geography, and history. This merging of Platonism, the liberal arts, and the new sciences was one of the distinguishing marks of the school of Chartres in the twelfth century.

William of Conches (c. 1080-1145), whom John of Salisbury calls the most richly endowed grammarian (John's epithet *opulentissimus* has also been interpreted as a reference to the high fees of grammarians), was a grammarian and wrote treatises of science and ethics. He was influenced by Thierry of Chartres and Peter Abailard in cosmology and theology, and he quotes Constantine the African about elements. William divides science into two species in his *Gloss on Boethius' Con-*

solation of Philosophy: eloquence and wisdom. Eloquence is the science of presenting what is known with the proper ornaments of words and sentences; it is a species of science because all science consists of only these two parts, knowing things and presenting what is known well. Eloquence is not philosophy, nor any part of philosophy, but without philosophy, eloquence is a hindrance rather than an aid. William's division of philosophy is Aristotelian rather than Stoic: practical and theoretical, each in turn divided into three parts, practical into ethics, economics, and politics, and theoretical into theology (the study of incorporeal things), mathematics (the quadrivium), and physics (the study of the properties and qualities of bodies). The proper order of learning is from the study of eloquence (from grammar through dialectic to rhetoric) to the study of practical problems to the study of theoretic problems, beginning with bodies in physics and proceeding through mathematics—arithmetic, music, geometry, astronomy—to the contemplation of incorporeal things and to the Creator in theology. *The Philosophy of the World* was written, according to William's Preface,[40] because he saw so many men arrogating to themselves the name of Master, who have dissolved the union between eloquence and wisdom, who spend their time sharpening a sword they never use in battle, and who know nothing of philosophy, yet blush to confess themselves ignorant of anything and, seeking solace for their lack of learning, proclaim to less cautious men that the things they do not know are of little utility.

The use of elements to organize bodies of knowledge and empirical data continues to employ two philosophical assumptions: that the invisible things of the world are understood by the things that are made,[41] and that the existence of causes

---

[40] The *De Philosophia Mundi* or the *Peri Didaxeon sive Elementorum Philosophiae Libri IV* has been ascribed to several philosophers and has been published as the work of William of Hirschau, the friend of St. Anselm (Basel, 1531), of the Venerable Bede (PL 90, 1127-78) and Honorius of Autun (PL 172, 39-102). The reference is to Book I, *Praefatio* (in the Honorius of Autun edition) PL 172, 41-43.

[41] The inference from visible to invisible, which is used by the pseudo-Clement

is proved from consideration of the characteristic of effects.[42] William opens his treatise with the definition of philosophy as " the true comprehension of things which are and are not seen and of things which are and are seen," and specifies that the first are incorporeal things, and the second corporeal things, whether they are possessed of divine or perishable bodies.[43] He treats incorporeal things first—God, the soul of the world, demons, and the souls of men. Since God can be known in this life, William undertakes to prove his existence to the incredulous by arguments from the creation of the world and from its daily disposition. The first argument begins with the fact that the world is compounded from contrary elements, hot and cold, wet and dry. This composition of the world might have been effected by nature, or chance, or some artificer. Not by nature, since nature flees contraries and seeks similars. Not by chance, since simpler constructions, like houses, are not made by chance, and, moreover, chance is the unexpected occurrence of a thing from a confluence of causes, but nothing preceded the world except the Creator. But the artificer was not man, since the world was made before man; nor an angel, since the angels were made with the world; therefore the artificer was God. The second argument, from the daily disposition of things proceeds similarly. Whatever is disposed is disposed in accordance with some wisdom, and in the case of the world it is not human or angelic but divine wisdom. From the daily disposition of things one attains to the divine wisdom, and from the divine wisdom to the divine substance.

and many of the Church Fathers, finds support in Paul (Rom. 1: 20, " For the invisible things of him from the creation of the world are clearly seen, being understood by the things that are made ") and elaboration in Platonic philosophies.

[42] The dependence of phenomena perceived by sense or reason on a transcendent cause, equally well established in the Christian tradition, finds like support in Paul (Col. 1: 16, " For by him were all things created, that are in heaven, and that are in earth, visible and invisible ") and its elaboration may have an *a priori* Platonic turn, in which man and the world are image, likeness, or imprint and reasoning about them proceeds by models, or an *a posteriori* Aristotelian or Stoic turn in which phenomena are effects and reasoning about first causes proceeds from effects.

[43] *De Philosophia Mundi*, I, 1-3, PL 172, 43B-C.

Philosophers say that in this Divinity, which is maker and governor of all things, power, wisdom, and will are present, corresponding to the persons of the Trinity, power to the Father, wisdom to the Son, and will to the Holy Spirit.

In this work William only touches on the world soul, enumerating three opinions about it. Some think the world Soul is the Holy Spirit, for all things which live in the world live by the divine goodness and will which is the Holy Spirit. Some think that it is a natural vigor placed by God in the world by which some beings only live and others live and perceive and think; some, finally, think that it is a kind of incorporeal substance which is whole in each body although it does not perform the same functions or operations in all because of the comparative slowness of some bodies. In his *Gloss on Boethius*, however, William states his own doctrine, characteristically combining aspects of the three: the world soul is a natural vigor by which all things have their being, their motion, their growth, perception, life, reason; its effects differ in different subjects; and the natural vigor is the Holy Spirit. William's discussion of the third kind of incorporeals, demons, is based, as his critics were quick to point out, on Plato as well as on Scripture and the Fathers. William argues that even Plato's division of good demons (*kalodaimones*) into two genera is not inconsistent with the Scriptural division of angels into nine orders, since Plato divides them according to the places they occupy and the Bible according to the functions they perform. The treatment of the fourth kind of incorporeals, souls of men, is postponed to the consideration of man in Book IV.

When William makes the transition from things which are and are not seen to things which are and are seen, he warns the reader that his manner of presentation must change since his exposition will use either statements that are probable and not necessary or statements that are necessary and not probable, " for as philosophers we posit the necessary even if it is not probable, and as physicists we add the probable even if

it is not necessary." [44]   His claim for his treatment is that
nothing more probable will be found in the works of " modern
physicists." Since things which are and are seen are bodies,
and since all bodies are composed of elements, his starting point
is with elements as Constantine defines them. " An element,
therefore, as Constantine says in the *Pantechne*, is a simple
and minimum part of any body, simple with respect to quality,
minimum with respect to quantity." [45]   William interprets this
to mean that an element is " a simple part, which has no
contrary qualities," which Constantine expands, in order to
exclude homogeneous wholes, like bones, by adding " a minimum part, which is a part of something in such wise that
nothing of the same sort is part of it." Letters are elements
in like fashion because they are parts of syllables in a way in
which nothing is part of them. Constantine undertook to derive
humors from the composition of the four elements, then homoeomeries or " consimilar parts," like flesh and bone, as well as
organic or " instrumental parts," like hands and feet, from
humors, and finally, the human body from these two kinds
of parts. Consequently, the elements are not " things which
are seen," the earth, water, air, and fire, which are commonly
called elements, for those are not simple in quality or minimum
in quantity, but each is seen to contain all the qualities, as
there is in earth, for example, something of hot, of cold, of dry,
and of moist.

William argues therefore that the *elements* of corporeal things
or *things which are seen* are incorporeal or *things which are
not seen*. Division is of two sorts: the human body can be
divided into members and homoeomeries *actually*, but only the
understanding divides homoeomeries into humors and into
elements. The power of the understanding, as Boethius points
out, is to disjoin the conjunct and to conjoin the disjunct. If it
is asked *where* the elements are, the answer is that they are in
composition of bodies as the letter is in the composition of
syllables but not in itself (*per se*) . Some thinkers, like simple

---

[44] *Ibid.*, I, 20, PL 172, 48C-D.   [45] *Ibid.*, 21, 48D-9A.

minds, know nothing unless they can comprehend it by sense, but the investigations of the wise man must be concerned more with insensible than with sensible things. The elements are simple and minimum parts determined by simple, non-contradictory qualities, as earth is by cold and dry. The parts which are seen are composites in which one of the elementary particles dominates, as the composite in which cold and dry particles predominate is called earth. If one wishes to apply separate names to the two, William says, the particles which are not seen may be called the elements, *elementa*, and the particles which are seen may be called the elemented, *elementata*, products or mixtures of elements.[46] Some philosophers who have read neither the writings of Constantine nor those of any other physicist say that the elements are the properties or *qualities of things which are seen*, that is, dryness, coldness, dampness, and heat. William uses quotations from Plato, Johannitius, and Macrobius to prove that the qualities are in the elements, and therefore, the elements are not the qualities. Other philosophers say that *things which are seen* are elements, and William argues that there is no contradiction between this position and that of Constantine, although they treat two different kinds of elements. Constantine treats the natures of bodies as a physicist, and he calls the simple and minimum particles of bodies " elements " in the sense of first principles. Philosophers who investigate the creation of the world rather than the natures of individual bodies call the four parts which are seen " elements " because the world is composed of them and they were created first. If it is said that these are not elements, because they are made of the four elements, and earth, for example, contains some water, and that Plato asks how one is to decide during the transmutation of elements whether to call it earth or water,[47] William's reply is that the earth in question is something porous and saturated with water, and even if it is dis-

---

[46] Cf. Theodore Silverstein, " Elementatum: its appearance among the Twelfth century Cosmogonists," *Medieval Studies*, XVI (1954), pp. 156-162.

[47] Plato, *Timaeus* 49B-C.

solved in water, it is not the element "earth" but the "earthly," which is "part of the element," which is dissolved. Therefore the *elements of bodies* are the particles and the *elements of the world* are accounted for by their conjunctions and mixtures.

William raises two more questions which have the same characteristic of relating the problem of how wholes are compounded of parts and how intelligible principles are used to structure sensible data, that is, how the incorporeal things of understanding are related to the corporeal things of sensible experience. They are the questions (1) of the composition of the universe or of the bonds by which elements are joined together in compounds and organisms and (2) of the origin of the universe or whether the elements were formed from a preexistent chaos or were present in the chaos. Both questions raise issues which are philosophic in character about the defining properties of elements which are qualitatively simple and quantitatively minimum in kind, and about how they "are" (corporeal or incorporeal) and "are understood" (sensible or intellectual).

William's treatment of the structure of the universe is based on Plato's demonstration that between extreme elements fire and earth, two and not more than two elements, air and water, are needed to establish the unity and cohesiveness of a universe.[48] Plato's argument is that that which comes to be must be corporeal and therefore visible and tangible, for the basic proportion underlying his account of creation is that being is to becoming as thought and reason are to opinion and sensation. William interprets Plato's statement that Divine Reason ordained that the universe be so constructed as to be perceptible to sight and to touch as a consequence of the purpose in creation that man should see even with his eyes in the creation and government of things the divine power and wisdom and goodness, should fear the power, venerate the wisdom, and imitate the goodness. But sight is impossible without fire and

[48] *Ibid.,* 31 B-32C.

touch is impossible without earth, and the conjunction of fire
and earth, which are opposed by contraries (since fire is subtle,
mobile, and acute and earth is corporeal, obtuse, and immobile)
required the interposition of one or more middle terms. William
distinguishes mixture (*commistio*), in which neither of the
contraries remains what it was before, from conjunction (*con-
junctio*), in which both the contraries remain what they were
before. Conjunction is impossible in the case of active qualities
(like hot and cold) unless they are separated by a middle term
to prevent one from dissolving the other. Wishing to conjoin,
not mix, fire and earth that both would remain what it is, God
created between the two elements, not one, but two more
elements, water and air. For if he had placed only water
between them it would be conjoined to earth more than to
fire, for it shares corporality and obtuseness with earth and
only mobility with fire, and that conjunction would not endure;
similarly, if only air were placed between, it would have
subtlety and mobility in common with fire and only obtuseness
with earth. To the objection that if one did not suffice, God
could make it suffice, William says that he does not put a
limit on God's power, but he says concerning things which are
that none could suffice nor could there be anything, according
to the nature of things, that would suffice.

Having shown that one would not suffice, he demonstrates
why there could not be anything that would suffice. Elements
may be separated by two contrary qualities or by three.
Between some binary pairs, one element would suffice as a
middle term; thus, in the case of earth, which is cold and dry,
and air, which is hot and damp, water (which shares coldness
with earth and dampness with air) is a term of separation and
connection. Between ternary terms there is no middle, since
any element would share one quality with one of the extremes
and two with the other. Moreover, even if fire and air are
treated in terms of two rather than three qualities no middle
could be found since fire is hot and dry, earth, cold and dry,
and any combination of the two qualities would be identical

with one of the two elements or the impossible combination, hot and cold.[49] Of the six combinations of the four qualities, four are possible and determine the four elements; and the remaining two combinations, hot and cold, dry and wet, are impossible.

[49] The demonstration of the harmony or unbreakable chain of elements binding the universe together, dependent on the interposition between fire and earth of two and only two elements, goes back to Plato, but the changes in the properties of the elements on which the demonstration depends mark changes in the doctrine of elements. Plato's argument depends on the nature of proportion and of numbers: if the universe had been a plane surface, one middle would have sufficed; since it is solid two middle terms are required. Macrobius gives a rough translation of this passage, omitting the references to proportions and square and cubic numbers; instead he discusses hot and cold, dry and moist. (*Commentarii in Somnium Scipionis*, VI, 23-33). The Medieval tradition, finally, presents the Platonic analysis of elements as permutation of sets of three qualities, elaborated and systematized from his account of the properties of elements resulting from the geometric forms assigned to them (*Timaeus*, 55C-56B). The systematic account of the six qualities of the elements is known as early as Nemesius, and scholars have argued that his source is a lost commentary of Posidonius on the *Timaeus* or a lost commentary of Porphyry. If the problem is treated in terms of three qualities, the two extreme elements of the universe are opposed by sets of contrary qualities—subtle, mobile, acute (fire) vs. corporeal, immobile, obtuse (earth), whereas if it is treated in terms of two qualities, the contraries separate the elements in groups of threes, but the two extreme elements are not opposed by contrary qualities—hot, dry (fire) vs. cold, dry (earth)—and therefore, according to Nemesius (V, 11, p. 64), the sequence of elements is not merely an ascent and a descent but a circle, since fire shares with earth the quality dry. Whatever the origin of the analysis in which each element is characterized by three qualities, the Latin writers of the Middle Ages learned the distinctions it employs from the Commentary of Chalcidius on the *Timaeus*. The sequence of elements between the two extremes, fire and earth, as set forth by Chalcidius, may be schematized as follows—

Ignis—	acutus	subtilis	mobilis
Aer—	obtunsus	subtilis	mobilis
Aqua—	obtunsa	corpulenta	mobilis
Terra—	obtunsa	corpulenta	immobilis

The two extreme pairs—fire-air and water-earth—share two qualities and are opposed in one; the sequence consists in the change of one quality at each step; the two extremes are opposed in all three contrary qualities. Chalcidius' translation and commentary (in the manuscripts that have come to us) are incomplete. The translation breaks off at 53C, immediately before the analysis of the mathematical forms which constitute the elements and of the sequence of the elements relative to each other. The Commentary is also incomplete: the list of topics enumerated is not completed; nonetheless the treatment of the elements is complete and it runs through all three forms of analysis. The theory of the elements as mathematical

Finally, the sequence of the elements from fire to earth is shown to involve an order of lightness and heaviness.[50]

The resolution of the second question, that of the place of the elements in the creation of the universe, according to William, is also worked out in opposition to a widely held position. Almost all philosophers say that the elements did not occupy fixed places in the first creation but were mixed in one mass and therefore moved up or down together. This position is derived from Ovid and Hesiod, but its proponents add a reason for it (that the Creator might show how great the confusion of things would be if they were not ordered by his power and wisdom and goodness), and they add the authority of Plato who said that God reduced the elements from an unordered scattering to order.[51] William argues that the position is false, the argument invalid, and the authority incorrectly interpreted. The position is false because elements must be bodies, or spirits, or properties of bodies or of spirits; he shows that they cannot be any of these except bodies, and bodies occupy place. The argument is invalid because before the creation there were neither angels nor men to show how great the confusion of things would be. The quotation from

forms is expounded and elaborated. The theory of the three qualities constituting the elements is developed (*Platonis Timaeus, Interprete Chalcidio cum eiusdem Commentaria*, XXI-XXII, ed. J. Wrobel, Leipzig, 1876, pp. 87-8) as commentary on Plato's argument that the elements are required to explain how the world is sensible (Timaeus 31C; it makes use, however, of distinctions from 55C-56C), since what comes into being must be material and capable of being seen and touched. The treatment of the two qualities (hot or cold and dry or moist) constituting the elements is part of the analysis of matter (*silva* or *hyle*), which is without qualities, and the transmutation of the elements (*ibid.*, CCCXVII-CCCXXIX, pp. 341 ff.). The excerpt on the four elements which appears in Cassiodorus' *Institutiones* is given without derivation (Mynor's note [p. 167] is "Quod unde dictum sit pudet me nescire"). The analysis set forth in the interpolated passage is clearly derived from Chalcidius' Commentary on the *Timaeus*.

[50] William's analysis combines the three modes of treatment of the elements that were observed in Nemesius—(1) two qualities, heavy and light, assigned to the elements in pairs of elements, (2) four qualties, hot, cold, dry, wet, assigned two to each element, and (3) six qualities, obtuse, acute, mobile, immobile, subtle, coropreal, assigned three to each element.

[51] *Timaeus*, 53B.

Plato is incorrectly interpreted because Plato did not hold that the elements were actually in an unordered scattering, but that they could be, and in the first creation they were where they now are, but they were thicker, in so far as they were mingled, and obscurer in as much as there were no sun, moon, or stars to light them. The stars, thus, were made from all four elements, the upper elements which are visible and mobile, and the lower elements which are obscure and immobile. The stars, which are visible, shining, and mobile, have their qualities from the interplay of the properties of the elements, and in that interplay each of the four qualities is found in the visible forms in which the elements appear. According to Constantine each of the elements has two qualities, one proper to itself, the other from another element; fire hot of itself, dry from earth; air damp of itself, hot from fire; water cold of itself, damp from air; earth dry of itself, cold from water.

The stars, being fiery in nature, began to move immediately on their generation and to heat adjacent air and, through it as intermediary, the further removed water. The various genera of animals were created from heated water, birds in the air, fish in the water, and other animals and man on the earth. The theory of elements gives organization to William's encyclopaedic examination of the world and of its parts. At the beginning of Book II, he describes Book I as a summary exposition, within the limits of his small powers, " concerning the particles of things which are and are not seen and concerning elements which some teachers present as visible things," and he proposes now to take up in turn each element and its embellishment (ornatus, i. e., kosmos).

The opening chapter of Book II is on ether and its ornatus. Fire is the space above the moon, and it is also called ether; its ornatus is whatever is seen above the moon, that is, the stars, both fixed and wandering. The book presents information concerning the planets and astronomical phenomena. The opening chapter of Book III is on air which extends from the moon to the earth and is damper and thicker nearer to earth.

The early chapters take up the zones of the air and the effect of the heat of the sun raising water to form clouds, and the transition from air to water is made in Chapter 14 on the tides of the Ocean. The book presents information concerning meteorological phenomena, snow, thunder, lightning, tides, fountains, and wells. Book IV is devoted to the remaining element, and begins with a chapter on earth and the world. After sketching some geographical questions—the qualities of earth, its inhabitants, the continents Asia, Africa, and Europe, a translation is made to man in Chapter 7. Since the creation of the first man, male and female, from dust was treated in Book I, William undertakes now to treat " of the everyday creation, formation, birth, ages, members of man, and of the functions and uses of his members." He begins with the sperm, traces man from the womb through infancy, examines his organs, digestion, sleep, senses, soul, virtues, and youth and old age largely in terms of the fundamental contraries. The book ends with five chapters on teaching and the order of learning.

William argues that man is by nature hot and cold and is tempered by the interplay of the four qualities, so that differences of virtue and temperament result from the intensification and remission of the contrary qualities.[52] He follows Constantine's localization of the functions of the mind in the three cells of the brain. The anterior cell is called *fantastic*, that is, visual or imaginative, because it is the seat of the power of seeing and understanding; it is hot and dry to attract the forms of things and colors. The middle cell is called *logistic*, that is rational, because it is the seat of the power of distinguishing; it is hot and moist that it may conform to the properties of things and distinguish better. The posterior cell is called *memorial*, because it is the seat of the power of retaining; it is cold and dry in order to retain better. This localization was determined, according to William, by observation of wounds of the head in which it was noted that injuries

[52] *De Philosophia Mundi*, IV, 20; PL 172, 93B-C.

to one of the cells resulted in the loss of the function associated with it without affecting the other functions.[53] Sensation is a function of the body which man shares with other animals; distinguishing and understanding are functions of the soul, peculiar to man. There are three powers of the soul: understanding (*intelligentia*) by which man perceives incorporeal things with the certain reason why they are thus; reason by which man perceives in what respects things agree with other things and in what they differ; memory by which man firmly retains what was known before.

The doctrine of elements provided William of Conches with more than the simple parts from which to construct things, organisms, and a universe; they were also principles for the examination of the relation of corporeal things perceived in sense experience to the incorporeal structures conceived by the mind and used to explain the nature of corporeal things. The processes of composition and resolution which related elements as qualitatively and quantitatively simple parts to composite wholes also crossed the line which separates seen from unseen and corporeal from incorporeal. William's analyses therefore have philosophic interest (since he explores the problems involved in these relations) and empirical content (since the structures which he abstracts are found embodied in things which are and are known). The elements serve similar functions in other twelfth century cosmologies, scientific treatises, and encyclopaedias, and they provide common principles for the work of William of Conches and the work of men like Thierry of Chartres and Peter Abailard who influenced him and of William of St. Thierry who criticized him.

Thierry of Chartres was Chancellor of the School of Chartres from about 1141 to about 1150. John of Salisbury calls him "the most zealous investigator of the arts," and another disciple says he was "preëminent among the philosophers of all Europe" (*totius Europae philosophorum precipuus*). Bernard Sylvestris dedicated the *De Universitate Mundi* to him, and two of his

[53] *Ibid.*, IV, 24, PL 172, 95.

pupils, Herman the Dalmatian (or Carinthian) and Robert of Chester (or Katene), in the dedication of their translation of Ptolemy's *Planisphere* to him, address him as the first anchor and sovereign of the second philosophy (the mathematical arts of the quadrivium), the immovable support of studies tossed by every tempest, in whom relives the soul of Plato descended from the heavens for the blessing of mortals, the true father of Latin Studies.

Thierry says that his method of commenting on the first part of Genesis is by distinctions which are literal and according to physics. There are four causes of earthly subsistences: an efficient cause, God the Father; a formal cause, the wisdom of God, or the Son; a final cause, the benignity of God, or the Holy Spirit; and a material cause, the four elements. To say *In the beginning God created the heaven and the earth* is to say that he created matter in the first moment of time. Once created, heaven could not remain immobile: in the revolution which constituted the first day, the highest element, fire, illuminated the lower element air. In the revolution of the second day, fire through the medium of air, heated the lower element water, vaporizing it into minute drops which can be suspended in air; the firmament was thus placed in the midst of the water, air being suspended between a layer of vaporized and a layer of condensed water. Since the condensed water below was diminished in that process, dry land appeared in the third revolution; the action of the heat of the superior air and the dampness of the earth produced herbs and trees. In the fourth day, the bodies of the stars were created by contraction, caused by heat, of the waters above the firmament. Heat was increased in the revolution of the fifth day by the motion of the stars, became vital, and produced fish in the waters and birds in the air. On the sixth day, the vital heat proceeded to earth, and the animals of the earth were created, including man made in the image and likeness of God. After the sixth day no new mode of creation was used, but new creatures were produced from the seminal causes inserted in the elements in those first stages of creation. Among the elements, fire is an active and efficient cause, earth a passive and material cause, while air and water are both active and passive, instruments and vehicles of causation. Among the seminal causes which determine processes and developments after the formation of the world are gravity and lightness which bring the elements into interrelations in local motion.[54]

Thierry proceeds from the creation of the world to an exposition according to the analysis of physicists (*secundum rationem physicorum*) of the motions of heaven and earth as determined by the properties and relations of elements. He argues that when Moses said that the earth was without form and void, and when he used other similar expressions, he was referring to the " informity," or rather the " uniformity," of the four elements. This " confusion " of elements, which the ancient philosophers called matter (*hyle*) or chaos, is what Moses signified by " heaven and earth."

The informity of those elements then consisted in the fact that each of them was almost of the same sort as the others and that the differences between them were minimum or almost nothing. Therefore that difference was held by the philosophers to be nothing, and they called the elements thus confused one unformed matter. Plato, however, considering the minimum which separates the elements, and knowing that the difference, although minimum, is present in the confusion, concluded consequently that matter, that is, the confusion of elements, underlies the four elements themselves, not in the sense that that confusion preceded the four elements in time or creation, but in the sense that confusion naturally precedes differentiation, as sound precedes word, or genus precedes species.[55]

When Moses went on to say that the spirit of the Lord moved upon the waters (Gen. 1: 2), he distinguished the operative cause from the material cause. The power of the artificer, whom he calls the spirit of the Lord, excels and dominates

---

[54] Thierry of Chartres, *De Sex Dierum Operibus*, ed. M. Hauréau, in *Notices et Extraits des Manuscrits de la Bibliothèque Nationale*, Paris, 1888, vol. XXII, Part 2, pp. 172-7.

[55] *Ibid.*, p. 179.

matter in order to inform and order it, in a relation similar to that which Plato, Hermes Trismegistus, and Virgil found between God or spirit or world-soul and matter or *hyle* or world. Having presented the two primordial causes of the creation, matter and operative power (*materia et virtus opera-trix*), Moses went on to demonstrate how and in what order the spirit of the Lord operated on matter, but Thierry pauses to examine the knowledge that man can have of the Creator from creation. He distinguishes four kinds of demonstrations (*genera rationum*) which lead from things to their creative cause—arithmetical, musical, geometrical, and astronomical proofs, but our manuscripts break off after an arithmetical analysis of unity and equality and their bearing on the existence of things.

Peter Abailard (1079-1142) developed a theory concerning the nature of universals in his treatises on logic and dialectic, and he drew conclusions concerning the nature of the artificer and the elements of the world in the treatises in which he used rhetoric or dialectic to interpret statements of Scripture and facts of history or to interpret doctrines of prophets and philosophers. He opens his *Commentary on the Epistle of S. Paul to the Romans* by observing that all Sacred Scripture has the objective of teaching and moving like a rhetorical oration,[56] and that the two Testaments are therefore divided into three parts: the law, to teach what should be done and avoided; the Prophets or the Epistles, to dissuade from evils or persuade to goods; and the histories, to provide examples. He interprets Paul's statement that the invisible things of God are understood by the things that are made, to mean that knowledge of the universe as a vast fabrication or as effects may lead to knowledge of its artificer as power, wisdom, and goodness. In his interpretation of the passage from Paul, Abailard finds a similar treatment of creation in Plato and Cicero; he argues that the perception of the power, wisdom, and goodness of the Creator

---

[56] *Commentariorum super S. Pauli ad Romanos Libri Quinque*, Prologus PL 178, 783B.

is the discovery of the marks of the Trinity; and he analogizes that knowledge to the perception, when a bronze statue is set before the eyes, that the bronze and the bronze statue are the same thing essentially and numerically and yet are diverse in their properties.[57] His rhetorical method is apparent in his *Expositio in Hexaemeron*, in which he undertakes a threefold interpretation—historical, moral, and mystic—" of the abyss of profundity " of Genesis. As first step in the historical interpretation, one must take into account the fact that Moses addressed a carnal and uneducated people and sought to raise them to a consideration of divine things. Moses therefore began his exposition with the creation and disposition of the world, for " God, who is invisible and incomprehensible in himself, conveyed to us the first knowledge of himself from the magnitude of his works, since all human knowledge arises from the senses." [58] To begin with creation is to follow the natural order in addressing a carnal people, committed to the corporeal senses, and not far advanced in spiritual understanding.

Christian philosophers had learned from Platonic and Stoic philosophers to treat problems of wholes and parts by distinguishing the artificer or the efficient principle causing the unity and the material principles compounded into wholes. Abailard's exposition of the creation marks off the stages of formation by means of the four elements and finds in the structure and embellishments of the world evidence for the unity and trinity of the Creator. The opening statement of Genesis, " In the beginning God created the heaven and the earth," means that the four elements were created first, " heaven " signifying the light elements, fire and air, " earth " signifying the heavy

---

[57] *Ibid.*, I, PL 178, 802D-5A. The doctrine of the Trinity is developed in detail in Abailard's *Theologia Christiana*, I, 2 and ff. (PL 178, 1124 ff.). Abailard says at the beginning of the second book of the *Theologia Christiana* that he has assembled in the previous book quotations from the prophets and the philosophers concerning the Trinity; in the second book he examines the relation between the philosophical disciplines and religion. (*Ibid.*, 1165 ff.) Cf. *Introductio ad Theologiam*, I, 8-10 and II. (*Ibid.*, 989C-95B, and 1035 ff.)

[58] *Expositio in Hexaemeron*, PL 178, 733A.

elements, water and earth; and they were created "in the beginning," because the first confusion or congeries of elements constituted the matter for the formation of other bodies. Fire and earth marked off the limits within which the other elements provided connecting bonds and limiting differentiations, and the whole constitution of the world consisted in the four elments.[59] The Trinity is expressed in the beginning of Genesis, and is developed more fully in the creation of man in the image of God on the sixth day, for it is in power, wisdom, and love that the likeness of the human soul to God is apparent.[60] The moral interpretation is based on the same distinctions as the historical interpretation. Much as the confused congeries of elements is later ordered, so too man, composed of soul and body, but in the beginning unformed and incomposite in moral character, is transformed from the initial confusion (symbolized by the fluid element water) first by the light of faith, then by hope, and finally by charity.[61] The mystical interpretation is an allegory of cultural history proceeding through six ages, in which the first age of primitive culture without law or art is symbolized by the confused congeries of elements, and subsequent ages follow like analogies to the days of creation, until in the sixth age the future is extrapolated from the history of the past.[62]

It is apparent that the problem of elements is a problem of parts and wholes, not in the simple sense that a whole is compounded of parts, but in the more complex sense that a whole persists through changes of parts and that a whole is identifiable although characterized by different properties. When changing wholes or inclusive wholes are under consideration, the problem of part and whole becomes a problem of same and other. Abailard distinguishes three senses of same and other (*idem et diversum*): as likeness, as essential sameness but not same in number, and as sameness in property,[63] for the

---

[59] *Ibid.*, 733C-7B.
[60] *Ibid.*, 739B, 760B-1D.
[61] *Ibid.*, 770C-1D.
[62] *Ibid.*, 771D-3A.
[63] *Introductio ad Theologiam*, II, 12, PL 178, 1065.

examination of data in a universe, which is a whole characterized by properties of dynamism, wisdom, and goodness, requires an analytic device by which to identify the wholes which remain the same essentially although characterized by different properties. One analogy runs through his works, the comparison of the distinction of Persons in the unity of God to the distinction of properties in a physical object: in his *Commentary on S. Paul* he uses the analogy of a bronze statue; in his *Introductio ad Theologiam*, a bronze seal; in his *Theologia Christiana*, a wax image. In the later two works he adds a third analogy, the characterization of man, to these two.[64]

Bronze is the " matter " on which an artificer works to form a seal; the seal, thus " mattered " (*materiatum*) and formed (*formatum*), is " sealable " (*sigillabile*), that is, adapted to impress an image on a soft substance like wax; when it is actually used, it is " sealing " (*sigillans*), that is, its act is the transfer of the form to another matter. When the wax is being sealed, the single bronze substance has three diverse predicates: bronze, sealable, and sealing; bronze is matter, sealable and sealings are " mattered." Abailard argues that the relation of the persons of the Trinity is similar: wisdom is a kind of power, as the bronze seal is a kind of bronze; benignity reforms the image of God in us that we may conform to the image of the Son of God, as sealing comes to be from bronze and the sealable. In the same way the genus, animal, is the matter of the species, man, for man is a kind of animal as the bronze seal is a kind of bronze.[65] " Matter " and " mattered " in a given image are the same, essentially, yet the matter precedes the mattered; and a like precedence is found in each of the related pairs of terms—constituent and constituted, cause and effect, generating and generated.[66] The distinction and the terms in which it is expressed are found in the eleventh century

---

[64] *Expositio in Epistolam ad Romanos*, PL 178, 804B-5A; *Introductio ad Theologiam*, II, 13-14, PL 178, 1068C-70B, 1073A-5A; *Theologia Christiana*, III, IV, PL 178, 1248B-9A, 1288A-90C.

[65] *Introductio ad Theologiam*, II, 13-14, 1068C-70B, 1073A-5A.

[66] *Theologia Christiana*, IV, 1288A-90C.

translations of Salerno. Alfanus, Archbishop of Salerno, distinguished *materia* from *materiatum* in his translation of Nemesius. After pointing out that some philosophers held that the soul is corporeal, while others held it was incorporeal, he gives a Neoplatonic refutation of the corporeity of the soul: the body needs a principle to hold it together; the principle is either incorporeal or corporeal; if it is corporeal, it in turn needs a principle to bind its constituents together. If the Stoics say that the principle is a motion, one asks what is the power or virtue (*virtus*) which causes this motion. If it is matter, the previous arguments are repeated; if it is not matter, it is "mattered" (*materiatum*), and the mattered will be different from matter, for "what participates in matter is called mattered." But if it is not matter, it is "immattered" and all body is "mattered." [67] The Stoic distinction of an operative and a material cause may, however, be joined to the distinction between "matter" and "mattered" without becoming involved in the Stoic materialism: "matter" is potentiality and the "mattered" is potentiality restricted by a form which confers a specific function or potentiality and from which a specific act follows, but the distinction does not entail the consequence that all things are corporeal.

William of St. Thierry (1085-1148) made elaborate use of the doctrine of elements, but was critical of the use of physical arguments to specify properties of God or the Trinity inferred from creation. He was the adversary of Peter Abailard and William of Conches and called their errors to the attention of St. Bernard. In his *Disputation against Peter Abailard*, his criticism of Abailard is that " he loves to think about all things

---

[67] Nemesii, *Premnon Physicon*, pp. 25-26. The distinction of *materia* and *materiatum* used by Abailard, of *elementum* and *elementatum* used by William of Conches, and of *natura naturans* and *natura naturata*, which came into use about the same time or a little later, have common origins in translations from Greek or from languages which preserve verbal forms of *materia, elementum,* or *natura* from which passive (and sometimes also active) particles can be formed and recognized. In the other languages the relation between *matter, mattering,* and *mattered* is lost in the circumlocutions of translation of a work which examines that relation and is inconspicuous in original inquiries into like problems employing the same data.

and wishes to dispute about all things, about divine things
and about secular things equally." [68] He criticizes Abailard's
use of power, wisdom, and benignity to differentiate the persons
of the Trinity. In particular, he criticizes his use of the analogy
of the bronze seal and the distinction between *materia* and
materiatum to explain the relation of the Father and the Son.[69]
He expresses the wish that Abailard would read the Evangel
of God with the same simplicity as he reads Plato and that
he would imitate his beloved Plato, who proceeds cautiously
and prudently from the creation to the incomprehensibilities
of the Creator.[70] He criticizes William of Conches for adding
a new philosophy to the theology of Abailard, confirming and
multiplying whatever Abailard said and adding more that he
did not say.[71] He says that William of Conches describes the
creation of the first man philosophically, or rather physically,
and holds that his body was not made by God, but by nature,
and that his soul was given to him by God, after his body had
been made by spirits, whom he calls demons, and by the stars.
William of Conches seems to him to follow the opinion of
certain stupid philosophers who say that nothing exists except
bodies and corporeal things, that God in the world is nothing
else than the concourse of elements and the harmony or temperature of nature, and that he is himself a soul in body.[72]

[68] Guillelmus Abbas S. Theodorici, *Disputatio adversus Petrum Abaelardum ad
Gaufridum Carnotensem et Bernardum*, 1, PL 180, 250A.

[69] *Ibid.*, 3, PL 180, 254C-7C. The analogy is also criticized by St. Bernard.

[70] *Ibid.*, 7, PL 180, 270C-D.

[71] *De Erroribus Guillelmi de Conchis ad Sanctum Bernardum*, PL 180, 333A.

[72] *Ibid.*, PL 180, 339A-40A. Walter of Saint Victor says that " William of Conches
held that all things are made from the concourse of atoms, that is, of the most
minute bodies," and that Peter of Poitiers used atoms to prove that the flesh of
Christ was not in Abraham or Adam. (*Contra Quatuor Labyrinthos Franciae*, IV,
25, ed. P. Glorieux, *Archives d'Histoire Doctrinale et Littéraire du Moyen Age*, XIX
(1953), 289.) In the *Dragmaticon* which is in dialogue form, William of Conches
replies to his interlocutor's question about Epicureanism, denying that he is an
Epicurean, but adding that there is no philosophic sect so false that it has no truth
mixed with its falsehood; the Epicureans are correct in saying that the world is
composed of atoms, wrong in supposing that the atoms were without beginning and
that the four bodies of the world were composed by the bombardment of large

William of St. Thierry is not opposed to the use of the doctrine of elements. His treatise *On the Nature of the Body and the Soul* treats its subject physically: Book I is entitled " The Physics of the Human Body " and Book II " The Physics of the Soul." All animal bodies are formed of earth, that is they are composites of the four elements; for the earth, from which they are formed, and what they consist of must be distinguished. William follows Constantine's analysis, defining each element by one quality to which a second quality is added from an element adjacent to it, and he quotes the argument of Hippocrates that the animal body would feel no pain if it were composed of one element. The elements are transformed into one another; they form the humors and nourish them; and the " children of the elements " follow the ways of their fathers, for the elements operate in the greater world as the four elements operate in the lesser world or microcosm, man.[73] William differentiates three virtues in the regimen of the body: the natural virtue localized in the liver, the spiritual virtue in the heart, and the animal virtue in the brain. His analysis of these three virtues follows Constantine's position in detail, and he shares his conclusions also on the localization of the functions of imagination, reason, and memory in the three cellules of the brain.[74] The five senses correspond to the four humours: sight is fiery; hearing, aerial; odor, smoky; taste, watery; and touch, earthly. William characterizes the method of his treatment of the exterior man as one in which he has considered not only the exterior man but also certain things within human bodies which are not subject wholly to the senses of man but are discerned by philosophers and physicists through reason and experience.[75]

---

particles. Peter of Poitiers uses the word " atom " in his argument that the flesh of Christ was not in Abraham, because there were not in Abraham as many atoms as there have been men descended from him by concupiscence. (*Sententiae*, IV, 7, 11, PL 211, 1164C).

[73] *De Natura Corporis et Animae*, I, PL 180, 695-8C.

[74] *Ibid.*, I, 700A-D and 702A-C.

[75] *Ibid.*, I, 707B-708A.

In his treatment of the soul, William of St. Thierry distinguishes the definition of the philosophers of this world, who say that the soul is a simple substance, a natural species, distinct from the matter of its body, and possessed of the power of life, from the definition of the ecclesiastical doctors, who say that the soul is a proper substance created by God, vivifying, rational, immortal, but convertible toward good and evil. The soul vivifies the body in three manners—for the purpose of living only, for the purpose of living well, and to provide opportunity for the succession of future goods.[76] God made man in his image and likeness, as a sculptor makes a statue, combining in him virtues of inanimate things, plants, animals, and angels. Moreover, since man is made in the image of God, his soul is related to his body as God is related to the world: it is everywhere and everywhere whole, whole in natural, in spiritual, and in animal operations;[77] and the image of the Trinity is found in man's body and in his soul, for the soul, which is one, is also memory, counsel, and will, and the body, which is one, is also measurable, numerable, and weighable.[78]

The works translated from Arabic and Greek, the epitomes of the translators, and the treatises of Western philosophers learned in the new sciences introduced further modifications in the doctrine of elements. Avicebron (whose *Fons Vitae*, in Latin translation, uses both *elementatum* and *materiatum*), Gundissalinus, Herman of Carinthia, and Adelard of Bath discuss the problems of determining simple parts and they use them in the classification and analysis of a wide range of data. The theoretic aspects of the problem become clear again in the exploration of the consequences of alternative approaches to elements; but the materials on which the schematisms are employed, once the new materials treated in the translations have become familiar, tend to fall into reiterative repetitions. There is some indication that the distinctions based on elements stimulated new observation in some fields, but the evidence is ambiguous because the task of assimilating the new materials

[76] *Ibid.*, II, 707-9.   [77] *Ibid.*, I, 702C.   [78] *Ibid.*, II, 722A-23A.

of the sciences was so great that what seems new is often the
interpretation of an old text newly acquired. It is ambiguous
also because the focus of inquiry was turning from the elements
or natures of things to the principles of motions or functions.
In that transition, the physical sciences of Aristotle are themselves interpreted in terms of elements rather than of principles.
Gundissalinus distinguishes natural bodies into simple and composite and then divides natural science into eight large parts:
the investigation (1) of what is common to natural bodies,
simple and composite, as in Aristotle's *Physics*; (2) of simple
bodies in heaven and earth, as in the *De Caelo et Mundo*;
(3) of the mixture and corruption of natural bodies and the
generation and corruption of elements, as in the *De Generatione
et Corruptione*; (4) of the principles of the accidents and
passions of elements and composites, as in the *De Impressionibus Superioribus*; (5) of bodies compounded of elements
and of bodies of similar or of dissimilar parts, as in the *De
Impressionibus Superiorum*; (6) of bodies compounded of similar parts which are not parts of a body compounded of diverse
parts, as in the *De Mineris*; (7) of what is common to the
species of vegetables and what is proper to each of them, as in
the *De Vegetabilibus*; and (8) of what is common to the
species of animals and what is proper to each of them, as in
the *De Animalibus*, the *De Anima*, and the books included up
to the *De Naturalibus*.[79] It is worth observing that the fact
that the title by which Aristotle's *De Caelo* was known during
the Middle Ages was *De Caelo et Mundo* suggested analogies
to the opening lines of Genesis concerning the creation of
the heaven (*caelum*) and the earth (*terra*). Aristotle conceived the history of natural philosophy to be an evolution
from elements as principles used by early philosophers to his
own methodical use of causes as principles. This history is
repeated in the transition from the eleventh to the twelfth
century, but ironically Aristotle's natural philosophy enters
into that transition as a philosophy of elements.

[79] Domingo Gundisalvo, *De Scientiis*, ed. P. Manuel Alonso Alonso (Madrid, 1954),
pp. 120-6.

After the first systematic commentaries on the newly translated scientific writings of Aristotle had appeared in the latter half of the thirteenth century, the problem of elements began to emerge again, and all the opposed conceptions were formulated in terminology borrowed from the Aristotelian writings. The discussion of least parts and simples in terms of kinds of motion led into theories of *minima* and *maxima,* and of simples and composites; the discussion of numbers and mathematical bodies as least parts and organizing principles of composites and organisms went from Platonic beginnings to mathematical elaborations; the Stoic elements and their efficient principles and the arbitrary models which used methods familiar to the skeptics were known in the Renaissance; the Epicurean atoms moving in a void were set forth by Gassendi in the seventeenth century. With the progress of medicine, astronomy, and mechanics in the Renaissance attention concentrated on the elements as principles again, and Boyle was able to assemble in the dialogue of the *Sceptical Chymist* a Corpuscularian, a Peripatetic, and a Spagyrist or modern Chemist, to discuss a large variety of theories of elements (including van Helmot's theory that all things are water fructified by seeds) .

The transition from the Renaissance to the seventeenth century is similar in what happened to the treatment of elements to the transition from the twelfth to the thirteenth century: more was known and the data were richer, but the opposed theories followed a similar pattern, and the discussion of elements again yielded to the discussion of laws and principles of motion—the issue in the seventeenth century was not primarily between Descartes' vortices, Leibniz' monads, and Newton's atoms but between their conceptions of mass and motion and their elaborations and applications of laws of motion. The Newtonian principles were used to organize a system of the world and a system of physical science in the eighteenth and early nineteenth centuries, but in the twentieth century our attention has turned again to elements and particles and to more subtle and better grounded forms of anti-

nomies and paradoxes of matter and energy, matter and
antimatter, machine and organism, simple and composite,
motion and rest. We have nothing to learn concerning the
substance of the twentieth century problem from what was
known about elements in the twelfth century or in the Renaissance, but the theoretic characteristics and consequences of the
opposed positions were thoroughly elaborated in the earlier
periods in statements which have echoes in contemporary
problems, and the ironical turn of history which transformed
rather than solved the problems of the earlier periods is preparation which might be useful for like transformations in the
problems faced today.

RICHARD McKEON

University of Chicago,
Chicago, Illinois.

THE ORIGINS OF THE PROBLEM OF THE UNITY OF FORM

ᖯᑐ

THE philosophical problem with which we are here concerned may briefly be formulated thus: Whether in one and the same individual, remaining essentially one, there are many substantial forms or only one.

A concrete thing of matter and form, the σύνολον, is one essence and one nature, but it possesses several perfections and activities. It is, in fact, a body, *corpus*, and it is such and such a body, a stone or a tree or a horse. A tree is a body, but it is a determinate body, quite different from a stone or a horse; besides being a corporeal thing, it is also a living thing. Now, as Boethius has it, it is the form that confers on matter the actual being: *omne esse ex forma est*.[1] A substantial form imparts an essential perfection, and an accidental form a relative or qualified perfection. Assuming that substantial form is the determining principle of a composite being, the difficulty arises of how to account for the various essential perfections of an individual. Does one substantial form give one perfection only, so that we have to look for as many substantial forms as there are perfections and activities; or does a single form suffice to determine the thing in its own nature, thus endowing it with all its perfections and activities? A stone is a corporeal thing as much as a piece of iron, and man is as much a living being as a tree or a horse; but as a horse possesses some perfections which a tree has not, for example, sensitive life, so man, besides having nutritive and sense powers, is also endowed with an intellective soul.

The whole point of the discussion, therefore, comes to this: Is a man—let us say *man*, for it was in connection with the human soul that the vexed question was first stated—a living

[1] Boethius, *De trinitate*, c. 2 (*The Theological Tractates*, ed. H. F. Stewart and E. K. Rand. London, 1926, p. 8; PL 64, 1250 B).

being by virtue of a distinct nutritive soul, an animal through a distinct sensitive soul, and finally rational by an intellective soul; or does he owe to one single substantial form, the intellective soul, not only his being a man, or rational, but also his being an animal, a living thing, and a corporal substance?

If with Aristotle one holds (i) that prime matter is a completely passive potency without any actuality of its own whatever; (ii) that privation is the disappearance of the previous form, and, consequently, has no part at all in the composition of the substance; and (iii) that substantial form is absolutely the *first* determining principle, which makes the thing to be what it is, the only root of actuality, unity and perfection of the thing; then, consistent with his stated principles, the conclusion forced upon us is that in one and the same individual there can be but one single substantial form: other forms, that come after the first, are simply accidental and not substantial forms. Since the thing is already constituted in its own being, they cannot give substantial being, but exclusively accidental or qualified being; they do not confer upon the concrete thing its own definite and specific kind of being, e. g., man, but only a qualified or relative state of being, for example, of being fair or dark, big or small, and the like.

On the other hand, if one contends (i) that primary matter is not absolutely passive and potential, but possesses in itself some actuality, no matter how incomplete or imperfect it may be: an *incohatio formae*, or any active power; (ii) that privation does not mean the complete disappearance of the previous form, so that matter is not stripped of all precedent forms in the process of becoming; or (iii) that substantial form either meets with some actuality in prime matter or does not determine the composite wholly and entirely, but only partially; from all this it will necessarily follow that there are in one and the same individual plurality of forms.

Briefly, the utimate philosophical issue resolves itself as follows:

(a) Do the various substantial forms, as imparting different essential perfections and virtues, remain *actually and simul-taneously* in a composite, which is essentially one, whether in juxtaposition, in co-ordination, disposed hierarchically, or in any other way implying actual persistence?

(b) Or must all previous forms pass away with the coming in of the more perfect substantial form, in such a wise that they are in the σύνολον only *virtually* as implied, synthetized, and comprised in the higher form, each essential perfection being gathered up into the unity of a single form, which *alone* gives to the individual its ultimate and specific determination?

The problem may be, and in fact had been, approached from two angles: the psychological and the metaphysical. Regarded psychologically, the problem was restricted to living beings, especially to man. Considered metaphysically, it was raised from as many aspects as there are things composed of matter and form, whether living or lifeless bodies (*mixta*), or simply from simple logical relations, such as genus and species viewed as matter and form, and their mutual predication.

The question was not fully elaborated all at once, but slowly and by degrees. The starting-point was whether the nutritive, the sensitive and the rational principles in man are one soul, one substance, or three distinct souls or substances.

To avoid confusion, it is important to bear in mind that the problem of the unity or plurality of the human soul is a different question from that of the unity or plurality of substantial form, whether in man or in any composite. Naturally enough, if there is plurality of souls, *a fortiori* there must be plurality of substances or forms. Substance, philosophically speaking, is equivalent to form. But the latter question is a more complex one; that is, assuming that there is in man one soul only, and even that the soul is the form of the body so as to constitute one essence, it still remains undecided whether the determining principle is one only or whether there are required as many principles, or forms, as there are perfections and powers.

There is a general consensus among scholars that it was St.

Thomas Aquinas who gave to the problem of the unity of substantial form its full significance. It is equally agreed that the question cannot have originated with him, since it was current in the schools as early as the first decades of the thirteenth century, though, it is true, it then turned on a single instance, namely whether the nutritive, the sensitive and the rational are in man one soul, one substance, or three distinct souls or substances. (We have already observed that to say *substance* is the same as saying *form*). Further, it should be admitted that many of the masters, who held that the three principles are in man not only one soul, but also one substance, did not fully grasp all its implications. Albert the Great was, perhaps, the first to see the general and wider principles involved; yet he too neither stressed the point nor deduced all the logical conclusions. With Aquinas, on the contrary, the debate entered a new phase. Refusing to regard it merely as a psychological theory, he considered it as fundamentally metaphysical, based on the principle of contradiction; he thus gave it stability, universality and full value. Since it is essentially metaphysical, it concerns the total range of matter-form composites, without exception, holding good not only in psychology, but also in logic, in the philosophy of nature and by inference in theology as well. It is precisely here that Aquinas' original contribution to the problem lies. Still, granted that St. Thomas' predecessors and contemporaries, chiefly because of their somewhat imperfect grasping of metaphysical principles, did not clearly perceive all the issues involved, the fact remains that the problem itself, in its psychological aspect, had already been discussed and propounded in the schools of Paris and Oxford for at least half a century before St. Thomas' time. And if in reality there were two contrary opinions, one must have been in support of plurality of substances, or forms, and the other in support of the unity of substance, or form. There is no alternative position.

The aim of this paper is not to discuss in detail the philosophical issues of the problem, but to attempt to trace its origins and to consider its impact on the early masters in Paris and Oxford.

*

*   *

The origin of the problem under discussion is obscure. On the assumption that it could arise only on the basis of Aristotelian principles, it would serve no purpose to search for its beginning before the rediscovery of the *libri naturales* and the *Metaphysics*. The twelfth-century thinkers, failing to understand the problem of change and becoming, could not perceive the value of the question of forms. They posited primary matter, not as the potential principle of which things are essentially constituted, but rather as a chaotic mass of the four elements, as something actual, and therefore already informed.[2] Similarly, they had no clear notion of the distinction between substantial and accidental forms. The substantial form was, for them, not the constitutive principle by which things are what they are, but more truly the collection of all the attributes by which a thing is discriminated from other things.[3] With a confused notion of matter and form, the question of the unity or of the plurality of substantial forms does not even arise. The times were not yet ripe for so refined a discussion.

To trace, then, the origin of the dispute and to investigate how and when the Schoolmen came for the first time into contact with it, we must turn to another field of inquiry.

In the height of the conflict against Aristotelianism in the last decades of the thirteenth century, there appeared a list entitled *Errores philosophorum*, written, in all probability, by

---

[2] See, for example, Alanus de Insulis, *Distinctiones dictionum theologicalium*, s. v. *silva* (PL 210,944 C); see also s. v. *aqua* (704 A); and *Regulae de sacra theologia*, reg. 5 (626 A).

[3] "Forma dicitur proprietas rei, unde Boetius: 'Considerat enim corporum formas,' id est proprietates." Alan de Insulis, *Distinctiones*, s. v. *forma* (796 D). "Forma est quae ex concursu proprietatum adveniens a qualibet alia substantia facit suum subiectum aliud." Nicholas of Amiens, *De arte seu articulis catholicae fidei*, Prologus (PL 210,597-8). Cf. among others, M. Baumgartner, *Die Philosophie des Alanus de Insulis im Zusammenhange mit den Anschauungen des 12. Jahrhunderts* (B. G. P. M., II. 4). Münster i. W., 1896, particularly pp. 47-60.

Giles of Rome,[4] in which Aristotle and Avicenna are made responsible for the thesis: *Quod in quolibet composito sit una forma substantialis tantum.* The author, who is on the whole familiar with the facts, argues that the unity thesis is a logical inference of the Aristotelian doctrine on change and movement. For, since the coming-to-be of a thing never takes place without the passing-away of another, and one substantial form is never introduced unless the one which preceded it is expelled—seeing that the matter of all things material is the same—it follows that there are no more substantial forms in one composite than there are in another. Nay if one stresses this point rightly, it seems necessary to maintain that there is in all compounds one substantial form only: and indeed this appears to be the Philosopher's position. In fact, in the *Metaphysics*, Book VII, in the chapter ' On the unity of definition,' he states that the attributes in the definition are one, not because they are present in one thing, but because they constitute one nature, one thing. If he means one thing composed of many forms, this view may be tolerated, but if he means one simple nature and that in the concrete thing there is one form only, then it is false.[5]

Doubtless in the Aristotelian system there can be no room for the theory of plurality of forms. St. Thomas more than once pointed out that *haec positio* (plurality of forms) *secundum vera philosophiae principia quae consideravit Aristoteles est*

---

[4] *Giles of Rome Errores Philosophorum*, ed. J. Koch (Milwaukee: Marquette Univ., 1944).

[5] Among Aristotle's errors: " 11. Ulterius, quia per viam motus nunquam est generatio unius, nisi sit corruptio alterius, et nunquam introducitur una forma substantialis, nisi expellatur alia, cum eadem sit materia omnium habentium eam (*De gen. et corrup.*, I. 3, 319 a 33-b 5; c. 5, 320 b 12-14), sequitur ex hoc quod non sint plures formae substantiales in uno composito quam in alio. Immo qui bene prosequitur viam istam, videtur esse ponendum in omni composito unam formam substantialem tantum; et ista videtur via Philosophi. Unde VII° Metaphysicae, capitulo ' De unitate diffinitionis,' vult partes diffinitionis non esse unum (Z. 12, 1037 b 22-27), ' quia sunt in uno,' sed quia dicunt unam naturam.—Quod si intelligit unam naturam compositam ex pluribus formis, posset tolerari; sed si intelligit unam naturam simplicem, et quod sit in composito una forma tantum, falsum est." *Ibid.*, p. 8. And in the *summa errorum*: " 11. Quod in quolibet composito sit una forma substantialis tantum." p. 12.

impossibilis.[6] Yet, since at the earliest stage the question was not discussed under this aspect, we are still far from knowing how and when the Schoolmen became aware of the problem.

We get nearer with Avicenna, who, according to the *Errores philosophorum*, explicitly maintained that *est una tantum forma substantialis in composito*. As a matter of fact, this thesis stands at the head in the enumeration of Avicenna's errors. Indeed, in his *Metaphysics*, section II, in the chapter ' On the division of corporeal substance,' Avicenna holds that the form of the genus is not made specific through anything extrinsic. By this he implies that the form of the species is not some essence besides the essence of the form of the genus.[7] This is a clear statement of the unity thesis. Elsewhere too, as for instance, in the *Sufficientia*, Avicenna firmly expresses the same view: one and the same substantial form makes matter a definite kind of body and a body: *Non est alia forma qua ignis est ignis et qua est corpus.*[8]

None the less, the weight of these arguments was felt only at a later and more developed period of the debate. At all events, we can trace its very beginning to Avicenna's *Liber sextus naturalium,* or *De anima,* translated into Latin at Toledo in the second half of the twelfth century by Dominic Gundissalinus and his associates, who also rendered into Latin Algazel and Ibn Gebirol's *Fons vitae.* Avicenna argues from the unity of the human soul to its substantiality. Since it is the soul that makes man what he is and constitutes him in his species, if there were in man diverse souls, man would be in diverse species.[9] Moreover, he posits unequivocally that the

----

[6] Cf. among others, St. Thomas Aquinas, *De spiritualibus creaturis*, a. 3 (ed. L. W. Keeler, Romae: Gregorianum, 1938, p. 42).

[7] " 1. Avicenna autem similiter videtur errasse ponens unam formam in composito, ut patet in II° tractatu Metaphysicae suae, capitulo ' De divisione substantiae corporeae ' (ed. Venetiis, 1508, fol. 76ra), ubi vult quod forma generis non specificetur per aliquod extrinsecum. Per quod innuitur quod forma speciei non sit aliqua essentia praeter essentiam formae generis." *Ibid.*, pp. 24-26. *Summa:* " 1. Quod est tantum una forma substantialis in composito." p. 34.

[8] Avicenna, *Sufficientia*, II, c. 3.

[9] " Anima ergo perfectio est subiecti quod est constitutus ab ea. Est etiam

human soul, while possessing a multiplicity of powers, namely vegetative, sensitive and rational, is essentially one; for it is one and the same principle that gives life and movement, and governs and acts in man.[10]

Gundissalinus is known to us not only as a translator, but also as an author. His treatises, in which he made full use of his own translations, chiefly of Avicenna and Gebirol, are important not so much for his personal contribution to medieval thought—for he is rather a compiler than an original thinker— as for his being the first to utilize and attempt a systematic exposition of the new learning, thus opening up fresh subjects

constituens speciem et perficiens eam. Res enim habentes animas diversas fiunt propter eas diversarum specierum, et fit earum alteritas specie non singularitate; ergo anima non est de accidentibus quibus non specificantur species, nec recipiuntur in constitutione subiecti. Anima enim est perfectio substantiae, non ut accidens." *De anima*, I, c. 3 (*ed. cit.*, fol. 4ra). I have collated Avicenna's text with Bodleian Library, Oxford, MS Bodl. 463 (S. C. 2456).

[10] " Postea autem declarabitur tibi quod anima una est ex qua defluunt hae vires in membra, sed praecedit actio aliquarum, et consequitur actio aliarum secundum aptitudinem instrumenti. Ergo anima quae est in omni animali ipsa est congregans principia sive materias sui corporis, et coniungens et componens eas eo modo quo mereantur fieri corpus eius; et ipsa est conservans hoc corpus secundum ordinem quo decet, et propter eam non dissolvunt illud extrinseca permanentia, quamdiu anima fuerit in illo, alioquin non remaneret in propria sanitate." *Ibid.*, fol. 3vb. Cf. P. V, cap. 7, fol. 27r ff.—Deviating, however, from his own principles, Avicenna held that the substantial forms of the elements remain entire in the mixed bodies, an inconsistency which cannot be explained save by assuming that he did not foresee all the consequences implied in his premises. See *Sufficientia*, I, c. 10, fol. 19rb; *Metaph.*, VIII, c. 2, fol. 97vb-98ra; *De anima*, IV, c. 5. Cf. St. Thomas, *Summa theologiae*, I, q. 76, a. 4 ad 4. It has also been urged that Avicenna's theory on the *forma corporeitatis* is in support of the pluralist view. That it may be interpreted as advocating pluralism is beyond doubt. In this sense it was understood and criticized by Averroes. The phrase itself is ambiguous, and because of its ambiguity it was avoided by Aquinas. Nevertheless, it seems to have a different meaning in Avicenna, as M.-D. Roland-Gosselin (*Le " De Ente et Essentia" de s. Thomas d'Aquin* [Bibliothèque Thomiste, VIII; Kain, 1926] pp. 104 ff.), A. Forest (*La structure métaphysique du concret selon saint Thomas d'Aquin* [Études de Philosophie médiévale, XIV; Paris, 1931] pp. 189 ff.) and others maintain. At any rate, Avicenna himself did not use it, it seems, in the sense assumed by the pluralists, namely as meaning the first substantial form that makes matter to be a body apart from, and previous to, its specific form. His teaching, that it is one and the same substantial form which makes matter a definite kind of body and a body, remained unaltered.

of inquiry and new approaches to old problems. It was through his treatise *De anima*, together with Avicenna's *Liber sextus naturalium*, that the question concerning unity of form reached the schools.

Gundissalinus deals with the question in Chapter **IV**: *Anima an una vel multae*, a faithful echo of Avicenna's *An sit una an multae*.

Following Avicenna closely, Gundissalinus discusses two distinct questions. The first is whether in all living beings there is one single soul which, though in itself one substance, in virtue of its manifold powers performs the function of vegetative life in plants, of sensation in animals, of intellect and reason in man. Thus, a single rational soul produces, according to its various powers, vegetation alone in the bones, hair and nails, in other parts of the body sensation and movement, and in the brain intellect and reason. Or again, to use a simile, just as one and the same solar ray causes different effects in different things, hardening the clay and melting the wax, so one and the same soul, according to diversity of bodies, operates diversely, bestowing upon some mere existence, upon others sensation, and making others rational beings.[11]

The other question propounded here is whether in man the vegetative, the sensitive and the rational are three distinct souls and substances, or one soul and one substance only. It is obvious that the former topic is not to be confused with the latter; they are two distinct problems.

The first opinion, qualified as erroneous, is rejected (*hunc errorem ita destruunt philosophi*). Gundissalinus argues against it that these three are in reality not only three powers, but three souls specifically distinct from each other, the vegetative which is in plants alone, the sensitive which is in brute animals, and the rational which is in man. The evidence that they are distinct from each other is that each one possesses a separate existence; hence one cannot be the other. The vegetative is like

---

[11] "The Treatise *De Anima* of Dominicus Gundissalinus," ed. J. T. Muckle, *Mediaeval Studies*, II (1940), 44.

the genus to its species; it is therefore in plants as well as in animals; but plants and animals are specifically diversified. Nevertheless, from the fact that each taken separately is specifically distinct, it does not follow that they are also distinct subsances when they are united. For instance, a palm tree and a vine are both a tree, that is, they are endowed with vegetative soul, a power of self-nurishment and growth. Yet for a palm or a vine there is not required another soul in addition to the vegetative soul, namely, the soul of a palm or of a vine. It is one and the same soul that makes the living, growing tree a palm or a vine.[12]

Likewise the three vital powers, vegetative, sensitive and rational, exist in man. Taken separately, each one is a substance distinct from the other, but this is not the case when they are jointly existing in man. As the sensitive includes the vegetative and has something else besides, that is, sensitivity, so the human soul is one single substance (*cum sit una simplex substantia*), implying in itself, not only the rational but also the vegetative and the sensitive, not however as distinct substances (*non tamen tres substantiae sunt in homine*), but simply as distinct powers. Moisture and heat, taken separately, are different, but conjoined in vapor they make one single thing.[13] The higher soul presupposes the lower, without which it cannot exist. Neither can the sensitive exist without the vegetative, nor the rational, in its turn, exist without the vegetative and the sensitive. But the lower form, when conjoined with the higher, has not a separate existence, but is implied in the higher,

---

[12] *Ibid.*, pp. 44-45.

[13] " Quamvis autem omnis anima sit substantia et hae tres simul sint in unoquoque homine, quoniam in homine est anima vegetabilis, et sensibilis, et rationalis, non tamen tres substantiae sunt in homine; humana enim anima, cum sit una simplex substantia, habet vires animae vegetabilis et vires animae sensibilis et vires animae rationalis; similiter et anima sensibilis habet vires animae vegetabilis. Et quamvis hae vires diversae sint inter se, ita ut una earum non praedicetur de altera, quippe cum unaquaeque earum sit species per se, tamen nihil prohibet eas simul haberi ab anima rationali. Quemadmodum, quia invenimus humorem in aere non separatum a calore, non tamen idcirco necesse est ut humorem et calorem qui sunt in aere non habeat aliqua una forma vel aliqua una materia. Sic et de viribus animarum." *Ibid.*, p. 45.

since the higher possesses all that the lower has and something more besides: the higher the soul, the greater the power, the more comprehensive its virtue. The power which supervenes, being stronger, becomes the principle of that which preceded and remains the only principle and cause of all the powers and virtues operating there. Similarly with regard to the sensitive and rational souls, just as when the sensitive soul supervenes, the vegetative is superseded, so with the appearance of the rational soul all the operations both of the vegetative and of the sensitive are effected by the rational. The latter virtually includes the former, not in the sense that we can distinguish in the sensitive two souls or substances, and in the rational three, but in the sense that one single soul, the highest, has the power to produce all the operations performed by the vegetative and the sensitive souls.[14]

Gundissalinus reaches the same conclusion in Chapter II, when he is discussing the substantiality of the soul. The soul is a substance and not an accident, since there is one soul only in a living composite, whether it be a tree, an animal or a man. To prove, in turn, the unity of the soul, he argues that it is the soul that makes man what he is and imparts to him his specific nature, for it is the self-same principle that bestows life and movement, and governs and acts in man. It is not by reason of two or more principles, but by virtue of the self-same prin-

---

[14] " Quaedam non recipiunt nisi animam vegetabilem tantum, quaedam vero amplius quia animalem; quaedam vero multo amplius quia rationalem. Quemadmodum si corpus unum ponatur ad solem cuius situs talis esse potest ut non recipiat a sole nisi calorem tantum; si vero talis fuerit eius situs ut recipiat ab eo calorem et illuminationem, tunc simul calefiet et illuminabitur, et lux cadens in illud erit principium calefaciendi illud: sol enim non calefacit nisi radio. Deinde si maior fuerit eius aptitudo ut etiam possit accendi, accendetur et fiet flamma, quae flamma erit etiam causa calefaciendi et illuminandi simul ita ut quamvis sola esset, tamen perficeretur calefactio et illuminatio, et praeter hoc calefactio poterat invenire per se sola, vel calefactio et illuminatio sola per se, quorum posterius non esset principium a quo emanaret prius. Cum autem omnia simul concurrunt, tunc id quod fuerat posterius fit principium etiam prioris et emanat ab eo id quod erat prius. Sic ergo dispositionem virium animarum facile intelligere poteris, si per corpus calefieri intelligas illud tantum vegetari, et per illuminari illud ab anima sensificari, per accendi vero animam rationalem sibi infundi." *Ibid.*, p. 46.

ciple, namely the soul, that an organic body is a body and a definite kind of body, that is, an animal or human body, since whatever perfection is superadded to an already constituted being does not impart a specific being, but merely an accidental being, or a mode of being. Unless we admit the patent contradiction that one and the same being could belong to two different species, we must agree that the soul confers on the organic composite a complete substantial being, and consequently that the soul is only one. In fact, as soon as the soul departs from the body, the body is no longer an animal or human body, but becomes something else, with an utterly different nature.[15] Professor E. Gilson has correctly remarked that there is complete agreement between Avicenna and Gundissalinus on the concept of the unity of the soul in a composite.[16]

I have dwelt at some length on this point, for it is of no mean importance in determining the exact source of the unity thesis. It is true that, strictly speaking, the discussion turned primarily on the unity of the soul; obviously, as we have already noted, a different question from that of the unity of substantial form. Nonetheless, Gundissalinus, presenting

[15] " Nam corpus proprium, in quo existit unaquaeque animarum, scilicet tam vegetabilis quam sensibilis quam etiam rationalis, non est id quod est ex complexione propria sed ex anima. Anima enim est quae facit illud esse illius complexionis, nec permanet in complexione propria in actu nisi quamdiu fuerit anima in illo. Anima enim sine dubio est causa per quam vegetabile et animal sunt illius complexionis; ipsa enim anima est principium generationis et vegetationis. Unde impossibile est ut proprium subiectum animae sit id quod est in actu nisi per animam. Non enim verum est ut proprium subiectum animae prius constituatur ab alio, cui postea adveniat anima quasi non habens partem in eius constitutione vel definitione, sicut accidentia quae consequuntur esse rei consecutione necessaria, non constituentia illud in actu. Immo ipsa anima constituit ipsum proprium subiectum et dat ei esse in actu. Cum vero anima separatur ab eo, succedit necessario cum separatione eius alia forma, quae est sicut opposita formae complexionali. Haec enim forma et haec materia, quam habebat dum aderat anima, non remanet post animam in sua specie, quoniam destruitur eius species et eius substantia quae erat subiectum animae." Ibid., chap. 2, p. 41.

[16] " Les deux philosophes se trouvent donc avoir du même coup une conception identique de l'unité de l'âme dans le composé." E. Gilson, " Les sources gréco-arabes de l'Augustinisme avicennisant," Archives d'hist. doctr. et litt. du M-A., IV (1929), 84.

Avicenna's treatment more systematically, provided the School-men with the main elements of the problem by asserting un-ambiguously (i) that the vegetative, the sensitive and the rational, though three distinct substances when taken sepa-rately, are one simple substance when united; (ii) that the higher principle includes the lower, which is only virtually present when the higher supervenes; (iii) that whatever per-fection is superadded to an already constituted being does not impart *specific* being, but merely accidental being; and conse-quently (iv) that the vegetative, the sensitive and the rational are in man not three distinct substances, but powers. The formulation, the arguments and similies set forth by Gundis-salinus will become a common patrimony and will be continu-ally used in more or less refined fashion by successive genera-tions of masters. Some confusion as to the unity of soul or sub-stance will linger for a time, but soon philosophers and theo-logians will accurately distinguish between the question of the unity of soul and the unity of substance or form.

Turning our attention now to the pluralist theory, Aquinas [17] traced its source remotely to Plato and proximately to Avice-bron (Ibn Gebirol). Both systems issue from the same root, both present as reality what is a mere distinction of the mind, and one is the sequel of the other.[18] The pluralist theory, in fact, follows logically from Platonic presuppositions. Plato holds that there are several souls in a body, distinct according to different organs and their various vital actions, such as the nutritive in the liver, the concupiscible in the heart, and the knowing in the brain.[19] Furthermore, he maintains that the human soul is united to the body not as form to matter, but merely as mover to the moved, just like a sailor in a boat; and again, that man is not composed of soul and body, but that

---

[17] St. Thomas, *De spiritualibus creaturis*, a. 3 (ed. Keeler, pp. 40-41).

[18] St. Thomas, *Summa theol.*, I, q. 76, aa. 3-4. " Et haec positio [Avicebron's], quamvis videatur discordare a prima [Plato's], tamen secundum veritatem rei cum ea concordat, et est sequela eius." *De spirit. creat., loc. cit.*

[19] Cf. St. Thomas, *QQ. disp. de anima*, a. 11: " Plato posuit diversas animas esse in corpore; et hoc quidem consequens erat suis principiis." Also *Summa theol.*, I, q. 76, a. 3.

man is a soul using a body. In all these cases the resultant union would not be essential but accidental. Now in things accidentally united there may be plurality of forms without any incongruity.

Nevertheless, the main true source from which the pluralist theory has come down to the Schoolmen is undoubtedly Avicebron.[20] The keystone of his system is his doctrine of the ' universal matter ' (materia universalis) and ' universal form ' (forma universalis): the two roots from which every thing, save God, comes forth and into which it is ultimately resolved.[21] Universal matter is one and the same, and is necessarily devoid of every form; it becomes substance by its composition with universal form. Substances are essentially different because they have diverse forms; each form conferring a special degree of being corresponding to its own nature, independently of the other. Since every thing possesses its special matter and its special form of which it is never stripped, and, at the same time, the new added form remains with the previous form or forms, it logically follows that in one and the same individual we must posit as many substantial forms as there are perfections or degrees of being.[22] " It must be taken for granted," he says, " that man owes his humanity to the human form, his animality to the animal form, his life to the vegetative form, his body to the form of corporeity, and his substance to the universal form." [23]

---

[20] " Circa ordinem formarum est duplex opinio: una est Avicebron et quorumdam sequacium eius." St. Thomas, Quodl. XI, a. 5. Cf. Comm. in II De anima, lect. 1 (ed. Pirotta, n. 225); In I De gen. et corrup., lect. 10 (ed. Leonina, n. 8); De spirit. creat., a. 1 ad 9; a. 3, etc. See M. Wittmann, Die Stellung des hl. Thomas von Aquin zu Avencebrol (Ibn Gebirol), (B.G.P.M., III, 3) Münster i. Westf., 1900.

[21] " Materia universalis et forma universalis . . . haec duo sunt radix omnium et ex his generatum est quicquid est, . . . haec natura praecedunt omnia, et in ea etiam resolvuntur omnia." Avencebrolis, Fons Vitae ex Arabico in Latinum translatus ab Iohanne Hispano et Dominico Gundissalino, primum edidit C. Baeumker (B.G.P.M., I, 2-4) Münster i. Westf., 1892-95. I, 5, p. 7.

[22] Fons vitae, II, 2 (ed. cit., pp. 26-27).

[23] " Tanquam certum . . . quod forma naturae est aliud a forma animae vegetabilis, et quod forma animae vegetabilis alia est a forma animae sensibilis, et

As Gundissalinus in his *De anima* made known the unity thesis of Avicenna, so it was he too who in his other treatises popularized Avicebron's theory. In the *De processione mundi* [24] we meet with the same description of matter and form as in Avicebron, whereas in the *De unitate* [25] (wrongly attributed to Boethius [26]) he reproduced almost verbatim Avicebron's teaching on the various degrees of forms. By bringing these theories to the fore, Gundissalinus contributed considerably to the spread of an utterly un-Aristotelian notion of matter and form which is at the base of all pluralism. Again, by proclaiming that other Avicebronian tenet, that *quicquid intellectus dividit et resolvit in aliquid, compositum est ex his in quae resolvitur*, he provided the pluralists with the fundamental principle on which their thesis stands.[27]

All things considered, we may unhesitatingly conclude that the main sources from which medieval speculation drew the philosophical problem with which we are concerned were Avi-

---

quod forma animae sensibilis alia est a forma animae rationalis, et quod forma animae rationalis alia est a forma intelligentiae." *Ibid.*, IV, 3 (pp. 215-216). Cf. III, 46 (pp. 181-2); V, 34 (p. 320).

[24] *Des Dominicus Gundissalinus Schrift 'Von dem Hervorgange der Welt'* (*De processione mundi*), ed. G. Bülow (B. G. P. M., XXIV, 3) Münster, 1925, p. 30: "Materia est prima substantia per se existens, substentatrix diversitatis, una numero. Item, materia prima est substantia receptibilis omnium formarum." Cf. *Fons vitae*, V, 22 (p. 298). Also *loc. cit.*: "Forma vero prima est substantia constituens essentiam omnium formarum." Cf. *Fons vitae, ibid.*

[25] *Die dem Boethius fälschlich zugeschriebene Abhandlung des Dominicus Gundisalvi De Unitate*, ed. P. Correns (B.G.P.M., I, 1) Münster, 1891, p. 8: "Quia igitur materia in supremis formata est forma intelligentiae, deinde forma rationalis animae, postea vero forma sensibilis animae, deinde inferius forma animae vegetabilis, deinde forma naturae, ad ultimum autem in infimis forma corporis: hoc non accidit ex diversitate virtutis agentis, sed ex aptitudine materiae suscipentis." Cf. *Fons vitae*, V, 20 (p. 295).

[26] St. Thomas has remarked that the *De unitate* was wrongly attributed to Boethuis: "Dicedum quod liber *De unitate et uno* non est Boethii, ut ipse stilus indicat." *De spirit. creat.*, a. 1 ad 21 (*ed. cit.*, p. 18).

[27] *De processione mundi*, ed. cit., p. 4; cf. *Fons vitae*, II, 16: "Quicquid compositorum intelligentia dividit et resolvit in aliud, est compositum ex illo in quod resolvitur" (p. 51). See St. Thomas, *loc. cit.* Cf. Wittmann, *op. cit.*, pp. 17-18; M. de Wulf, *Le traité 'De Unitate Formae' de Gilles de Lessines* (Les Philosophes Belges, I), Louvain, 1901, p. 35.

cenna for the unity thesis and Avicebron for the pluralist theory, Gundissalinus being the immediate channel through which the same problem reached the schools.

In thirteenth-century writings Avicebron is expressly mentioned less than Avicenna (the Schoolmen, it seems, were somewhat shy of referring to him by name) ; yet his influence is not to be underrated, chiefly among the so-called Augustinians and in the Franciscan school, particularly at Oxford.

There were, however, other factors which helped to strengthen the pluralist theory. Not least among these was the *De differentia spiritus et animae* of Costa-ben-Luca,[28] the Constabulinus of the schools. This short treatise exerted no little influence on medieval physiological and psychological thought. From it Gundissalinus in his *De anima* borrowed Plato's and Aristotle's definitions of the soul.[29] It helped to sanction the difference between 'spirit' and 'soul'[30] and to posit an intermediary uniting the soul to the body. The soul is united to the body by means of a corporeal 'spirit,' which, inasmuch as it comes forth from the heart, produces life, breath and beating of the pulse; as proceeding from the brain, it causes sensation and movement.[31] Further, Costa-ben-Luca holds that the three powers of the soul, the vegetative, the sensitive and the rational, are forms and genera of soul, and may at choice be called *animae*.[32] Thus, by introducing an ambiguous terminology, he rendered an already involved theory even more confused.

The *Liber de causis*, springing from the same Neo-Platonic

---

[28] *Excerpta e libro Alfredi Anglici De motu cordis. Item Costae-ben-Lucae De differentia animae et spiritus liber translatus a Johanne Hispalensi*, ed. C. S. Barach (Bibl. Phil. Med. Aetatis, II), Innsbruck, 1878.

[29] Cf. Gundissalinus, *De anima*, chap. 2 (ed. Muckle, pp. 37-41).

[30] The difference between *spiritus* and *anima* is also clearly stated by Isaac Israeli in his *Liber de definitionibus*, translated by Gerard of Cremona, ed. by J. T. Muckle in *Archives d'hist. doctr. et litt. du M.-A.*, XI (1937-38), 318-19.

[31] Costa-ben-Luca, *De differentia animae et spiritus*, cap. 4 (*ed. cit.*, p. 138); cf. cap. 1, pp. 121, 124, and cap. 2, pp. 124, 130.

[32] "Nunc loquarum de virtutibus animae, et dicamus, quod primae virtutes animae, quae sunt ei formae et genera, sunt tres: prima, scilicet vegetativa, secunda sensibilis, tertia rationalis, et hae virtutes vocantur ad placitum animae." *op. cit.*, cap. 3, p. 137.

source as Avicebron's *Fons vitae*, supplied a fresh argument in support of the pluralist view. We have it from Roland of Cremona, that some, to prove that there are three souls in man, based their contention on the authority of the book *De pura bonitate*, proposition I.[33] (It is well known that in some ancient manuscripts the *Liber de causis* is entitled *De pura bonitate*.) On the other hand, Albertus Magnus adduces this very same first proposition to demonstrate that such an assumption is untenable. " To admit three souls in man," he argues, " would destroy the order of formal causes, which is against the Philosopher's[34] teaching in the *De causis*, that the causes are disposed in a certain order: being, living, sentient, intelligent. For in that case the second cause would in no way be influenced by the first cause, whereas it is by virtue of that influence that a cause *is* and is a cause."[35]

These are the main sources from which the Schoolmen derived their knowledge of the problem under consideration and drew their arguments in favor of or against either opinion. Secondary channels, however, concurred to feed the stream. We may mention, for instance, the pseudo-Augustinian *De spiritu et anima*,[36] utilized by John de la Rochelle,[37] St. Albert

[33] " Et probant illud idem per primam propositionem quae est in libro *De pura bonitate*." Text edited by Dom Odon Lottin, *O. S. B.*, " L'Unité de l'âme humaine avant saint Thomas d'Aquin," *Psychologie et Morale aux XIIᵉ et XIIIᵉ siècles*, 2nd edition (Gembloux, 1957), I, p. 465.

[34] The *Liber de causis* was attributed to Aristotle in the thirteenth century until Aquinas discovered its true origin when William of Moerbeke translated the *Elementatio theologica* of Proclus from the Greek (Viterbo, 18 March 1268).

[35] " Hoc autem dato (quod vegetativum, sensitivum, intellectivum sint per substantiam separata), sequuntur duo inconvenientia, quorum unum est. . . . Aliud autem est, quod destruitur ordo causarum formalium: quia secunda causa non habebit a primaria quod est, et quod causa est. Sunt enim ordinatae causae formales, esse, vivum, sensitivum, intellectivum, ut dicit Philosophus in libro *De causis*." *De anima*, III, tr. V, c. 4 (ed. Borgnet, V, 418 b).

[36] *De spiritu et anima*, PL 40, 779-832. It was attributed to St. Augustine by many in the thirteenth century, but not by St. Thomas. See G. Théry, " L'authenticité du ' De spiritu et anima ' dans saint Thomas et Albert le Grand," *Revue des Sciences philosophiques et théologiques*, X (1921), 373-377.

[37] " Dicamus ergo secundum Augustinum in libro *De anima et spiritu*: 'Una et eadem est animae substantia vegetabilis, sensibilis et rationalis, secundum diversas

and others [38] in support of the unity thesis, and by the pluralists for their embryo-genesis theory.[39] Medieval thinkers would
make their approach from various standpoints. Arguments
were drawn from the most disparate sources; a simile, an *obiter
dictum* frequently offered ample matter for speculation. What
might seem to us quite an insignificant, tentative suggestion
sometimes gave rise to long and important controversies. It is,
therefore, not surprising that there were indeed other factors
which mingled with these to strengthen the development and
growth of the problem.

*

*   *

The next question with which we are confronted is when did
the problem itself reach the Universities of Paris and Oxford?

Although it is beyond doubt that the problem was discussed
in the schools in the first decades of the thirteenth century, at
the latest, it would surely be rash, in our fragmentary knowledge of this period, to assert definitely who were the first
masters to introduce it.

It is rather disappointing that Daniel of Morley makes no
allusion to it in his *Philosophia*.[40] In one so familiar with
Avicenna and Arabic learning, we should expect to find an
echo of the discussions held at Toledo on psychological mat-

potentias diversa vocabula sortitur ' [c. 13, PL 40, 788-9]." *La Summa De Anima
di Frate Giovanni della Rochelle*, ed. T. Domenichelli (Prato, 1882), p. 138. Cf.
also Richard Rufus of Cornwall, for whom see D. A. Callus, " Two early Oxford
Masters on the Problem of Plurality of Forms: Adam of Buckfield—Richard
Rufus of Cornwall," *Revue néoscolastique de Philosophie*, XLII (1939), 439.

[38] Albertus Magnus, *Summa de creaturis*, II, q. ,7 a. 1: " Ex his omnibus accipi-
tur, quod sententia omnium philosophorum est, quod vegetabile, sensible, et
rationale in homine sunt una substantia. Et hoc expresse dicit Augustinus in libro
De spiritu et anima." (ed. Borgnet, XXXV, 90 b).

[39] *De spiritu et anima*, cap. 9: " Vegetatur tamen (humanum corpus) et movetur
et crescit et humanam formam in utero recipit, priusquam animam rationalem
recipiat. Sicut etiam virgulta et herbas sine anima moveri et incrementum habere
videmus." (PL 40, 784-5)

[40] " Daniels von Morley *Liber de naturis inferiorum et superiorum*," ed. K.
Sudhoff, *Archiv für die Geschichte der Naturwissenschaften und der Technik*, VIII
(1918). See A. Birkenmajer's remarks on this edition, *ibid.*, IX (1920), 45-51.

ters; but he has purposely, it seems, avoided the subject to devote himself entirely to cosmology and astronomy: *ostenso itaque ex quibus diversitatibus homo constet, tum in anima tum in corpore, quoniam ad praesens non spectat negotium in huiusmodi diutius morari, ad constitutionem mundi, unde sermo venit, prius stilum inclino.*[41]

Alexander Nequam taught in Paris at the school of Petit Pont in the last quarter of the twelfth century, and about 1190 was lecturing in theology at Oxford. Seemingly he was in a position to know the main questions of the day. Yet in the *De naturis rerum* and in the *De laudibus divinae sapientiae* summing up the problems concerning man, which were then current in the schools,[42] he has not a word on our topic, though he was familiar with the connected question, whether the soul and the body are united by means of a medium.[43] Moreover, in Books III and IV of his theological work, the *Speculum speculationum*,[44] he has a short treatise on the soul, which would have offered him a good opportunity of introducing the point at issue, considering especially his acquaintance with Avicenna's *De anima*. Again, in Chapter XC, *De viribus animae*, he has a long discourse on the powers of the soul, and in Chapter XCIV, *De sensualitate*, under which heading theologians generally discussed our question, he makes no allusion

[41] *Ibid.*, p. 9.

[42] *Alexandri Neckam De naturis rerum libri duo, with the poem of the same author, De laudibus divinae sapientiae*, ed. T. Wright (R. S.), London, 1863, cap. 173, p. 299. Another set of similar questions is found in *De laud. div. sap.*, dist. X, p. 499. M.-D. Chenu (" Grammaire et théologie aux XIIe et XIIIe siècles," *Archives d'hist. doctr. et litt. du M.-A.*, X (1935-36), 5-28; and " Disciplina. Notes de lexicographie philosophique médiévale," *Rev. Sc. phil. et théol.*, XXV (1936), 686-92) has shown the great profit that can be derived from these topics in order to trace the origin and development of much medieval speculation.

[43] " Nonne maior est contrarietas inter animam et corpus, quae tamen sine aliquo medio coniuncta sunt? " *De naturis rerum*, cap. 16, *ed. cit.*, p. 55.

[44] The *Speculum speculationum*, written between 1204 and 1213, is extant in one manuscript, British Museum, MS Royal 7 F. I. On Alexander Nequam and other early masters, see R. W. Hunt, " English Learning in the late twelfth century," *Transactions of the Royal Historical Society*, 4th ser., XIX (1936), 19-42; D. A. Callus, *Introduction of Aristotelian Learning to Oxford* (Proceedings of the British Academy, XXIX, 1943).

to it, as though he had never heard of the Aristotelian distinction of the vegetative, the sensitive and the rational.

Alfredus Anglicus, or Alfred of Sareshel, well versed in medicine and in the natural sciences, was one of the very first to make extensive use of the new Aristotelian learning. His *De motu cordis*, dedicated to Alexander Nequam (d. 1217), was introduced in the university curriculum of studies as *pars inferior philosophiae naturalis*. It contains in a curious mixture a large body of doctrine common to Neo-Platonic metaphysics and Aristotelian biological and natural philosophy. The repeated assertion that the soul is one only in every living being, seems to suggest that Alfred had some inkling of the question. He teaches with Aristotle that no living being is without the vegetative soul, since nutrition is indispensable for every thing that grows and decays: a living being must therefore have within itself a principle by which it acquires growth and undergoes decay, that is, soul. Animals are not only living but also sentient beings. But since one and the same principle, not a distinct one, produces life and sensibility, in every living being there must be one soul only. Consequently animals have not two distinct souls, one vegetative and the other sensitive, for from the same soul the operations of life and sensibility arise. By one single principle an animal is a living and a sentient being.[45]

Obviously, this is not an ordered exposition or a thorough treatment of the question, which is rather touched upon occasionally and only in passing; it is more presupposed than explicitly and directly stated. The principles upon which the structure of the doctrine is built are laid down, the conclusion inferred is there; but it is referred to only incidentally insofar as it is raised in connection with the general subject matter.

---

[45] *Des Alfred von Sareshel (Alfredus Anglicus) Schrift De Motu Cordis*, ed. C. Baeumker (B. G. P. M., XXIII, 1-2), Münster i. Westf., 1923. " Hanc (animam) in quolibet animato unam esse constans est " cap. 13, p. 65; " unius autem una est anima " cap. 8, p. 31; " anima enim animalis simplex et una est; ex ea autem tantum vivit et sentit animal; ex una igitur causa. Ex ea igitur animal est. A causa igitur uniformi vivit et sentit " cap. 10, p. 43.

None the less, it is noteworthy that in establishing his point, namely, the unity of the soul in every living being, Alfred urges the same argument advocated before him by Avicenna, and which later will be more elaborately used by Aquinas.

Turning our attention now to the Paris theologians of the period, we meet with no explicit mention of the problem in Peter of Poitiers (d. 1205), in Simon of Tournai (d. 1203), Praepositinus of Cremona (d. 1210), Robert Curzon, William de Montibus (d. 1213), or Stephen Langton. William of Auxerre (d. 1231), so keen to turn to profit in his *Summa aurea* (c. 1220) every new topic, and perhaps the first theologian to make wide use of the new learning, is equally silent.

The earliest, to my knowledge, clear and unmistakable account is found in the faculty of Arts, in the treatise *On the Soul* of John Blund, written not later than 1210.[46] Its main source is undoubtedly Avicenna. This treatise, representative of both Paris and Oxford, is a striking example of the deep penetration in the schools of Avicennian theories, under the cloak of Aristotle, at the beginning of the thirteenth century. Like Gundissalinus and Alfredus Anglicus, John Blund belongs to a period of transition, and joins in the attempt to utilize Eastern philosophy in Western thought, linking up the Arabian world with Scholasticism.

The elementary way in which the question is treated points unmistakably to its early stage. Its very title, *utrum anima vegetabilis. sensibilis et rationalis sint in homine eadem anima an diversae,* bears the impress of Avicenna. In the table of contents it is described *quomodo anima vegetabilis se habeat ad animam sensibilem et rationalem.* The chief point of the discussion, in fact, appears to be more logical than psychological, though this is not excluded, namely, whether ' anima ' or ' animatum,' the vegetative soul is a genus or a species; and if a genus, how it is predicated of its species, namely the nutritive soul of animal soul and of rational soul.

[46] See D. A. Callus, " The treatise of John Blund *On the Soul,*" in *Autour d'Aristotle. Recueil d'études offert à Mons. A. Mansion* (Louvain, 1955), pp. 471-495. This treatise will be published shortly.

The debate opens by setting forth the evidence in support of the unity view. Three arguments are brought forward: the first two are drawn from the univocal predication of ' animatum ' and ' substance.'

(1) *Animatum* is univocally predicated of a living body, of animal and of man. Now a thing is said to be animated inasmuch as it possesses a soul. Since, therefore, *animatum* is predicated according to the same formal notion signified by the name ' animated,' similarly the soul pertains to each thing possessing a soul according to the same formal notion. Consequently, one and the same is the soul of a living body, of animal and of man.

(2) Again, ' substance ' is univocally predicated of body, of living body, and of each of its inferiors; and it is specified by the addition of gradual differences, such as corporeal, living, sentient, and so on. Likewise the soul is specified by the addition of vegetative, sensitive, and rational. Now as ' substance ' is a genus with respect to its species, so ' soul ' is a genus with respect to its species. But it cannot be said that there are many substances in one species of substance. For the same reason it should not be said that there are three souls in man, but one soul only. Accordingly, the vegetative, the sensitive and the rational are not three souls, but one soul only.

(3) Moreover, if these were three diverse souls, there would be in reality three souls in man, which is contrary to Avicenna, who teaches that in man it is from the same rational soul that the vegetative life, the sensitive life and the rational life are derived.[47]

That they are diverse souls might be argued as follows:

(1) If the vegetative, the sensitive and the rational were one soul, then as the rational is incorruptible, so also the vegetative and the sensitive souls would be incorruptible; and as

[47] " Si sint diversae animae, contingit hominem habere tres animas in effectu, quod est contra Avicennam, qui dicit quod ab anima rationali est in homine vegetatio, sensibilitas, rationalitas." Cambridge, St. John's College, MS 120, fol. 125rb.

the rational soul can be separated from the body, enjoying perpetual life, likewise the souls of a tree or of an ass would live
forever.

(2) The second argument aims at proving that ' soul ' is not
a genus; for, since the genus contains something more than each
of its species, no genus is equal to its species. Consequently, the
vegetative, the sensitive and the rational are three distinct
species, not a genus.

Blund's answer is that this word soul (*hoc nomen ' anima '*)
means the genus of the vegetative, of the sensitive and of the
rational souls. Sensitive soul is a subaltern genus, inasmuch as
it is a genus with respect to the rational soul, and a species
of the vegetative soul. But in man there is only one single
soul which imparts vegetative life, sensitivity and reason.[48]

Doubtless, John Blund's treatment is still quite embryonic,
and the real issue is more implied than expressed. Nevertheless,
Blund is a definite witness, not only to the fact that the question was discussed in the schools by the masters of Arts in the
first decade of the thirteenth century, but also to the fact that
its first solution was in favor of the unity thesis. Its significance
lies in this, that we have in this account, however inarticulate
it may be, some of the same arguments which were later advanced in the heyday of the conflict by both opponents and
defenders: that of the corruptibility or incorruptibility of the
soul was adduced by all the pluralists, whereas the supporters
of the unity thesis insisted that it is one and the same principle that gives life, sense and reason to one individual.

A few years later Roland of Cremona, the first Dominican
master in the University of Paris (1229-1230), attests that the
question had reached the faculty of theology. His statement
bears considerable weight for its accuracy and conciseness.

There are, he says, three species of souls: the vegetative soul,

---

[48] " Solutio. Dicimus quod hoc nomen ' anima ' significat genus animae vegetabilis et animae sensibilis et rationalis. Et in homine est una sola anima a qua est
vegetatio, sensus et ratio. Et anima sensibilis est genus subalternum, quia anima
sensibilis est genus animae rationalis et species animae vegetabilis." *Ibid.*, fol.
125va.

which is in plants; the sensitive soul, which is in dumb animals; and the rational soul, which is in man alone. Yet there are not three souls in man, as some think. According to these thinkers, there are really three souls in man: the vegetative, the sensitive and the rational. But this is untenable, for of one and the same thing there cannot be but one first perfection, since one and the same thing can have but one existence (*unicum esse*). Now all agree that the soul is the perfection of an organized body holding life in potentiality. The vegetative soul, therefore, is the perfection of this body, and likewise the sensitive and the rational soul. It follows, then, that if there were three souls, this body would be perfected in virtue of the first perfection, which is impossible. Again, if the first endows the body with its perfection, the second or the third would serve no purpose.[49]

Those who claim that there are three souls in man are persuaded by this reason: they see that the embryo, even before it is perfected by the sensitive and the rational soul, grows. But growth is exclusively caused by the vegetative soul. Consequently, it seems that the vegetative soul is in the embryo before the sensitive and the rational soul. They prove this from the first proposition of the book *De pura bonitate*. However, they labor in vain (*frustra nituntur*). The embryo is not self-growing or vegetating, but grows in virtue of the mother, inasmuch as, previous to the infusion of the rational soul, it is in a certain manner a part of the mother, since the embryo is united to the matrix by cotyledons.[50] Accordingly, it remains that the

[49] " Neque sunt tres animae in homine, quemadmodum quidam putant. Dicunt quod in homine est anima vegetabilis, et anima sensibilis, et anima rationalis. Sed hoc non potest stare, quia unius rei unica est perfectio prima, quia unius rei unicum est esse. Constat autem quod anima est perfectio corporis organici potentia vitam habentis. Ergo haec anima vegetabilis est perfectio huius corporis, et haec anima sensibilis, et haec anima rationalis. Ergo habet hoc unicum corpus vi perfectionis primae, quod esse non potest. Iterum, si prima perficit, pro nihilo venit secunda vel tertia." Text edited by Dom O. Lottin, *Psychologie et Morale aux XIIe et XIIIe siècles*, 2nd edition (Gembloux: Duculot, 1957), p. 465.

[50] See, e. g., Alexander Nequam, *De naturis rerum*: " Cum enim cotilidonum nexu familiari foetus adhaerens matrici quodammodo pars sit ipsius matris " (*ed. cit.*, p. 240); Albertus Magnus, *De animalibus*, XVI, tr. II, c. 7: " Qualiter per cottilidiones fit incrementum embrionis " (ed. Stadler, 1131-3); and tr. I, c. 2.

vegetative and the sensitive in man are not distinct souls, but powers of the rational soul.[51]

Assuredly the development of the problem is as yet at its first stage. The discussion turns on the unity or plurality of souls in man. The solution gives the impression that it is merely outlined and unfinished; it is none the less clear and categorical, and the treatment of the whole question is extremely instructive. Roland based his reasoning on the Aristotelian definition of the soul, regarded as axiomatic. *Constat autem quod anima est perfectio corporis organici potentia vitam habentis.* The argument brought forward is the same one that Aquinas will urge and develop to its utmost value in upholding the unity of form not only in man, but in all composites: *unius rei unica est perfectio prima, unius rei unicum est esse, si prima perficit, pro nihilo venit secunda vel tertia.* There can be no doubt that the first reaction of the Schoolmen in both faculties of Theology and of Arts was in favor of the unity thesis: the vegetative and the sensitive are not distinct souls in man, but powers of the rational soul.

On the other hand, the same argument from the vital operations of the embryo was constantly adduced by the pluralists as the most cogent in stressing their view. It is found wherever the problem is discussed, often with the biblical text, Exodus, 21:22, and always with the same physiological reflection. It was later corroborated with the authority of Aristotle, *De generatione animalium*, II. 3 (*De animalibus* XVI. 3, 736 b 1 ff.).[52] To refute this argument William of Auvergne dedicated a full chapter to it in his *De anima*,[53] and in St. Thomas' *Quaestio disputata De anima*, a. 11, to cite one more instance, no less than nine objections out of twenty are drawn from the embryo-genesis theory. When, however, Roland, trying to argue against this view contends that the embryo grows *vege-*

---

[51] " Sensibilis et vegetabilis sunt vires animae rationalis in homine." *Ibid.* On Roland of Cremona, see E. Filthaut, *Roland von Cremona O. P. und die Anfange der Scholastik in Predigerorden* (Vechta i. O., 1936).

[52] See the discussion of this point in Albertus Magnus, *De animalibus, ad locum.*

[53] *De anima*, cap. 4, P. II (ed. Orleans, 1674), fol. 105 b-106 b.

tatione matris suae, he is assuming an erroneous fact, though it was taught by many physicians in his day.[54]

In conclusion:

(i) The immediate and main sources of the problem of the unity or plurality of souls and substances in man are Avicenna and Avicebron. The former stood for the unity thesis in every living being; the latter advocated plurality of forms in all compounds.

(ii) The problem was formulated by Dominic Gundissalinus, and it reached the schools through him. Under the influence of Avicenna he transmitted the unity thesis in his *De anima,* but he popularized the opposite view through his other writings drawn chiefly from Avicebron.

(iii) Various elements of diverse kind mingled with the main sources: the Platonic-Galenic teaching on the tripartite distinction of the soul and on embryo-genesis; the theory of Costaben-Luca and of Isaac Israelita on the vital *spiritus* as distinct from the soul and as a medium of union with the body; the *Liber de causis.* All these secondary sources contributed to reinforce the pluralist stream.

(iv) The first reaction of the Schoolmen was in support of the unity thesis, both in the faculty of Arts and in the faculty of Theology. Theologians in general held the thesis of one soul, one substance in man; they held that the vegetative, the sensitive and the rational in man are not three souls and three substances, or one soul and three substances, but *one soul* and *one substance.* St. Albert the Great voicing their view maintained that " *error pessimus est dicere unius subiecti plures esse substantias, cum illae substantiae non possunt esse nisi formae.*" [55] And again: " *Hunc errorem hucusque in diem sequuntur quidam Latinorum philosophorum, praecipue in sen-*

---

[54] Cf. Albertus Magnus, *De animalibus,* XVI, tr. I, c. 2, where he ascribes such a view to some " de medicorum imperito populo "; St. Thomas, *Contra gentiles,* II, cap. 89.

[55] *De unitate intellectus contra Averroem,* cap. 13 (ed. Borgnet, IX, 455 b).

*sibili, vegetabili et rationabili, qui dicunt esse diversas sub-
stantias et unam animam in corpore hominis.*" [56]

(v) With Philip the Chancellor (c. 1230) the problem entered into its second stage of development. The discussion
turned, then, not on the unity or plurality of souls, but definitely on the unity or plurality of substances, whether the vegetative, the sensitive and the rational are one or three substances
in man. Theologians discussed it in their commentaries on
Book II, dist. 17, of the *Sentences,* and also in their *quaestiones
disputatae* and *quodlibetales,* and later in special treatises.

(vi) The masters of Arts generally raised the question in
their commentaries on Aristotle's *De anima,* at the close of
Book I or at the beginning of Book II. We have an illuminating
clue in Adam of Buckfield (c. 1250) as to their procedure in
setting the question. In this passage (411 a 26-411 b 11), he
tells us, Aristotle deals with two questions. The first is whether
the attributes of the soul, namely understanding, opinion, desire and the like, appertain to the soul as a whole, or whether
each particular operation is dependent on a particular part;
that is, whether the soul as a whole thinks, desires, perceives,
or whether one part thinks, another perceives, another desires.
The second question is this: Does life reside in one single part
of the soul, or in more than one, or in all parts? According to
some, however, Aristotle's intention is to investigate a different
problem, namely whether the vegetative, the sensitive and the
rational are distinct with respect to their operations, or with
respect to a diversity of substance. Buckfield believes that
this interpretation is based neither on our translation (*nostram,*
i. e., the Greek-Latin version) nor on the other (*aliam,* i. e.,
from the Arabic). Aristotle simply meant to maintain against
Plato that the soul is not divided into various parts which in
turn are located in different organs. Since, therefore, the
problem concerning one or more substances in man was left
unsolved by the Philosopher, there is room for further inquiry.

---

[56] *De anima,* I, tr. II, c. 15 (ed. Borgnet, V, 184 a); III, tr. V, c. 4 (417 b ff.)
et alibi passim.

DANIEL A. CALLUS

Et est hic quaestio: utrum in anima hominis sit eadem substantia intellectivae, sensitivae et vegetativae, an sint substantiae diversae.[57]

(vii) The question was also raised in the commentaries on Aristotle's *Metaphysics*, particularly in connection with the " unity of definition " (Z. 12, 1037 b 22-27), as quoted in the *Errores philosophorum* (see *supra*, p. 263). For instance, we find it discussed at great length in an anonymous commentary by a secular Oxford master of Arts in the first half of the thirteenth century.[58]

(viii) Finally, the Aristotelian distinction of the soul into rational and irrational in the *Nicomachean Ethics* (I. 13) offered another opportunity to theologians and masters of Arts to discuss the question. St. Albert was well aware that this

---

[57] " In hac parte intendit [Aristoteles] de opinionibus aliorum, et sistit sua determinatio in prosecutione cuiusdam quaestionis. . . . Cum ita sit, quaestio est, utrum omnes istae actiones attribuantur animae secumdum se totam, ita scilicet quod secundum se totam intelligat, et secundum se totam sentiat, et sic de aliis, an secundum diversas partes sui in diversis membris existentes diversas faciat operationes, ut, scilicet, secundum unam partem sui in uno membro existentem intelligat, et secundum aliam in alio membro existentem sentiat, et sic de aliis.— Adhuc quaerit ulterius, si secundum diversas partes sui in diversis membris existens diversas faciat operationes. Tunc est quaestio adhuc, utrum ab una illarum partium tantum insit vita animali, aut a pluribus, aut ab omnibus; hoc est quaerere, utrum quaelibet pars animae vivificet suum membrum in quo est, aut non. Ista tamen quaestio principalis secundum quosdam aliter intelligitur, ita scilicet, ut intendat Aristoteles quaerere, utrum anima, cum sit una et eadem secundum substantiam et radicem, habeat operationes diversas, an diversificetur substantia ita, scilicet, quod substantia vegetativae sit alia a substantia sensitivae, et substantia sensitivae alia a substantia intellectivae, sicut et operationes diversae sunt. Ista tamen quaestio nec per nostram translationem nec per aliam videtur praetendi. . . . Cum iam manifestum sit secundum intentionem Aristotelis in hac ultima parte quod anima est indivisa secundum situm et subiectum, et non videtur esse determinatum ab ipso utrum, cum sit indivisa secundum situm et subiectum, similiter sit indivisa secundum substantiam, propter hoc circa hoc est dubitandum. Et est hic quaestio: utrum in anima hominis sit eadem substantia intellectivae, sensitivae, vegetativae, an sint substantiae diversae." See D. A. Callus, " Two early Oxford Masters," *ed. cit.*, pp. 434-5.

[58] Although in this commentary the question is discussed in Book IX, it refers to the unity of definition. Cf. G. Gàl, " Commentarius in *Metaphysicam* Aristotelis cod. Vat. lat. 4538 fons doctrinae Richardi Rufi," *Archivum Franciscanum Historicum*, XLIII (1950), 216: " Sed modo quaeri potest: si diffinitum . . ." cf. p. 237.

topic, strictly speaking, was unrelated to the text. Nevertheless, because there were various opinions, Albert thought it
fitting to inquire into the question, together with the kindred
question about whether the powers of the soul are distinct or
identical with the essence of the soul.[59] We meet with similar
questions in an anonymous commentary on the *Ethica nova* by
a master of Arts of the first half of the thirteenth century.[60]

But by this time, mid-thirteenth century, the debate was
well advanced, and the treatment of the problem was greatly
developed. A few years later, the genius of St. Thomas Aquinas
will bring its solution to full maturity.

DANIEL A. CALLUS, O.P.

Blackfriars
Oxford, England

---

[59] " Quamvis considerare horum differentiam [rationabilis et irrationabilis] non
pertineat ad hanc scientiam, sicut ipse [Aristoteles] dicit, tamen quia de hoc sunt
opiniones, quaeritur, utrum. . . .   See G. Meersseman, " Die Einheit der mensch-
lichen Seele nach Albertus Magnus," *Divus Thomas* (Frib.), X (1932) 86 ff.

[60] These questions have been published by Dom O. Lottin, *Psychologie et Morale*,
ed. cit., I, pp. 511-12.

THE CELESTIAL MOVERS IN MEDIEVAL PHYSICS

∾

IN the spring of 1271 John of Vercelli, Master General of the Order of Preachers, sent a list of forty-three questions to three Dominican Masters in Theology for their consideration. Independently of each other, the three theologians were to consider each question carefully and reply promptly keeping in mind the directive of the Master General: (i) Do accepted authorities, the *Sancti*, maintain the doctrine or opinion contained in the articles listed? (ii) Apart from the weight of authorities, does the consultor maintain the aforesaid doctrine or opinion? (iii) Apart from the consultor's personal views, could the aforesaid doctrine or opinion be tolerated without prejudice to the faith?[1] Clearly the purpose of this questionnaire was to safeguard the truths of faith, even where the question raised was one of philosophical opinion or strictly natural science.

St. Thomas Aquinas had previously given his decision on most of these questions in two private communiques to the lector of Venice, Bassiano of Lodi.[2] The official questionnaire of the Master General contained nothing of importance which had not already been considered by St. Thomas in his two private replies. The questions are for the most part idle curiosities and useless fantasies, as the consultors themselves realized. However, the official questionnaire was sent to three outstanding Masters in the Order, and not all the questions are without interest to the modern reader. St. Thomas' reply to the official questionnaire has always been known to Thomists, even though little studied. The reply of the second consultor,

---

[1] St. Thomas, *Responsio ad fr. Joannem Vercellensem de articulis XLII*, prooem., ed. R. A. Verardo, O.P., *Opuscula Theologica* (Turin: Marietti, 1954), I, p. 211. In this list the original q. 8 is missing.

[2] *Responsio ad Lectorem Venetum de articulis XXX* and *Responsio ad eundem de articulis XXXVI*, ed. R. A. Verardo in *Opuscula Theologica*, pp. 193-208.

Robert Kilwardby, later archbishop of Canterbury, was discovered and published by Fr. M.-D. Chenu, O. P., about thirty years ago.[3] Now with the discovery and publication of the reply of the third consultor, the great St. Albert himself,[4] we are in a position to compare the views of the three Dominican Masters point by point.

Among the relatively few interesting questions in the list of forty-three, the first five stand out as particularly important for the historian and philosopher of science. They have to do with the cause or causes of celestial motion. In the order of appearance they are as follows:

1) Does God move any physical body immediately?

2) Are all things which are moved naturally, moved under the angels' ministry moving the celestial bodies?

3) Are angels the movers of celestial bodies?

4) Is it infallibly demonstrated according to anyone that angels are the movers of celestial bodies?

5) Assuming that God is not the immediate mover of those bodies, is it infallibly demonstrated that angels are the movers of celestial bodies?

To the casual reader these questions, too, might appear to be useless in this age of scientific progress. Angels, it is frequently thought, have no place in a discussion of scientific questions. Some Catholic scientists, and even some Thomistic philosophers feel considerable embarassment at the mention of angels; they would rather not mention them at all, or at least not mention them as having anything to do with the real world in which we live. In medieval literature the problem of celestial movers was not created by theologians, nor did it take its origin in any point of Catholic faith, although St. Thomas was keenly

[3] M.-D. Chenu, O. P., "Les Réponses de s. Thomas et de Kilwardby à la consultation de Jean de Verceil (1271)," in *Mélanges Mandonnet* (Bibl. Thomiste XIII: Paris 1930), vol. I, pp. 191-222.

[4] James A. Weisheipl, O. P., "The *Problemata Determinata XLIII* Ascribed to Albertus Magnus (1271)," in *Mediaeval Studies*, XXII (1960), 303-354.

aware of the guiding role of faith in this matter. The problem of celestial movers was entirely a scientific one having many ramifications. But here, as in other problems of medieval science, it is not sufficient to know what a particular author maintained. It is far more important to understand the scientific problem in its philosophical context and to evaluate the arguments leading to the solution proposed. After all, the best of medieval science is not to be found in the lapidaries, herbals or bestiaries of the Middle Ages; least of all is it to be found in pious legends, sermons or morality plays. Rather it is to be found in the speculative commentaries, treatises and disputations of the schoolmen. These writings, emanating largely from various faculties of the university, are not readily intelligible to modern readers, as anyone who has tried to read them can testify. To understand the writings of medieval authors one needs a considerable background in the sources, a speculative competence to follow the argumentation, and a familiarity with medieval practice. Neither the questionnaire of the Master General nor the replies of Albertus Magnus, Thomas Aquinas or Robert Kilwardby can be evaluated correctly without reference to the sources, the argumentation and medieval practice.

In a review of Chenu's edition of Kilwardby's reply to the questionnaire, Fr. Mandonnet noted the similarity between the view of Robert Kilwardby and that of John Buridan, the fourteenth century proponent of " impetus " to explain violent motion. Inspired by the thesis of Duhem's *Études sur Léonard de Vinci* (3me série), Mandonnet was quick to point out the modernity of Kilwardby's universal mechanics.[5] This suggestion was developed at some length by Fr. Chenu in a special study devoted to the origins of " modern science." [6] Whatever may be said of the validity of Duhem's well-known thesis, one may perhaps doubt the utility of isolating a particular medieval thesis—in this case one of dubious modernity—to extol the

[5] P. Mandonnet, O. P., *Bulletin Thomiste*, III (1930), 137-9.

[6] M.-D. Chenu, O. P., "Aux origines de la 'Science Moderne,'" in *Revue des Sc. Phil. et Théol.*, XXIX (1940), 206-217.

modernity of medieval science. Even if there should happen to be considerable similarity between some aspect of medieval science and a current scientific view, this would be no more than an interesting curiosity, unless we come to grip with an objective philosophical problem and analyze the issues historically and scientifically.

A short paper such as this cannot sketch even in broad outlines a picture of medieval astronomy or the history of its development.[7] All that can be attempted here is an examination of the problem as seen by each of the three Dominican Masters consulted by the Master General, and an explanation of the views proposed, especially in their response to the official questionnaire. Since our purpose here is to understand the medieval view, we need not be concerned about the true historical intent of ancient sources, but only about how the medieval schoolmen interpreted them. That is to say, it is not essential here to understand what Plato, Aristotle, Ptolemy or Al-Biṭrûjî really meant; it is essential only that we understand what St. Albert, St. Thomas and Kilwardby thought them to mean. There is always the possibility that these great schoolmen misunderstood or misinterpreted their sources, but this makes little, if any, difference to the medieval view of the scientific problem.

Preliminary Observations

In the traditional division of the speculative sciences derived from Plato and Aristotle, astronomy occupied a peculiar position. By astronomy we do not mean the elementary calculation of movable feast days, the Epact or the Golden Number; nor do we mean identification of the signs of the zodiac or prognostications from conjunctions. By astronomy is meant the theoretical sciences which attempts to make celestial phenomena intelligible by means of mathematical principles. The peculiar position of this theoretical science can be recognized clearly in the writings of the three consultors.

---

[7] An outline can be found in P. Duhem, *Le Système du Monde* (Paris: Hermann, 1954), vol. III.

In the first place, astronomy was classified with optics, mechanics, harmonics and other *scientiae mediae* between the sciences of pure mathematics and natural science.[8] As a science intermediate between mathematics and physics, astronomy was considered from three points of view. First, it was considered in relation to the higher science of mathematics, to which it is subalternated and on which it depends for its scientific validity. Astronomy, it was said, accepts as established all the conclusions of geometry and applies them to the known measurements of celestial phenomena. In this consideration, astronomy and the other *scientiae mediae* "have a closer affinity to mathematics, because what is physical in their consideration functions as something material, while what is mathematical functions as something formal." [9] Intelligibility in every science was taken as derived from the principles, the formal element, as contrasted to the material element which is the conclusion, or fact now understood scientifically.[10] We know that mathematical astronomy did not begin until Eudoxus of Cnidos accepted the challenge from Plato " to find out what are the uniform and ordered movements by the assumption of which the phenomena in relation to the movements of the planets can be saved." [11] The obviously irregular motions in the heavens, tabulated for centuries before Plato, could not be made intelligible except by reducing them, at least in theory, to perfectly regular movements of geometric spheres. In other words, astronomy was taken formally to be a mathematical type of knowledge, extending to measurable quantities of celestial phenomena, such as size, distance, shape, position and velocity.

Considered in its own right, astronomy was presented as a true speculative science, demonstrative within its own limits. Unless there be some true demonstrations in astronomy, true

---

[8] St. Thomas, *In I Post. Anal.*, lect. 1, n. 3; *In II Phys.*, lect. 3, n. 8; *In Boeth. de Trin.*, q. 5, a. 3 ad 5-7; *Sum. theol.*, I-II, q. 35, a. 8; II-II, q. 9, a. 2 ad 3.

[9] *In Boeth. de Trin.*, q. 5, a. 3 ad 6; *Sum. theol.*, II-II, q. 9, a. 2 ad 3.

[10] *In I Post. Anal.*, lect. 41, n. 11; *Sum. theol.*, II-II, q. 1, a. 1; q. 9, a. 2 ad 3.

[11] Simplicius, *De caelo*, ed. Heiberg (Comm. in Arist. Graeca, VII), p. 488, 18-24.

causal dependencies between principle and conclusion, this knowledge would not deserve the name of science. The mathematical principles of astronomy are themselves demonstrated in one of the purely mathematical sciences. Moreover, in theory " mathematical principles can be applied to motion," [12] and sometimes the application is clear. But very often geometrical figures and principles must be assumed as applicable to the celestial phenomenon under consideration, as in the case of Eudoxus' four spheres to explain the motions of Jupiter, Callippus' seven spheres and Ptolemy's epicycle. Nevertheless, the relationship between the principles assumed, even assumed as applicable, and the celestial phenomenon to be saved can be one of necessity. This connection of necessary dependency of the conclusion on the assumed principles is sufficient to establish astronomy as a demonstrative science. It was in this sense that St. Thomas and St. Albert interpreted Aristotle's statement that, " It is the business of the empirical observers to know the fact, of the mathematicians to know the reasoned fact." [13] Between the mathematical principle and the quantified aspect of the fact, there may well be a *propter quid* relationship, that is, the immediate, proper and convertible middle term of the measured facts of the conclusion may be the mathematical principle invoked. To this extent astronomy should be called, and was called a true science subalternated to mathematics. To be sure, astronomical science fell far short of the ideal of scientific knowledge described by Aristotle in the *Posterior Analytics*. It did not demonstrate through the immediate, physical cause of celestial phenomena; at best, it demonstrated through a kind of extrinsic formal cause (*secundum causam formalem remotam*) of the natural phenomena.[14] Even this, as has already been suggested, is most often in a tentative, dialectical and hypothetical manner.

Considered in relation to the physically real celestial bodies

---

[12] St. Thomas, *In Boeth. de Trin.*, q. 5, a. 3 ad 5.

[13] *Post. Anal.*, I, c. 13, 79a2-3. St. Thomas, *In I Post. Anal.*, lect. 25, n. 4; St. Albert, *Lib. I Post. Anal.*, tr. III, c. 7.

[14] St. Thomas, *In I Post. Anal.*, lect. 25, nn. 4 & 6.

and their movements, astronomy was recognized fully as hypo-thetical. The true causes of celestial motion are extremely difficult for any science to discover. " These matters into which we inquire are difficult since we are able to perceive little of their causes, and the properties of these bodies are more remote from our understanding than the bodies themselves are spatially distant from our eyes." [15] Simplicius, and possibly Plato before him, was aware that the aim of astronomy is to give some rational account of celestial phenomena, saving all the known facts (Σώζειν τὰ φαινόμενα).[16] But as it turns out, all the known facts of astronomy can be explained by a variety of hypotheses. Of course, when a new fact is discovered which cannot be accomodated by the existing hypothesis, then some new hypothesis must be devised to account for the new fact. St. Thomas, commenting on the homocentric spheres of Plato and Eudoxus, observes:

The hypotheses which they devised (adinvenerunt) are not neces-sarily true, for although the appearances are saved on the assump-tion of those hypotheses, one does not have to say that they are true, because the phenomena of celestial bodies may perhaps be saved in some other way not yet known to man.[17]

An astronomical hypothesis which accounts for all the known facts is indeed worthy of provisional credence. But every astronomical hypothesis by its very nature was considered by St. Thomas to be provisional and indemonstrable. Speaking of this type of reasoning, St. Thomas notes:

Reasoning is employed in another way, not as furnishing an adequate proof of a principle, but as showing how the existing facts are in harmony with a principle already posited; as in astron-omy the theory of eccentrics and epicycles is considered as estab-lished, because thereby the sensible appearances of celestial move-ments can be explained; it is not, however, as if this proof were

---

[15] St. Thomas, In II De caelo, lect. 17, n. 8.

[16] Cf. P. Duhem, " Σώζειν τὰ Φαινόμενα. Essai sur la notion de théorie physique de Platon à Galilée," Annales de philosophie chrétienne (Paris), 4 série, VI (1908), 113 ff., 277 ff., 352 ff., 482 ff., 561 ff.

[17] St. Thomas, In II De caelo, lect. 17, n. 2.

[demonstratively] adequate, since some other theory might explain them.[18]

The tentative and hypothetical character of astronomical theories was commonly recognized from the thirteenth century onward, that is, after the acceptance of both Aristotle and Ptolemy in Latin translation. The homocentric hypotheses of Eudoxus and Callippus were taught in the faculty of arts together with the Ptolemaic hypotheses of epicycles and eccentrics. The schoolmen frequently discussed the preferability of one over the other in their commentaries on Aristotle.

This brings us to the second peculiar characteristic of astronomy recognized in the Middle Ages, namely that mathematical astronomy was ordained to the discovery of true physical causes in nature. The mathematical character of astronomy was clearly evident to the schoolmen. But as mathematical, it abstracted from all questions of efficient, final and material causality; its concern was with the quantitative formalities of celestial phenomena related functionally to assumed mathematical principles. [*Astronomi*] *non considerant motum caelestium secundum principia motus, sed potius secundam numerum et mensuram quantitatis suae.*[19] This being the case, one might have expected such an abstract science to be an end in itself, a purely speculative science sought for its own sake. In actual fact, however, this was not the view of Albertus Magnus, Thomas Aquinas or Robert Kilwardby. These three men, it is true, did not consider the functional use of astronomy in the same way, but they did consider astronomy to have a functional use in discovering real physical causes beyond quantity.

In the Second Book of the *Physics* Aristotle had raised the problem concerning the relation between the mathematical sciences and natural science.[20] Taking the case of astronomy, Aristotle posed the dialectic: astronomy is obviously a part of mathematics, but it is also a part of natural science since it

[18] St. Thomas, *Sum. theol.*, I, q. 32, a. 1 ad 2.

[19] St. Albert, *Lib. XI Metaph.*, tr. II, cap. 10, ed. Borgnet (Paris: Vivès, 1890-1899), VI, 628a.

[20] Arist., *Phys.* II, c. 2, 193b22-194a12.

considers the sun, moon and stars; therefore mathematics also
is a part of natural science. In reply Aristotle distinguished
purely mathematical definitions from those of natural science;
this is sufficient to establish the sciences as distinct. In confirmation Aristotle pointed to the *quasi*-physical character of
optics, harmonics and astronomy, which he called τὰ φυσικώτερα
τῶν μαθημάτων (*Phys.*, II, 2, 194a7). Modern translators give
the more probable rendering of this phrase as " the more
physical of the branches of mathematics." It was in this sense
that Averroes (text. comm. 20) and St. Albert (*ibidem*) had
understood the text. William of Moerbeke, however, rendered
this phrase with equal grammatical correctness as *magis physica
quam mathematica*. This translation presented St. Thomas
with the opportunity of explaining how astronomy, harmonics
and optics pertain, in a certain sense, rather to natural science
than to mathematics:

Sciences of this kind, although they are intermediate between
natural science and mathematics, are here described by the Philosopher as more natural than mathematical, because each thing is
denominated and specified by its ultimate term; hence since investigation in these sciences terminates in natural matter, though by
means of mathematical principles, they are more natural than
mathematical. . . . Hence astronomy is more natural than mathematical.[21]

Both St. Albert and St. Thomas recognized two types of
astronomy: mathematical astronomy, such as was studied by
Eudoxus, Ptolemy and others, and physical astronomy, such as
Aristotle discussed in the *Physics* and *De caelo et mundo*. This
latter astronomy was considered an integral part of natural
philosophy. Unlike mathematical astronomy, physical astronomy attempts to discover all the physical causes of celestial
phenomena, the ultimate efficient and final cause as well as the
material and intrinsic formal cause. For Albert and Thomas
physical astronomy alone indicates the real system of the universe. The difficulties involved in discovering the real system

---

[21] *In II Phys.*, lect. 3, nn. 8-9. See also *Sum. theol.*, II-II, q. 9, a. 2 ad 3.

of the universe, the moving causes of celestial motion, their number and order, are obvious. Consequently this part of natural philosophy abounds with tentative views and arguments, having need of mathematical astronomy to suggest possibilities. Discussing the number of celestial movements, Aristotle himself realized the need of " that one of the mathematical sciences which is most akin to philosophy, namely of astronomy." [22] He was unable to determine the exact number of distinct celestial motions, but he tentatively adopted the astronomical hypotheses of Callippus minus eight uncertain motions, taking the number of spheres to be forty-seven. From this he argued that " the unmovable substances and principles also may probably be taken as just so many; the assertion of *necessity* must be left to more powerful thinkers." [23] That there must be many movements and movers was accepted by St. Albert and St. Thomas as certain, but their exact number was hypothetical and not essential to the argument pursued.[24]

In other words, for St. Albert and St. Thomas mathematical astronomy and the other physical parts of mathematics are considered as ordained to the discovery of physical causes in natural philosophy. The mathematical sciences are, as it were, the dialectical preparation for the real demonstrations in natural philosophy. Since all mathematics, even the more physical parts of mathematics, prescind from motion and sensible matter,[25] they are that much removed from reality and need to be evaluated by that science which studies nature as it really exists, *in motu et inabstracta*. That is to say, the mathematical sciences are subordinated to and ordained to the philosophy of nature. Consequently, " if there were no substance other than those which are formed by nature, natural science would be the first science." [26]

---

[22] *Metaph.*, XII, c. 8, 1073b4-5.

[23] *Ibid.*, 1074a15-17.

[24] St. Albert, *Lib. XI Metaph.*, tr. II, c. 17 & c. 27; St. Thomas, *In XII Metaph.*, lect. 9, n. 2565; lect. 10, n. 2586.

[25] Boethius, *De Trinitate*, c. 2.

[26] *Metaph.*, VI, c. 1, 1026a28-29, and XI, c. 7, 1064b9-10.

Robert Kilwardby, on the other hand, represents a different tradition in medieval thought.[27] His is the Platonic tradition of Robert Grosseteste, Pseudo-Grosseteste and Roger Bacon, which considered natural science ordained to the mathematical, and mathematics ordained to metaphysics. The Platonic hierarchy of the sciences was seen to correspond to a real priority of forms in nature, not, of course, existing apart from sensible reality, but within physical bodies. Thus motion and sensible qualities, the object of natural science, are radicated in the prior forms of pure quantity, the object of mathematics; the forms of quantity, in turn, are radicated in the prior form of nude substance, the concern of metaphysics. Kilwardby, discussing the four mathematical sciences, sees a perfect hierarchy of priority and dignity among the mathematical forms. The lowest of all the mathematical sciences is astronomy, for it considers celestial motion through the principles of geometry; hence astronomy is prior to and more abstract than natural science.[28] Since discrete quantity is simpler and prior to extension, all the sciences which deal with number are prior to geometry. Among these the lower is the ideal harmony of numerical proportions; the science of numerical harmony, therefore, is prior to geometry.[29] The highest and most abstract of all the mathematical sciences is arithmetic, or algebra, *quia ipsa ut sic, nulla aliarum indiget*.[30] Thus arithmetic, the sciences of pure number, is *quasi mater aliarum [scientiarum]*.[31] But as Kilwardby failed to distinguish the numerical " unity " discussed in mathematics from the entitative " unity " convertible with being, he said that it belongs to the metaphysician to explain the cause of plurality in mathematics.[32]

It may perhaps be a fair interpretation of Kilwardby's mind

---

[27] See my " Albertus Magnus and the Oxford Platonists," in *Proceedings Am. Cath. Phil. Assoc.*, XXXII (1958), 124-139.

[28] Kilwardby, *De ortu scientiarum*, cap. 16 ad 1. Merton College, Oxford, MS 261, fol. 25v.

[29] *Ibid.*, cap. 24 ad 4, fol. 32ra.

[30] *Ibid.*, cap. 19, fol. 27va.

[31] *Ibid.*, cap. 22, fol. 28vb.

[32] *Ibid.*, cap. 24 ad 1, fol. 29rb; also cap. 14 ad 2, fol. 24vb.

to say that if there were no metaphysics, arithmetic would be the supreme universal science. This contrast, however, with the view of St. Albert and St. Thomas is not perfectly symetrical, since Kilwardby did not consider metaphysics to rest on the real existence of " substance other than those which are formed by nature." Nevertheless a clear contrast can be seen between the Platonic orientation upward from nature to mathematics and the Aristotelian orientation subordinating mathematics to natural philosophy. St. Albert and St. Thomas both defended the autonomy of natural science within the limits of its own *principia propria illuminantia,* distinct from metaphysics and superior to mathematics.[33]

The third peculiar characteristic of astronomy recognized in the Middle Ages was the special role it had in the discovery of God's existence. This characteristic was not entirely new. In pagan mythology the celestial bodies were themselves considered gods or at least the inhabitation of the gods. Pagan philosophers such as Plato and Aristotle did not hesitate to call celestial bodies divine. Ptolemy himself saw in astronomy the only secure path to theology:

For that special mathematical theory would most readily prepare the way to the theological, since it alone could take good aim at that unchangeable and separate act [God], so close to that act are the properties having to do with translations and arrangements of movements, belonging to those heavenly beings which are sensible and both moving and moved, but eternal and impassible.[34]

Al-Biṭrûjî, St. Albert frequently points out, had this advantage over the complicated system of Ptolemy that he considered all celestial motions to be derived from a single first mover, who is God.[35] For Kilwardby the path to God rose more tortuously

[33] Cf. J. A. Weisheipl, " Albertus Magnus and the Oxford Platonists," *ed. cit.,* pp. 136-139.

[34] Ptolemy, *Almagest,* Bk. I, chap. 1, trans. by R. C. Taliaferro (Great Books of the Western World, 16; Chicago, 1952), p. 6.

[35] Al-Biṭrûjî, *De motibus celorum,* III, 10-14, trans. by Michael Scot, ed. Francis J. Carmody (Berkeley: Univ. of California, 1952), pp. 79-80; St. Albert, *Problemata Determinata,* q. 1, *ed. cit.,* p. 321; *Liber de causis,* I, tr. IV, c. 7, ed. Borgnet X, 426b-427b; lib. II, tr. II, c. 1, ed. Borgnet X, 479b-480a *et alibi.*

from nature through astronomy, geometry, harmonics, arithmetic to the One of metaphysics; for him the proper subject of metaphysics is God precisely as the first cause of all plurality, material and immaterial.[36]

St. Albert's view of the matter is most interesting. Throughout the *Metaphysics* and *Liber de causis* St. Albert repeatedly rejected the " Platonic view " which would admit into philosophy certain separated substances totally unrelated to celestial movement. " The statement of certain Platonists that there exist separated substances not related to movable bodies, is entirely outside the realm of philosophical discourse, since this cannot be proved by reason." [37] The separated substances called angels by Avicenna, Algazel, Isaac and Moses Maimonides have nothing to do with celestial movement or with celestial bodies; they are independent intermediaries between God and man. For Albert the only demonstrative way to separated substances and to God is through the study of celestial motions. Consequently not only are angels, as revealed in Sacred Scripture, outside philosophical discussion, but the *intellectus universaliter agens* of celestial motions can be none other than God. That is to say, the first cause of the *primum mobile* and its diurnal motion is God, and not an intermediary. That God is " the immediate natural mover " of the universe in its diurnal motion is taken by St. Albert as true and demonstrated among those who know anything about philosophy.[38]

Whatever modern Thomists may have to say about the famous *quinque viae* of St. Thomas, it cannot be denied that for Thomas all the proofs progress from terrestrial phenomena through celestial phenomena eventually to God. The question of angels in St. Thomas' philosophy will be considered later. For the present it is important to establish only that in St. Thomas' proofs celestial phenomena do have an important part to play. This is not to say that the validity of those proofs

---

[36] Cf. Kilwardby, *De ortu scientiarum,* cap. 26, fol. 32rb-va.

[37] St. Albert, *Liber XI Metaph.,* tr. II, c. 17, ed. Borgnet VI, 638a; cf. *Problemata determinata,* q. 2, *ed. cit.,* pp. 323-327

[38] St. Albert, *Problemata determinata,* q. 5, *ed. cit.,* p. 328.

depend upon the antiquated astronomy of the Middle Ages. The principle of each proof has universal validity and the line of argumentation transcends all astronomy, ancient, medieval and modern. Nevertheless to see the proofs as St. Thomas saw them, it is necessary to accept, at least historically, the system of the universe as he understood it.

There can scarcely be any doubt that St. Thomas' first proof is derived historically from Aristotle's *Physics* and *Metaphysics*. This is clearly evident in the detailed analysis presented in *Summa contra gentiles*, I, c. 13, where Aristotle is explicitly cited as intending to prove the existence of God *ex parte motus duabus viis*. The first way is a paraphrase of *Phys.* VII, c. 1 to VIII, c. 5, text. 35; the second corresponds to *Phys.* VIII, c. 5, text. 36, to the end. The first starts with the example of solar movement and ends disjunctively with Plato's self-mover of the first sphere or Aristotle's separated mover of the whole. The second starts with various types of self-movents, showing how all must be reduced to some *primum movens se quod sit sempiternum*, and ends with God as a self-movent. " But since God is not a part of any self-movent, Aristotle in his *Metaphysics* further discovers from this mover which is a part of a self-movent, another mover entirely distinct, who is God." Two objections to the Aristotelian argument are easily handled. The first, that it assumes the eternity of motion contrary to the Catholic faith, is shown to be irrelevant, for it makes no difference whether or not motion is eternal; there is still need of an adequate mover. The second, that Aristotle assumes the animation of celestial bodies contrary to the view of many, is likewise shown to be irrelevant, for even if the celestial bodies are animated, one must still conclude according to Aristotle's principles to an unmoved mover entirely separated from bodies. A simplified form of this *manifestior via* is the only one presented by St. Thomas in his *Compendium theologiae* for Brother Reginald of Piperno.

The involvement of celestial bodies in the other proofs for God's existence is not so patent in the text of St. Thomas. However, it ought to be obvious that the argument from efficient causality includes the universal agency of celestial bodies operating in elementary bodies and in animal reproduction:

> Even among naturalists it is admitted that above those contrary agencies in nature there is a single first agent, namely the heaven, which is the cause of the diverse motions in those lower bodies. But since in the very heaven there is observed a diversity of position to which the contrariety of lower bodies is reduced as to a cause, [this diversity] must further be reduced to a first mover who is moved neither *per se* nor *per accidens*.[39]

Similarly the argument from possible and necessary beings includes not only terrestrial necessities and contingencies, but also the sempiternal celestial bodies and spiritual substances, which are radically necessary beings. Their necessity for being can, indeed, be seen as derived; therefore beyond them there must exist an absolutely necessary being whose necessity is in no way derived.[40] The Platonic, or more specifically, the Avicennian [41] argument concerning perfections clearly includes the immutable celestial bodies in the participated inequality of being and goodness, an inequality which needs to be derived from a single source which is essentially being, goodness and supreme perfection. The fifth argument likewise includes the influence of celestial bodies and separated intelligences on natural operations.[42] Natural terrestrial operations, influenced by celestial motions, the light and heat of the sun, are apparently purposeful operations of nature; all such operations of nature require the direction of intelligence (*opus naturae est opus intelligentiae*).

Historically, then, the five proofs of St. Thomas for the existence of God involve celestial bodies and their movement as he understood them. Therefore a careful consideration of celestial phenomena in the physics of St. Thomas is not without

---

[39] St. Thomas, *De pot.*, q. 3, a. 6.

[40] St. Thomas, *De pot.*, q. 5, a. 3.

[41] *De pot.*, q. 3, a. 5.

[42] *De verit.*, q. 5, a. 2; *Sum. contra gentiles*, I, cap. 13. Cf. Averroes, *In II Phys.*, comm. 75.

value to the modern Thomist, however much the modern Thomist may wish to adapt the traditional arguments.

To understand the problem of celestial movers in medieval physics, it is necessary to present the views of Albertus Magnus and then those of Robert Kilwardby before examining the crucial problem in the doctrine of St. Thomas.

St. Albert the Great

For St. Albert both physics and metaphysics attain the existence of God, but under different formalities and in different ways. Physics, although it demonstrates through all the real causes in nature, is primarily concerned with the efficient and material cause: " if we have said anything about the form or about the end [in physics], this was only of form insofar as it is mobile and of end only insofar as it is the termination of the motion of a mover." [43] But metaphysics deals with substantial being and its causes; therefore in metaphysics " we directly show that the first efficient cause is the universal end, that from him flow all mobile substances, and that he is like a leader of an army with respect to the universe." [44] This task is proper to metaphysics, and in this respect nothing is borrowed from natural science. It is true that natural science proved by way of motion the absolute immobility of the first mover, but it did not reveal him *prout ipsum est causa universi esse et forma et finis.* This is proper to metaphysics. Hence, Albert concludes, it is evident that metaphysics is a loftier contemplation by far than physics.

The task of physics is to explain all changes in nature, both terrestrial and celestial. Terrestrial movements, alteration, generation and corruption can be explained in large measure by the celestial bodies, but since these celestial bodies themselves are moved, the ultimate source of this movement must itself be immovable. This ultimate unmoved mover, proved in the *Physics,* is considered by St. Albert to be God, the

---

[43] St. Albert, *Lib. XI Metaph.,* tr. I, c. 3, *ed. cit.,* VI, 584b.
[44] *Ibid.*

Christian God. But the approach is different in metaphysics. Since the term of terrestrial movement and alteration is *per se* the generation of a substantial being,[45] and since the substantial being of the very heavens must be produced, beyond the physical universe there must exist a *principium universi esse*, who is the efficient source of being, the formal principle of all being, and the universal end of all things.[46] Hence it belongs to both physics and metaphysics to consider celestial phenomena and God, but physics considers these through the principles of motion (*secundum principia motus*), while metaphysics considers these through the principles of being (*essendi*). In other words, the natural philosopher arrives at the existence of God as the first mover, but the metaphysician arrives at His existence as the efficient cause, the formal principle and the ultimate end of all being.

This does not mean, Albert points out, that the metaphysician gives the *propter quid* reason for changeable substance, and the physicist the *quia*, as some would have it. "For if the physicist borrowed from the metaphysician, it would follow that physics is subalternated to first philosophy, which from the opening pages of this science we have shown to be false."[47] Thus physics and metaphysics are each autonomous sciences with special principles of investigation proper to each. However, unless it is first demonstrated in physics that there exists some real separated substance, there is no need for the subsequent investigation called metaphysics. The Platonists, Albert repeatedly points out, postulated ideas and mathematical entities separate from matter in order to explain sensible being; but these cannot exist apart from matter, and if they did, they could not be responsible for motion in the universe.[48] Therefore if some separated substance exists to be studied in metaphysics, this substance can be demonstrated

[45] St. Albert, *Lib. VIII Phys.*, tr. II, c. 4, *ed. cit.*, III, 572a.
[46] St. Albert, *Lib. XI Metaph.*, tr. I, c. 3, *ed. cit.*, VI, 584b-585a.
[47] *Ibid.*
[48] St. Albert, *Lib. XI Metaph.*, tr. I, cc. 4 & 8; lib. I, tr. V, cc. 8, 12 & 14; lib. VII, tr. II, c. 3, *et alibi*.

only as the cause of motion, specifically as the cause of celestial motion.

St. Albert accepted the order of celestial spheres commonly taught by the Arabian astronomers. The spheres were considered generically to be ten in number: the *primum mobile* causing diurnal movement of the whole universe, the sphere of fixed stars, the spheres of Saturn, Jupiter, Mars, the Sun, Venus, Mercury, the Moon, and the terrestrial sphere of active and passive elements.[49] It was well understood by all that each so-called sphere was subject to many distinct motions, each of which required some kind of mover. But it was simpler to talk in terms of the clearly visible planets, the fixed stars and the unseen cause of diurnal motion, than in terms of the precise number of celestial motions postulated to save the appearances of each planet. Similarly, it was understood among the better informed that the notion of " sphere " was postulated to regularize the errant motions of the planets and to give intelligibility to their complicated movements. Those spheres were no more " solid," contrary to some modern interpretations, than the familiar sphere of terrestrial change.

In the view of Avicenna each sphere was moved and ruled by a separated substance, whatever may have been the number of distinct movements required for each planet. It is within this context that St. Albert discusses the problem of celestial movers. But Avicenna further identified those intelligences and the proximate mover (*anima nobilis*) with angels.[50] St. Albert, as has already been noted, was unwilling to identify the separated substances of the philosophers with the angels of Sacred Scripture. Further, the tenth intelligence for Avicenna was the *intellectus agens hominum*, which ruled the terrestrial realm of mutable substances by infusing forms from without. This *dator formarum* was invoked by Avicenna to explain the apparent generation of new substances in the world of nature. St. Albert

[49] St. Albert, *Problemata determinata*, q. 2, ed. cit., p. 324; see *ibid.*, note 9.

[50] An excellent discussion of this has been given by Henry Corbin in his *Avicenna and the Visionary Recital*, trans. by W. R. Trask (New York: Pantheon, Bollingen Series 66, 1960), pp. 46-122.

repeatedly rejected the Avicennian innovation with sound Aristotelian arguments, which need not concern us here.

The real problem for St. Albert was the obvious difference between terrestrial changes arising from nature and celestial motions which could not arise from nature. The term "nature" is a technical one and it designates that "principle of motion and rest in those things to which it belongs properly (per se) and not as a concomitant attribute (per accidens)." [51] Technically it was contrasted with soul (anima, ψυχή) and with intelligence (intelligentia, νοῦς), particularly in Platonic and neo-Platonic writings; and it was also contrasted with art (ars, τέχνη) and with chance (casus, αὐτόματον) by Aristotle. Nature as an intrinsic principle always acts in a determined manner for a predetermined end. [52] This nature must always be efficiently produced by some generator of the form. Once this natural form has been generated by an efficient cause, that nature spontaneously moves toward the unique end proportioned to it and rests in the possession of the end. "Hence place and motion are given by the generator just as the form is, but the form is given principally, while place and motion are given per consequens, just as proper accidents are given to the form by generation." [53] Moreover, strictly speaking, "nature" designates the internal power of inanimate substances (natura non est nisi virtus inanimatae substantiae). [54] Finally, nature is a source of individual attainment, and not of transient activity. Hence "locomotion is never derived [efficiently] from nature as 'the principle of motion and rest in those things to which it belongs properly and not concomitantly,' as defined by Aristotle in Physics II; for which reason, as we have said, locomotion must be derived either from the generator or from one removing an impediment or from a soul." [55] In other words,

---

[51] Aristotle, Phys., II, c. 1, 1921b21-23. Cf. James A. Weisheipl, "The Concept of Nature," in The New Scholasticism, XXXVIII (1954), 377-408.

[52] Cf. Albert, Lib. VIII Phys., tr. II, c. 4, et passim.

[53] Ibid., ed. cit., III, 572a-b.

[54] St. Albert, Lib. XI Metaph., tr. I, c. 13, ed. cit., VI, 604.

[55] St. Albert, Problemata determinata, q. 2, ed. cit., p. 325.

since celestial motions do not attain any end, these motions cannot arise spontaneously from the nature of celestial bodies. For St. Albert, as for Plato and Aristotle before him, celestial motions must be derived immediately from some kind of *soul*, or self-mover.

Comparing the views of Plato and Aristotle,[56] Albert notes that both agree on three points: (i) that all natural motions must be reduced to some self-movent; (ii) that a celestial body cannot move itself, but must be moved by a spiritual substance which is either a soul or an intellect; (iii) that the spiritual mover of the body must itself be indivisible, without magnitude, possessing adequate power to move the celestial body. However, Albert notes, Plato and Aristotle differ on two essential points: (i) Plato considered the conjoined mover to be the ultimate mover, while Aristotle considered this soul to be the instrument of a higher intellect entirely separated from all matter; (ii) Plato considered the celestial soul to be perpetual and descendent from the stars, while Aristotle conceived the conjoined mover to be produced by the separated intellect and moved by it. In other words, Aristotle, according to St. Albert's understanding, admitted a conjoined mover for each celestial motion, a mover which was somewhat similar to a spiritual, intellectual soul, but without sense faculties. This conjoined mover explained how a celestial body like the *primum caelum* could be moved perpetually without attaining any end or finality intrinsic to itself. However, the conjoined mover itself was moved by reason of the celestial body; that is, the *anima caeli* moved concomitantly (*per accidens*) with the celestial body, much as the human soul is moved by the movement of the body. Therefore, the *anima caeli* is a moved mover, needing to be moved by another, a substance entirely separated from matter not only in definition, but also in existence. The spiritual *anima caeli* can be moved only by intellection and desire. The initial intellectual light emanating from the subsisting act-

---

[56] St. Albert, *Lib. VIII Phys.*, tr. II, c. 8.

ing intellect, giving the soul the idea and the desire to move, is the true immediate mover of the universe.

As St. Albert understands it, when Aristotle speaks of the heavens or the celestial bodies, he usually means the composite of soul and body, mover and moved; the heavens are for Aristotle animated substances (*substantiae animatae*). While it is easier to talk of the sun as though it were a simple substance, the movement of the sun is complex and due to many animated substances. For Aristotle at least the diurnal, longitudinal and latitudinal motions are distinct; each of these is caused by an animated celestial body. Ultimately these motions of the sun and all other planetary motions are due to the diurnal motion of the entire universe, the *primum caelum*, the first animated cause of the universe.

Now the animated substance is the cause not only of inanimate substances, but also of their order and motion. According to the teaching of the Peripatetics, this animated substance is the *corpus caeli*. Moreover, it was shown in Book VIII of the *Physics* that the first mover, which is a composite of mover and moved, or pushed, is the first heaven (*primum caelum*). In this manner it was therefore shown that the animate precedes the inanimate. We have likewise shown in that same place at the end of Book VIII of the *Physics*, first that the first mover is absolutely simple, and that this, since it is related to the first body as its mover, unquestionably will have the character of soul, and not nature (*pro certo habebit rationem animae et non naturae*), because nature never moves that body whose nature it is according to local motion.[57]

Plato, according to St. Albert, stopped here with the *anima mundi* as God, but Aristotle realized that each soul, since it is moved along with the body, must be moved by the desire for some absolutely separated intelligence. Thus for Aristotle the separated intelligence known and desired by the first animated mover is the actual source of all physical movement and the ultimate end of every celestial motion. There is, in other words, a hierarchy of intelligences proportioned to the various orders of animated substances. There is, for example, at least one illu-

[57] St. Albert, *Lib. XI Metaph.*, tr. I, c. 13, *ed. cit.*, VI, 604b.

minating intellect for all the animated movers of Venus, another for Jupiter, and so forth. The highest separated intelligence is the true immediate mover of the entire universe, the *primum caelum*. The mind and will of God are obediently accepted and executed by the animated substances, who consequently move as moved movers.

When discussing this matter on his own terms, St. Albert prefers to keep three elements distinct: the celestial body, the soul-like mover, and the separated intelligence. The reason for this is that Albert could not accept Aristotle's concept of celestial " souls " as the substantial form of the body. For Albert these " souls " could not be the substantial form of an inorganic, insensitive body, such as the moon and sun; this kind of body would be entirely useless for intellectual processes. Consequently these " souls " move the body only as an efficient cause, not as a formal cause.[58] In his early work, the *Summa Parisiensis*, Albert was willing to reconcile Aristotle's " souls " with the Catholic doctrine of angels.[59] Later, however, Albert became most insistent that the angels of revelation should not be identified with celestial souls or intelligences. According to Giles of Lessines, a disciple of St. Albert, *Haec est positio multorum magnorum et praecise domini Alberti quondam Ratisponensis episcopi, ob cuius reverentiam rationes praedictam positionem confirmantes addidimus.*[60] Albert's strong views distinguishing angels from intelligences and souls were shared by Theodoric of Freiberg, another disciple of his.[61] The

[58] " Nos cum Sanctis confitemur caelos non habere animas, nec esse animalia, si anima secundum propriam rationem sumatur. . . . Operatur autem ad corpus ut nauta ad navem, hoc est, secundum rationem movendi ipsum et regendi." *Summa de creaturis*, tr. III, q. 16, a. 2, ed. Borgnet XXXIV, 443a. In this edition " natura " is erroneously printed for " nauta."

[59] " Ita non est contrarium fidei quosdam angelos iuvare naturam in movendo et gubernando sphaeras caelorum, quos Angelos moventes sive intelligentias Philosophi dicunt *animas*." *Ibid.*, ad 6, p. 445b.

[60] Giles de Lessines, *De unitate formae*, P. II, c. 5, ed. M. de Wulf in Les Philosophes Belges, I (Louvain, 1902), p. 38.

[61] " Est autem et hoc circa iam dicta tenendum, quod dicti philosophi, loquentes de intelligentiis, non loquebantur de angelis, de quibus scriptura sacra loquitur, quae loquitur mysteria abscondita a sapientibus et prudentibus et revelat ea par-

reason for Albert's view is clearly stated in the reply to John of Vercelli's questionnaire: the separated intelligence known to philosophers is entirely immobile locally, *nec mittitur nec venit nec recedit*.[62] This is entirely contrary to what we know of Gabriel, Raphael and Michael according to the Scriptures. Further, the separated intelligence is known to philosophers solely as the cause of celestial motion and of inferior forms, while the angels of Scripture are the messengers of God, a function which cannot be proved by natural reason.[63]

To understand St. Albert better, we must consider celestial motion itself and its three distinct causes, namely the body, the soul-like mover, and the separated intelligence.

St. Albert clearly insists throughout all his writings that celestial motion cannot be accounted for by the nature of the celestial body. That is to say, perpetual motion of the spheres cannot originate spontaneously from " nature " as from a formal principle. Scholastic philosophy, following Aristotle, distinguished two uses of the technical term " nature." [64] The primary and principal use of the term was to designate an intrinsic active source of regular, teleological activity and attainment; nature in this sense was called a formal principle, since form is the ultimate source of these activities. In a secondary and analogical sense the innate, passive receptivity for the form could also be called " nature," since potency is a true principle of change; nature in this sense was called a material or passive principle. For St. Albert none of the characteristics of nature as a formal principle could be verified in

vulis." Theodoric of Freiberg, *De intellectu et intelligibili*, P. I, cap. 12, ed. E. Krebs in *Beiträge z. Gesch. d. Phil. d. M.-A.*, Bd. V, heft 5-6 (Münster, 1906), pp. 132*-133*. Cf. *ibid.*, P. II, cap. 34, pp. 164-165*. I am grateful to Fr. William A. Wallace, O. P., for allowing me to utilize his transcription of Theodoric's *De intelligenciis et motoribus celorum* and *De corporibus celestibus quoad naturam eorum corporalem* from MS Vat. lat. 2183.

[62] St. Albert, *Problemata determinata*, q. 2, ed. cit., p. 323.

[63] *Ibid.*, q. 5, ed. cit., p. 328.

[64] Cf. J. A. Weisheipl, " The Concept of Nature," *loc. cit.* above in note 51 and reprinted in *Nature and Gravitation* (River Forest: Albertus Magnus Lyceum, 1955), pp. 1-32.

celestial motions. Nature as a formal principle always moves toward a determined end, and when it has attained it, rests in that attainment. " The reason for this is that nature does not cause local motion except *per consequens*, for in moving toward the form it consequently moves to the place which belongs to its form." In the celestial motions there is never any attainment and possession. " The mover of the heaven never moves to any position, but to move out of it again. But to move into a position and to move out of it again is not from nature, but from soul." [65] For this reason Albert frequently insisted that celestial motions are not from nature, but from intelligence (*caeli motus non dicitur naturae motus, sed intelligentiae*).[66] Albert undoubtedly would have admitted that celestial motions are " natural " in the sense of coming from a passive principle, the celestial body. But invariably he prefers to deny the natural character of celestial motions, insisting always that they are not from nature, but from soul or intelligence. Precisely because the body itself is not the source of its perpetual movement, it is said *to be moved*. " Everything which *is moved* has a mover conjoined to itself, as was proved in the Seventh Book of the *Physics*." [67]

The nature of the conjoined mover is difficult to determine in the writings of St. Albert, largely, no doubt, because Albert retained the Aristotelian terminology while denying the substantial union of the two " parts " of the sphere. The conjoined mover is clearly a spiritual substance, indivisible, and separated from all matter, at least in definition.[68] It moves the body by its knowledge and desire of something higher.[69] " Since

---

[65] " Adhuc autem natura non movet nisi ad unum, et cum pervenerit, quiescit in illo. Cuius causa est, quia natura non est causa motus localis nisi per consequens: movendo enim ad formam, per consequens movet ad locum qui est illius formae. Motor autem caeli non movet unquam ad aliquem situm, nisi moveat etiam ex illo. In aliquid igitur movere et ex illo non est naturae, sed animae." St. Albert, *Lib. XI Metaph.*, tr. I, c. 13, *ed. cit.*, p. 605b.

[66] St. Albert, *Lib. II Phys.*, tr. I, c. 2, *ed. cit.*, p. 95b.

[67] St. Albert, *Lib. XI Metaph.*, tr. II, c. 3, *ed. cit.*, p. 614a; see *Lib. VII Phys.*, text et comm. 10.

[68] St. Albert, *Lib. XI Metaph.*, tr. II, cc. 12-13.

[69] *Ibid.*, c. 13, *ed. cit.*, p. 605a.

every motion of the heaven is according to the form which is in the intellect, as the artistic idea is in the mind of the artist, so in the intellect of the mover there is the image to be effected by its motion; otherwise its motion would be unintentional, a chance result and an accident." [70] At times St. Albert does call this conjoined mover a " soul," particularly the *anima nobilis* of the *Liber de causis* (prop. 3). But more frequently he conceives the mover as a luminous form of intelligence and desire, produced by the separated intelligence. " Since the intelligence by its light produces every form in its sphere and order, and since those forms are its light (*lumen*) and this light desires to produce beings in existence (*lumen desiderans ad esse deducere*), the proximate mover of the orb moves the orb and by moving produces forms in existence." [71] The conjoined mover, therefore, is an intelligent form, but not the " soul " of the sphere. " Thus it is evident that the intelligence is not an angel; and if it were, it would still not be the proximate mover of any celestial sphere." [72]

It is important to note that for St. Albert the luminous forms, the conjoined movers of celestial bodies, are the true causes of everything which is produced within that sphere. That is to say, the luminous form, obedient to a higher intelligence, is the active principle of such mysterious phenomena as animal reproduction, and the spontaneous generation of living things from inanimate matter.[73] " Every lower motion which is in the matter of generable things is reduced to the motion of the heavens, which is the cause and measure of lower motion by means of (i) the form of the moving intelligence, (ii) the form of the celestial orb, and (iii) stellar rays." [74] The active powers of light, heat, conjunctions of the planets and stars are, for St. Albert, instrumental causes of the celestial forms whereby the natural powers of the elements can be pro-

---

[70] *Ibid.*

[71] St. Albert, *Problemata determinata*, q. 2, ed. cit., p. 327.

[72] *Ibid.*

[73] St. Albert, *Lib. XI Metaph.*, tr. I, cc. 6 & 8.

[74] *Ibid.*, c. 8, ed. cit., p. 594a; cf. *Problemata determinata*, qq. 7-15 and qq. 34-36.

ductive of higher forms. One can say that these higher forms produced preexist in the elements *virtually* insofar as these elements are instruments of celestial movers. Of course, the celestial mover is itself a voluntary, intellectual instrument of the absolutely first intelligence, which is God. Similarly the male sperm virtually and actively contains the living and sentient souls of the embryo, but only as the instrument of celestial forces and intelligences. In other words, the natural heat, density, mobility and structure of the male sperm are used instrumentally by celestial agents to produce an effect higher than their own active powers.[75] It was in this way that St. Albert understood and explained the famous Aristotelian phrase, *Homo ex materia generat hominem et sol.* (Phys. II, 2, 194b13).[76] The only qualification which Albert, the philosopher and theologian, makes to this phrase is the direct creation of the human soul.[77]

Finally, for Albert, the separated movers of celestial bodies are the active intelligences (*intellectus agens*). Each intelligence is like a practical intellect of an artist who conceives the image to be produced and implants this in his instruments as he uses them. The instruments of the active intelligence are three-fold, namely the conjoined spiritual mover, the celestial body itself, and the inherent powers of terrestrial nature. Consequently the ultimate mover of each celestial body is, in fact, the separated active intelligence proportioned to the spheres. Since, however, all celestial spheres depend upon the diurnal motion of the first heaven, the absolutely first mover of all the celestial bodies is the separated, active intelligence commanding the *primum caelum*. This absolutely first mover is the *primum principium universi esse*, the cause not only of all

---

[75] St. Albert, *Problemata determinata*, q. 34; *De animalibus* XVI, tr. I, cc. 11-13.

[76] " Quod enim impressiones separatorum a materia generabilium sint in materia patet per hoc quod ex materia hominis homo generat hominem, et sol et motor solis; et ideo oportet considerare separata in quantum impressiones earum per motum caelestium sunt in generabilibus et corruptibilibus." St. Albert, *Lib. II Phys.*, tr. I, c. 11, ed. cit., pp. 113-4. See Averroes, *ibid.*, comm. 26.

[77] *Problemata determinata*, q. 33; *De nat. et orig. animae*, tr. I, c. 5; *De animalibus*, lib. XVI, tr. I, cc. 11-12; *Summa de creaturis*, P. II, q. 5, a. 4.

motion, but also the absolute efficient cause, formal principle and ultimate end of all being. He produces not only the hierarchy of conjoined celestial movers, their bodies and motion, but he is also the first efficient cause, formal principle and final end of each intelligence. The first principle of universal being is commonly designated by St. Albert as the *intellectus universaliter agens*, who, as has already been noted, is God Himself. As first mover of the heavens He is attained in natural science; as first cause of being He is attained in metaphysics.

Once Albert has established in his reply to the Master General that angels are not the same as intelligences discovered by the philosophers, he can easily dismiss the first five questions as fatuous. The existence of angels, the messengers of God, cannot be proved in philosophy; they have nothing to do with problems of natural science; and even if God were not the first mover of the heavens—which He really is—the existence of angels would still not be demonstrated. God, for St. Albert, is the first cause of celestial motions, not as a form conjoined to the universe, but as a separated active intelligence commanding the motions of all, " since Aristotle says that the first cause moves the first heaven, to the motion of which all motions of celestial bodies are referred, as all movements of organic members are referred to the movement of the heart." [78] The only body which God moves immediately as conjoined to Himself is the body of Christ, joined hypostatically to the Word.

ROBERT KILWARDBY

The approach of Kilwardby is very different from that of St. Albert. Kilwardby, in fact, reflects much more the schools of Oxford than those of Paris, despite his own regency in arts at Paris (c. 1237-c. 1245). He had been a Master in Theology of Oxford about fifteen years when he was asked to reply to the questionnaire of John of Vercelli. We cannot be certain that Kilwardby always maintained the views presented in the reply of 1271, but we can be certain of his views at that date.

---

[78] *Problemata determinata*, q. 1, *ed. cit.*, p. 331; cf. Aristotle, *De caelo et mundo*, II, c. 2, 284b6-286a2.

Replying to the first question, Kilwardby explicitly denies that God is the immediate mover of the heavens moving either eternally or temporally in place: *certissime tenendum est et asserendum quod Deus non movet primum caelum nec aliquod corpus immediate motu locali.*[79] He admits that Aristotle seems to consider God as the first mover of the eternal spheres, " but the truth is that God does not move any body immediately " by continual locomotion. If God did move any body in this way, He would be either the substantial act of that body and a part of the whole or a simple mover like a man on a horse. The first alternative is obviously erroneous. The second is awkward and unreasonable for it implies that the first heaven is moved by violence: *secundo modo caelum primum videretur moveri violenter.* Kilwardby, however, does admit that God can and does move bodies immediately by a certain supernatural change, as in creation, the production of light, the formation of Eve and similar events. In such events God operates without the assistance of nature or angels. Concluding his reply to the first query, Kilwardby categorically states:

From these considerations, therefore, the reply to the question must be that God moves no body immediately by continuous motion, but only by His word when a body is changed instantaneously so that something supernaturally begins to exist.

The second question has to do with natural motions and their dependence on angelic movers of the celestial bodies. Kilwardby first distinguishes between natural and violent motions. Nature is an intrinsic principle of motion; only bodies which have such a principle *per se* are said to move naturally. Motions are called violent when their moving force is extraneous, the subject contributing nothing to the motion (*quando principium motivum est extraneum, passo non conferente*). Among natural motions Kilwardby enumerates continuous movement of bodies, instantaneous transmission of light, the irascible and concupiscible emotions of spiritual beings, and intellectual activity. Clearly, intellectual and appetitive activities of spiritual

---

[79] Kilwardby, *Responsio*, q. 1, ed. Chenu, *loc. cit.*, p. 194.

beings are not affected by celestial movement; rather, such spiritual activities are productive of celestial motion. There are for Kilwardby two types of celestial motion. The first emanates from celestial bodies in the form of energy and light rays affecting all the active and passive powers of terrestrial bodies, both elementary and composite. This cosmic influence is produced by the celestial bodies, but the influence is subjectively located in terrestrial bodies. " And perhaps if this influence of light and energy were withdrawn from elements and composites, all active and passive powers of bodies would cease to act or react; hence this influence seems to be the *per se* cause of natural activity and movement in the elements." [80] There is, however, another motion located in the celestial body itself; this is the continual rotation of the sphere. Kilwardby does not consider this rotational movement of the spheres to have any direct or proper bearing on natural terrestrial motion. Such motions do provide variations of temperature, humidity and the like, but this is secondary to the direct cosmic influence affecting natural changes.

Finally Kilwardby proceeds to discuss the crucial question of celestial movers. He notes that there are three opinions concerning the motion of celestial bodies. The first is that of Aristotle and certain other philosophers. Kilwardby's interpretation of Aristotle's view is essentially that of St. Albert: " celestial bodies are animated, having animal life and intelligence by which they perceive the will of the first cause, and motion in place by which they fulfill the known will of God; by this motion of theirs they conserve things and preserve generation and the limited being of generable natures." [81] In this view celestial bodies are moved by spirits which are their " souls " just as man is moved by his spirit, or soul. It is interesting to note in passing that the author of *Errores philosophorum* does not attribute animation of the heavens to Aristotle or Averroes, but exclusively to Avicenna:

---

[80] *Ibid.*, q. 2, ed. cit., p. 196.
[81] *Responsio*, q. 2 § *De tertio*. For this part of the reply we rely on the emended edition published by Chenu in *Revue des Sc. Phil. et Théol.* XXIX (1940), 211.

Again [Avicenna] erred on the subject of the animation of the heavens. For he held that the heavens were animated. He said that the soul of the heavens is not only a suitable moving power, as the Philosopher and the Commentator were intent upon saying, but that a single being is produced by the union of the soul of the heavens with the heavens, just as by the union of our soul and our body.[82]

Concerning this presumed view of Aristotle, Kilwardby notes that it is philosophically sound and supported by reason: " since those bodies seem to be more noble than living bodies, they ought to have a higher form of life." Nevertheless in 1277 the Bishop of Paris condemned the proposition " that celestial bodies are moved by an intrinsic principle, which is a soul." [83] And St. Albert, as we have seen, clearly rejected celestial animation as alien to the Catholic faith.

The second opinion listed by Kilwardby is in reality that of St. Thomas: " others hold that those bodies are moved by angelic spirits who govern and move them in such a way that they are not their act, or form." Kilwardby dismisses this view as unphilosophical, and he remarks, " Nor do I recall it being approved by any of the *Sancti* as true and certain." However, Kilwardby does admit in passing that it could be held *absque errore* by Catholics.[84]

Kilwardby's own view of celestial motion is presented succinctly as the third opinion:

Just as heavy and light bodies are moved to a place in which they rest by their own inclinations and tendencies, so celestial bodies are moved circularly in place by their own natural inclinations similar to weight (*quasi ponderibus*) in order to conserve corruptible things lest they suddenly perish and fail.

Some spheres rotate naturally from West to East, others from

---

[82] Giles of Rome, *Errores philosophorum*, VI: Avicenna, 10, ed. Josef Koch, trans. by J. O. Riedl (Milwaukee: Marquette, 1944), p. 31.

[83] *Chartularium Univ. Paris.*, ed. H. Denifle, O. P., I, n. 473, p. 548, prop. 92; see also prop. 213. Cf. E. Krebs, *Meister Dietrich*, in *Beiträge z. Gesch. d. Phil. d. M.-A.*, Bd. V, heft 5-6 (Münster, 1906), pp. 75-76.

[84] Cf. J. A. Weisheipl, " The *Problemata Determinata* Ascribed to Albertus Magnus," *loc. cit.*, p. 304, note 8.

East to West, and still others move naturally as epicycles, and others on the eccentric. To each planet and orb God gave an innate natural inclination to move in a particular way in rotational motion; to each He accorded an innate order, regularity and direction without the need of a distinct agency like a soul, an angel or Himself here and now producing the motion. " Just as the forces (*pondera*) of heavy and light move bodies consistently, not permitting them to stray outside a determined path, so it is with the forces of each and every celestial body." Consequently rotational motion is as natural to celestial bodies as gravitational motion is to heavy bodies. Both arise spontaneously from *nature* as an intrinsic active principle, *instinctu propriorum ponderum* (q. 3). It was commonly recognized among the schoolmen that heavy bodies need nothing more than their own generated nature to account for gravitational motion; heavy bodies need no conjoined mover to account for the continued downward fall.[85] Kilwardby wished to explain celestial motions by a similar intrinsic formal principle. Terrestrial bodies are unattached and hence move rectilinearly to a place of relative rest. But for Kilwardby the heavens are spherical; stars and planets are attached to their proper orbs within a sphere. Consequently the only " natural " motion the heavens could have is rotational, a continual rotation of each orb on its axis. The combination of various rotations on suitable axes together with the required uniform velocity of each rotation produced the apparent motion of the planet. Kilwardby thus dispenses with the need of any conjoined or separated mover, whether that mover be called a soul, an angel, intelligence or God. It is clear from this that Kilwardby could not prove the existence of God through physical motion. He cannot even prove the existence of a separated substance.

Because of the great diversity of opinion concerning celestial movers, Kilwardby maintained that it is impossible to prove that angels move the spheres (q. 4). Philosophers think that they have infallibly demonstrated the existence of spiritual

[85] Cf. J. A. Weisheipl, *Nature and Gravitation*, ed. cit., pp. 19-21, 25-28.

movers for the heavens, but these are certainly not the angels discussed by Catholics. Even assuming that God is not the immediate mover of the heavens—which according to Kilwardby He is not—it is in no way proved that angels have to be celestial movers (q. 5). Unlike St. Albert, Kilwardby conceives the physical universe as perfectly self-contained, perfectly "natural," having no need of immaterial agencies directing and moving the heavens. His is the closed world created by God in the beginning with sufficient innate tendencies to move rectilinearly and rotationally.

This view was not original with Robert Kilwardby. Fr. Daniel A. Callus has pointed out that this idea can be traced to the earliest days of Aristotelianism in Oxford. Some sixty years before Kilwardby's reply, John Blund gave as his considered opinion that the heavenly bodies are not moved by souls, nor by intelligences, but by their own active nature moving *orbiculariter*.[86] As is commonly known, this opinion found favor among many in the fourteenth and fifteenth century.

Fr. Chenu saw in Kilwardby's view an anticipation of John Buridan's famous suggestion about celestial motions, that an impetus (given by God) is also found in the celestial spheres, but one which cannot be diminished by resistance, since celestial matter offers no resistance.[87] In all terrestrial projectiles impetus is diminished and overcome by nature resisting the violent force. But in Aristotelian theory celestial bodies could offer no resistance, since they had no weight or gravity; they were considered completely passive, having " nature " only as a passive principle of motion. Consequently Buridan's suggestion of an initial impetus for celestial motion was a perfectly obvious one; it presupposes Aristotle's doctrine of the pure passivity of those bodies. In other words, it is precisely because

[86] " Dicimus quod firmamentum movetur a natura, non ab anima, et alia supercelestia." The full passage is published by Daniel A. Callus, O. P., " The Treatise of John Blund On the Soul," in *Autour d'Aristote* (Louvain, 1955), pp. 487-9.

[87] Cf. Pierre Duhem, *Études sur Léonard de Vinci*, III (Paris: Nobele, 1955), p. 42.

such bodies have no active "nature" that they can, in the scheme of Buridan, receive a perpetual impetus for continued motion. This is quite different from Kilwardby's conception of celestial spheres actively inclined to circular motion, for here the "nature" of celestial bodies is an active principle. The final result of both views may be similar or even identical, but the theoretical foundation of Buridan's theory of impetus for the heavens is profoundly dissimilar to the views of Kilwardby.

Kilwardby's view, however, was common enough in later centuries. It was favored particularly by Platonists and semi-Platonists. Notably Nicholas of Cusa attempted to explain the circular motion of the heavens by an appeal to their orbicular shape; their matter, being different from terrestrial matter, naturally tended to move orbicularly, that is, by rotating.[88] Copernicus himself explained the circular motion of the heavenly bodies by their spherical nature:

Now we note that the motion of the heavenly bodies is circular. Rotation is natural to a sphere and by that very act is its shape expressed. For here we deal with the simplest kind of body, wherein neither beginning nor end may be discerned, nor, if it rotates ever in the same place, may the one be distinguished from the other.[89]

For Copernicus, as for Kilwardby before him, the substantial form of a spherical body naturally tends to move spherically. Surprisingly, for Copernicus the outermost sphere of the fixed stars, though spherical by nature, was said to be at rest.[90] It must be admitted, however, that Copernicus was not concerned with explaining the physical causes of celestial motion, as this is beyond the scope of mathematical astronomy.

We may seriously doubt that Kilwardby's reply influenced later writers; it certainly did not influence John Buridan. Nevertheless it does represent an important medieval view concerning celestial motion.

[88] Nicholas of Cusa, De ludo globi, lib. I (Basel, 1565), pp. 210-214.
[89] N. Copernicus, De revolutionibus orbium caelestium, lib. I, c. 4 (Thorn, 1873), p. 14; also c. 8, pp. 21-24.
[90] Ibid., c. 10, pp. 28-29.

St. Thomas Aquinas

The reply of St. Thomas is the shortest and most succinct of the three. He adheres strictly to the *forma* expected, appealing to the *Sancti* (Scripture, Augustine, Pseudo-Dionysius, Gregory, Jerome) and evaluating all questions in the light of Catholic faith. " It seems to me safer," he says in the prooemium, " that doctrines commonly held by philosophers which are not contrary to the faith be neither asserted as dogmas of faith (although they may sometimes be introduced as philosophical arguments) nor denied as contrary to the faith, lest occasion be offered to men learned in human wisdom to ridicule the doctrine of faith."

In his important theological treatise, *De substantiis separatis*, St. Thomas considers the relative merits of Plato and Aristotle on the question of angels.[91] Plato—really Proclus—is understood by St. Thomas to have postulated various orders of spiritual substances between the human soul and God. Under God, the supreme unity and goodness, there is the order of secondary gods who are the Forms or Ideas eternally radiant. Inferior to these is the order of separated intellects, " which participate in the above-mentioned Forms in order to have actual understanding." Next come the various orders of soul, each one inhabiting a certain kind of body. Celestial souls animate celestial bodies and move them, in such a manner that " the highest of the bodies, namely the first heaven, which is moved by its own motion, receives motion from the highest soul, and so on to the very lowest of the heavenly bodies." Below celestial souls are the demons who inhabit unearthly bodies. The lowest intellectual soul is man, who although he inhabits a visible body " as a sailor in a ship," also has another nobler body belonging to the soul, incorruptible and everlasting, even as the soul itself is incorruptible. Souls below man, such as plant and animal souls, lack intelligence and immortality. If all these views of Plato were true, notes St. Thomas,

---

[91] Cap. 1-4. For the treatise *De substantiis separatis* we rely on the excellent English version of Fr. Francis J. Lescoe (West Hartford: St. Joseph College, 1959).

then all orders between God and man would be called ' angels '
by Catholics.

The fundamental weakness of Plato's position, as St. Thomas
sees it, is that it is without proof, for his separated intelligences
are merely postulated, not demonstrated. " That is why Aristotle proceeded by a more manifest and surer way, namely, by
way of motion, to investigate substances that are separate from
matter." St. Thomas' interpretation of Aristotle is substantially that of St. Albert and Kilwardby. Since all generable and
celestial bodies are moved, they must be moved ultimately
by a substance which is not material. The immaterial soul conjoined to celestial bodies is moved concomitantly with the
body, therefore it is moved by knowledge and desire of absolutely separated intelligences. " Therefore each of the heavenly
bodies is animated by its own soul and each has its own separate appetible object which is the proper end of its motion."
For Aristotle, then, there are as many intelligences as there
are celestial souls, and as many celestial souls as there are
motions. It was Avicenna, according to St. Thomas, who erroneously limited the number of separated intelligences to ten,
thinking that the multiple motions of a planet could be " ordered to the motion of one star." In any case, according to the
position of Aristotle, between man and God " there exists only
a two-fold order of intellectual substances, namely the separated substances which are the ends of the heavenly motions,
and the souls of the spheres, which move through appetite and
desire." [92] Aristotle and Plato both agree that all immaterial
substances have their entire being from God, that they are
entirely immaterial, and that they are ruled by divine providence. They differ, however, with respect to the number and
precise character of separated substances as well as to their
relevance to the physical order.

For St. Thomas the theologian, Aristotle made three serious
errors concerning angels. First, he erroneously limited their
number to what could be ascertained by celestial motion; there

[92] *Ibid.*, c. 2, n. 10; cf. *In II De caelo*, lect. 18, n. 16.

is no demonstrative reason why they cannot be more numerous, as Catholic theology teaches.[93] Second, he erred by considering some to be substantially united to celestial bodies as their soul; such a union is unreasonable and contrary to Catholic teaching.[94] Finally, Aristotle erred in considering angels and the universe to have existed from all eternity; such eternity cannot be demonstrated by reason.[95] St. Thomas himself never doubted that Plato and Aristotle admitted another mode of " coming-into-being " besides physical generation for immaterial substances and the universe. " Over and above the mode of becoming by which something comes to be through change or motion, there must be a mode of becoming or origin of things, without any mutation or motion through the influx of being *(per influentiam essendi)* ." [96] St. Thomas goes on to say that, although Plato and Aristotle did posit that immaterial substances and even heavenly bodies always existed, " we must not suppose on that account that they denied to them a cause of their being." [97] On this point they did not depart from the position of the Catholic faith.

We can now return to St. Thomas' reply to the official questionnaire. His reply to the first three questions simply states that God normally rules His creation through intermediaries, the lower and more gross bodies being ruled by the higher and more subtle. The divine power, however, is in no way limited to the order it has established. Assuming that angels are the

[93] *Ibid.*, c. 2, nn. 12-13; cf. *Sum. contra gent.*, II, c. 92.

[94] *Ibid.*, c. 18, nn. 100-101; cf. *De spirit. creat.*, a. 5; *Sum. contra gent.*, II, c. 91; *Sum. theol.*, I, q. 51, a. 1; *De pot.*, q. 6, a. 6.

[95] *Ibid.*, c. 2, n. 14; cf. *Sum. theol.*, I, q. 46, a. 1; *Sum. contra gent.*, II, cc. 31-38; *De pot.*, q. 3, a. 17; *De aeternitate mundi.*

[96] *Ibid.*, c. 9, n. 49.

[97] *Ibid.*, n. 52. For this reason St. Thomas frequently insists that those who interpret Aristotle's God as a mere physical mover or a mere final cause are in complete error. For St. Thomas Aristotle's God is a *causa essendi ipsi mundo*, a *causa quantum ad suum esse*, a *factor caelestium corporum.* " Ex hoc autem apparet manifeste falsitas opinionis illorum, qui posuerunt Aristotelem sensisse, quod Deus non sit causa substantiae caeli, sed solum motus eius." *In VI Metaph.*, lect. 1, n. 1164. Also *In VIII Phys.*, lect. 3, n. 6; *In I De caelo*, lect. 8, n. 14; *In II Metaph.*, lect. 2, n. 295.

celestial movers, then no learned man can doubt that all natural motions of lower bodies are caused by the motion of celestial bodies (q. 3). Dionysius himself notes that the sun's rays induce the generation of sensible bodies, generate life itself, nurture, strengthen and perfect it. All of this is within the power of angels.

For some reason St. Thomas omitted to answer the fourth question directly. It asks whether it is infallibly demonstrated according to anyone that angels are the movers of celestial bodies. In two earlier replies to the lector of Venice, St. Thomas answered this very question in clear terms:

The books of the philosophers abound with proofs for this, proofs, which they consider demonstrations. It seems to me therefore that it can be demonstrated that celestial bodies are moved by some intellect, either by God immediately or by means of angels moving them.[98]

Consequently his reply to the fifth question comes as no surprise. He categorically insists that if God does not move those bodies immediately, then some other spiritual substance is demonstrated as mover, either a celestial soul or a separated angel. The fundamental reason for this assertion is stated clearly: *Quod autem corpora caelestia a sola natura sua moveantur, sicut gravia et levia, est omnino impossibile.*[99] In other words, for St. Thomas it is absolutely impossible that circular motion be explained by nature as an active (formal) principle within celestial bodies. This view is directly opposed to the position represented by Kilwardby.

Throughout all his writings St. Thomas insisted on the essential difference between rectilinear motion and rotational motion. Rectilinear motions, such as those of heavy and light bodies, arise spontaneously from within bodies, from nature as an active (formal) principle. Nature in this sense is predetermined to a certain end and to the means of attaining it. The

---

[98] St. Thomas, *Resp. de art. XXXVI*, a. 2; also *Resp. de art. XXX*, ad 4.

[99] St. Thomas, *Resp. ad Joan. Vercel.*, q. 5; cf. *Sum. contra gent.*, III, c. 23 *per totum.*

end, therefore, is already within the intentionality of nature as form. Once nature has attained the end, it must rest in its acquisition, since it is its *good*. Physically there is no need for any " conjoined mover " to account for this motion downward or upward. Nature itself spontaneously moves toward the end which is its goal. " There is in heavy and light bodies a formal principle of its motion, because, just as other accidents proceed from the substantial form, so does place and, consequently, movement toward place; not however that the natural form is a mover (*motor*), but the mover is the generator which begot such a form upon which this motion follows." [100] Therefore nature as an active principle is always ordained to rest in the possession of some good proper to itself.

For St. Thomas the profound difference between celestial and terrestrial phenomena lay in the motions. The heavens move continuously in time, aiming at no rest or possession of a goal. Whether the heavens are eternal or created in time is not relevant to the question. Likewise it makes no difference whether the celestial bodies in motion are real spheres or independent planets; in either case the motion is always ordered to further motion. Clearly these motions cannot be striving for a rest as yet unattained, since such a rest would be disastrous for the celestial body and no nature can desire its own destruction as a good. Nor can it be said that the purpose of such motion is motion itself. Motion by its very nature is a tending, a continual otherness; it has within its very nature a deformity which is incapable of being the final cause of any natural agent. " Therefore it is impossible that nature intend motion for the sake of motion." [101] Now for St. Thomas, if there is no intrinsic end attainable by a body in motion, then that motion cannot have sprung spontaneously from nature as form. Like the

---

[100] St. Thomas, *In II Phys.*, lect. 1, n. 4. Also *In I De caelo*, lect. 18, n. 1; II, lect. 2, n. 6; III, lect. 7, nn. 5-9; *In II Phys.*, lect. 5, n. 5; IV, lect. 12, n. 9; VIII, lect. 8, nn. 5-7; *Sum. cont. gent.*, III, cc. 82, 84; *De pot.*, q. 5, a. 5.

[101] " Impossible est igitur quod natura intendat motum propter seipsum." *Sum. cont. gent.*, III, c. 23, § 6. Also *De pot.*, q. 5, a. 5: " impossible est quod aliqua natura inclinet ad motum secundum se ipsum."

matter in generable substances, the celestial body must be moved by another, by one in continual contact with it. Consequently celestial bodies have " nature " only in the sense of a passive (material) principle, which means the natural aptitude to be moved by another. Hence "the motion of a celestial body, as far as its active principle is concerned, is not natural, but voluntary and intellectual; however, in relation to its passive principle, the motion is natural, for a celestial body has a natural aptitude for such motion." [102] In this matter, notes St. Thomas, it makes no difference whether we conceive the celestial bodies to be moved by intellectual substances conjoined to the body after the manner of a soul or by one entirely distinct like an angel. *Non autem esset via solvendi, si moverentur per solum naturae impetum, sicut corpora gravia et levia.*[103]

It is true that for St. Thomas celestial bodies can have only a passive nature whether the mover be a conjoined soul as Aristotle wished or a separated angel, as he himself believed. Nevertheless in establishing the existence of God along Aristotle's lines, it does make a difference. St. Thomas, as St. Albert before him, was well aware that the First Mover of the *Physics* was for Aristotle identical with the First Being of *Metaphysics* XII. That is to say, St. Thomas knew St. Albert's interpretation to be correct. However, there is a serious difficulty. If the celestial movers are not souls, but angels, as St. Thomas himself held with the *Sancti*, then Aristotle's argument is not conclusive. A soul conjoined to the sphere is necessarily moved *per accidens*, that is, concomitantly with the sphere. Since this kind of mover is insufficient to account for the primary source of physical motion, one can validly conclude to the existence of an intelligence which is entirely separated from matter. And if one erroneously limits the number of spiritual substances to the number of celestial movements, then the separated intelligence moving the first animated sphere (*primum caelum*) must be God. On the other hand, if the immediate

---

[102] *Sum. cont. gent.*, III, c. 23, § 8. Also *In II Phys.*, lect. 1, n. 4; *in II De caelo*, lect. 3, n. 2, and lect. 18, n. 1; *De pot.*, q. 5, a. 5 ad 12.

[103] St. Thomas *In II De caelo*, lect. 18, n. 1.

mover of the celestial bodies is not a soul, then it is in no way moved *per accidens*. This immediate mover could be God Himself or an angel. And if the number of angels is greater than Aristotle conceded, then it is impossible to demonstrate that God is the immediate mover of the heavens. This is precisely the difficulty envisaged in St. Thomas' reply to the fifth question: assuming that God is not the immediate mover, then it is indeed demonstrated that an angel is the mover. This assumption, however, cannot be made on philosophical, much less on physical grounds. This is not to say that Aristotle failed to prove the existence of God in *Metaphysics* XII. Quite the contrary. St. Thomas was convinced that Aristotle perceived that other mode of becoming *per influentiam essendi*, whereby every spiritual substance is necessarily dependent on the first cause of being. It is this other mode of " being moved " that St. Thomas sees in Aristotle's conception of the conjoined mover of the first heaven.[104] It is the totality of movers which are in some true sense *moved* that validates the Aristotelian argument for St. Thomas. " Hence, unless the celestial bodies are moved immediately by God, they must either be animated and moved by their proper souls or be moved by angels, *quod melius dicitur*."

Concluding his reply to the fifth question, St. Thomas notes that there are some philosophers who would have God move the first heaven by means of its *anima propria*, and the other heavens by means of intelligences and souls. St. Thomas' own view is that God directs the universe through a hierarchy of angels, only the lower of which directly move the celestial bodies.

The view of St. Thomas is openly defended in the anonymous *Quaestio de motoribus corporum caelestium*, a work formerly attributed to St. Thomas and still published among his works.[105]

---

[104] For example, *In XII Metaph.*, lect. 7, nn. 2519-2522; lect. 8, nn. 2539-2543; *In II De caelo*, lect. 18, n. 6.

[105] *Opera Omnia* (Parma: Fiaccadori, 1869), XXIV, pp. 217a-219b. This treatise was first published by Thomas Boninsegnius, O. P., in his edition of the *Summa* with Cajetan's commentary (Venice: apud Juntas) in 1588. The first folio an-

Strangely, there is no known manuscript of this work extant, but it seems to be of English origin, written, as Grabmann has pointed out, some time after June 1271.[106] In it the author rejects at length the tradition represented by Robert Kilwardby as well as the animation theory presented by Simplicius. The author defends vigorously the Thomistic view that celestial movers are two-fold: the passive nature of the celestial body and the active power of angels ministering to the will of God.

The medieval views of celestial movers which we have outlined in this paper are rarely considered today. Yet they are important for an understanding of St. Thomas, and they do have serious implications which deserve the attention of modern Thomists, implications of interest to theologians as well as to philosophers of nature.

JAMES A. WEISHEIPL, O. P.

Albertus Magnus Lyceum
Dominican House of Studies
River Forest, Illinois

nounced: "Quaestiones duae S. Thomae de Aquino nuper repertae ac in lucem editae, una de principio individuationis, altera vero de motoribus coelestium corporum, quae nuper repertae fuerunt Florentiae in bibliotheca S. Marci." This new manuscript was copied for San Marco by order of Cosmo de Medici and notarized on June 5, 1587; this document is published on fol. 2r of the edition. Boninsegnio rests his argument for the authenticity of the treatise (fol. 2v ff.) on the Thomistic character of the doctrine and on the credibility of the manuscript, which also contained St. Thomas' *De potentia*. The same scribe had written the two new questions on folios 287-290 of the original manuscript, which is now lost.

[106] M. Grabmann, *Die Werke des hl. Thomas von Aquin*. 3rd ed. (Münster, 1949). *Beiträge z. Gesch. d. Phil. u. Theol. d. M.-A.*, Bd. XXII, heft 1-2, p. 415.

GRAVITATIONAL MOTION ACCORDING TO
THEODORIC OF FREIBERG

ᕫᑎᕫ

THE recent appearance of Marshall Clagett's *The Science of Mechanics in the Middle Ages* [1] has focussed attention once again on the wealth of material made available by scholars in the " Dark Ages " for the development of science as we now know it. Concentrating on " the mechanical doctrines of the medieval period which were framed in mathematical terms or had important consequences for a mathematical mechanics," [2] Clagett reproduces most of the important texts in this area and analyzes them for the conceptual content that contributed to the revolutionary seventeenth-century development. By intent he avoids the study of methodology, nor does he attempt to evaluate the complex relationships that existed between physics and natural philosophy during this period. Yet even these areas have not been without their share of attention in the recent literature. Three significant studies of medieval scientific methodology have appeared in succession,[3] and Anneliese Maier has recently concluded the fifth volume of her monumental *Studien zur Naturphilosophie der Spätscholastik* [4] with some weighty observations on the transitional philosophical concepts that gave rise to the new

[1] University of Wisconsin Press: Madison, 1959, xxix + 711 pp.

[2] *Ibid.*, p. xxii.

[3] A. C. Crombie's *Robert Grosseteste and the Origins of Experimental Science,* Oxford, 1953; my own *The Scientific Methodology of Theodoric of Freiberg,* Fribourg, 1959; and J. A. Weisheipl's *The Development of Physical Theory in the Middle Ages,* London, 1959.

[4] *Zwischen Philosophie und Mechanik,* Rome, 1958, particularly pp. 373-382. The five volumes, which we shall henceforth refer to as *Studien* I, II . . . etc., are entitled respectively: I. *Die Vorläufer Galileis im 14. Jahrhundert* (1949); II. *Zwei Grundprobleme der scholastischen Naturphilosophie* (1951); III. *An der Grenze von Scholastik und Naturwissenschaft* (1952); IV. *Metaphysische Hintergründe der spätscholastischen Naturphilosophie* (1955); and V. *Zwischen Philosophie und Mechanik* (1958).

192   W. A. WALLACE

science. All of these works are fruitful sources of study for the Thomistic philosopher of science who would evaluate modern science in light of the traditional concepts of natural philosophy. It is to be hoped that the time will not be long before some penetrating studies in this area may help solve the stubborn problems that have frustrated and divided adherents to the philosophy of St. Thomas during the past several decades.[5]

Meanwhile these works have also signalized the importance of studying manuscript sources to fill the gaps in our knowledge of medieval science. Clagett's work, by his own admission, would have been quite impossible without the prior paleographical efforts of Maier and Moody. It is in a spirit similar to that in which the latter research was undertaken that I should like to offer this brief study of gravitational motion according to Theodoric of Freiberg (c. 1250-c. 1310). Theodoric's contributions to medieval optics and scientific methodology are sufficiently well known not to require further attention, but by some peculiar oversight the views of the German Dominican on the problem of gravitation have generally not been recorded.[6] I shall attempt to fill this lacuna by a résumé of the unedited opusculum *De elementis corporum naturalium inquantum sunt partes mundi*,[7] which contains

[5] I have in mind the long-standing debate over a so-called " specific distinction " maintained by some to exist between Thomistic natural philosophy and modern science, which has impeded the study of a host of philosophical problems concerning the nature of matter, gravity, mass, energy, light, the elements, etc., all arising in modern science.

[6] The literature on Theodoric is given in my *Scientific Methodology of Theodoric of Freiberg* (Studia Friburgensia, No. 26), The University Press, Fribourg: Switzerland, 1959. Miss Maier mentions him in several footnotes throughout her volumes, but otherwise has only a brief treatment of his doctrine on the elements in *Studien* III, pp. 58-69, without considering the relation of the latter to falling motion.

[7] This opusculum was probably written about the year 1300. Two complete manuscript versions are known: Cod. Maihingen (Fürstliche Bibl. Schloss Harburg, II, 1 qu. 6), henceforth referred to as M, and Cod. Vat. Lat. 2183, henceforth referred to as U. In addition, some fragments of the opusculum are to be found in Cod. Vat. Lat. 1121, henceforth referred to as T. When a reading of the Latin text is given below, it is generally a composite text based on all available manuscripts, as indi-

Theodoric's complete doctrine on this subject. It is not my intention to enter into a detailed analysis of the doctrine presented, but rather to sketch the essential content of Theodoric's teaching, supporting this by substantial citation from the manuscript versions of the opusculum. In thus utilizing the space alloted to me, I also forego the opportunity to point out possible relationships between Theodoric's doctrine and more recent thought on gravitation. I trust, however, that the material presented will have some bearing on further analyses of the causes of gravitational motion that may be forthcoming from Thomistic philosophers.

GRAVITY AND THE ELEMENTS

The elements, for Theodoric, are material components of natural bodies, "principles according to the formality of matter," or, more explicitly, "whence a thing is materially composed." [8] As such, they can be studied by the metaphysician, who is interested in them "from the viewpoint of their substance, how they pertain to the genus of being precisely as being," or they can be studied by the natural philosopher "insofar as they are natural bodies and accordingly related to motion and change." [9] The latter consideration again permits of a twofold division, for the natural philosopher may investigate them in a way similar to that of the modern physicist, insofar as they are "the first parts of the universe," or in a way similar to that of the modern chemist, insofar as they contain a "principle of transformation by which one element can be simply generated from another, or compounds formed from elements." [10] Gravity is of primary interest to the physicist, thus characterized, as Theodoric explains in the following passage:

---

cated with the foliation. I have already furnished a critical Latin edition of the prologue and first eight chapters of this opusculum in my *Scientific Methodology*, pp. 324-331.

[8] Prologue, (ed. Wallace) pp. 324-325.
[9] Cap. 7, p. 329.
[10] *Ibid.*

194   W. A. WALLACE

Certain accidents or qualities are in elements as they are parts of the universe, namely, gravity and levity, and, deriving from these, natural motions either to or from its center. . . . Through such motions bodies are disposed in their proper places in the material universe, considering the latter quantitatively in its extensive and dimensional integrity as well as in its specific diversity. Such accidents are in elements as parts of the universe, making up the universe precisely as actual, for actual parts are those which have a species. Thus it is that gravity and levity are first found in [elemental] bodies complete according to species, and that they are their very first accidents as parts of the universe. . . . Wherefore, if there be any bodies or natures simpler than these, of which the forementioned elements might in turn be composed, light and heavy would not be proper to such bodies or natures, nor would these be parts of the universe specifically and quantitatively, except possibly in an originative way.[11]

Gravity, then, is one of the first qualities of bodies considered in relation to other bodies making up the universe, and is properly attributable to the elemental constituents of such bodies, themselves specifically complete, as the ultimate source of their natural or gravitational motions. This suggests for Theodoric some observations as to whether gravity is an absolute quality, or merely relative, and whether it is subject to intensification or not. Surprisingly enough, such questions were not commonly discussed at the turn of the fourteenth century; Clagett has pointed out that the first evidence of the concept " specific weight " is only to be found in the pseudo-Archimedean treatise *De insidentibus in humidum*, itself dating from the thirteenth.[12] There is no direct use by Theodoric of the quantitative notions found in *De insidentibus*, but he does speak of an " intensity " of gravity, as is clear from the following citation:

There is a twofold modality of heavy and light. One is according to absolute quality, whose formality consists in this, that heavy and light are principles of a determinate tendency to some place in the universe. Under this formality heavy and light are distinguished in bodies in the following way, viz., some are heavy and light simply,

[11] *Ibid.*, pp. 329-330.   [12] *Op. cit.*, pp. 93-95, 674.

as fire and earth, which go to the extremities of straight-line motion; others are such comparatively, in the sense that they are heavy or light with reference to various boundaries, as air and water. But there is another modality of heavy and light which is noticed in the intensity of these qualities, whereby it happens that in the case of two bodies, even such as tend to the same terminus, one will be heavier or lighter than the other, in the sense that one will have more weight than the other. And this can result from one of two causes, viz., because of the aggregation of more parts of the same body, as a larger portion of earth has more weight than a small piece; or from the complexion and nature of the body itself, as lead or gold is heavier and has more weight than earth or stone of an equal size.[13]

Thus there is in Theodoric's thought a recognition of specific weights, although he gives no mathematical treatment of them, and in fact is not interested in their effect on gravitational motion. His position is rather that the first modality mentioned above, " according to absolute quality," is proper to bodies as they are parts of the universe, and this alone determines the proper place or region to which a body tends, whether it be element or compound. If it is a compound, it will tend to a region determined by what is " predominant " in it, not by " proportional parts, even an exceeding one." What he means by this " predominant " is not too clear: he describes it as being " according to the property and nature of the complexion in which the species of the body is rooted, which itself is one and simple." Yet the practical consequence of his view is easily discerned, for he holds that " fiery bodies," i. e., " shooting stars and comets," tend to the proper place of fire, while " earthy bodies " such as " minerals and stones " tend to the place of earth.[14] This is clearly in accord with Aristotle's doctrine in De caelo et mundo [15] and itself adds little to the latter's development. Had Theodoric been discussing the

---

[13] Cap. 8, p. 330.

[14] Ibid., p. 331. For the medieval understanding of the expression, " comets tend to the place of fire," see Lynn Thorndike's Latin Treatises on Comets Between 1238 and 1368 A. D., Chicago, 1950, passim.

[15] Book IV, chap. 4, 311a30-b3.

velocities of fall of such bodies, and not the places to which
they tend, his elimination of specific weights as of incidental
importance would have shown rare insight for his time. But
there is no mention of velocities in this opusculum, and this
discovery had still to await the researches of Galileo.

It is by pursuing such a line of thought, however, that
Theodoric comes to some interesting questions about composite
motions and how these can be resolved into component parts,
for which he proposes noteworthy answers. He maintains, in
accordance with the teaching just proposed, that there are no
" intermediary places . . . beyond the four places of the four
primary bodies," although allowing that a particular compound
might have a proper place to which it tends in " some one of
these first regions," determined by its " relation to some part
of the heavens or the horizon." [16] Against this position he notes
the objection, already in Aristotle, that simple bodies ought
to have simple motions and composite bodies composite motions. He replies to this by making precise the sense in which a
motion is " composite "—not because its terminus is composite,
but rather because " the manner in which it tends to that
terminus is composite." This manner of tending, he points out,
need not be composite, for we find that both simple and composite bodies undergo simple motions " according to the nature
of the predominant." In fact, he notes, such simple motions
are what manifest the natures of the simple bodies or elements,
and it matters little whether the body undergoing motion be
simple or composite when the motion itself is simple and manifests the simple nature that is its principle.[17]

Yet it is a fact that some composite bodies have simple
natural motions, while others have composite natural motions—

[16] Cap. 10, M 14vb, U 141vb: Non est eciam aliquis locus medius, vel ut ita
dicam mixtus, preter hec quatuor loca quatuor corporum primorum. Unde necessarium est omne corpus recti motus ferri ad aliquem istorum quatuor secundum
predominans, et si fuerit aliquis locus proprius alicui mixto secundum habitudinem
ad aliquam partem celi vel orizontis, hic erit pars alicuius istorum primorum locorum
et presupposita natura ipsius.

[17] Cap. 11, M 15ra, U 142ra.

and this even when living things are excluded and one treats only of objects that move precisely as light or heavy. This leads Theodoric to a significant question: " Why do certain composite bodies move naturally with a simple motion, and certain others with a composite motion? " [18] The answer he proposes, while hardly consonant with modern scientific thought on the subjects he treats, provides an insight into the way in which the medievals explained such divergent motions as those of currents, magnets, tides, and heavenly bodies, and may be suggestive of analogous approaches available to the natural philosopher of the twentieth century for evaluating modern theories dealing with these same topics.

COMPOSITE MOTIONS

In summary form, the general answer that Theodoric gives to this question, which he then goes on to elaborate through twelve chapters of the opusculum, is contained in the following statement:

It should be noted that there are many differences among bodies that are moved by nature either with composite or simple motions. Some are moved as parts of wholes, without being separate from such wholes. Others are moved somewhat as wholes themselves, and this in a twofold way, for some are moved by an intrinsic natural principle, while others are moved by an extrinsic principle, as will become apparent when we consider them singly.[19]

To illustrate the meaning of this observation, we may note that for Theodoric the natural motions of fluids, such as those comprising the atmosphere and the hydrosphere, are generally composite motions. Some of these are composite in the sense that they are motions of the parts of a fluid medium; the movement of such a part he resolves into two interacting

---

[18] Cap. 12, M 15ra, U 142ra-b.

[19] *Ibid.*: Est sciendum quod corporum que moventur motu composito seu simplici per naturam multiplex est differencia. Quedam enim moventur ut partes in toto, non tamen separate a toto, quedam autem ut tota quedam, et hoc dupliciter, quia quedam moventur ab intrinseco principio naturali, quedam ab extrinseco, ut de singulis patebit.

components, one impressed on it by adjoining parts, another arising intrinsically within the part itself. Other composite motions are those of clouds, vapors and winds, when these are considered as integral wholes apart from any internal movements that might characterize their parts; such motions he analyzes as deriving partly from the intrinsic elements of which such wholes are composed, and partly from the forces that generate them, which he sees as endowing them with added dispositions to fulfill special purposes intended by nature. Still other motions, such as those of rivers and whirlwinds, are composite because of the reaction of the fluid with its boundaries or because of the interaction that results when two natural motions converge from different directions. In practically all of these cases, as we shall see, the natural motion which is attributed by Theodoric to the elemental constituents of the fluid is a simple, straight-line motion towards the center of gravity, while the component that makes the total motion composite derives from an outside source and does not come directly from the fluid's intrinsic components.

The case of the complex movement of parts of a fluid medium is not particularly noteworthy, except for the fact that Theodoric there uses notions associated with Averroes' solution to the projectile problem,[20] which may be indicative of his own ideas concerning impetus. Theodoric does not commit himself to any particular theory of impetus—in fact he explicitly refrains from discussing this matter [21]—but he does speak of the influence of the parts of a fluid on each other by which they continue to be in motion after the source of their initial disturbance has ceased.[22] Since the cases of fluid and projectile

[20] Cf. *Commentarium in VIII Physicorum* (ed. Venetiis, 1550), Tom. IV, 195va-196ra.

[21] For the Latin text, see Maier, *Studien* V, p. 290, fn. 1.

[22] Cap. 13, M 15rb, U 142rb: Tale enim corpus, cum receperit motum in aliqua suarum parcium, huiusmodi pars movet aliam vel alias, et sic deinceps, quod absque aliquali subinteraccione parcium ad partes fieri non potest, propter talium corporum spiritualitatem, ut dicit Commentator super octavum *Physicorum*. Partes autem sic mote et propulse, alias secum trahunt propter continuitatem. Cum autem per talem mocionem partes sursum vel alias extra locum suum actu fuerint, quasi per

motion are quite dissimilar, at least in the sense that the first is that of a continuous medium in direct contact with its disturbing force, while the second is that of an object obviously separated from its mover, one should not make too much of this argument, but there does seem to be a suggestion here of some motive power being communicated to parts of the fluid and thus accounting for its continued motion.

In discussing the motions of fluids considered as wholes, such as winds, clouds, mists, rain, etc., Theodoric develops this notion further. He considers these as " incomplete entities not yet separated from their generator," and maintains that they have some motive principle, apart from the intrinsic gravitational principle associated with their elemental constituents, by which they fulfill a particular end intended by nature.[23] The gravitational principle, he notes, is analogous to the intrinsic principle that might be induced into a body by the action of an altering agent, and here he gives the interesting example of a magnet's action on iron, which he observes causes the iron " to tend towards it in a straight line wherever it might be, whether through air, water, or a metallic container." [24]

violentam alterius partis impulsionem vel attractionem, motu suo naturali redeunt rursum ad locum suum proprium et ipse tales partes et impellentes. Et sic per talem impulsionem, tractionem parcium, subinteraccionem, fit quedam inundacio talis corporis humidi in suis partibus. Quo fit eciam ut non statim cesset huiusmodi motus ad cessacionem primi moventis primam partem, quia sicut dictum est huiusmodi motus componitur ex naturali et violento, qui ex disposicione sibi, ex mutua disposicione seu alteracione vel influencia indita, sepius super seinvicem replicantur, cum in huiusmodi naturalis motus sequatur violentum, et violentus causetur a naturali.

[23] Cap. 15, M 15rb, U 142rb.

[24] Cap. 16, M 15va, U 142va-b: Et huiusmodi motus per naturam non solum competit rebus que moventur ad aliquem naturalium locorum mundi secundum determinatam habitudinem ad centrum et circumferenciam mundi, et hoc secundum aliquod principium inexistens per mocionem generantis, sed eciam sic moventur secundum naturam principii inexistentis per approximacionem alicuius corporis alterantis seu aliquo modo afficientis ea. Cuiusmodi est motus ferri ad magnetem, quod non impeditum, secundum lineam rectam tendit ad ipsum ubicumque fuerit, sive per aerem, sive per aquam, sive per vasa metallina, ut patet ad sensum. Sic patet de quibusdam compositis qua racione moventur per naturam motu recto, quia scilicet moventur per principium intrinsecum.

Unfortunately he does not discuss the character of the extrinsic principle in this context. However, when attempting later to account for the fact that mists arise naturally from ponds and move in determined directions, he explains that the generating agent " continually induces some natural disposition into such bodies," which is not gravity but " which presupposes and requires this qualitative principle," and is similarly related to a determinate place.[25] Such an added disposition, he observes, is the means by which "universal nature " provides for the needs of the various parts of the universe, as for example by moving rain clouds to particular areas where water is needed.[26] The added disposition he also calls a " generative principle," and notes that its action is not a violent one, even though attraction and propulsion characterize its operation. He would prefer to speak of the propulsion as arising from " whatever induces the form or disposition which is the principle of the motion," and to understand the attraction as being merely in the order of final causality.[27]

Thus Theodoric analyzes certain composite motions found

---

[25] Cap. 17, M 15va, U 142vb: Sed si sunt alia aliqua corpora huius inferioris mundi que moveantur per naturam motu tortuoso vel composito vel circulari, huiusmodi eciam movebuntur ab exteriori principio, et hoc sive a generante, inquantum videlicet talibus corporibus continue influit aliquam disposicionem naturalem qua acquiratur eis continue locus post locum, non semper secundum habitudinem recte distancie que attenditur inter centrum et circumferenciam secundum lineam rectam. Talis enim motus principium est generans, secundum quod ingenerat corporibus has simplices et absolutas qualitates que sunt gravitas et levitas. Predictis autem corporibus aliquando acquiritur locus continue secundum habitudinem ad aliquam partem orizontis, ut si surgat aliquis vapor in parte australi et per naturam tendat versus septentrionem. Hoc autem fit secundum aliquam aliam disposicionem huiusmodi corporibus inditam, que nec est gravitas neque levitas. Presupponit tamen et preexigit hoc qualitativum principium, sic inditum per naturam, gravitatem et levitatem in corpore in quo est, sicut et locus in quo vel ad quem moventur huiusmodi corpora est pars alicuius locorum gravium et levium.

[26] Cap. 18, M 15va, U 142vb-143ra.

[27] Cap. 19, M 15va, U 143ra: Huic motui corporum que moventur per principium generativum commune assimilatur motus et nutrimenti per corpus. . . . Intelligenda est pulsio et tractio modo predicto proporcionaliter, sicut in predictis corporibus partibus mundi, ut scilicet dicatur pellens eo quod dat formam vel disposicionem que est principium motus, trahens autem intelligatur secundum racionem et intencionem finis. . . .

in nature and attributes their composite aspect to two component principles, one being the gravity or levity of the predominant elements of which the bodies are composed, accounting for the straight-line component of their motion to or from some center of gravity, the other being a natural form added to the gravitational principle by a generating force, and accounting for the non-linear component of their motion. This suggestion is pregnant with consequences if it could be understood as applying to the case of the heavenly bodies, and the question naturally arises if Theodoric, writing at the latest in the first decade of the fourteenth century, could have anticipated this seventeenth-century development of celestial mechanics.

The answer is to be found in another unedited opusculum of Theodoric entitled *De intelligenciis et motoribus celorum.*[28] Here he introduces the notion of composite motions once again, and precisely in the context where one might expect him to do so, namely, in connection with the astronomical theories of eccentrics and epicycles. Theodoric specifically rejects Averroes' adherence to the literal text of Aristotle, maintaining that Aristotle need not be understood as meaning that heavenly bodies must revolve in circular orbits *exactly* concentric with the midpoint of the universe, as Averroes interprets him, and suggesting that " perhaps he [Aristotle] wished ' center ' to be understood more generally, for the natural center of any natural circle whatsoever," as opposed to the center of the world.[29] His reason for urging a different interpretation of the Aristotelian text is based on " the efficacy of the demonstrations " in Ptolemy's *Almagest*; here, as in other places, Theodoric is more convinced by the observational evidence " of the astrologers " than he is by the authority of Aristotle.[30] Granting the

---

[28] This opusculum was probably written in the first decade of the fourteenth century. There are two manuscript copies extant: Cod. Vat. Lat. 2183, henceforth referred to as U; and Cod. Vindobon. (Dominikanerkloster) 138/108. Where readings of the Latin text are given below, they are based on U.

[29] Cap. 11, U 58va: Fortassis generalius voluit intelligi medium, videlicet, quodcumque medium naturale cuiuscumque circuli naturalis. . . .

[30] Capp. 11 et 14; *De elementis,* cap. 9—cf. *Scientific Methodology,* p. 126.

mathematical explanation of eccentrics and epicycles, however, he is still at a loss for a physical explanation as to why this peculiar motion of the heavenly bodies occurs, and in seeking such an explanation has recourse to his concept of " composite motion."

In this treatment, as in *De elementis*, there is again a lack of quantitative analysis. Theodoric's argument is in fact very brief, and merely suggestive of an analogy that might obtain between straight-line motions and circular ones when both are considered as natural motions. He first notes that there is a certain relativity to be found in linear gravitational motions, when the principles of such motions are considered precisely as related to the surrounding environment.[31] If extrinsic factors introduce a type of composition into motions that should be simple when explained in terms of their intrinsic principles alone, he sees no reason why a similar type of composition might not also be found in circular motions:

If this is the case in such straight-line motions, as has been said, it is not extraordinary or incomprehensible to interpret the Philosopher's [Aristotle's] treatment of circular motion, when he speaks of it as rotating about a center, as not to mean the exact center of the universe, but the natural center of any natural circle in which there is something having the nature of a terminus, as for example the mid-point of the revolution, insofar as a revolution includes in its very notion movement to a point and away from a point, both being understood with reference to the center of the circle. . . . If therefore different relations to various termini can introduce composition into straight-line motions, so also different centers can

---

[31] Cap. 16, U 59ra-b: Quia in talibus transformacionibus que sunt recti motus attenditur *tercio* aliquis terminus—nichil enim tali motu incipit moveri secundum naturam quod non potest pervenire ad terminum secundum naturam intentum— hinc est quod in talibus motis secundum diversitatem talium terminorum invenitur nonnulla distraccio et aliquis recessus a pura et omnimoda simplicitate, ne talia corpora, quamvis habeantur per simplicibus, ad eosdem terminos vel secundum eosdem moveantur. Videmus enim alium esse terminum ad quem naturaliter movetur ignis in regione sua, quia ad superficiem infimam spere lune, alium autem terminum perpendimus ad quem movetur aer in spera sua, qui si esset in spera ignis ab ea recedet naturaliter. Et ita videmus diversitatem terminorum in aqua et in terra quoad proprias secundum naturam regiones eorum.

introduce plurality and composition into circular motions, and these too can be composed of many circular motions, of which each is itself simple and one.[32]

The composition which Theodoric here attempts to explain in terms of physical or natural causes is thus not the composition that would result from a straight-line gravitational tendency to a center to which had been added a principle of tangential motion, as this was to be proposed by Newton in the seventeenth century, but rather a composition of rotary motions consistent with the geometrical picture of the universe already sketched by Ptolemy. What is interesting about Theodoric's view, however, is his willingness to account for the deviations from perfect circularity detected by astronomers of his time in planetary, lunar and solar motions, by allowing for the possibility of different centers of gravity within the universe, and this while viewing these centers not merely mathematically, but also as terms of proper natural motions from intrinsic principles. This represents a very definite break with the Averroist-Aristotelian tradition, and at the same time provides the basis for accomodating Aristotelian thought to a plurality of gravitational centers, in the sense of universal gravitation as it was ultimately to be understood by Newton.

Another interesting development of Theodoric's thought regarding composite motions is his attempt to explain the complex motion of the tides in terms of natural principles. This

[32] Cap. 17, U 59rb-va: Si inquam sic se habet in istis motibus rectis, ut dictum est, quid mirabile vel inconveniens si sic vult intelligi Philosophus illud quod tractat de motu circulari, dicens ipsum fieri circa medium, non sumendo medium omnino pro centro universi, sed pro quocumque naturali medio cuiuscumque circuli naturalis in quo invenitur eciam aliquis habens naturam termini, puta medium centrum circa quod volvitur, que circumvolucio includit in se et importat naturam motus ad terminum et a termino, quod utrumque intelligitur in respectum ad centrum talis circuli. Moveri enim circa centrum est moveri quodammodo ab ipso et ad ipsum; unde habet naturam et racionem termini motus. Si igitur habitudo diversa ad diversos terminos motus rectos, ut visum est, sic eciam quoad motum circularem secundum diversa media centralia, quorum quodlibet habet naturam et racionem termini, potest plurificari et componi motus, ut sit motus compositus ex pluribus circularibus motibus quorum quilibet in se simplex et unus est. . . .

he undertakes to do in the opusculum *De elementis*, where he works out an explanation that is rather ingenious, even though quite implausible from the viewpoint of modern science. The motion of the tides, for Theodoric, is yet another case where "universal nature" provides for the needs of the universe by a composite motion, and this by inducing a motive principle that comes "effectively" from the heavenly bodies (particularly the moon), and "passively" from sea water as being naturally adapted to receive this influx.[33] The mode of transmission of the force deriving from the heavenly bodies is based on an interpretation of Proclus,[34] whereby Theodoric conceives of some generic influence, originating with the separated substances, as being more and more determined and composed as it works down through the heavenly spheres, finally receiving its ultimate determination from the moon.[35] Theodoric does not regard this influence as an attraction which exerts a pull on the sea, but rather conceives it as somehow effecting an alteration within the sea water, which makes it expand and thus extend its boundaries on land, thereby accounting for the rise (and fall) of the tides.

Interestingly enough, Theodoric proposes a mechanistic type of explanation for this motion which is not without empirical foundation. As far as he can discern, tidal motions are restricted to bodies of sea water, and are not found in fresh water.[36] Thus he proposes that sea water can be regarded as

[33] Cap. 22, M 15vb, U 143ra-b.

[34] Cap. 23, M 16ra, U 143rb-va: Sicut dicit Proclus, 135 proposicione et 136 proposicione, dicit quod omnes illarum substanciarum separatarum potencie desursum inchoantes, et per proprias medietates procedentes usque ad extrema, perveniunt et ad loca circa terram. . . . Sicut dicit Proclus 54 proposicione, sic: omne quod a secundis producitur, et a prioribus et a causalibus producitur eminencius.—The references are to the *Elementatio theologica*. Cf. *Proclus, The Elements of Theology*, A Revised Text with Translation, Introduction and Commentary, by E. R. Dodds (Oxford: Univ. Press, 1933), Props. 135-6, pp. 120-121, and Prop. 56 (cited as Prop. 54 by Theodoric), pp. 54-55.

[35] Cap. 23, M 16ra, U 143rb.

[36] Cap. 24, M 16va, U 144ra: Sufficiant illa que dicta sunt nonnulla racione, cui racioni concordat hoc quod videmus in aquis dulcibus, sive sint fluentes sive sint stagna, scilicet, quod non videmus ibi notabiliter eas vaporare et moveri extra

a mixture of salt and fresh water, which is not strictly a new chemical compound, and whose components can therefore be separated " by the application of some force." [37] He conceives the action of the moon as being such a force, which effectively is able to " vaporize " the fresh (or " sweet ") component of sea water, thereby causing the whole body of the sea to expand and overflow its banks " as the moon approaches the meridian." [38] Thus there are two natural causes of this com-

consuetum modum suum, quia non est facilis separacio parcium talium aquarum, sicut dictum est de aquis que sunt in mari.

[37] *Ibid.*, M 16rb, U 143vb: Quando humida aliqua adinvicem confunduntur, et fuerint substancie diversarum naturarum, et fuerit unum eorum subtilius altero et passibilius et facilius obediens agenti, faciliter abinvicem separantur, maxime si fuerint valde distantis nature, vel si fuerit unum eorum in alio sic virtute, ut possit ex eo faciliter generari. Et sic se habent aqua et vinum, que ex hoc aliqua arte separantur. Sicut autem dictum est de aqua et vino, sic se habet et in aliis talibus, puta in aqua salsa et dulci. Dico autem aquam salsam cuius substancia est sal, ut putei salis. Et talis est aqua maris in sui substancia, et propter hoc coquitur sal ex eo. Constat autem quod substancia dulcis aque et aqua maris sunt valde diverse, et distantis nature in subtilitate et grossitudine multum differentes. Et propter hoc, permixta, possunt aliqua vi abinvicem separari. Manifestum est autem quod dulces aque pluvium permiscentur mari; omnia enim flumina intrant in mare, et multi et maximi imbres et pluvie cadunt in ipsum. Si ergo sicut experimento probatur, ars aliqua potest separare vinum ab aqua vel aliquid huiusmodi simile facere, multo forcius natura potuit facere et fecit, determinans ad simile faciendum unum naturale instrumentum, confluentibus ad hoc, ut premissum est, aliis causis superioribus. ' Confluentibus ' inquam, quasi in unam virtutem et naturalem potenciam faciendi hoc, cuius effectus apparet in motu solius lune.—For Theodoric's teaching that this kind of mixture does not make a strict (chemical) compound, see *De miscibilibus in mixto*, cap. 9 (ed. Wallace, *Scientific Methodology*), p. 339.

[38] *Ibid.*, M 16rb-va, U 143vb-144ra: Fit per istum modum, videlicet, quod partibus dulcis aque sparsis per mare, luna, immo totum celum quasi mediante luna tamquam per maxime determinatam causam secundum predicta, facit sua virtute dictas dulcis aque partes vaporare, secundum Tholomeum, ex supra inducta auctoritate, et resolvi in fumum humide substancie. Hic enim accipiatur hoc modo esse vapor, videlicet, fumus humide substancie, quem oportet extendi quantitative intra corpus maris ad omnem dyametrum, et sic incomparabiliter ultra corpus ex quo vaporat quantitative, id est dimensionaliter, ingrossari. Luna autem appropinquante ad meridianum, in quo magis viget natura et virtus operacionis sue, huiusmodi partes dulcis aque vaporant, et sua vaporacione extendunt substanciam maris cui permixte sunt, et mare sic extensum fluit quasi extra sinum suum et versus vacuitatem litoris. Et recedente luna a meridiano circulo a loco ad quem fluxerat, mare refluit, et mare sequitur lunam recedentem et euntem versus litus continuum. ' Sequitur ' inquam, non secundam eamdem partem sui qua iam fluxerat, sed

posite motion, one being the moon as efficient cause, the other
being the passive nature of sea water, which is capable of
receiving the moon's influence because of its peculiar material
composition.

EXTRINSIC MOVERS

Having thus accounted for several composite natural motions,
Theodoric turns to a question which was much agitated by
medieval scientists, and whose resolution gradually prepared
the way for the new mechanics that was to arise with Galileo
and Newton. This was the problem of identifying the extrinsic
mover that is responsible for falling motion, i. e., gravitational
movement to a center. Theodoric has referred previously to a
" generative principle " as accounting for the composite character of some natural motions; this resembles the traditional
Aristotelian doctrine that the generator is the *per se* cause of
simple natural motions, and thus the question arises whether
Theodoric also regards the generator as being the effective
principle that moves a body falling in straight-line gravitational
motion. Theodoric's answer to this question is negative. While
developed in the context of Aristotle's natural philosophy, his
solution is again representative of a transitional type of reasoning that in some ways anticipates the development of
sixteenth-century mechanics, and on this account, at least, is
worthy of note.[39]

Theodoric's line of argumentation is directed principally
against those who interpret Aristotle to mean that gravitating
bodies are moved by the generator in the sense that they have
their form and species from the generator, and just as they
have these, so " they have all the natural accidents which
follow from the species, one of which is natural motion with
respect to place." [40] Such was not an uncommon interpretation

secundum aliam sui partem que in loco continuo ad presenciam lune vaporat et
extenditur et fluit, sicut dictum est. . . .

[39] See Maier, " Das Problem der Gravitation," *Studien* III, pp. 143-254.

[40] Cap. 28, M 16vb-17ra, T 184r, U 144va: Dicunt autem quidam quod gravia et
levia et universaliter ea que moventur localiter per naturam in hoc inferiori mundo

of Aristotle in Theodoric's time, being in fact proposed by various of his contemporaries, including Siger of Brabant, Godfrey of Fontaines, John Peter Olivi and Duns Scotus.[41] But our German Dominican does not regard this explanation as consistent with the remainder of Aristotelian doctrine, and gives seven arguments why it should be rejected.

The first is drawn from the processive motion of animals, to which Theodoric would apply a similar analysis to the one here invoked for the local motion of heavy objects, insofar as it too derives from a natural form. This would result in an animal's locomotion being caused by its generator (i. e., its parent), which Theodoric calls " absurd." [42] The second argument is drawn from a similar application to the heavenly bodies: Theodoric merely points out that all metaphysicians agree that the latter are moved by another, but no one claims that they are moved by their generator.[43] His third argument is for those who are dissatisfied with the argument from animal locomotion, and is concerned with the motion of the heart and arteries: these are clearly vital motions, and as such must come from within—therefore they cannot proceed from the generator.[44]

Should one reply to these arguments, moreover, that they concern living things whose motions proceed from an active intrinsic principle, while falling bodies (as such) are non-living and only have a passive principle of motion within them, Theodoric will concede the objection. But then his fourth argu-

moventur a generante, eo quod habent formam que est principium motus a generante, a quo sicut habent huiusmodi formam et speciem, sic habent omnia naturalia accidencia que consequuntur speciem, quorum unum est naturalis motus secundum locum. . . .

[41] For details, see Maier, *Studien* III, pp. 158-164. This was also the teaching of St. Thomas Aquinas (*In II Phys.*, lect. 1, n. 4; *In III De caelo*, lect. 7, nn. 8-9; *In V Metaph.*, lect. 14, n. 955), but there are subtleties in Thomas' exposition that have been commonly overlooked by historians. For a clear presentation of the original Thomistic doctrine and its relation to Arab and late scholastic thought, see James A. Weisheipl, O. P., *Nature and Gravitation*, (River Forest, 1955), pp. 19-32.

[42] Cap. 29, M 17ra, T 184r, U 144vb.

[43] Cap. 30, M 17ra, T 184r, U 144vb.

[44] Cap. 31, M 17ra, T 184r, U 144vb-145ra.

ment is based on the very passivity of gravitating bodies. By the terms of the objection, every passion must be accompanied by a simultaneous action, and thus, if the generator is the moving agent, it must actually accompany falling bodies " with a continual influx of motion," and this " we do not see." [45] A fifth argument he draws from mathematics. A generator causes a triangle, and thus according to the explanation under discussion, causes all the natural accidents which flow from its quiddity, including that its angles equal two right angles; but it is " absurd " to say that the triangle in itself does not have this property, and gets it continually from the generator.[46]

The sixth argument depends on the supposition that fire, or any other element, might be eternal, and on this supposition would not have a generator. Theodoric maintains that naturally " it still would be moved up," without the action of the non-existent generator.[47] His seventh argument, finally, he draws from the nature of motion itself, which is an imperfect act and as such requires an " actual mover producing the influx of motion." Therefore, if the generator is the mover, " it must actually coexist with and touch the object in motion, which is contrary to what is apparent to the senses." [48]

Having thus disposed of a prevalent interpretation of Aristotle, Theodoric turns to his own explanation of what the Stagyrite means when he says that falling bodies " are moved by the generator as by their principal and essential mover, and by whatever removes an impediment as by their accidental mover." The interpretation he proposes is based on distinctions between substantial and accidental being already developed in opuscula other than those now under examination. This doctrine is exposed elsewhere; [49] here I merely report the distinctions among accidents that are enumerated in *De elementis* as relevant to the problem of gravitation.

---

[45] Cap. 32, M 17rb, T 184v, U 145ra-b.
[46] Cap. 33, M 17rb, T 184v, U 145rb.
[47] Cap. 34, M 17rb-va, T 184v, U 145rb.
[48] Cap. 35, M 17va, T 184v, U 145rb.
[49] See my *Scientific Methodology*, pp. 26-32, 80-91, 152-161.

There are some accidents, notes Theodoric, which are purely accidental in the sense that they have no *per se* order to any causal principle found in the subject by reason of its species, nor to the *per se* cause of the subject (i. e., its generator), but can be present or not without affecting the nature of the subject. For example, heat or cold in a stone are purely accidental in this way.[50] Other accidents are naturally in the subject according to its species, either always or for a certain time, and have a *per se* order to some causal principle in the subject. This group of accidents is further divisible into two types. Some are naturally produced by the subject itself, and are found only in things which have a natural diversity of parts. The organs of living animals are an example of this type.[51] Another type is that of accidents produced by some causal principle not itself found in the subject, but which produces the subject (e. g., the generator). These accidents are found *per se* and naturally in homogeneous things, of which an example is wetness in water. Since they cannot come from any intrinsic principle, but must come from an extrinsic one, and this cannot be the end, they must be produced by the efficient agent of the subject, which is the generator.[52] The *per se* accidents of which Theodoric is here speaking come " under the essential order of the generator," and are produced by the same action which terminates in the substance or nature of the subject, so that they do not need any other essential mover

[50] Cap. 36, M 17va, T 184v, U 145va.

[51] Cap. 37, M 17va, T 184v, U 145va.

[52] Cap. 38, M 17vb, T 184v-185r, U 145va-b: Alia vero accidencia secundum naturam que reducuntur ad aliquod principium causale, non quidem repertum in subiecto, sed quod est ipsius subiecti causa factiva, puta generans. Et ista sunt omnia ea accidencia que secundum naturam et per se insunt rebus homogeneis, ut sunt humidum et frigidum virtuale in aqua, frigidum et siccum virtuale in terra, grave et leve, et similia. Hec igitur, quia insunt per naturam et sunt per se accidencia, necesse est ea reduci tamquam in causam aliquid eorum que sunt subiecti per se et secundum naturam. Nec hoc potest esse aliquid intrinsecum, secundum predictam racionem. Igitur oportet quod principium eorum sit aliquid extrinsecum, quod sit per se causa subiecti. Finis autem non est principium factivum alicuius rei, sed movet per intentionem solum. Relinquitur ergo efficiens sive generans esse talium encium factivum principium.

to educe them from potency to act, as would be the case if they were produced through alteration.[53]

In this division, then, the first group of accidents are such that, when not present in the subject, the subject is simply in potency to them. This means for Theodoric that even when all impediments are removed, they are still not actually present in the subject, but require an extrinsic agent to educe them from potency to act, and this agent further presupposes a subject already existing with this potency.[54] The second class of accidents, found in the organic world, also presupposes a subject already constituted in a determined species. Since, however, they come to be from some causal principle within the subject itself, they likewise are not made actually present by the generator, although their principle is from the generator.[55] As to the third class—which is of main interest here insofar as it includes gravity and levity—it is manifest that their subjects are not simply in potency to them, although it might happen that the subject be accidentally in potency to them should they be blocked by an impediment, if the accident be of such type that it could be impeded. But in any case they do not require an essential mover to educe them from potency to act. They are already generated with the species, and their essential mover was the generator while actually generating.[56]

[53] Cap. 39, M 17vb, T 185r, U 145vb.
[54] Cap. 40, M 18ra, T 185r, U 146ra.
[55] Ibid.
[56] Cap. 41, M 18ra, T 185r-v, U 146ra-b: Ea autem que sunt tercii generis, secundum es que predicta sunt de hoc genere, manifestum est quod res habens suam completam speciem non est in potencia simpliciter et per se ad aliquam talium disposicionem, sed forte erit in potencia secundum accidens, scilicet propter impedimentum, si fuerit talis disposicio cui possit accidere impedimentum. . . . Hinc est quod gravia et levia habencia suam speciem non moventur nisi a motore accidentali qui est removens prohibens, et non a generante, si vere et proprie loquamur de huiusmodi motis et motuum eorum principiis. Sed tunc solummodo et vere moventur a generante ad huiusmodi naturalia accidencia, cum per mocionem generantis secundum substanciam exeunt de potencia ad actum sue forme substancialis. Actio enim generantis, ut predictum est, simul terminatur ad speciem rei et huiusmodi per se accidencia. . . .

This supplies Theodoric's basic answer to the difficulty presented by falling bodies. Heavy bodies already have their
gravity from their generator or essential mover. They do not
need the generator's action any further once they are generated;
all that they henceforth require is an accidental mover to
remove any impediments. Once such impediments are removed,
gravity is immediately and actually present, and the subject
is not in potency to it in any way, either accidentally or
essentially.[57]
This still leaves unanswered the question as to what is the
efficient principle of the motion which follows from gravity.
As Theodoric has just shown, this is not the generator, nor is it
the falling body, nor is it the " disposition " which the body
acquires, nor can it be a " natural consequent " of its specific
nature, nor can it be whatever removes the impediment to its
motion (i. e., its accidental mover), which merely functions
in a negative way.[58] Rather, in considering such an existential

[57] Cap. 42, M 18rb, T 185v, U 146rb: Ex predictis liquet quod ea que insunt a
generante, constante re ipsa secundum suam speciem et cessante omni impedimento,
postquam eciam res separata fuerit a generante, mox acquisita sunt rei et statim
insunt, ut ostendit Philosophus in quarto *Physicorum* de propriis locis gravium et
levium. Non enim iam manet res ipsa in potencia aliquo modo ad huiusmodi
disposiciones; quia non accidentali, eo quod non sit impedimentum, nec essenciali,
propter dictam racionem, scilicet, quia res habens suam speciem non est in potencia
essenciali ad aliquam talium naturalium disposicionum. Hinc est quod ea que
secundum dictum modum insunt, sunt forme vel nature habentes se per modum
habitus circa subiectum, quorum esse est totum simul et in indivisibili, quum in
instanti talia acquisita sunt rei, sive in termino generacionis, sive eciam post,
remoto impedimento. . . .
[58] Cap. 45, M 18vb, T 185v, U 146rb-147ra: Constante re secundum suam speciem,
et impedita per aliud ne possit esse in sua naturali disposicione, si removeatur
impedimentum, movere potest; quid sit per se agens et faciens rem esse in tali
disposicione? Generans enim non facit, eo quod res iam ponitur separata a generante.
Nec res ipsa seipsam agere potest ad huiusmodi disposicionem, secundum predicta.
Nec ipsa disposicio seipsam facit in esse, cum ipsa nondum sit, et non ens non
ducit seipsum ad esse. Nec potest inesse per naturam cuiusdam consequencie. . . .
Actus autem non complet potenciam secundum racionem consequendi, absque factivo
principio actu agente. . . . Nec sufficit dicere quod movens per accidens, id est,
removens prohibens, hoc faciat; non enim sufficit ad productionem seu factionem
rei non existentis solum removere impedimentum factionis, nisi sit aliquid actu
per se faciens.

thing as motion, itself an acquisition of being, Theodoric holds
that another factor must be taken into account, and this is the
dependence of things on a *principal* essential cause, not only
for their coming-to-be, but also for their continued being. In
his own words:

It must be understood that things able to be generated, considered
with respect to their acquisition of being, have a twofold relation
to the cause generating them: first, according to the conversion
of potency to substantial act, which has the formality of a coming-
to-be; secondly, according to the act acquired through the generator's causality, which is the formality under which it is already
constituted in being. In both these ways a thing comes under the
essential ordering of its generating cause. I wish ' generator ' to be
understood here as the *per se* and essential and principal cause of
the substance of the body, so as to exclude any instrumental cause
or other causes that may be accidental. I also understand ' essential
ordering ' to be that by which a thing depends essentially on its
cause, which not only holds for its coming-to-be . . . but also for
the perfection of its act once acquired. . . .⁵⁹

His thought here has a definite Neoplatonic flavor, although it
is not without some affinity to the Thomistic analysis of divine
causality, for Theodoric conceives the principal essential cause
as that which sustains and connects the whole natural order,
that on which natural things depend for " a certain continuation of their being through a continual influx " deriving from
it as an essential cause.⁶⁰ The influx of this cause is what

⁵⁹ Cap. 46, M 18vb, T 185v, U 147ra: Sed considerandum quod res generabiles,
quantum ad acquisicionem sui esse, dupliciter se habent ad causam dantem esse per
generacionem: uno modo, secundum exitum potencie ad actum substancialem, et
sic habet racionem eius quod est fieri; alio modo, respicit huiusmodi causam
secundum racionem actus acquisiti per talis cause causalitatem, et secundum hunc
modum res est in facto esse. Utroque autem istorum modorum, res stat sub ordine
essenciali cause generantis. Volo autem intelligi generans quod est per se et essen-
cialis et principalis causa substancie rei, ut excludatur causa instrumentalis, vel
eciam alie cause, si que sunt accidentales. Dico autem ordinem essencialem quo res
per suam essenciam dependet a sua causa, quod quidem non solum convenit rei
secundum suum fieri, scilicet, quantum ad accepcionem sui esse quoad exitum
potencie ad actum per mocionem generantis, sed eciam attenditur in causa huiusmodi
ordinis secundum perfectionem iam acquisiti actus. . . .

⁶⁰ *Ibid.*: Non est aliud quam quedam ipsius esse continuacio per continuum ipsius
cause influxum per essenciam. . . .

sustains every natural substance in being. It is also, for Theodoric, what gives it actuality during its transitional stage, or sustains its motion:

The influx of this cause is found not only when the thing has been constituted in being, but also in a certain way in its changing, for otherwise the influx would already have ceased, and if this were the only action of the universally first cause, then the being of the thing would not be restricted to a certain and determined period.[61]

Thus Theodoric's solution reduces simply to this, that the efficient principle of gravitational motion is the first principal cause in the order of nature, or, in other words, " the motion of which we are treating is reducible, as to its principal cause, to the essential cause of the substance of the body in motion." [62]

The singular merit of Theodoric's solution would appear to lie in the fact that he has simplified the search for the cause of gravitational motion by eliminating the generator altogether, as not being in the direct line of efficient causality effecting the motion. Thus he does not consider it correct to say that the generator is the cause of such motion by the form he puts in the falling body. This, for him, is to confuse the meta-physician's way of looking at the problem with that of the natural philosopher. From the point of view of the natural philosopher, the generator is the motive principle in the production of the body; once the body is produced, the only principle of its motion that need concern him is the accidental mover, which removes any impediments that might restrain an efficient causality deriving directly from the principal essential cause of the universe. He considers further that there is

---

[61] Cap. 46, T 185v: Huiusmodi igitur cause influxus non est solum in facto esse, sed eciam est in fieri quodammodo, alioquin iam olim cessasset influere, et si hec esset solum causa universaliter prima, tunc esse rei non clauderetur certa et determinata peryodo.—The manuscript versions all give different readings for this chapter, and none is clear and unambiguous. I give here only the reading as found in T, which is the briefest and most intelligible. The English above is not a literal translation, but conveys what I believe to be the sense of the passage, as far as this is discernible.

[62] Cap. 46, M 18rb, T 185v, U 147rb: Motus huiusmodi de quo agitur reducitur sicut in causam principalem in causam videlicet essencialem substancie rei mote.

"a twofold accidentality to be noted in such motions, both coming from whatever restrains or impedes bodies of this type; one is an [accidental] potency by which it 'happens' that they can be moved; the other by which it 'happens' that they are moved successively, for otherwise, once all impediments are removed, they would move instantly." [63] Unfortunately Theodoric does not elaborate this very interesting observation, but immediately adds the colophon and *explicit*, bringing his opusculum on the elements to rather an abrupt close.

As to the precise mechanics favored by Theodoric for explaining the quantitative aspects of gravitational motion, one can only adduce indirect evidence. Two views were current among his contemporaries, one deriving from Averroes, which would have the velocity of fall directly proportional to the motive force and inversely proportional to the resistance of the medium, the other deriving from Avempace and having the velocity proportional to the difference between the motive force and the resistance of the medium. [64] Theodoric seems to

[63] Cap. 47, M 18vb-19ra, T 185v, U 147rb: Sed ex hoc frustrum nititur quis rectificare errorem suum quo asserit huiusmodi moveri a generante eo modo qui improbatus est, scilicet, in habendo formam seu speciem a generante. Aliud est reducere aliquid in aliud sicut in causam essencialem, secundum consideracionem primi philosophi, qui considerat rerum essencias secundum racionem suarum quidditatum; aliud est querere de alicuius principio motivo, secundum quod physicus habet considerare. Unde aliquid potest reduci in causam propriam secundum quod primus philosophus considerat, quod non potest reduci in ipsam ita quod ipsa sit principium motivum. Et sic se habet in proposito quantum ad motus gravium et levium, ut patet ex prehabitis. Unde generans non est principium motivum nisi quando actu movet per generacionem rei. Est autem principium causale [tale U] eciam postquam generavit, sed removens prohibens est principium motus, attamen per accidens inquantum physicus considerat de motu, videlicet, inquantum motus. Et secundum istum modum cucurrit questio proposita de motibus gravium et levium, et negatur quod moveantur a generante. Sed est hic advertenda duplex accidentalitas in motibus istorum, et utraque est a prohibente seu impediente huiusmodi mobilia. Una est secundum potenciam ad motum qua accidit eis moveri, alia est qua accidit eis successive moveri; alias enim, remoto omni impedimento, mutarentur in instanti, ut predictum est. Hec igitur sufficiant de elementis inquantum sunt partes mundi; alibi enim de ipsis tractatum est inquantum sunt miscibilia et partes mixti. Explicit. . . .

[64] For details, see Maier, "Platonische Einflüsse in der scholastischen Mechanik?," *Studien* V, pp. 237-285.

favor the Averroistic explanation, as evidenced by this text where he explicitly rejects Avempace's solution:

It is obvious from what has been said that Avempace's position, which the Commentator [Averroes] treats in the context of the fourth book of the *Physics,* is false. This states that if all impediments be removed, taking away even corporeal media through which heavy and light bodies move, supposing imaginatively that the medium were void, that nonetheless heavy and light bodies would be moved by nature with a determinate velocity and slowness in time. According to the foregoing, however, this is only possible where the mover and the thing moved are actually distinct, and where the mover is also actually conjoined to the moved according to a determinate proportion between the power of the mover and the thing moved, as is the case with animals and heavenly bodies. This would also render false the demonstration of the Philosopher [Aristotle] in the fourth book of the *Physics,* where he shows that heavy and light bodies do not move in a void, as the Commentator sufficiently explains, nor need we delay over this.[65]

Theodoric's treatment of gravitational motion is consistently concerned with the natural or physical causes of such motion, and is devoid of quantitative or mathematical considerations. In this respect his methodology in mechanics is significantly different from that found in his optical studies, where experimental and mathematical techniques reached their highest development within the *hochscholastik* period. This difference was noted in my earlier study, where I assigned it to the obscurity of the principles available for explaining gravitational motion (and chemical change), forcing Theodoric to remain at the qualitative and dialectical level when treating these matters.[66] Yet the conclusion need not be drawn that Theodoric's opuscula were without value for the later development of the science of mechanics. Both Maier and Clagett have shown how the mid-fourteenth century opuscula of writers like Buridan began to change the ' climate of opinion,' and

---

[65] Cap. 44; Latin text given by Maier, *Studien* V, p. 246, fn. 14.
[66] *Scientific Methodology,* pp. 127, 246-247.

prepare the way for the seventeenth century development, by considering gravitational force and impetus less as the *cause* of mechanical motion and more as an *effect* of the motion itself.[67] Theodoric had not yet arrived at this conception, but he perhaps cleared the way for it by eliminating gravity (and its generator) entirely from the realm of *efficient* causality. In this endeavor, and particularly in his attempt to point out existing confusions between a physical and a metaphysical approach to such problems of mechanics, Theodoric had something distinctive to offer to early fourteenth century physics.

W. A. WALLACE, O. P.

Dominican House of Philosophy,
Dover, Massachusetts.

---

[67] *Studien* V, pp. 380-382; *Science of Mechanics*, pp. 548-678.

"MINING ALL WITHIN"

CLARKE'S NOTES TO ROHAULT'S *Traité de Physique*

ᴄ⅋ᴐ

SAMUEL CLARKE, the son of a prominent Norwich family, was just sixteen when in 1691 he entered Gonville and Caius College, Cambridge. A quarter of a century earlier Roger North had remarked on " a general inclination, especially of the brisk part of the university," [1] to follow the teaching of Descartes; in 1691 Clarke found Cartesian philosophy established and his own tutor, John Ellis, a " zealot " for it. [2]

One of the reasons for the Cartesian success had been the excellent textbook on physics published in 1671 by Jacques Rohault, a Cartesian whose ability as a teacher had been partly responsible for the vogue for science in the French capital. His *Traité de Physique* [3] had been quickly translated into Latin by Théophile Bonet, and an edition of this translation was published in London in 1682. Edition after edition of the *Traité* continued to appear in both French and Latin, [4]

[1] R. North, *Autobiography*, Univ. Lib. Cambridge, MS. Baker 37, fol. 163-163v. Cited in M. H. Curtis, *Oxford and Cambridge in Transition* (Oxford, 1959), p. 257.

[2] B. Hoadley in Samuel Clarke, *Works* (London, 1738), I, p. i.

[3] For accounts of Rohault's work and especially of the *Traité de Physique*, see P. Mouy, *Le Développement de la Physique Cartésienne* (Paris: Vrin, 1934), pp. 108-138, and R. Dugas, *La Mécanique au XVIIᵉ siècle* (Neuchâtel: Éditions du Griffon, 1954), pp. 252-263.

[4] Mouy's account of these editions (*op. cit.*, p. 137) has many errors. George Sarton's " The Study of Early Scientific Textbooks," *Isis* XXXVIII (1947-8), 137-148, is more satisfactory. A fuller list is as follows:

French editions, published in Paris: 1671 (1st ed.), 1672 (2nd ed.), 1676/5 (3rd ed. corrigée), 1676 (4th ed., reveüe & corrigée), 1682 (4th ed., tres-exactement reveüe & corrigée), 1683 (6th ed.), 1692 (6th ed., tres-exactement reveüe & corrigée), 1705, 1708 (12th ed.), 1723, 1730.

French editions published in Amsterdam: 1672, 1676.

Latin translation by Bonet: 1674, Geneva: 1682, London; 1682, Amsterdam, with notes of Le Grand; 1700, Amsterdam, with notes of Le Grand.

Latin translation by Clarke and with his notes: 1697 (1st version of notes),

217

but although still unrivalled, it was by Clarke's day becoming seriously out of date. Leaving aside Newton's optical papers (1672-6) and his epoch-making *Principia* (1687), several important works on Cartesian physics had appeared since 1671,[5] and the many observations and experiments carried out, especially by Fellows of the Royal Society, had led to numerous detailed improvement in knowledge. Another reason for dissatisfaction in Cambridge was the poor quality of Bonet's translation.

In Clarke, Ellis had a pupil of unusual gifts. Before coming to Cambridge he had shown promise of the linguistic ability that later in life led him to prepare editions of such different authors as Caesar and Homer; and at Cambridge he made his mark in natural philosophy by defending a Newtonian thesis in the Schools.[6] His insight into the forbidding *Principia* was shortly to impress no less a figure than William Whiston, who later succeeded Newton in his professorship. On meeting Clarke, Whiston " was greatly surprised that so young a man as Mr. Clarke then was, not much I think above twenty-two years of age, should know so much of those sublime discoveries which were then almost a secret to all, but a few particular

London; 1702 (2nd version), London; 1708 (2nd version, with notes of Le Grand), Amsterdam; 1710 (3rd version), London; 1713 (? 2nd version, with notes of Le Grand), Cologne; 1718 (3rd version), London; 1739, " 6th edition," Leiden.

English translation of John Clarke with 4th version of Samuel Clarke's notes: 1723, London; 1728/9, London; 1735, London.

The various versions of Clarke's notes are discussed below. The term ' edition ' is perhaps misleading in this connexion, for the successive versions are radically changed; and it is therefore not appropriate to speak of " the " notes by Clarke. Sarton's inability to obtain a copy of the 1697 edition prevented him from realizing this. One of the few writers to draw attention to the changes in Clarke's notes is F. Cajori, *Newton's Principia* (Berkeley: Univ. of California, 1934), p. 631.

[5] Including Malebranche, *La Recherche de la Vérité* (1st ed., 1674/5), Régis, *Système de Philosophie* (1st ed., 1690), Perrault, *Essais de Physique* (1st ed., 1680), Le Clerc, *Physica* (1st ed., 1695).

[6] Hoadley in Clarke, *Works*, I, p. i.

mathematicians." [7] Ellis accordingly suggested to Clarke that he should prepare a new Latin translation of the *Traité*.[8]

This invitation put Clarke in something of a dilemma: for on the one hand he knew, as Ellis did not, that Newton's *Principia* had not only made serious inroads into the Cartesian position, but had in practice developed a rival cosmology; yet, on the other hand, neither Newton's lectures nor his book had had much impact on the university, and an improved Cartesian textbook was an urgent necessity. If Whiston's memory for dates is accurate, Clarke's doubts must have persisted into 1697, the very year in which his translation appeared, for it was then that he introduced himself to Whiston in a Norwich coffee-house " to ask my opinion about the fitness of such a translation. I well remember the answer I made him, that ' since the youth of the university must have, at present, some System of Natural Philosophy for their studies and exercises; and since the true system of Sir Isaac Newton's was not yet made easy enough for the purpose, it is not improper, for their sakes, yet to translate and use the system of Rohault . . . but that as soon as Sir Isaac Newton's Philosophy came to be better known, that only ought to be taught, and the other dropped.' " [9] Newton stood in far greater need of an interpreter than Descartes; until one was forthcoming, Rohault must be taught.

In the Preface to his 1697 edition, Clarke explains his motives. The existing translation is faulty, and he gives examples of this. But in addition, he says, he is not a man to make an oracle of his author, and although critics have failed to discredit many of the things in the book, some parts have been overthrown by subsequent experiments and some have been emended by later writers. He has therefore supplied some short notes, in which he has tried to give " a full answer to such objections made against the author as seem not to

[7] W. Whiston, *Historical Memoirs of the Life of Dr. Samuel Clarke* (London, 1730), p. 6.

[8] *Ibid.*, p. 5.

[9] *Ibid.*, pp. 5-6.

have any just foundation, and a great many things in natural philosophy, which have been since found out by the pains and industry of later philosophers, are here selected from the best writers; and there are also several things added out of the observations of the ancient writers of natural philosophy and natural history, where they seem to explain and illustrate matters." [10]

Clarke was not the first to annotate Rohault's text; Antoine Le Grand had provided *animadversiones* to the edition of Bonet's translation published in Amsterdam in 1682. The Bonet-Le Grand version was published again in Amsterdam in 1700, and Le Grand's notes were later appended to Clarke's translation and notes when these were published in Amsterdam in 1708 and in Cologne in 1713. In total length the two sets of notes are much the same. But whereas those of Le Grand are individually of some length, most of Clarke's are slight, and he refers to a bewildering variety of earlier authors: to classical writers like Aristotle, Pliny, Seneca, Livy, Plutarch and Macrobius, to Cartesians such as Régis, Malebranche, Perrault and Le Clerc, and to accounts of experiments by the *Accademia del Cimento*, Hooke and Boyle, as well as to the writings of Newton himself.

Newton is first mentioned in a note to the passage where Rohault, following Descartes, concludes from the identity of matter and extension that a vacuum is not possible. Clarke notes that this is *controversa et plena dissensionis inter Philosophos,* and refers the reader to Régis, where he will see that the objections brought against Descartes are only slight. He then adds, almost as an afterthought: *sed lancem deprimit Clariss. Newtonus,* and gives a reference to the *Principia.*[11] There is another reference to the *Principia* in a note on the propagation of sounds.[12] In the notes to the chapter

---

[10] Where appropriate, English translations are cited from John Clarke's 1723 edition. Samuel Clarke made curiously few alterations in his Prefaces, even when the role played by the notes he is introducing clearly change.

[11] II, p. 187.

[12] II, p. 208.

on light Newton comes more into his own, for Clarke gives an account of his work on refraction and its implications for the construction of telescopes.[13] He also lists phenomena associated with prisms, and after mentioning the views of Descartes, Hooke and Barrow, continues: *His igitur omissis, propero ad Clariss. Newtoni Theoriam (nam hypothesim eam appellare fas non duco) qua superius memorata phaenomena, aliaque omnia luculentissime explicantur.* Clarke then shows how each of the phenomena can be explained by Newton, and concludes with a hint of better things to come: *Permulta alia omni luce dignissima de colorum natura et proprietatibus invenit Clariss. Newtonus, quae aliquando in lucem edere dignetur efflagitat orbis literarius.*[14]

In the cosmology of Part II, Newton is quoted for a more exact estimate of the shape of the earth [15] and for the relative density of the earth and moon [16]; and in a note on comets Newton's doctrine of their essential similarity to planets is shown to be consistent with their observed behavior.[17] Newton is not mentioned in the notes to Part III, on terrestrial phenomena, and Clarke at no time provided any notes to Part IV, on physiology and medicine.

The reader of Clarke's notes, then, would learn something of Newton's prismatic experiments and his doctrine of colors; but of his great cosmological synthesis, little more than his views on the nature of comets. Newtonian attraction is not so much as mentioned. The Cartesian *plenum*, the three elements, Rohault's condemnation of attraction, all are allowed to pass without comment. It is true that the notes on the prism and on comets are the longest of all, but the other notes of substance are usually confined to discussions of the views of Cartesian commentators. Clarke gives the views on solidity of Descartes, Malebranche and Perrault,[18] the laws of Régis on elastic impact,[19] the views of Régis, Perrault, Malebranche and Le Clerc on rest,[20] Perrault's explanation of the direction of free fall,[21]

[13] II, pp. 212-3.
[14] II, pp. 214-9.
[15] II, p. 225.
[16] II, p. 227.
[17] II, pp. 227-30.
[18] II, pp. 198-200.
[19] II, pp. 191-3.
[20] II, pp. 189-90.
[21] II, pp. 231-2.

and so on. There is no suggestion of a systematic refutation of the text and argument in favor of Newtonian philosophy, although historians who have confused the 1697 notes with those of later editions have often supposed Clarke to offer just this.[22] In fact, the notes are tucked away at the back of the book, and are referred to on the title page and in the Preface by the diminutive *annotatiunculae*. They represent the tentative first steps of a newly-fledged graduate.

By 1702, when a second edition was required, Clarke's intentions had undergone a major change. His notes are now enlarged to about a fifth of the length of Rohault's text and are dignified with the title *annotata*. Some of the improvements are credited to Whiston and to another Clare physicist, Richard Laughton; others indicate Clarke's own interests, as when he tells us of some of his experiments[23]; but it is the name of Newton that appears on the title pages[24] as the chief source of the notes. This promise of a more hostile attitude towards the Rohault text is soon confirmed by the notes themselves. Thus, when Rohault suggests that the essence of matter consists in extension, Clarke retorts that a similar argument would make its essence consist in existence, and that it in fact consists in impenetrability.[25] Of the identification of matter and space he now declares roundly, *Hoc quidem falsum est*,[26] and he dismisses the supposed equal quantities of matter in a vessel of lead and a vessel of wax with *omnino hoc falsum*.[27]

On the more constructive side, Clarke now feels at liberty

---

[22] Hoadley, who clearly lacks Whiston's personal knowledge of these events, is perhaps the first to fall into this error. " His aim was much higher than the making of a better translation of it. He resolved to add to it such notes, as might lead the young men insensibly, and by degrees, to other and truer notions " (Clarke, *Works*, I, p. ii). At the other extreme, R. Dugas and P. Costabel date the Newtonian notes from the 1723 English edition (*Histoire Générale des Sciences*, ed. R. Taton [Paris, 1957-], II, p. 465).

[23] " I have tried it with quicksilver . . .," notes p. 13; " I have oftentimes ordered the glass . . .," notes p. 55.

[24] Plural, because the 1702 edition (like the 1710 and perhaps others) was reissued with a new title page. Newton's name occurs on both.

[25] Notes, p. 2.   [26] Notes, p. 3.   [27] Notes, p. 4.

to introduce longer notes, notably of Boyle's hydrostatical paradoxes and his experiments on taste, smells and so on.[28] And, most important of all, he provides a brief but uncompromising exposition of Newtonian gravitation, in his views of the cause of which he was further from the Cartesian position than Newton at times seemed to be.[29] In Part I he remarks in passing that " it is now allowed, that gravity does not depend upon the air or aether, but is an original connate and immutable affection of all matter," [30] and he develops the theory in a series of three notes near the end of Part II. The Cartesian account of gravity is now dismissed as " a very ingenious hypothesis," and it is Newton who has " established the true system of the world beyond all controversy." [31] His admiration is expressed in the highest terms: Newton " in his wonderful book of the *Mathematical Principles of Natural Philosophy* has explained the true system of the world, and shown the true and adequate causes of all the celestial motions almost beyond the genius of a man." [32]

Clarke explains that, according to Newton, gravity is associated with every pair of particles, wherever they are, whatever the bodies in question, and whatever the time; it is proportional to the quantities of matter, and inversely proportional to the square of the distances. This being so, it follows (he says) that gravity is an ultimate fact: " gravity of the weight of bodies is not any accidental effect of motion or of any very subtle matter, but an original and general law of all matter impressed on it by God, and maintained in it perpetually by some efficient power, which penetrates the solid

[28] Hydrostatical paradoxes, notes pp. 23-26. On taste, notes pp. 35-36. On smell, notes pp. 36-38. Boyle is mentioned in some ten notes altogether, and Dr. M. Boas' remark (*Rev. d'Hist. des Sc.*, IX (1956), 124) that Boyle's experiments are quoted almost as often as those of Newton is true of the 1702 notes.

[29] On Clarke's views as expressed in his other works, see H. Metzger, *Attraction Universelle et Religion Naturelle chez quelques Commentateurs Anglais de Newton* III (Act. Sci. Ind. 623), (Paris, 1938), pp. 113-139. On the relations between the views of Newton and Clarke, see A. Koyré, *From the Closed World to the Infinite Universe* (Baltimore: Johns Hopkins, 1957), pp. 300-301.

[30] Notes, p. 18.   [31] Notes, p. 80.   [32] Notes, p. 72.

substance of it; for gravity is never in proportion to the super-ficies of bodies or of any corpuscles, but always to the solid quantity of them. Wherefore we ought no more to enquire how bodies gravitate, than how bodies began first to be moved." [33]

In the other two notes Clarke gives a taste of the power of the Newtonian conception. In the first he outlines, informally, how gravity explains the first two Keplerian laws of planetary motion [34]; in the second he follows Halley in using gravity to explain the motion of the tides.[35] Here at last the English undergraduate was given a glimpse of the power of the New-tonian theory; one wonders what continental readers made of these notes when they were republished in Amsterdam in 1708, no longer hidden at the back of the book, but displayed as footnotes to Rohault's text.[36]

Although in the 1702 notes Clarke's views are unmistakable, surprisingly large sections of the Rohault text are still allowed to pass unchallenged. Sometimes this is because Clarke does not yet go out of his way to pick quarrels with his author—for example, he does not exploit Newton's teaching on comets as an argument against the Cartesian vortices—but sometimes it is because Clarke is still hampered by Newton's failure to publish a more widely-ranging account of his views.

In 1704, however, Newton's *Opticks* at last appeared, and it was Clarke himself who prepared the Latin translation of 1706.[37] When a new edition of his Rohault translation was published four years later, Clarke made numerous references in his notes to the *Opticks*, many of them accompanied by

[33] Notes, pp. 81-83.
[34] Notes, pp. 70-72. An improved version of this note, with some mathematics, was published in the 1723 edition.
[35] Notes, pp. 83-85.
[36] The influence, if any, of this early popularization of Newtonian cosmology on the continent does not appear to have been studied. Clarke's forthright views on the nature of attraction are unlikely to have commended themselves to Cartesian readers.
[37] With additional queries, in particular the one which later became Query 31, from which Clarke quotes nearly two dozen passages in his 1710 notes.

lengthy quotations. Some of these references are in the extended comments to the chapters on light, but by no means all.

Encouraged in his criticisms by this new ammunition, Clarke now carries the war into the enemy's camp. His earlier discussion of the application of gravity to the motion of planets is now preceded by four arguments showing that " the vortices of matter in which the planets swim, are mere fictions and contrary to the phenomena of nature." [38] Rohault's paragraph headed " that these three elements are not imaginary," previously allowed to pass, now has a note beginning " these three elements *are* to be looked upon as fictitious and imaginary." [39] The Cartesian subtle matter is now a " fiction . . . very weak, and contrary both to reason and experience." [40] At last Clarke's notes begin to provide a systematic refutation of the text.

At the same time the positive teaching in the notes is greatly increased. Perhaps nothing illustrates their role in this respect better than the inclusion of " six whole dissertations " by Charles Morgan, a contemporary of Clarke at Cambridge and later Master of Clare College. These were important enough to merit republication as a separate tract in 1770, long after the Cartesian controversy had been settled in Newton's favor. Three of the dissertations, on the motion of falling bodies, on the motion of projectiles, and on the descent of bodies falling in a cycloid, together form a single footnote occupying over a dozen pages of small print and ostensibly provoked by Rohault's innocuous remark that falling bodies accelerate.[41] Clarke clearly feels that he must take opportunities of complementing the text over and above what is strictly necessary to the establishment of Newtonian philosophy.[42]

One particularly interesting note contains Clarke's doctrine

[38] P. 311.

[39] P. 105, my italics.

[40] P. 25.

[41] The acknowledgement to Morgan is made in the Translator's Preface. Clarke's presentation copy to Morgan is in the possession of Clare College, Cambridge.

[42] Mouy (*op. cit.*, p. 137) erroneously supposes these dissertations to be by Clarke and to be " ses critiques principales."

of the efficient cause of gravity. "Since nothing acts at a distance," he says, "that is, nothing can exert any force in acting where it is not, it is evident, that bodies (if we would speak properly) cannot at all move one another, but by contact and impulse. . . . Yet because besides innumerable other phenomena of nature, that universal gravitation of matter . . . can by no means arise from the mutual impulse of bodies (because all impulse must be in proportion to the superficies, but gravity is always in proportion to the quantity of solid matter, and therefore must of necessity be ascribed to some cause that penetrates to the inward substance itself of solid matter), therefore all such attraction is by all means to be allowed as it is not the action of matter at a distance, but the action of some immaterial cause which perpetually moves and governs matter by certain laws." He goes on to quote several passages from the *Opticks*, adding the gloss "not bodily impulse" to Newton's "What I call attraction may be performed by impulse." [43]

With the publication of the 1710 edition Clarke's notes assumed almost their final shape. On the title pages Newton's name is actually given greater prominence than those of author and editor; the notes have grown to between one-quarter and one-third the length of the text [44] with a corresponding increase in quality, and they are now displayed as footnotes with references in the index.[45] Clarke left these notes unaltered in the 1718 edition, which suggests that after his famous controversy with Leibniz,[46] in which he acted as Newton's champion, he saw little reason to alter his opinions—above all, on the nature of gravity. But he did make a few minor alterations

---

[43] Pp. 50-51.

[44] As the title-page of a reissue accurately observes, they have been increased by half.

[45] The continental edition of 1708 has footnotes, but these are not referenced in the index. The references in the 1710 edition are presumably to the notes Clarke himself regarded as important.

[46] See H. G. Alexander (ed.), *The Leibniz-Clarke Correspondence* (Manchester: Univ. Press, 1956).

in the notes for the English translation published in 1723 by his brother John: the discussion of Kepler's laws [47] and Morgan's dissertation on the rainbow are enlarged,[48] there is mention of Newton's view of the origins of novae (taken from the 1713 edition of the *Principia*),[49] and a handful more quotations are culled from the Queries in the *Opticks*,[50] but otherwise almost all the changes are echoes of changes in the second English edition of the *Opticks* (dated 1717, but published too late for use in Clarke's 1718 notes).

The English translation with notes was republished twice, in 1728/9 and 1735, and the Latin translation with notes appeared in Leiden as late as 1739, over forty years after the first set of notes and more than half-a-century after the publication of the *Principia*. Benjamin Hoadley and Whiston both testify to the popularity of the Clarke-Rohault text in Cambridge even after the editor's death in 1729, Hoadley remarking with mixed feelings, " To this day his translation of Rohault is, generally speaking, the standing text for lectures; and his notes, the first direction to those who are willing to receive the reality and truth of things in the place of invention and romance." [51] Playfair may well be right in ascribing this popularity to the dual system of college and university teaching in Cambridge [52]; whatever the views of a college tutor over the merits of Descartes and Newton, his students could use Clarke's book. The work of Newton's supporters would have been difficult indeed, if Clarke had not returned twice to make a thorough revision of the hesitant and deferential *annotatiunculae* of his early graduate days.

MICHAEL A. HOSKIN

Whipple Science Museum
Free School Lane,
Cambridge, England.

---

[47] II, p. 75.

[48] II, pp. 233-235.

[49] II, p. 71. *Principia* (1713 edition), p. 481.

[50] II, pp. 137-8; II, p. 193.

[51] Hoadley in Samuel Clarke, *Works*, I, p. ii; Whiston, *op. cit.*, p. 6. The text was also used at Yale until 1743, cf. Sarton, *op. cit.*, p. 145.

[52] Cf. Cajori, *op. cit.*, pp. 631-2.

PART THREE

PHILOSOPHY OF SCIENCE

DARWIN'S DILEMMA *

ᛣᛚ

D ARWIN reared his theory of Natural Selection upon the basis of three observable facts in the world of living things, and two deductions which he made from these observations. The first two observations are the following: organisms tend to increase their numbers in a geometrical ratio such that, if unchecked, the individuals of a given type of organism would quickly become so great in number that no country could support them. On the other hand, and this is the second observation, the numbers of a given type of organism do in fact remain relatively constant.

The first deduction made from these first two observations to account for them is what Darwin called "the struggle for existence." For if nature produces more individuals than can survive, the greater number of them must, for some reason or other, be destroyed. Now this Darwin accounted for by competition between organisms, resulting in survival of those that are sufficiently equipped by their quality, or are favored by circumstances, such as the seed that falls on fertile ground.

Darwin's third observation was that organisms tend to vary. His first example is that of variation under domestication, of wheat, for instance, of pigeons, of horses, and of hounds. Now this is attributed to man's power of selection. These variations are intended by man. However deliberate the choice, not all of these variations that are brought about are actually the result of a deliberate selection—not all. Deliberate choice, improvement of environment, or cross-breeding, are not all there is to this selection. Darwin pointed out that,

. . . eminent breeders try by methodical selection, with a distinct object in view, to make a new strain or sub-breed, superior to any kind in the country. But for our purposes, a form of Selection, which may be called Unconscious, and which results from everyone

---

* These pages are the transcript of a recording.

trying to possess and breed from the best individual animals, is more important. [Notice, the breeding or deliberate improvement of, say, the quality of wheat or the quality of horses is accompanied by an improvement that was not intended; that is not deliberate, an unconscious selection is taking place.] Thus, a man who intends keeping pointers naturally tries to get as good dogs as he can, and afterwards breeds from his own best dogs, but he has no wish or expectation of permanently altering the breed. Nevertheless we may infer that this process continued during centuries, would improve and modify any breed, in the same way as Bakewell, Collins, etc., by this very same process, only carried on more methodically, did greatly modify, even during their lifetimes, the forms and qualities of their cattle.[1]

I have quoted this long passage because of the importance of what Darwin calls "Unconscious Selection," unconscious "insofar that the breeder could never have expected, or even wished to produce the result that ensued—namely the production of two distinct strains." This unconscious selection is important to Darwin's second deduction, namely, Natural Selection. The distinction which he makes brings us face to face with two different types of selection; the first is deliberate, with a distinct object in view; the second was unintended unexpected, nor even wished for. So far as man's purpose in this particular intervention is concerned, the new strains produced by the second type are fortuitous. Actually, they are products of nature. The natural principle, as distinguished from the conscious, deliberate one, is called Natural Selection.

There is no doubt that Darwin was reasoning here on the basis of an analogy or proportion between art and nature, and that the term for transition was selection. In other words, unconscious selection is first revealed as a by-product, so to speak, of conscious selection, and an unconscious selection is going on in nature all the time. This was sound reasoning, it seems to me, given the observations—particularly the one that all organisms tend to vary considerably—which should in fact

[1] Charles Darwin, *The Origin of Species*, chap. I (New York: Modern Library, n. d.), p. 32.

be warranted by experience, and in some measure they are. (Whether they are or not warranted is none of our concern at this moment or in this particular paper.) The point is that I see no problem in unconscious selection going on in domestication and in nature untouched by man. Right now I am particularly interested in the analogy and the more so because Darwin himself dwells upon it. [Between conscious selection, and that natural selection which accompanies it but lies outside man's intention, Darwin sees a proportion.] He makes a tight case of it. Listen to this from Chapter Three of *The Origin of Species.*

I have called this principle, by which each slight variation, if useful, is preserved, by the term Natural Selection, in order to mark its relation to man's power of selection. But the expression often used by Herbert Spencer of the Survival of the fittest is more accurate, and is sometimes equally convenient. We have seen that man by selection can certainly produce great results, and can adapt organic beings to his own uses, through the accumulation of slight but useful variations, given to him by the hand of Nature. [But Natural Selection, as we shall hereafter see, is a power incessantly ready for action, and is as immeasurably superior to man's feeble efforts, as the works of Nature are to those of Art.]

If Darwin's analogy holds good, it implies that both art and nature proceed by determinate ways or means to produce some final product. Another point worthy of attention is that to Darwin's mind the works of nature are immeasurably superior to those of our art or craft. We must not interpret Darwin as believing that art cannot produce certain works that nature could not bring about, in which respect art is superior to nature. Nature does not amputate a gangrenous foot, supply spectacles, or false teeth. Here we can do something that is useful and that nature cannot do. Darwin only meant that nature's ways, in producing her own works, are immeasurably more subtle, and relatively obscure to us, than our own ways and means in producing artifacts. Nature's selection is superior to our own. That is Darwin's position, and notice that he still calls it selection.

Before dwelling on this second deduction, namely natural selection, let us return for a moment to the first, the struggle for existence, which Darwin attributes to every organism. And here is where we will encounter our dilemma. We all know what the expression " struggle for existence " means as referring to man's activity, as when he struggles to get somewhere, say, physically, to get up a hill, or against an enemy, or to make a living, or to get a job. In this context the word " struggle " is quite clear. It can be verified immediately. But what does it mean when applied to *all* organisms, to beasts, and even to plants as Darwin holds? He was keenly aware that he was not using the expression in its readily verified meaning. And here I quote from the very same Chapter Three.

I should premise that I use this term in a large and metaphorical sense including dependence of one being on another, and including (which is more important) not only the life of the individual, but success in leaving behind progeny. Two canine animals, in a time of dearth, may be *truly* said to struggle with each other which shall eat food and live. But a plant on the edge of a desert is said to struggle for life against the drought, [and here the meaning of " struggle " is going to be somewhat diminished], though more properly it should be said to be dependent on the moisture. A plant which annually produces a thousand seeds, of which only one of an average comes to maturity, may be more truly said to struggle with the plants of the same and other kinds which already clothe the ground. The mistletoe is dependent on the apple and a few other trees, but can only in a far-fetched sense be said to struggle with these trees, for, if too many of these parasites grow on the same tree, it languishes and dies. But several seedling mistletoes, growing close together on the same branch, may *more truly* be said to struggle with each other. As the mistletoe is disseminated by birds, its existence depends on them; and it may methodically be said to struggle with other fruit bearing plants, in tempting birds to devour and thus disseminate its seeds. In these several senses, *which pass into each other,* I use for convenience' sake the general term Struggle for Existence. [Italics added.]

There stands the dilemma. The first one is clearly expressed when he says, " I use this term in a large and metaphorical sense." This is nonetheless most equivocal. The second is the example of the plant. He allows that a plant struggles, but of course a plant does not struggle in the way a dog does; and a dog does not struggle in the way a man does to solve a problem. Further, we must notice that, still within the realm of plants, in one case we can say more truly that they struggle than in other cases. But a meaning of struggle is still retained somewhat. It is not quite the struggle of a man, it is not quite that of a beast, but it is not confined to that of a plant merely needing moisture either. One plant can somehow compete with another and, as a result, the most favored, either by quality or by circumstance, will survive, or its progeny. "The mistletoe . . . may methodically be said to struggle with other fruit-bearing plants." So that the plants, in a sense, truly struggle after all.

This passage from the *Origin of Species* reminds us of Aristotle's caution in using the simple term "life." If we compare plants to animals, he says, they are not alive; but compared with other forms of matter, they are indeed alive. So "alive" or "life" are equivocal terms, they have many meanings. There is a meaning of life verified in a beast, not verifiable in the plant; and one of man, that is not verifiable in a beast. Aristotle held that such terms are homonymous by design, not by chance (as the word "seal"). Terms or expressions that are equivocal by design are called analogous. Bertrand Russell speaks of "systematic ambiguity." But Darwin said that he was using "struggle for existence" in a large and metaphorical sense. Now analogy and metaphor are not the same. I mean that a "large sense," and a "metaphorical sense" are not necessarily the same, and that is where we run into difficulty.[2] Take for instance the word "light," or the word "to see." "To see" means first of all, "to see with my eyes." But when you explain to me some problem

[2] Not even those of Darwin's followers who opt for sheer metaphor quite succeed in circumventing such words as "good," "favorable," "advantageous," "better," "improvement," and the like. This is strikingly borne out in an excellent paper, "Darwin and Religion," by Prof. John C. Greene, which appeared in the *Proceedings of the American Philosophical Society*, CII (1959), 716-725.

and I say, " Oh I see," I do not mean that I see with my eyes, since the figures on the blackboard I see with my eyes are not exactly what it is that I understand. Seeing is said here of *understanding*. So " seeing "—the word—is still materially the same, but it has a prior meaning, and we use the same word because this sameness expresses the passage that our mind makes from what we know less to what we know more. " To see " is an analogous term.

Take the word " light " for a second instance: " sunlight," " candlelight," " the light of reason," or, " to examine a problem in the light of calculus." Is " light " used as a metaphor, or as an analogous term? It all depends. If you have changed the meaning of the term " light "—extending it to identify this new kind of thing that you want to designate by it—if you have actually stretched the meaning of the word, then it is an analogous term. But if you retain exclusively the first meaning of the word as in " candlelight " or " sunlight," and have not changed what we call the imposition, then your application of this word in the " light of geometry " is a metaphor. An analogous term may have first been used as a metaphor, such as the word " tongue " when meant of speech. But eventually the word was intended to mean both organ and language. " The English tongue," or " la langue française " are not metaphors. But not all metaphors can become analogical terms. " Brief candle " is a fine metaphor for human life, but we would hardly say that our life is such in a large sense of " brief candle "; or that a heart is of stone in the large sense of stone. Nonetheless Darwin, explaining why he uses a metaphor, is actually giving reasons which, to an Aristotelian, make the expression an analogous one, although Darwin calls it metaphorical. It is actually analogy and I will show you why. We should say " in a large, extended sense," as distinguished from a metaphor whose sense has not changed when applied to something else, although the mode of signifying does change.

You may now wonder what the purpose is in going into the

question of naming as I do. It is my simple intention to show what strange views we may be led to, unless we clear up this particular problem of naming in connection with the theory of evolution—with the theory of evolution, at least as it was begun by Darwin. Theories of evolution were around long before then, but Darwin can be said to have begun the scientific investigation of the problem and to have proposed a scientifically sound theory, at least for his time.

One of these strange views—and I should not use the word " strange " in too forceful a way—we find in Sir Julian Huxley's interpretation of general Darwinian theory. Darwin allowed that one plant may be said to struggle " more truly " than another plant, according to circumstances, or according to kind, or according to the kind of plant or kinds of plants with which it has to struggle. Now this is surely very different from saying that a stone is more truly a stone than a heart of stone, because in the latter case we have not changed the imposition of the word " stone "; we have retained the first meaning and applied it without imposing a new meaning upon it. There is a change in the mode of signifying, but not in the significance of the word. For the " heart of stone " is in no sense truly a stone at all. But Sir Julian takes Darwin's " metaphorical sense " quite literally. Take, for instance, the term tending in " tendency of all organisms to increase in geometrical ratio." Is the word " tendency " used here as a metaphor, or is it taken as an analogous term? For instance, it is a metaphor in " the tendency of a variable to its limit." This is not tendency by which a man tends to do this, or tends to do that; or by which a dog intends to get the bone. The " tendency of a variable to a limit " is in this context plainly a metaphor.

Sir Julian Huxley writes that " at first sight, the biological sector seems full of purpose. Organisms are built as if in purposeful pursuit of a conscious aim." But the truth, he adds, " lies in those two words ' as if.' As the genius of Darwin showed, the purpose is only an apparent one." Darwin's contribution, according to Sir Julian, consists precisely in this—

in the discovery that there is no purposeful activity going on in nature and that everything must be explained without having any resort whatsoever to purpose; and that if there appears to be purpose in nature it is only in appearance, so that when you use terms that are related to purpose in beasts or plants, you are using the term as a sheer metaphor. There is no room for a " large " sense of purpose.

It is not my intention to show here that nature acts for a purpose. I merely want to attract your attention to the strange antinomies we are led to when we deny purpose in nature. I am just going to present the antinomies; my present purpose does not extend beyond this. Let me then make four points regarding purposeful activity and nature, in the context of Huxley's assertions which I have just quoted.

(1) Sir Julian, along with Lord Russell, is emphatic that action for a purpose is clearly recognized in human making and behavior. He accepts that man acts for a purpose, acts for the sake of something; and this is verified in man's case unmistakably according to both these authors; they are both quite critical and accept as little as possible, which is in itself a praiseworthy attitude. They say, and allow us to say, that man truly acts for a purpose. Far from denying such action, Huxley asserts that " the future of man, if it is to be progress and not merely a standstill or degeneration, must be guided by a deliberate purpose. And this human purpose can only be formulated in terms of the new attributes achieved by life in becoming human." Purposeful activity is therefore a radically new kind of reality that arises uniquely in the case of man. It is not to be found in nature itself. Man himself cannot be said to have been brought about for the sake of something. Yet man, as we have stressed, is in many respects unique among animals: a purposeful agent is brought about without intent in any possible sense of this word.

Until this purposeful agent appeared on the scene, " The purpose manifested in evolution, whether in adaptation, specialization, or biological progress, is only an apparent purpose.

It is just as much a product of blind forces as is the falling of a stone to earth or the ebb and flow of the tides. It is we who have read purpose into evolution, as earlier men projected will and emotion into inorganic phenomena like storm or earthquake. If we wish to work towards a purpose for the future of man, we must formulate that purpose ourselves. Purposes in life are made, not found."

Sir Julian offers no reason why, though at first sight the biological sector seems full of purpose, the purpose manifested in evolution is only an apparent purpose. He offers no reason for this, but I will explain the seeming plausibility of this hypothesis a bit later.

We must concede that if there is action for a purpose in irrational nature, that is, outside of man, it will be very different from the kind we find in man, to the point where purpose or action for a purpose will have a different meaning when said of man, when said of beast, and when said of a plant. If there *is* that kind of action in nature, if the term purpose is deserved, if it is applicable, it will have to carry a new meaning, but a meaning related to and dependent upon the one we first imposed. If it is stretchable, as it were, if it can be enlarged, then we will have to accept that it will have a different connotation in these different cases.

This we ask of Sir Julian. Is it so obvious that a purpose is either human or no purpose at all? If a purpose is indeed either human or no purpose at all, then of course Sir Julian's position would be quite irrefutable. He suggests that it is we who read purpose into nature, that is, we project into nature certain things that are actually characteristic of, and exclusively found in man. And this is no doubt often the case. But are we not being anthropomorphic, we ask, in a more sophisticated way when we imply that nature's purpose is either human or no purpose at all? Isn't that another kind of anthropomorphism? On the other hand if organisms are built by nature in " purposeful pursuits," does this mean that nature must have a " conscious aim "? I mean, is purposeful action restricted to conscious action? That is a further assumption and it ought to be justified. Darwin justified it when he spoke of the plant living on the edge of the desert. He showed us that he was stretching the meaning of the word " struggle for existence " and " struggle for survival," a survival, which, of course, is understood as a good. Dogs struggle to acquire food because they like it. But if a plant is going to struggle after its food, can you mean that the plant likes it? We assume that a plant by definition at least has no sensation, so how could the plant like food? Yet plants struggle, as Darwin points out. We have to stretch our words, with Darwin. But Sir Julian refuses to stretch them: he does not allow a new, related, meaning whose difference is based upon a proportion found between the things intended by the same word.

Allow me to mention in passing the over-emphasis on change in Darwin and in Huxley, an over-emphasis which has been recently criticized rather ably by Loren Eiseley in a book written on the occasion of Darwin's centenary. These thinkers have so emphasized the passage from one form of life to another that they have lost sight of the remarkable stability that can go along with this change. Now the stability of an organism needs explanation too, and change alone is not going to explain stability. We bring in this example simply to point out the idea of what we mean by action for an end in nature or what is called final cause, although I am wary of the term final cause, so easily misunderstood. It is not found in Aristotle who teaches that things act " for the sake of something." " Causa finalis " is found in scholastic philosophy. St. Thomas uses it, as a matter of fact, but I am wary of it in English because it tends to be technical. With Aristotle a man acts for a purpose and beasts act for a purpose too; and, while plants do also, this is very obscure and we must at any rate extend the meaning of purpose. The term " good " has likewise several meanings—a whole orderly group of them co-ordinated some-how one with the other, all covered by that single term " good "; as for instance in a " good steak," a " good man."

" Good " means something quite different in each case. There is not a unique meaning here, but actually many co-ordinated meanings.

(2)   Take an organ such as an eye or a tooth. We say that eyes are for the sake of seeing, that incisors are for the sake of cutting and molars are for grinding. When we say this are we using metaphor? We can go way back to Empedocles who said that we have eyes not for the sake of seeing but we see because we have eyes. Another philosopher said that man is the wisest of animals because he just happens to have hands. It is far more thorough, I think, to hold that man has hands in view of making. Why should one position exclude purpose as a cause—I mean a good as " that for the sake of which "? Nature acts for a purpose; of course, not exactly in the way we do, since there is, after all, a radical difference between nature and reason, but in a proportional way: there is a proportion between the way we act and the way nature acts. There is no true identity, but only a proportion, and an irreducible one, between them. Can we accept this? It is not our problem here. I merely want to show, in a dialectical way, what we are led to when we deny that nature acts for a purpose, even in this remote yet analogous sense of the term.

Now, my question is about this struggle. Does that which finally comes about after a certain activity possess the nature of good? It is good to have the molars in the back (allow me this example from Aristotle) and our cutting teeth in the front. Is this disposition produced by a proportional cause or by chance? Do we understand why the molars should be in the back to grind, why the grinding should go on there and the cutting out in front? Do our teeth make sense? If their disposition were reversed, it would be unreasonable, it would be monstrous. That is how we distinguish monsters from non-monsters.

Now, if we allow that nature produces such end products *because* they are good, we imply that nature acts for a purpose, but in doing so we must be aware that we have extended the meaning of " end " and " action " and " purpose."

(3)   Now, once we have recognized goodness in these things, we can still ask whether nature acted "for the sake" of this goodness, or whether it came about for no purpose at all, just by chance, as some of the ancient philosophers held, in common with some more recent ones. The Darwinian philosophers who deny action for a purpose in nature should realize that they have been anticipated by the earliest philosophers; they are somehow regressing to ancient positions.

Sir Julian's view is that all can be rendered intelligible without purpose—by blind forces. Just what is meant by "blind forces," by "blind," on the one hand, and "forces" on the other—not to mention the equivocity or ambiguity of the two words taken together in "blind forces"—is not clear. I know what a "blind man" is, but a "blind stone" is something else—I mean that a stone is not *expected* to see. This makes a considerable difference. I know fairly well what I mean when I say that stones have neither eyesight nor understanding (and even Sir Julian insists upon the uniqueness of man as to understanding and purposeful action).

Remember Darwin's plant struggling at the edge of the desert. Huxley will state that this struggle and its result are the product of blind forces, as in the falling of a stone. Darwin did not say this, although he did leave us with a dilemma when he stated that he was using "struggle for existence" in a *large and metaphorical sense*. Darwin would not have held that stones struggle to fall, and to say that they do would be poor metaphor. But if taken as a mere metaphor apropos of living things, why should it then be good? What does it convey that the fall of a stone does not? If I understand him correctly, Sir Julian would make no distinction here. The result is that "struggle for existence" said of plants and beasts is not only poor metaphor; it is also utterly misleading. We must admit all the same that Darwin made it possible for some people to to hitch on to a metaphorical sense, which, upon closer analysis, turns out to be unfelicitous and unscientific; and for others to allow an extended, large, and yet true meaning. He might have unfolded himself a bit more.

(4)   Fourthly, we are faced with two paradoxes, which I will mention briefly. For Sir Julian, Reason ought to be satisfied with a theory which seeks to explain everything, including Reason itself, as arising from something which has nothing in common with Reason, and for a reason no different from the reason stones fall to earth. Notice the different meanings here imposed upon this word " reason." It means one thing in " man is endowed with reason "; it means another in " a man has no reason to do this rather than that "; and something else again when we say " the man fell for the reason that he slipped on a banana peel." Sir Julian does not mean that things occur for no reason at all; he intends that outside human activity all things occur aimlessly and are accounted for without invoking intelligence behind them. He deserves credit for seeing that, if purposeful action be held to exist in nature, this can only be on the supposition that nature is the work of an intellectual agent—that *quodlibet opus naturae est opus alicujus substantiae intelligentis*—which is precisely what we hold (let it be immediately added that the difficulty of our position is not unappreciated by us). In other words, so far as nature is concerned, Sir Julian will understand rational to mean no more than reason in " the reason stones fall "; with the consequence that, compared to human reason or to any other understanding or intellectual agency, all the things and events of nature proceed from utter unreason, and for no other than the reason stones fall to the earth. Human reason itself is sufficiently accounted for as a product of blind agency. " Explanation," " interpreting," " providing proof " can never be more than an attempt to show that everything in nature is the product of aimless " blind forces." Man, then, the avowedly purposeful agent, came about for no purpose at all. This unfortunate animal finds itself in the curious position of being burdened with all the reason or intelligence there is, and with all the purposeful action there is. He alone has reason, for a reason which can only be blind.[3]

---

[3] " Natural Selection can determine the direction of change, but has no goal.

Now I am all in favor of economy in explanation. If the existence of what Darwin called " good species " (notice his use of the word " good ") can be accounted for by, say, random mutations, then random mutations it is. But can these species be so accounted for? And, by the way, just what does this word " random " mean? I know what it means in " to throw dice at random." I deliberately so throw them, just as when I aim randomly distributed pellets at a duck. In these cases there is no opposition between randomness and purpose. If the word must be applied to nature, it will either become a metaphor or acquire an extended meaning. And what do certain biologists intend when saying that all species are the product of random mutations and, in the same breath, that therefore they are products of mere chance? Does randomness mean the same as chance?[4] If so, we are imposing a new meaning on

It pushes evolution blindly from behind." Julian Huxley, "Man's Place in Nature," in *The Destiny of Man* (London: Hodder and Stoughton, 1959), p. 19. In the *Sunday Times* (Feb. 3, 1957) Sir Julian writes: "The real wonder of life is the fact that the automatic and non-purposeful process of biological evolution should eventually have generated true purpose in the person of the human species."

[4] Elsewhere I expressed some difficulty in understanding Sir Julian Huxley's position in this matter. Take, for instance, the following statement: "Natural Selection is an ordering principle. It takes the disorderly material provided by 'random' or 'chance' variation, builds it up into orderly patterns of organization, and guides it into ordered paths of change." ("Man's Place in Nature," *ed. cit.,* p. 14) As J. W. C. Wand remarks in the same booklet (p. 42): we believe "that 'the mechanism which directs the course of evolution' and its 'ordering principle' are guided by a divine mind to a good and beneficent purpose." Plainly, Sir Julian sees no need for such a mind. Still, whether or not randomness and chance are for him the same, whether chance here means pure chance or something less than pure chance, he indeed insists upon an ordering, guiding principle. Might we, in order to avoid all suggestion of purpose, take the "ordering" or "guiding" as having the meaning these words would have when a river-bed is spoken of as channelling, and as directing and guiding its waters to the sea? But the analogy cannot stand. For the river-bed too, was somehow formed at random (we would say *ex necessitate materiae*), and the sea itself, is a random distribution. One ought not to ask Sir Julian "How do you account for the ordering principle?" for the reply would likely be "It's just there." No, we are driven back to the monkeys pounding at random. Now, when they allegedly produce all extant literature, are their random poundings led to this by an "ordering" and "guiding" principle? Sir Julian must surely admit that the terms are now vividly out of place. The principle now cannot be

either or both of these terms. Upon what grounds? When we throw dice at random, we do not know which sides will in fact turn up, though we know the possible alternatives; when we aim birdshot at a duck, we do not know which of the pellets will actually bring it down, though we may be confident that some of them will do the work. Something is known here, but there is also something unknown: we are blind as to which sides of the dice will turn up, or which pellet or pellets will strike. (Notice that we in fact use the random distribution of many pellets to compensate for the uncertain course of a single bullet.) Now there is also something blind about chance or fortune in human affairs. Socrates did not go to the market this morning to meet the debtor he had been wanting to meet, yet he met him all the same, by chance, for he did not know his debtor would be there. So here too there is blindness. Could this be the reason randomness and chance are said to be one and the same?

I have dwelt for a few moments on Sir Julian's position—not irreverently, I hope—merely to point out its paradoxical nature. Let me add, in all fairness, that whoever holds that nature does act for the sake of something ought to be aware of the obvious difficulties of such a position. If it is maintained, for example, that a bird builds a nest for the sake of offspring as yet unborn, and does so quite unwittingly, it is after all, far from obvious how anything that does not as yet exist can already be a cause—especially in the case of blind agency. Purposeful activity in nature is also readily oversimplified, and made to look like the argument concluding *et voilà pourquoi votre fille est muette*; it is obviously good for a man to have hands, but this does not show how he acquired them. Tele-

anything more than the mere possibility of these particular arrangements of letters, which just happen to be meaningful. In virtue of what principle is "a million monkeys" meaningful, and "the slithy toves" not, if both are arrived at by aimless monkeys? Where is the reason why the former and not the latter arrangement should be judged *favorable?* Cf. *The Hollow Universe* (Oxford University Press: London, 1960), pp. 97-110; "Abstraction from Matter" (III) in *Laval théologique et philosophique*, 1960, n. 2, pp. 174-188.

ological mechanisms may help to explain. Meantime, we must remember that the good was first recognized by Aristotle [5] as a special kind of cause—the first but most obscure of all causes. But though it would be foolish to ignore the difficulties which this doctrine must entail, will it be any less foolish to conclude that it is therefore unscientific? I fail to see why Natural Selection must be understood as devoid of purpose, or why " the struggle for existence " is to be taken as sheer metaphor.

CHARLES DEKONINCK

Université Laval,
Québec, Canada.

[5] Plato also considered the good as a cause, but not as a cause *sui generis.*

ΦΥΣΙΣ

ονο

*The Meaning of 'Nature' in the Aristotelian
Philosophy of Nature*

SOMETIMES there are many things in a word. If such is the case, it is to the philosopher's advantage to trace out the relation between the various meanings of a word, insofar as the later and secondary significations are to be more fully understood only when seen in the light of a primary imposition, first and best known to us. The extension of the word to include further meanings retaining the relationship to this first and most known can be for the human mind a safeguard from meaningless abstractions and a reminder of the principles and trajectory of our knowing. At the same time, if the order is not seen, the extension can be a source of confusion and error.

The advantage of bearing this order in mind and the danger of ignoring it are of particular importance in the case of the word *nature*; for although it is one of the most common terms in philosophy, many of its possible significations have yet to be explored more fully. The purpose of this article, accordingly, is twofold: (1) to trace out some of the more important meanings of this word with a view to determining its particular use in the Aristotelian and Thomistic philosophy of nature, and (2) to show that even this particular meaning is continually modified within the science of nature. Our order of procedure shall be as follows: I. After a preliminary review of the meanings of *nature* given by Aristotle in Book V of his *Metaphysics*, we shall turn to his *Physics* in order to determine more explicitly which of these meanings are proper to philosophy of nature. II. Next we shall develop certain implications of the definition of nature given in the *Physics* by detailing various ways in which nature can be taken as either an active or a passive principle. III. Finally we shall examine the extended meanings that the word nature assumes as philosophy of nature is elaborated. To my knowledge the possibility of this progressive

247

enlargement of the term *nature* corresponding to the gradation of mobile beings in the philosophy of nature has not been considered: this possibility the present study aims particularly to investigate.

I

SOME MEANINGS OF NATURE

In Book V, Chapter 4, of his *Metaphysics*, Aristotle runs through several meanings of φύσις, which in Latin becomes *natura* and in English *nature*. Let us recall them briefly.

1. Taking φύσις to be derived from φύεσθαι, "to grow," Aristotle gives as the first meaning *the genesis of growing things*. Hence φύσις means the process of a thing's coming into being by growing from something, as a plant comes into existence by growing from a seed. In this sense, then, the word is used for the generation of a living being.—Our English word *nature* would not have this meaning, of course, nor does the Latin *natura*, though *nativitas*, the process of birth, does have a similar signification.

2. Secondly, the word is taken to mean what the growing being grows from, a source within the growing being.

3. From this second sense is derived a more general meaning of nature: nature as the intrinsic source, not only of generation, but of the primary movement (including any type of change) which is in a natural being by virtue of what it is.

Thereupon, the meaning becomes more determinate, as this inner source of movement or change is identified:

4. First, with the formless primary stuff, of which a natural thing consists or out of which it is made. It was in this sense that the ancient "physicists" called the elements of natural things their nature.

5. Secondly, with essence or form (οὐσία), for we cannot say that those things which are or come to be by nature have their nature unless they have their form and shape, even though the matter (that from which they come) is present.

Aristotle then retraces his steps in order to make certain

precisions: nature is the primary matter, whether this latter be absolutely first or first only in a certain order;[1] and nature is the form or essence as well, which is the *end* of generation.[2]

6. By "an extension of meaning," finally, any essence (οὐσία) is called nature, whether it be the term of generation or not, because a nature is one kind of essence. It is in this sense that we can speak of the nature of a circle or of an immaterial substance.[3]

In conclusion, Aristotle makes the point that it is the form that is primarily and most properly nature, for the matter is called nature insofar as it is receptive of the form, and generation and growth are called nature because they are movements proceeding from it:[4] "And nature, in this sense, is the source of movement in natural things, which is in them in some way, either potentially or actually."

---

[1] The examples given by Aristotle are in keeping with the views of certain of his predecessors. Thus, for primary matter he gives not his own absolutely prime matter, but something composite, one or several of the elements; and for the form he gives—quoting Empedocles—not the substantial form, but the primary composition of a thing. His purpose obviously was to show that the word *nature* was in fact being used for primary matter and for form whatever these might be understood to be.

[2] Form, therefore, is a principle of a natural thing as a formal cause and a principle of generation as a final cause.

[3] It might be noted in addition that form or essence may be called nature, not only as an end of generation, but as a source of accidental physical movement or change, and that this meaning may be extended to include form or essence as principle of movement in a more common sense, including any operation, even spiritual. This would give us a more proper sense in which we could speak of the nature of an immaterial substance, one closer to the original signification than essence taken simply. In his *De Ente et Essentia*, St. Thomas gives this extended sense as one of the meanings of *nature* ("a thing's essence as ordered to its proper activity") and even indicates that this seems to be what Aristotle means by *nature* in *Metaphysics V*, where he says that in a certain sense every substance is a nature (cf. no. 6, above).

[4] The form of the thing to be generated is a principle of generation as the end, whereas the form of the progenitor is the active principle from which the generation proceeds, the progenitor being the agent. Generation, of course, implies change within the progenitor, the latter being a moved mover. As principle of this change, the form is obviously a source of change in that in which it is and as such can be taken to be nature. Just how the form of an agent, an active principle moving another as such, may nevertheless be termed nature, a principle of change *within* the changing being, will be discussed in the last footnote of this article.

Such, in brief, is Aristotle's delineations of various meanings of nature.[5] It is to be noted that all the senses except the last include a relation to movement, and this last Aristotle is careful to set off from the others by indicating that it involves " an extension of meaning." Nature, then, is to be seen principally as a source of movement in things.

Before proceeding to the *Physics*, it is of interest to note St. Thomas' introductory comment upon this chapter of the *Metaphysics*: " Though the consideration of [*nature*] does not seem to belong to first philosophy, but rather to natural philosophy, [Aristotle] nevertheless distinguishes the meaning of this word here [in first philosophy] because *nature* according to one of its senses is said of every substance." In this passage Aquinas is obviously referring to the extended meaning of *nature*; the other meanings, then, would apparently belong properly to philosophy of nature.

This is precisely what we find when we turn to the *Physics*, Book II, Chapter 1.[6] Let us briefly review Aristotle's procedure: First he points out that things which exist by nature are seen to differ from artifacts in that the former have within

---

[5] These, of course, are not the only ways in which Aristotle uses the word. For a comprehensive list of the meanings of φύσις in Aristotle, see H. Bonitz, *Index Aristotelicus* (Graz, 1955).

[6] St. Thomas establishes the meaning of *nature* in philosophy of nature right at the beginning of his commentary of the *Physics*. In lesson 1, Bk I of his commentary he shows the subject of the science of nature to be that which depends on matter for both its being and its definition, as distinct from mathematical entities and the subject of metaphysics. St. Thomas then explains: " Because everything that has matter is mobile, consequently the subject of natural philosophy is mobile being. For natural philosophy is about natural things, which are those whose principle is nature. Now nature is the principle of motion and rest in that in which it is. Natural science, therefore, is about those things which have in themselves a principle of motion." Natural being is here clearly identified with mobile being and mobile being with sensible material being. Nature has the meaning, not of what the thing is or the essence simply, but of principle of movement or change, such as movement according to place or even of generation. Movement, inasmuch as it is given as implying matter, is obviously to be understood in the strict sense, as *actus imperfecti*, and not according to an extended meaning which could also include any type of operation, even thought. Otherwise the natural and mobile being would not necessarily be a material being, as it is explicitly stated to be, since there are operations which do not presuppose matter.

them a source of movement or change in respect of place or size or some quality or other, whereas products of art have no inner tendency to change, except insofar as they are made of a natural substance. From this he concludes that *nature is this principle or cause of being moved and being at rest in that in which it is,* and he adds by way of precision, *in which it is primarily, in virtue of itself and not accidentally.*

This definition, it will be noticed, is the third meaning given in the *Metaphysics,* but with certain additions. Nature is defined here not merely as a principle but as a cause as well. According to St. Thomas, this is to indicate that nature may be either a passive source (principle) or an active source (cause). These two senses of nature will constitute the subject for the second part of this article; and in the third part we shall consider the word *primarily.* The words *in virtue of itself and not accidentally,* we may note here, are meant to exclude such intrinsic principles as the art of medicine in virtue of which a doctor cures himself. The movement of being cured belongs to the man *per se* as a patient, not as a doctor; it is only accidentally that the doctor is also the patient.

After defining nature, Aristotle proceeds to make certain distinctions concerning the use of the word: those things are said " to have a nature " which have this principle of movement and they are substances; and both the subject which has its being from nature and the accidents which are caused by this nature are said to be natural or according to nature.

Nature is then identified, as it is in the *Metaphysics,* with " the first material substratum of all things which have in themselves a principle of movement and change "; and then with the form of these things, insofar as " what is potentially flesh or bone does not have its nature until it receives the form by which we define what flesh or bone is." Both matter and form are nature but each in a different way, and unequally, since form is nature even more than matter is: " for a thing is more properly said to be what it is when it is in act than when it exists only potentially."

In the *Physics,* accordingly, nature is seen to be the form insofar as a thing does not have its nature unless it has the form " by which we define what the thing is." This form might appear to be the essence, taken absolutely, without reference to movement, unless we bear in mind what has gone before. For Aristotle not only defined nature as a principle of movement but also stated that those things are said to have a nature which have this principle. Accordingly, the form must be taken as nature precisely because, in making the thing to be what it is, it is the root of its particular activities and its particular tendencies to change. It is in this sense that the thing would not have a nature if it did not have a form.

But there is another sense in which the form is nature. The natural thing is one that is the result of change, the product of a natural process of becoming (which, according to Aristotle, was also called φύσις) . The form of a natural being is one that fulfills a potency of matter, and it was to this form that the matter tended in the process of generation. The form, then, as nature, is also an end of movement: " What grows *qua* growing grows from something into something. Into what then does it grow? . . . Into that to which it tends. The form then is nature." [7] In time, it is true, the form is at the term of generation, but, absolutely considered, it is a principle, and a principle prior to the matter according to the essential order of things. The form, consequently, whether it be considered as the origin of activity or as the end of generation, is nature as a principle of movement. (It can also, of course, be nature as the active principle in the progenitor *from which* generation proceeds. But this sense, mentioned in the passage from the *Metaphysics* and indicated at least at one point in Chapter 2, Book II, of the *Physics*,[8] belongs properly to a later stage in the philosophy of nature, that which deals with the living natural being as such.)

---

[7] Aristotle, *Physics*, Bk II, ch. 1, 193 b 17 *et sqq.*

[8] " Man is born from man, but not bed from bed. That is why it is said that not the shape but the wood is the nature of the bed, for, if the bed sprouted, not a bed but wood would come up. But if the form is art, so also is the form nature; for man is born from man." *Physics*, Bk. II, ch. 1, 193 b 9 *et sqq.*

In short, it is as a principle of movement accepted in the strict sense [9] (movement involving a material substratum) that nature is identified severally with matter and with form. Clearly it is not to be taken either as essence, the root of spiritual operations, or as essence without reference to movement in any sense.[10] Nature, in fact, is something proper to material beings, since all natural beings are mobile beings and all mobile beings are material beings. In this meaning of nature, it might be added, we find the basis for distinguishing between philosophy of nature and metaphysics as to mobility and immobility, materiality and pure immateriality.

II

NATURE AS BOTH AN ACTIVE AND A PASSIVE PRINCIPLE

For a fuller understanding of nature, the various ways in which it is both an active and a passive principle must be examined. It has already been indicated that nature can be both active and passive. Does this division coincide exactly with the division of nature into matter and form? This might seem to be the case since in the commentaries of St. Thomas the passive principle is usually associated with matter or what is material (*principium passivum et materiale*) and the active with form or what is formal (*principium activum et formale*).[11] At times, however, St. Thomas identifies the form with a passive principle as he often does when he speaks of the intrinsic principle of falling bodies.[12] We might be inclined to dismiss the difficulty with the distinction that when it is not a question of living things both form and matter must be included under

---

[9] This sense is not the strictest since it includes generation and corruption, as well as movement taken in the strictest sense involving two positive terms (cf. Arist., *Physics*, V, ch. 1). It is a strict sense in that it excludes operations such as thought.

[10] It could be taken as essence considered as a *composite* principle of accidental movements (strict sense). For example, the composite nature of a living being, including both matter and form, is a principle of growing, more adequate than either matter or form taken alone.

[11] Cf. *In VII Metaph.*, lect. 8, n. 1442Z.

[12] Cf., e. g., *In II Phys.*, lect. 1, n. 4.

passive principle, while *principium activum et formale* would be reserved for the principle by which a thing moves itself by itself. But this answer creates difficulties as soon as we observe that in other places the principle of falling in heavy bodies is explicitly given not as a passive but as an *active* principle.[13]

The solution to this apparent contradiction lies in an explanation of what is meant by active principle. The formal principle is not necessarily active as in an agent, or in a living being in which one part moves another. In the passage in which the form of a heavy body is said to be an *active* principle, what is meant apparently is not that the form moves the body as an agent cause or even that it is a principle by which the body moves itself, but that it is the ever-present *source* of the motion—of the activity. In this way, it is distinguished from a passive, i. e. receptive, principle which requires for the transition into act the presence of an agent, as when water is being heated. Even in non-living things, consequently, nature may be regarded as an active principle, though in living beings it is active in a special way.

When St. Thomas states, then, that the form of the heavy body is a passive principle and explains further that the body is moved rather than moves, his intention in these passages, evidently, is to distinguish the heavy body from the living being.[14] For though the falling body moves, and moves indeed without the actual influence of an agent cause, it, nevertheless, does not move itself in the sense that it is an agent (a mover) with respect to itself, as is the living being. The mover in the case of the falling body would be the original maker that produced the form it has, making it the type of thing it is, with all its concomitant characteristics, including its tendency to fall when raised from the ground.[15]

The passive *material* principle, on the other hand, is a receptive principle. It is especially prime matter with its appetite

[13] Cf., e. g., *Contra Gentiles*, IV, 97.

[14] Cf. Arist., *Physics*, VIII, ch. 4; St. Thomas, *In VIII Phys.*, lect. 8, n. 7, where *principium passivum* is distinguished from the *principium motivum aut activum*.

[15] Cf. St. Thomas, *In II Phys.*, lect. 1, n. 4.

for form. We may consider prime matter in general as having an appetite for form in general, or as the matter in a particular substance (e. g., an acorn) having an inclination to a determinate form (namely, the form of an oak tree) —the determination of the appetite being due, of course, to the form possessed (i. e., the form of the acorn). But the passive material principle also includes secondary and accidental principles of receptivity as in the case of water, which becomes warm when exposed to fire. Such an accidental passive principle, of course, even though material (i. e., receptive), springs as a characteristic fundamentally from the substantial form just as does the active (or, if you prefer, passive) formal principle of being drawn downwards for the stone.

However, a new difficulty now arises, for to say that nature may be merely a passive potency seems to do away with the distinction between nature and art. Nature differs from art in that nature is an intrinsic, art an extrinsic principle. But if this intrinsic principle that is nature may be no more than a passive potency, which of course is also required by art, the active principle being, like art, extrinsic, where would the difference lie? St. Thomas saw this difficulty, as is evident in his commentary on Book II of the *Physics*,[16] where he makes the precision that in the case of nature this potency must be a *natural potency*. In Book VIII, ch. 4, of the *Physics* Aristotle distinguishes a violent movement from a natural one by the fact that the latter is one to which the thing was in potency. St. Thomas comments: " These things are naturally moved, when they are moved to their proper acts, to which they are in potency according to their nature." [17] " To their proper acts " implies that these things are not in potency to just any acts or even to many acts, but to certain determinate acts fixed by their nature (i. e., by their form, primarily) —to certain perfections wherein they find their fulfillment. Implied here is an order of appetite intrinsic to the things. The passive potency in the case of nature, then, involves a determinate inclination,

[16] *Lectio* 1, n. 4.   [17] *In IX Phys.*, lect. 8, n. 1.

an appetite, not to be found in the passive potency of art. Although the potency in the case of the matter of artificial things is limited to certain forms (e. g., wood cannot be used in the making of any and all artifacts), nevertheless there is no *positive* inclination to any form. There is simply a non-repugnance. The determination that there is in art must come from the extrinsic active principle, from the mind of the artist. The potency itself, in the case of art, is a passive potency only insofar as there is no repugnance to an act that man wishes to impose upon it; it is a potency then only in relation to the human mind, a sort of " obediential potency." The natural potency, on the other hand, is intrinsically related to an act— the act also being considered natural, even though in certain cases it can be supplied only by a non-natural agent.

It was by an application of this principle that St. Thomas showed the movement of the heavenly bodies to be natural.[18] For although they were moved by forces extrinsic to nature, the separated intelligences, nevertheless from the point of view of the passive potency, implying a determinate inclination or aptitude to circular movement, the movement was said to be natural. Another application may be seen in the case of evolution. Though the active principle must certainly have been outside of nature, the whole process would have been natural from the standpoint of the passive inclination of matter, always " desiring " as an end the more perfect fulfillment of its potency. The act conferred was natural, corresponding to a natural potency, though the power that conferred it was not.[19]

It should be noted, moreover, that although the natural potency in a thing implies an intrinsic order to an act, giving rise to a relation between an appetite and a good, this good need not be considered as a perfection of the thing in its own particular being. Indeed, in the case of non-living things, it

[18] Cf. St. Thomas, *Contra Gentiles*, III, 23.

[19] It might be asked if the active principle in such cases would be an example of art cooperating with nature. It seems that it would not be—at least not in the strict sense. Art, it seems, *cooperates* with nature when it acts in conjunction with an *active* principle operating in nature, as is the case with medicine.

is very difficult to determine just what is the good for them. But it is sometimes a different matter if we look at such things in the general scheme of the universe. Then their observed tendencies to certain acts very often appear as contributing to the order and good of the whole, they are seen within the framework of the general intention of universal nature.[20] This was the case even of the heavenly bodies. One could say that they did not tend to movement as to a perfection for them, but that such movement was intended by nature for the generation of rational beings. By such movement they were constituted in their given role of causes of alteration in the universe. The tendency known as " gravity " can also be seen as contributing to a general order. Even the tendency of water to be warmed, sometimes given by St. Thomas as a simple example of an intrinsic passive principle of natural movement, could be seen as contributing to the good of the whole.

To complete the general picture, however, the passive potency should be seen in relation not only to its act, as we have been viewing it, but also to the agent which confers the act. In his commentary on Book VII of the *Metaphysics*,[21] St. Thomas explains natural potencies in terms of forms *and* agents: " The difference between the matter of natural things and the matter of artificial things is that in the matter of natural things there is a natural aptitude for the form *and it can be reduced to act by a natural agent*; this does not happen in the matter of artificial things." (Italics mine.) Indeed, the universe may be considered as a whole composed of parts so interrelated that they are acting upon one another or being acted upon by one another, so that everything according to its particular nature is related to something else or to many things as either patient or agent, or both, though not of course in the same respect—and all for the good of the universe as a whole. Thus, to use a simple example, water would be related to both fire and the north wind as passive, fire and the north wind to

[20] Nature taken as the whole system of interrelated individual natures.
[21] *Lectio* 8, n. 1442Z.

water as active. This does not presuppose a determinate inclination in the water either to be warmed or to be cooled,[22] but an intrinsic aptitude for either, which, unlike the indifferent potency in the wood, as the matter of a table, for example, gives rise to a relationship and order to other things *in nature*. The movements resulting from these relations are natural. Art, on the other hand, would imply an interference, or at least an intervening in this order by the human intellect, extrinsic to nature—an intervention, moreover, usually not aimed at the fulfillment of a natural (i. e., intrinsic) potency.[23]

In resumé, then, a movement corresponding to an intrinsic passive inclination to a determinate act as an end and a good is termed natural, even though the active principle be quite extrinsic to nature. However, natural movements usually take place in subjects having a potency to an act which can be supplied by a natural agent; in this case, even when the passive potency is not a determinate inclination to one act but is rather an indeterminate inclination to opposite acts, it is still a case of nature insofar as by these potencies the subject is related to corresponding agents within nature and the order thus established can be seen as fitting into the general scheme of the universe. The order of appetite and good in the universe as a whole, then, is what determines whether or not a movement is natural.

III

VARIATIONS IN THE MEANING OF *Nature* THROUGHOUT THE STUDY OF NATURE

Returning now to Aristotle's definition of nature given in the *Physics* (Bk. II, ch. 1), we find that there is a qualification that requires further development, the word *primarily*. And it is with a consideration of this point particularly that

---

[22] A passive potency in the general scheme of nature can be related to more than one agent—even to agents producing opposite effects—and therefore it can be ordered to opposite acts, both of which would be a good for the whole. It is the active, not the passive, principle, in both animate and inanimate things, that as nature is determined *ad unum*.

[23] An exception could be made for those arts that cooperate with nature.

we become aware of a special divergence in the use of the word *nature* throughout the philosophy of nature.

In his explanation of this word, St. Thomas says: " Nature is the principle of the movements of composite things, but not primarily. Thus the fact that an animal moves downwards [i. e., falls] does not proceed from the nature of the animal as animal but from the nature of the dominating element." [24] Nature, then, is a principle primarily of those movements that belong to things in virtue of what is most fundamental in them.[25]

Nor is this the only instance in which St. Thomas adverts to this idea. When, for example, Aristotle speaks of generation as the activity the most natural of all living things, St. Thomas explains that it is a movement common to all mobile beings, even to the inanimate.[26] Again, St. Thomas, speaking of the vegetative soul, reserves the term *nature* for what living and non-living things have in common: " Now this principle is not nature. Nature does not move in opposite directions, for all plants grow not only upwards or downwards, but in both directions." [27] It seems, then, that in these passages the soul is taken to be nature only insofar as it is the principle of movements common to all mobile beings—though in other places of the *De Anima* it is clear that the soul as such is regarded as nature.[28]

What is most common, of course, is also what is most fundamental in any mobile being; and this, we are saying, is what is

---

[24] *In II Phys.*, lect. 1, n. 5.

[25] John of St. Thomas takes the word *primarily* to mean that the nature of a being is not a secondary and instrumental principle, such as an accident would be, but a fundamental principle, i. e., substantial. That nature must be primary in this sense is readily evident. St. Thomas, however, seems to see another meaning in the word *primarily*.

[26] Aristotle, *De Anima*, II, 4, 415a22 *et sqq.*; St. Thomas, *In II De Anima*, lect. 7, n. 312.

[27] St. Thomas, *In II De Anima*, lect. 3, n. 257.

[28] Cf. Aristotle, *De Anima*, I, 1; St. Thomas, lect. 2, where it is established that the study of the soul belongs to philosophy of nature insofar as the proper activities of the soul involve modifications of the body. Also, Aristotle, *De Anima*, Bk. II, 4, 415 b 22 *et sqq.* where the soul is seen as a principle of movement.

most natural.[29] This fact is significant especially in the case of living beings where one can distinguish between various types of movements, some more fundamental than others. We could say that movements such as being generated (in a broad sense) and falling would be more natural than growing, and growing more natural than sensing, and sensing more natural than understanding (which is not natural at all in the strict sense given to *natural* in the philosophy of nature).

Now why is it that what is most common and most fundamental is also the most natural? We have said that nature is a principle of movement in that in which it is. It is therefore a principle of movement in the mobile—in the moving or moveable thing. A mobile thing implies potency and passivity. It does not necessarily involve activity; this is the mark of the mover. Nature then is intimately related to matter. Though form is nature more perfectly than matter is, since matter would not be a principle of movement without its relation to form, and no being would be a natural being in act were it not for form; nevertheless, form is nature only insofar as it determines matter, because otherwise it would not be a principle of movement at all. Where there is no matter, there is no nature. And in the measure that form rises above matter it reaches beyond mere nature, as it becomes, first, a principle not only of being moved but also of moving, and then a principle not only of movement but of operations that are not strictly movements at all.

Let us look more closely at this gradation in natural beings. One step above the bottom, we have the plants, differentiated from inanimate things by the vegetative soul. Now, this soul, like any other, even the human soul, is most fundamentally

---

[29] It must be noted that we are taking *nature* and *natural* absolutely. Thus, absolutely considered, sensing is less natural than growing though relative to the animal it is more natural, since it is proper to the animal nature and growing is not. Likewise, understanding and willing are more natural for man than sensing, though in an absolute sense they are what is least natural in him, if they are natural at all, and what is most natural of all is anything he has in common with the lowest thing in nature.

substantial form. As such, it is nature insofar as it was a principle in the generation of the thing of which it is the soul and also insofar as it is the principle of movements, such as falling, that are natural to mobile beings already constituted. As soul, in what is proper to it, it is a principle as well of the vegetative operations. These, it is true, are still movements in the strict sense, involving activity, passivity and alteration, all in the strict sense. However, they are movements in which the living being properly moves itself. The soul, unlike any mere substantial form, constitutes the being as an agent with respect to itself. It is still nature, insofar as it is a principle of being moved, intrinsic to the moving being. However as an *active* potency, it is a principle of moving rather than of being moved, and of moving *another* as such [30]—in fact, the living being moves itself only inasmuch as *one* part moves *another* part. Thus as an active, motive principle, it has something different from and more than mere nature.

Then, a more perfect soul, the sentient, is capable not only of these operations but of sense perception as well, which considered in itself, is not movement in the strict sense, but an operation that is an *actus perfecti*.[31] It is movement in some sense, however, " a sort of alteration," as Aristotle calls it, for it involves a transition from potency to act. If the sentient soul is considered to be nature insofar as it is a principle of movement in a secondary sense, in this respect it can only be nature according to an extended meaning. On the other hand, sensation involves movement in the strict sense, insofar as it requires a corporeal organ; and it can result in movement in the strict sense, since it can arouse the passions which involve bodily modifications and at times also give rise to locomotion. Because all these movements are proper to the sentient soul as such, it too is properly termed nature.

[30] Aristotle, *Metaph.*, V, 12, 1019a15 *et sqq.*; St. Thomas comments: "An active principle of movement must be in something other than that which is moved." (*In V Metaph.*, lect. 14, n. 955.)

[31] Aristotle, *De Anima*, III, 7, 431a6 *et sqq.*; St. Thomas, *In III De Anima*, lect. 12, n. 766. Cf. also, *De Anima*, II, 5; St. Thomas, *In II De Anima*, lect. 10 & 11.

Finally, an even more perfect soul, the rational, can be a principle of intellection which, since it does not require an organ, does not involve movement at all. It is an *actus perfecti* and is called movement only because like sensation it requires a transition from potency to act. Since the intellectual operation is no more than metaphorically movement [32] (or, at least, movement according to an analogical extension even beyond that required to include sensation), the rational soul as its principle, considered precisely in this way, is nature only in the same improper (or extended) sense. However, because the proper operation of the rational soul cannot take place without the instrumentality of the senses which do involve movement, the study of this soul, also, belongs to philosophy of nature. It must be remembered too that there are some properly human movements that spring from the rational soul as such—laughing and talking, for example. What is more, the soul is an act corresponding to a natural potency, the form of a natural body. And it is as a *rational* soul that it is the form of a particular type of body, a human body. In this respect, the human soul, even as rational, is properly nature.

Hence, as the form emerges from matter, the thing which it determines rises above passivity, and then above movement, and therefore above mere nature also. Not that it loses what belongs to nature. It has all this and something more. And, in each case, this something more constitutes what is most proper to the particular thing, e. g., sensation for the animal, understanding for man. In this sense, then, we can say that what is primary or most fundamental in a thing is also most purely natural. Indeed, it is what is least perfect in a natural being that is also what is most fundamental. And this is also what is most common since in nature the more perfect things always keep something of the less perfect.

We might note too, incidentally, that as the form rises above

---

[32] Note that in his commentary on the *De Anima*, I, lect. 10, n. 160, St. Thomas says: "In the least proper sense of all, indeed only in a metaphorical sense, is movement to be found in the intellect." See nn. 157 to 162 for a distinction of the three kinds of movement found in the soul's activities.

matter, a characteristic of nature, its *determinatio ad unum*, diminishes in a proportional degree. Because of their materiality, both non-living things and plants are limited to one form, their entitative, natural form. Since one form cannot give rise to contrary active inclinations, in this way they are determined *ad unum*. Already in plants, however, there is a certain beginning of indetermination insofar as they can grow up and down—their growth being not mere local movement but the development of an organism, a body of heterogeneous parts; there is a certain spontaneity in that they can adapt themselves to varying circumstances. Hence St. Thomas's distinction in his commentary on the *De Anima* between nature and the vegetative soul. As form rises above matter, the thing emerges from the purely entitative and becomes capable of the intentional. As such it is not limited to its own form. The inclinations of the thing are not merely those springing from its entitative (natural) form but also those that rise from certain acquired forms, its forms of knowledge. An animal can have now one intentional form, now another, and therefore, can have now one tendency, now another. Man, however, can possess intellectually at the same time a form and its opposite. Hence, precisely as rational, he is above nature insofar as he is not at all determined *ad unum* but must determine himself— and therein, by the way, lies his freedom.[33]

To return now to the development in meaning of *nature*: it might be observed that the variation is based on the different senses of two elements in the definition of nature. Nature, it will be recalled, is defined as a principle of movement in that in which it is. It is an *intrinsic* principle and it is a principle of *movement*. We have seen that the active principle by which living beings move themselves is not in every way intrinsic;[34]

---

[33] It is interesting to note that although the plant is more determined in its *operations* than the beast and the beast more than man, as to their *being* the order is the reverse: man is more determined than the beast and the beast more than the plant. The more perfect the form the more determined a thing is in its being and the less determined in its operations.

[34] With respect to this "innerness" of nature we might go even further and

furthermore, that the principle of sensation in animals *as such* is not a source of movement in the strict sense and the principle of intellection in men has even less reason to be considered as a cause of movement. This last extension of meaning, however, does not coincide with the sense that is broad enough to include even the essence of immaterial substance as root of spiritual activity. It is still proper to philosophy of nature, for though the operation in question as spiritual is not movement, still as the operation of a form in a body, it must take place in conjunction with activities that *are* movements. The rational soul, as a form in matter, cannot effectually be a principle of understanding unless it be at the same time a principle of movement. At this point, however, the extension of the word has reached a limit beyond which the meaning would no longer be proper to philosophy of nature.

The word *nature*, consequently, though it has a sense proper to philosophy of nature, admits of a wide variety of meanings even within this science. In the *Physics*, we have seen, *nature* is said most obviously of matter and most properly of form, but of both insofar as they are principles of movement in the strict sense. Matter is such a principle by its aptitude for form, thus implying an inclination to being. Form as fulfilling this aptitude, and as an end of generation, is also a principle of movement. Once the natural being is in existence, form is nature as the active principle of movements necessary for its preservation in existence and the attainment of its good in general or of movements contributing to the good of the uni-

consider the active principle of the generating agent relatively to the generated. Here the active potency is undoubtedly the mover of *another*. There is a sense, though, in which even this active principle can be called nature, for although it is extrinsic to the particular mobile being that is the product of the generation, nevertheless both mover and moved coincide in the same natural species. (Cf. St. Thomas, *In VII Metaph.*, lect. 6, nn. 1386-1393.) What is more, the universe could be considered as a whole having heterogeneous parts acting one upon the other. In this case, the form that constitutes anything as an agent with respect to something else could be considered as a principle intrinsic to the moving whole (although extrinsic to the particular thing it moves) and as such could be called nature.

verse as a whole; and it is the form, too, that accounts for the particular passive potencies by which a natural being is related to natural agents, fits into the scheme of the universe and thus contributes to the good of the whole. As for this whole system of interrelated active and passive potencies, it too is commonly called Nature. Then, in the study of the soul and subsequent treatises, form again is nature, but now as a special type of active principle by which the living being can move itself. Finally, the form, as soul, is a principle of various activities, some more strictly movement than others; and as the meaning of movement varies, so does the meaning of nature. But from first to last, nature is considered not as essence, nor even as principle of operation in the broad sense, but in one way or another as principle of movement in the strict sense of the term.

SHEILAH O'FLYNN BRENNAN

St. Mary's College
Notre Dame, Indiana

ORDER IN THE PHILOSOPHY OF NATURE

༄

ORDER is an outstanding characteristic of the man of wisdom.[1] He is a man who has discovered and observed the due order in his reasoning processes. He has imposed a rational order over the acts of his will and emotions. And he stands in wonderment at the great order of all nature, an order that he himself has not made, but only contemplates.[2] It is the discovery of order—of *logos*—in the world that impels him to set up a science of nature by which he will understand the intelligible necessities and manifold beauties of the universe that is his home.

As a man of wisdom the philosopher of nature seeks not only the order inherent in reality itself, but also an order for investigating that reality.[3] For he realizes that not only the exigencies of the real order, but also those of the order of his mind will rule the development of his science. When the natural philosopher is a teacher as well as a searcher for wisdom, he knows that his exposition will have to be modified by another order, that required to direct the minds of his students to the comprehension of the truths amassed by a long tradition of devoted masters.

No arbitrary plan of investigation nor casual order of treatment will do justice to the science of nature. There must be a definite order that will be the result of the interplay of several factors on the science—factors whose demands are essential.

---

[1] St. Thomas Aquinas, *In Metaphysicam Aristotelis Commentaria* (ed. Cathala) Proemium; *In Decem Libros Ethicorum Aristotelis ad Nichomachum Expositio* (ed. Pirotta), I, 1, n. 1-2; *Summa Theologiae*, I, 1, 6; I-II, 102, 1; *Summa Contra Gentes*, I, 1; II, 24.

[2] Cf. St. Thomas, *In De Physico Auditu Aristotelis* (ed. Leonina), VIII, 3, n. 3; *Sum. cont. Gent.*, II, 24.

[3] "Processus scientiarum est opus rationis, cujus proprium est ordinare; unde in omni opere rationis ordo aliquis invenitur, secundum quem proceditur ab uno in aliud " (St. Thomas, *In I De Caelo et Mundo* [ed. Leonina] Proem., n. 1).

To ignore these will severely blemish the science achieved and particularly the teaching of that science.

It will be profitable, therefore, to make a synthetic study of the principles of order governing the philosophy of nature.

Two texts of St. Thomas can serve to introduce the question.

The concept of order includes three elements: first, the idea of *before and after*; hence there is order in all those ways by which one thing can be before another, by place, time, and so forth. Order also includes *distinction*, because only distinct things have any order. But this is rather presupposed than signified by the word " order." The third element is a *principle of order*, according to which order is divided into its species. Hence there is an order according to place, another according to dignity, and another according to origin.[4]

Succession, distinction, and a principle of order: all these are pertinent to the consideration of order in the philosophy of nature. St. Thomas elaborates on the principle of order in the second text:

Order always has reference to some principle. Therefore, since there are many kinds of principle—namely, according to site, as a point; according to intellect, as the principle of demonstration; and according to each individual cause—so there are many kinds of order.[5]

It is the order according to intellect that mainly interests us, because we are here considering the problem of ordering a science. The principle of that order will in some way coincide with " the principle of demonstration." Since demonstration is the means for achieving scientific knowledge, the order within

---

[4] " Ordo in ratione sua includit tria, scil. rationem prioris et posterioris; unde secundum omnes illos modos potest dici esse ordo aliquorum, secundum quos aliquis altero prius dicitur et secundum locum et secundum tempus et secundum omnia huiusmodi. Includit etiam distinctionem, quia non est ordo aliquorum nisi distinctorum. Sed hoc magis praesupponit nomen ordinis, quam significet. Includit etiam tertio rationem ordinis, ex qua etiam ordo in speciem contrahitur. Unde unus est ordo secundum locum, alius secundum dignitatem, alius secundum originem " (*Super Libros Sententiarum*, I, d. 20, 3, 1. Cf. *Summa Theol.*, II-II, 26, 1).

[5] *Summa Theol.*, I, 42, 3, transl. A. Pegis, *Basic Writings of Saint Thomas Aquinas* (New York: Random House, 1945).

natural philosophy will have to conform to the exigencies of the logical process of demonstration. Among the many requirements of demonstration is this one, that the principles of a demonstration, i. e. the definitions and premises, have to be foreknown, even reducible to self-evident propositions, so that the mind may be led from the known to the yet unknown. The first point of our study will be the order in which the mind is led from the known to the unknown.

The order of learning [6]

The learning process may be likened to the way in which nature operates a cure. It may do so through its own intrinsic powers, or it may be helped along by the art of the physician and the instrumentality of his medicines. By analogy, there are two ways of acquiring science. " In one way, natural reason by itself reaches knowledge of unknown things, and this way is called discovery (*inventio*) ; in the other way, when someone else aids the learner's natural reason, and this is called learning by instruction (*disciplina*) ." [7] There follows from this a fundamental principle of organizing a science. "A similar thing takes place in acquiring knowledge (*scientia*). For the teacher leads the pupil to knowledge of things he does not know *in the same way that one directs himself through the process of discovering something he does not know.*" [8]

Therefore, the *via inventionis* and the *ordo disciplinae* coin-

[6] L. M. Régis, O. P., *Epistemology* (New York: Macmillan, 1959), Chap. IV " The Angelic Doctor's Method." Chap. XII. " Infallible Knowledge of Mediate Truth." R. Garrigou-Lagrange, *The One God* (St. Louis: B. Herder Book Co., 1943), " The Method of St. Thomas," pp. 9-26.

[7] *Truth*, 11, 1, transl. J. V. McGlynn, S. J. (Chicago: Henry Regnery Co., 1953).

[8] *Ibid*. Italics ours. St. Thomas teaches the same doctrine elsewhere. " Scientia acquiritur dupliciter: et sine doctrina, per inventionem; et per doctrinam. Docens igitur hoc modo incipit docere sicut inveniens incipit invenire: offerendo scilicet considerationi discipuli principia ab eo nota, quia *omnis disciplina ex praeexistenti fit cognitione* (I *Poster.*, 1, 1; 71a), et illa principia in conclusiones deducendo; et proponendo exempla sensibilia, ex quibus in anima discipuli formentur phantasmata necessaria ad intelligendum " (*Contra Gent.*, II, 75. Cf. *Summa Theol.*, I, 117, 1; *In II De Anima*, 11, n. 372; *De Spir. Creat.*, a. 9, ad 7).

cide from the point of view of order. Is there an *ordo doctrinae* that is different from these? Sometimes it is asserted that in building up a body of scientific knowledge one would use the order of discovery, but in teaching others the fully achieved science one would use an inverse order, the order of doctrine. Such a position would equate the order of doctrine with two other orders: the *order of nature* or with the *via iudicii*. We shall show that both these identifications are incorrect. Actually, the *ordo doctrinae* and the *ordo disciplinae* coincide. As St. Thomas wrote at a later period of his life, " The names ' doctrine ' and ' discipline ' pertain to the acquisition of knowledge. For doctrine is the action of him who makes something known; discipline, however, is the reception of knowledge from another." [9] The *ordo doctrinae* is not, therefore, the inverse of the *via inventionis*.[10] In fact, *ordo doctrinae* should be translated " order of teaching."

Mention has been made of the *order of nature* or the real order. What is the relation between this and the order of learning? At the beginning of his commentary on the *Physics* of Aristotle, St. Thomas lays down a principle of learning that he reiterates many times in his other works.[11] Our knowledge starts from what is more known to us and proceeds to things that are ontologically more perfect and hence more knowable. We must start from sensible things, lower in the order of nature, but more accessible to our knowledge; it is through these sensible things that we ascend to the contemplation of higher and ultimately of divine things.[12] Moreover, the study of

[9] *Exposition of the Posterior Analytics of Aristotle*, transl. Pierre Conway, O. P. (Quebec: Le Librairie Philosophique M. Doyon, 1956), I, 1, n. 9.

[10] Cf. R. Garrigou-Lagrange, *La Réalisme du Principe de Finalité* (Paris: Desclee, 1932), p. 255; P. Coffey, *The Science of Logic* (London: Longmans, Green and Co., 1918), II, pp. 15-16.

[11] *In I Phys.*, 1, n. 7-11. Cf. *In I Anal. Post.*, 2, n. 8; *In VII Meta.*, 2, n. 1297-1305; *Summa Theol.*, I, 85, 5; *In De Trin.*, 6, 1, ad qu. 1.

[12] " Cum enim omnis disciplina fiat per ea quae sunt magis nota addiscenti, quem oportet aliqua praecognoscere ad hoc ut addiscat, oportet disciplinam nostram procedere per ea quae sunt magis nota quo ad nos, quae sunt saepe minus nota secundum naturam, ad ea quae sunt notiora secundum naturam, nobis autem minus nota " (*In VII Meta.*, 2, n. 1301).

sensible things is easier than that of immaterial things, and in teaching and learning, the preferable order is to start with what is easier.[13] Thus, the order of learning is the inverse of the order of nature.

What is to be said of the *via iudicii* and the order of learning? As a first approach we may note that St. Thomas opposes the *via iudicii* to the *via inventionis*,[14] the latter of which parallels the order of learning. The *via inventionis* is a procedure from the sensible to self-evident principles and thence to the conclusions flowing from them; herein is there a true " discovery " of truth. The way of judgment is the inverse of this.[15] It consists of resolving or analyzing a mediate truth into its principles. It verifies and evaluates already acquired knowledge by tracing conclusions back to self-evident premisses.[16] Thus, in a science, when there has been a chain of demonstrations one following from the other, a conclusion can be resolved or analysed back to first principles by retracing the course of the demonstrations developed through the *via inventionis*. The way of judgment is not then the essential order of learning or of teaching, though it is secondarily involved in learning and teaching as the process of verification of demonstrations. The way of judgment, how-

---

[13] *In V Meta.*, 1, n. 752; *In De Trin.*, 7, 1, qu. 2, ad 3; *In II Anal. Post.*, 16, n. 6; *Summa Theol.*, II-II, 189, 1, ad 4.

[14] *De Veritate*, 10, 8, ad 10; 14, 1; 15, 1; 22, 2; *Summa Theol.*, I, 79, 8; 9; I-II, 57, 6; 68 4; II-II, 9, 1.

[15] " Cum autem homo per naturalem rationem assentit secundum intellectum alicui veritati, dupliciter perficitur circa veritatem illam; primo quidem, quia capit eam; secundo, quia de ea certum iudicium habet " (*Summa Theol.*, II-II, 9, 1). The references in the preceding note sufficiently describe the way of judgment.

[16] The way of invention, from the point of view of *content*, proceeds by either analysis or synthesis, these two terms being used in a variety of ways. However, from the point of view of the *logical process*, invention is synthetic: putting together of a syllogism. The way of judgment analyses or resolves a syllogism into its elements in order that the intellect may give its assent to the conclusion. On analysis-synthesis, cf. L.-M. Regis, "Analyse et synthèse dans l'oeuvre de saint Thomas," in *Studia Mediaevalia in Honorem Admodum Rev. Raymundi Josephi Martin* (Brugis Flandrorum: De Tempel); *idem., Epistemology*, pp. 422-457; S. E. Dolan, " Resolution and Composition in Speculative and Practical Discourse," *Laval Theologique et Philosophique*, VI (1950), 9-62; F. X. Calcagno, *Philosophia Scholostica* (Napoli: D'Auria, 1950), I, pp. 216-219.

ever, may seem to be the order of teaching to those who use the thesis method in which the conclusion is first presented authoritatively and then justified. At most, the conclusion should be presented only as a question, the solution of which must be arrived at by the way of discovery.[17]

Distinction of natural philosophy from other sciences

The question of the relation of the real order to the order of learning raises the problem of the relation of natural philosophy to other sciences, especially to metaphysics, the queen of the human sciences. The same material being is known in different ways by different sciences. If we are to establish order in natural philosophy, then this science must be distinguished from metaphysics, theology, and empirical science.[18]

In many texts St. Thomas explicitly states that metaphysics is to be taught after natural philosophy.[19] Metaphysics is, in fact, the last of the sciences to be learned, the queen of human sciences, the culmination of human wisdom, ancillary to none but supernatural theology. Natural philosophy and metaphysics are distinct sciences, each with its proper principles. Natural philosophy uses proofs with middle terms that contain common sensory matter in their definitions. Metaphysics uses concepts that are negatively immaterial, that is, containing no matter in their definitions, but able to be existentially realized either in matter or apart from matter. Two sciences proceeding according to such distinct manners of conceptualization are at different levels of intelligibility and point up different degrees of necessity in their objects. They are thus irreducibly distinct.[20]

---

[17] The above distinction between invention and judgment is not the same as the distinction between inventive logic (largely dialectics) and judicative logic, which is concerned with the matter and form of the demonstrative syllogism. Cf. *In I Anal. Post.*, 1, n. 6.

[18] " Ordo absque distinctione non est. Unde ubi non est distinctio secundum rem, sed solum secundum modum intelligendi, ibi non potest esse ordo nisi secundum modum intelligendi " (*De Pot.*, 10, 3).

[19] *In III Sent.*, d. 35, 1, 2, 3; *In VI Ethic.*, 7, n. 1209-1211; *In Librum de Causis*, 1; *In De Trin.*, 6, 1.

[20] *In I Anal. Post.*, 41; *In De Trin.*, 5, 1; *Summa Theol.*, I, 85, 1, ad 2.

Nevertheless, there are close and necessary relations between the two sciences. Natural philosophy is preparatory to metaphysics.[21] It acquaints the learner with many concepts existing in material reality, but able to be extended to a metaphysical plane. Notions such as substance and accident, potency and act, cause and effect are metaphysical concepts, commensurate with being as such; but they are used and studied in natural philosophy insofar as they apply to its subject.[22] After becoming acquainted with them at the level of sensory matter, where they are relatively easy to grasp, a student can more conveniently understand them in their metaphysical context. Natural philosophy is preparatory to metaphysics also because it proves the existence of immaterial being, without which metaphysics would have no formal subject and thus would yield its primacy to natural philosophy.[23]

Even though metaphysics comes later in the order of learning, it is first in the order of nature and dignity.[24] Therefore, it gives an extrinsic guidance to natural philosophy, a guidance that the beginner will scarcely realize or one which he will have to take on authority. Moreover, the defense of the principles of natural philosophy is the function of metaphysics. It is the metaphysician who justifies the validity of our knowledge and who critically investigates the common principles that other sciences borrow and use.[25]

This brief discussion of the relation of the two sciences should suffice to justify a few practical points pertinent to our present study. Due order requires that purely metaphysical questions be eliminated from natural philosophy. Relevant examples would be such topics as creation, pantheism, eternity, the glory of God as final cause of the universe. The immortality of the

---

[21] In De Trin., 5, 1, ad 9.

[22] In IV Meta., 5, n. 591; XI, 4, n. 2206-2210; In II Phys., 5, n. 360.

[23] We have studied elsewhere the relation of natural philosophy and metaphysics: " The Formal Subject of Metaphysics," The Thomist, XIX (1956), 59-74; " Being and Metaphysics," The Modern Schoolman, XXXV (1958), 271-285.

[24] In De Trin., loc. cit.

[25] Ibid.; In IV Meta., 5, n. 590-591.

human soul must not be treated metaphysically in natural philosophy; the proof, in order to be physical, must rest on the intrinsic incorruptibility of the soul. The *de facto* question of the immortality of the soul, proved from the wisdom and goodness of God, must be saved for metaphysics, or at most must be presented in natural philosophy in dialectical status. The origin of the soul and its status after death are questions raised in natural philosophy, but which are unable to be settled by the principles of natural philosophy; the metaphysical light is necessary.[26] Natural philosophy must always present its proofs on the basis of its own principles. Positions should not be held because of metaphysical repercussions, but proofs should be constructed by the intellectual processing of sensory data in the light of properly physical principles. Metaphysical proofs can be accepted only as dialectical in the lower science. It is true that metaphysics casts a fuller light over the world of nature; it gives the ultimate reasons for the truths discovered by the physicist. But the distinction necessary for highlighting the true nature and order of natural philosophy demands that metaphysical insights be presented in the status of footnotes or appendices, which are accepted, not as apodictic, but as dialectical, until they can be seen in their proper perspective within the science of metaphysics.

Even more important, it is necessary that teachers effectively shake off the Wolff-Leibnizian influence and discontinue presenting natural philosophy as an *application* of metaphysics.

---

[26] " Sed quomodo se habeant formae totaliter a materiae separatae, et quid sint, vel etiam quomodo se habeat haec forma, idest anima rationalis, secundum quod est separabilis et sine corpore existere potens, et quid sit secundum suam essentiam separabile, hoc determinare pertinet ad philosophum primum " (*In II Phys.*, 4, n. 10. Cf. *In De Sensu et Senato*, 1, n. 4; 2, n. 317; *In III De Anima*, 12, n. 785). Just as the above-mentioned questions should be removed from natural philosophy, so it would seem that the discussion of the final natural end of man belongs to natural philosophy. Every science treats the principles, causes, and properties of its subject (*In Meta.*, Proem). The final end of man is determined by nature (*In III Ethic.*, 13, n. 524; VI, 2, n. 1131). It is the ultimate term of the natural motion of desire (*Ibid.*, I, 9, n. 197). Ethics borrows from natural philosophy the doctrines of man's nature and end; it is, therefore, subalternated to natural philosophy.

Often the doctrine of hylomorphism, for instance, is treated as an application of the metaphysical doctrine of potency and act to material things, which implies a genetic primacy of metaphysics over natural philosophy. The presentation of natural philosophy before metaphysics is important for all who would give a synthetic picture of Thomism, even for those historians who claim to describe the philosophical doctrine of St. Thomas, rather than his theology.

It is equally essential to distinguish natural philosophy from theology. There is no theoretical difficulty to this. But sometimes the theological interest of authors impels them to give undue prominence to problems that have theological import, even to treat theological matters in philosophy, such as the manner of the Eucharistic presence of our Lord and the possibility of miracles. The due order and proportion of natural philosophy require footnote status for strictly theological problems, no matter how worthy or interesting they may be in themselves. Special caution must be exercised in taking proofs bodily from St. Thomas' theological writings and using them uncritically in natural philosophy. The theological light, or perhaps a metaphysical orientation, may make a given proof incompatible with the proper method of natural philosophy. Extracontentual arguments are a disservice to natural philosophy.

Another clarification is necessary for the purposes of keeping due order in natural philosophy. What is the relation between natural philosophy and modern empirical science? This is not the place to treat this question *ex professo*, but we may lay down a few propositions. Natural philosophy must not be content with mere generalities; it must extend its investigations into the realm of the specific. At its general stage it is still confused knowledge awaiting further actualization. It must apply its light to the whole cosmos and to all its parts. The human drive for understanding will not be satisfied with less.[27]

Modern science's monopoly of detailed phenomena causes

[27] Cf. *In I Meteorologicorum*, 1, n. 1; R. J. Nogar, O. P., "Cosmology without a Cosmos," in *From An Abundant Spring* (New York: Kenedy, 1952), pp. 363-392.

at least an overlapping, if not a real conflict. A partial resolution is certainly possible. Insofar as empirical science is factual, its data are required as preliminary to causal demonstration at the various levels of natural philosophy, for a rich experience is prerequisite to natural philosophy. Insofar as empirical science is mathematicized, it is a *scientia media* distinct from natural philosophy.[28] But if mathematics is used as an instrument for the investigation of facts, and if the facts have thereby been certainly established, they may be taken over by the natural philosopher and demonstrated in the light of his proper principles. From this point of view, mathematicized science is instrumental to philosophy.[29] Insofar as modern science is hypothetical, its relations with natural philosophy can be only on the level of a dialectical continuation of philosophy. At this stage of modern science we can argue that there is a *de facto* influence of philosophy upon the scientist, whether it be mechanism, logical positivism, or—are we anathema for suggesting a *desideratum?*—Thomism. At least, if nature is to be *understood*, rather than merely catalogued or used, then natural philosophy must shed its light even into the dark corners of scientific theory.[30]

One point is most noteworthy. Natural philosophy does not depend on scientific theory, but rather vice versa. The doctrine of hylomorphism, for instance, is not built on the shifting sands of scientific theory. Aristotle elaborated his doctrine long ago on the basis of common observation. The discoveries and theories of the passing centuries have not overturned that doctrine, but rather look to it to introduce intelligibility and order into the confused maze of modern facts and theories.[31]

[28] *In De Trin.*, 5, 3, ad 6.

[29] *In I De Coelo*, 3, n. 6.

[30] We have studied the relevance of these principles to the science of psychology in "Toward an Integrated Psychology," *Proceedings of the American Catholic Philosophical Association* (1958), 139-148.

[31] "It is enough for us to remark that rectitude of conscience in scientific research has led modern thought to the threshold of the only philosophy which can give a reasonable interpretation of the results obtained by experimentation. . . . The theory of matter and form, of potency and act, is capable of illuminating the

Obviously, the order intrinsic to natural philosophy demands full clarity on the distinctions and relations obtaining between it and empirical science.

Internal order of natural philosophy

Once we have ordered natural philosophy in the sense of distinguishing it from other sciences, we may turn our investigation to its own intrinsic order. In this we have the assistance of St. Thomas in the various *prooemia* to his commentaries on the works of Aristotle.

First, we must make a necessary distinction between the order of demonstration and the order of definition. A number of books on natural philosophy so divide their matter as to treat first of the properties of natural being: motion, quantity, time, and place; then as a culmination of that part of natural philosophy widely called " cosmology," comes a study of the nature of material bodies, a determination of the first principles, matter and form. The study of the properties is presented, explicitly or implicitly, as part of the inductive search for the definition of bodies through their first principles.

Such a process, however, does not do justice to the logical doctrine of demonstration. It is *propter quid* demonstration that yields strictly scientific knowledge. The theoretical discussions among scholastics on the principles of division of sciences presuppose the Aristotelian and classical Thomistic concept of science. Scientific knowledge, in this precise and technical sense of the word, is not merely a collection of facts nor inductive searches ending in definitions. It consists of demonstrating attributes, whether properties or causes, through the use of middle terms that are both definitions of the subject and proper causes of the attributes. There would be no reason

requirements of modern science with a light which closely agrees with the results of experimentation. . . . It is easy to catch a glimpse of the great usefulness which so profound a philosophy can have in aiding science to clarify the problems of nature " (" The Perennial Philosophy and Modern Science," Address of Pope Pius XII to the Intenational Thomistic Congress, September 14, 1955). *The Pope Speaks*, II (1955), 220-221.

for distinguishing sciences according to the manner of conceptualizing the subject (*obiectum formale sub quo*), if the definition of the subject were the terminal point of the science, rather than the starting point. The definition is rather the very light that reveals the necessary connection of the attributes with the subject. The definition must be predicated of the subject in the minor premiss of a *propter quid* demonstration; it must be shown as the proper cause of the attribute in the major premiss. The knowledge of both these premisses is prior to the drawing of the scientific conclusion.[32] Therefore, the study of the principles of natural being must come at the beginning of natural philosophy.[33]

The order of procedure intrinsic to natural philosophy is set out at the beginning of the *Physics* and of St. Thomas' commentary on it. We must start with the general characteristics of material beings and later proceed to their specific notes.[34] A reason of pedagogical convenience is given for this: otherwise it would be necessary to repeat these truths many times while treating the particular manifestations of them.[35] There is also a proper reason for this procedure from general to particular. A thing is knowable according to its separation from matter; this is the principle for the specification of sciences. Even within a science the same principle holds for the division of parts.[36] We advance in the scale of knowledge insofar as we transcend potency and make manifest more actual notes; in other words, we proceed from confused to distinct concepts. The more general concepts are more potential; the specific are more actual. Therefore, in natural science we must start with the study of mobile being in general, with its principles, causes and properties. Later, by a process of concretion or application,

---

[32] Cf. M. Glutz, C. P., *The Manner of Demonstrating in Natural Philosophy* (River Forest, Illinois: 1956).

[33] *In I Anal. Post.*, 41, n. 9. Cf. Wm. H. Kane, O. P., "The Nature and Extent of Natural Philosophy," *The New Scholasticism*, XXXI (1957), 85-97.

[34] *In I Phys.*, 1, n. 5.

[35] Aristotle, *Parts of Animals*, 1, 1, 639a15-b7.

[36] *In De Sensu et Sensato*, 1 ,n. 2.

we treat those mobile beings that are the proper subjects of specific types of change.[37] The same process of concretion is used in the special branches of the science, e. g. psychology treats living beings first in general, then in particular. At each stage of concretion we must assign the commensurate principles, causes, and properties. The further we proceed in concretion, the more difficult it becomes to demonstrate facts causally, although quite often the final cause of phenomena will be apparent, and from it we can "trace the links of causation." [38]

Order to the minds of students

We have discussed order in natural philosophy from the aspect of distinction and priority. Now we must investigate it from the aspect of relation to the student.

A science is a body of knowledge that is intended to be communicated to others. It is significant that the word "doctrine," which, when used substantively, signifies a body of truths, comes from the word "to teach." The exposition of the philosophy of nature can never abstract from this ordination to the minds of other men, and so the internal order of the science must necessarily envision some audience, whether beginers, graduates, or specialists. We shall confine ourselves to considering natural philosophy in relation to the undergraduate student.

The most important fact about the undergraduate is that he is a beginner in philosophy. He is struggling through a new and strange terrain. His insights are superficial; his knowledge

---

[37] G. J. McMahon, S. J., *The Order of Procedure in the Philosophy of Nature* (Quebec: La Librairie Philosophique M. Doyon, 1958) Chap. 5-7; C. DeKoninck, "Introduction à l'étude de l'âme" in S. Cantin, *Précis de psychologie thomiste* (Laval University, 1948) pp. xlvi-xlvii, and in *Laval Théologique et Philosophique*, III (1947) 9-65.

[38] Aristotle, *Parts of Animals*, 1, 5, 645a10 The first book of this work gives a summary of the method to be pursued in studying the various types of animal life from the general to the specific. 645b1-646a6 show how demonstrations are to be given in terms of final causes.

is often largely a memorizing of formulae. He must be helped by his teacher to understanding, and this with the aid of a text book that features clarity of exposition. The undergraduate is not yet prepared for delving into ancient sources; at least, he cannot use the works of Aristotle and the commentaries of St. Thomas in place of a text book. These are for more advanced students. Moreover, these ancient treatises, valuable as they are in themselves, are not adapted to the modern student, who has had some amount of modern science before coming to the study of philosophy. Our exposition of natural philosophy must take cognizance of modern science, even though philosophy is not founded on scientific theory. We must also give at least bowing recognition to the many competing theories for each thesis in the philosophy of nature, even though they may sometimes be little more than historical oddities.

All learning proceeds from previously acquired knowledge. This knowledge not only is a starting point; it also conditions the acquisition of further doctrine. Because of his previous education a student very easily slips into mechanistic modes of thought. The concept of formal causality may come hard to him. Analogical concepts may be frustrating. The student must be gently led into the philosophical mode of thinking. Many examples of formal and final causality must be given him so that his concepts will be clear and deep. A well-ordered exposition of the philosophy of nature must satisfy this need of the modern student.

The presentation of topics within natural philosophy must not be given in a cut and dried thesis method. The natural relation between a human mind and a not-understood fact of nature is expressed in wonderment. As wonderment initiated the science of philosophy among the early Greeks, so too it will stimulate the individual mind to true philosophical inquiry. The order of a science consists in the progress from wonderment to its contrary, the understanding of causes.[39] Hence it is

[39] Cf *In I Meta*, 3, n. 66.

necessary to arouse this state in the minds of students by presenting the topics of natural philosophy as questions, the *aporia* of Aristotle. These questions are hedged in by doubts, and it is only in resolving the doubts in the light of certainly established definitions and demonstrations that the mind comes to rest. Proper order demands that the questions and doubts be first proposed.[40] The thesis method is not well adapted for the first imparting of knowledge, but rather for remembering, reviewing, and for disputing.

The nature of the student's mind demands that a hunt be made for all definitions. Definitions have value only when one understands how they have been acquired and through what kind of defining principles they are stated. Merely to state them without justifying them is equivalent to an appeal to authority. To state the definition and then to justify its elements is to proceed in reverse order. To define after an inadequate preparation for the definition is to play the midwife to a puny and scrawny brainchild, as Socrates would put it. We can learn a valuable lesson by observing St. Thomas painstakingly proceeding through three or four articles before finally stating their outcome in a definition.

The core of science is the *propter quid* demonstration. All else in the science, observations of facts, definitions, *quia* demonstrations, hypotheses and other dialectical material are all ordered to *propter quid* demonstration. This order must be made evident to the student. He must be shown how all hinges on the first principles of science and how one demonstration follows upon another. Particularly, he must be able to evaluate the type of demonstration and to situate it in the context of the whole science. It must be admitted that one looks far and wide before he finds philosophy books that make use of the doctrine of demontration as proposed in the logic texts. The nature of the science itself demands this structure, and its order to the minds of the students requires that the methodology be empha-

---

[40] This is, of course, the method of St. Thomas in the *Quaestiones Disputatae* and in the *Summa Theologiae*. Cf. R. Garrigou-Langrange, *The One God*, pp. 9-26.

sized, both in its abstract principles and in its concrete application. Only thus will students be led to philosophic wisdom.

It is wisdom that we intend to give our students. Even the meager participation of full human wisdom which the philosophy of nature gives is of great value.[41] Such wisdom is communicated to students through a twofold process on the part of the teacher, information and formation. The teacher is interested in teaching the students to think for themselves, to acquire firm habits of correct reasoning, to achieve personal insights, to understand rather than to memorize formulae. This formation is given, not by abstract exercises, but through a process of information wherein the student assimilates the wisdom of the ages, the fruits of a rich tradition. There can be no question of wasting time by letting untrained students try to discover for themselves the wisdom that it took more than twenty centuries to acquire. A realistic ordination of natural philosophy to the minds of undergraduate students will emphasize information by which minds will come into posession of the basic doctrines of the science. But if natural philosophy is presented with correct order, the cherished goal of formation will be achieved in and through the process of information.

Order, then, is the key-word to the correct presentation of the philosophy of nature. Definite order is required by the nature of the human mind and its goal of science. Order is existent in physical reality and imposes itself on the science of that reality. The minds of students of philosophy, conditioned by special modes of receptivity, require a particular ordination of natural philosophy to their own degree of development. We may say, by analogy, that order is the soul of the universe, " the form that knits the whole world." [42] The contemplation of this order in the science of nature will elevate

---

[41] Cf. *Contra Gent.*, II, 1-4.

[42] Dante, *The Divine Comedy*, Paradiso, Canto 33, 1.92, transl. Lawrence Binyon (New York, The Viking Press, 1947). Cf. *Contra. Gent.*, II, 39; III, 97.

our minds and hearts, according to the beautiful words of
Dante:

> The Power primordial and ineffable
> Made with such order all that circling speeds
> Through mind or space, that he who looks on it
> Cannot but taste Him, as thereon he feeds.[43]

MELVIN A. GLUTZ, C.P.

Immaculate Conception Monastery
Chicago, Illinois.

---

[43] *Ibid.*, Canto 10, 1 3-6.

MOTIONLESS MOTION

༄

S OME years ago a modern mathematician who had at that time become interested in Aristotelian-Thomistic philosophy asked me if it would be possible to employ symbolic logic to set forth the proofs for the existence of God. In the attempt to show him that the difficulties in these proofs derived from something other than their logical form, I discovered that most of the terms I was using meant something quite different for him. This was particularly true of the term " motion." I, of course, was referring to *actus entis in potentia inquantum huiusmodi*. When I tried to show him how this notion required an analysis of matter, form, and privation he expressed typical Cartesian astonishment. In the discussion which followed he referred to an idea of motion by a neo-Kantian which he said fairly well expressed his own concept of motion:

All determination of place . . . is a work of the mind: *omnis locatio mentis est opus*. From this point the way is open to Galileo's foundation of dynamics: for since place has ceased to be something real, the question as to the *ground* of the place of a body and the ground of its *persistence* in one and the same place disappears. Objective physical reality passes from *place* to *change of place*, to motion and the factors by which it is determined as magnitude. If such a determination is to be possible in a definite way, the identity and permanence, which were hitherto ascribed to mere place, must go over to motion; motion must possess ' being,' that is, from the standpoint of the physicist, numerical constancy. This demand for the numerical constancy of motion itself finds its expression and its realization in the law of inertia.[1]

He also was of the opinion that quite a number of the modern scientists and philosophers would agree, at least in general, with this idea of motion. I was inclined to agree with him on

---

[1] Ernst Cassirer, *Substance and Function* (La Salle, Illinois: Open Court Publishing Company, 1923), p. 362.

the latter point but on the first one I had to say that such motion was " motionless " and that only by using the concept developed by Aristotle could we arrive at the *prima via*. Furthermore, while admitting that motion as conceived by modern science has a certain validity in the explanations of the mathematical physicist, I said that to attempt to make this the basis of any kind of a complete explanation of the ultimate principles of the universe could lead to a very unacceptable philosophy. I do not recall whether my mathematician friend was convinced or not. In the present paper I would like to elaborate some of these notions.

Cassirer himself, in his *Substance and Function*, attempts to make this idea of " motionless motion " the basis of a new explanation which will replace that of Aristotle. In the first chapter he shows how the new developments in logic must necessarily replace the logic of the Philosopher, founded as the latter was an a now out-moded metaphysics. His conception of the Greek synthesis in his analysis of the problem of knowledge shows his appreciation of the work of both Plato and Aristotle:

There is no denying that Plato shaped his conception of knowledge on the pattern of mathematics, and his theory of ideas not only owes separate fundamental insights to mathematics but is determined throughout its whole structure by this science. On the other hand, his theory far transcends whatever Greek mathematics could present in the way of stable results, and Plato seems to have given to the mathematics of his time much more than he took from it. . . .

What Plato had done for mathematics, Aristotle did for biology. Not only did he conceive of it as a self-contained whole; he was the first to provide a conceptual language for its separate parts. . . .[2]

What he has in mind here is shown in the rest of his Introduction to this work. He shows how the work of Descartes, Leibniz, and Kant has discovered a new basis for the interpretation of Nature. As he says:

---

[2] E. Cassirer, *The Problem of Knowledge* (New Haven: Yale University Press, 1950), p. 12.

The Renaissance proved itself in very truth a new birth, in that it not only revived the various philosophical theories of antiquity but also recovered the spirit by which they had been created. The first centuries of the Renaissance were content in general to tie up with some doctrine or other. But so long as they sought to establish anew the Platonic, the Aristotelian, the Stoic, the Epicurean, and the Skeptic systems, all these remained mere heirlooms of which it was impossible to take complete possession. Descartes, precisely because of his unhistorical temper, was the first to succeed in the historic act of liberation. For he never merely took over conclusions but reembodied in himself the original power of philosophical thinking. He filled all science with this power and he thereby discovered a new universal form of science, and the Cartesian method and the Cartesian system are but the discovery of science and establishment of this new form.[3]

That this new approach to science will result in a new "ontology" is shown by his appreciation of the Greek synthesis in the very beginning of this work where he says:

The more deeply reason is absorbed in its own being, and the more conscious it becomes of its own true worth, the further it penetrates into the Being of things. For there is no sharp line that separates truth from reality, thought from Being. This fundamental meaning of Greek philosophy is fully realized in Plato. With him the problem of being and the problem of knowledge, ' ontology ' and ' logic ', are bound together in indissoluble unity.

That this analysis of the Greek achievement has some basis in fact would be generally admitted. However, in order to see its lacunae more precisely, some further comparison with the Aristotelian " synthesis " will be necessary. We might begin with the problem of being or " ontology."

Aristotle studied being in the science which is today often referred to as " metaphysics." He called this " first philosophy," " theology," and sometimes " the divine science." In his conception of this discipline there were at least two very important aspects: it is a science, and the knowledge of it is in some way above the capacity of the human intellect. When he referred to it as a science he was speaking in terms of the ideas estab-

[3] *Ibid.,* p. 13.

lished in the *Posterior Analytics*. He held that there is a kind of knowledge in which the human intellect, starting from principles which it grasps with certitude, is able to arrive at true and certain conclusions. When the syllogism of the *Prior Analytics* is employed in this way the result is a demonstration, the knowledge is science. We attain this knowledge most easily and often in mathematics. It is found in other disciplines but with greater difficulty. One study that presented problems to this kind of analysis was the science of Nature, another was the science of being or first philosophy.

Heraclitus had said that " Nature loves to hide." Aristotle was able to show more clearly why this is so. He discovered that the objects studied in this science contained an inherent lack of intelligibility. For this reason the student will sometimes be forced to content himself with an inductive argument which will show that a proposition is true without giving a scientific reason. At other times he must use an argument from analogy. Science in the meaning given that term in the *Posterior Analytics* will be very difficult to arrive at in this discipline. Still, Aristotle was convinced that only by building on the ideas laboriously worked out in the science of Nature would the human intellect be able to come to a knowledge of the objects of first philosophy. Here, as Cajetan might say, is something which seems to have escaped the notice of many modern followers of the Philosopher. There are many today who teach that motion is *actus entis in potentia inquantum huiusmodi*. There are not so many who, after presenting this notion, go on to explain it along with its properties, time and place, and its kinds, both quantitative and qualitative. There are even fewer who, after having done this much, go on to speak of first motions and first movers. Many teachers today are of the opinion that this part of Aristotle's *Physics* is hopelessly tied to the out-dated cosmogony of Greek science. This makes it easy for them to ignore totally all the other physical works, with the possible exception of his *De Anima*. Even with this last named work there are only a very few teachers who are not prepared to use St. Thomas' *Summa Theologiae* in place of the more natural exposition of these principles. However, while there are only a few who give much more than lip service to Aristotle's treatment of Nature today, the number of those who stand ready to expound his metaphysics or first philosophy is legion. Some even go further and, with the vague and ambiguous notions of metaphysical principles derived from such an anti-Aristotelian procedure, attempt to find out how things are in Nature. This is truly an attempt to proceed from the unknown to the known. Swift's comment on these disciples is apt:

Having a desire to see those ancients, who were most renowned for wit and learning, I set apart one day on purpose. I proposed that Homer and Aristotle might appear at the head of all their commentators; but these were so numerous, that some hundreds were forced to attend in the court and outward rooms of the palace. I knew, and could distinguish those two heroes at first sight, not only from the crowd, but from each other. Homer was the taller and comelier person of the two, walked very erect for one of his age, and his eyes were the most quick and piercing I ever beheld. Aristotle stooped much, and made use of a staff. His visage was meager, his hair lank and thin, and his voice hollow. I soon discovered, that both of them were perfect strangers to the rest of the company, and had never seen or heard of them before. And I had a whisper from a ghost, who shall be nameless, that these commentators always kept in the most distant quarter from their principals in the lower world, through a consciousness of shame and guilt, because they had so horribly misrepresented the meaning of those authors to posterity. . . . But Aristotle was out of all patience with the account I gave him of Scotus and Ramus, as I presented them to him; and he asked them whether the rest of the tribe were as great dunces as themselves.[4]

In the study of Being the human intellect also finds difficulties, according to Aristotle. The obstacle here is not matter and its basic unintelligibility, as it was in the science of Nature. Rather the very intelligibility of the object studied here so far exceeds man's nature that our intellect looking at these objects

---

[4] Jonathan Swift, *Gulliver's Travels*, Part III, ch. VIII.

is " like the eyes of the owl when in the light of day." The Greeks in general, and Aristotle in particular, were very conscious of the fact that while man has an intellect there are other intellects in the universe. What is more, they were quite thoroughly convinced that the human intellect was the weakest of all. It is, I think, a tribute to the Greek genius, especially as it was realized in Aristotle, that it was able, by capitalizing on its very inadequacies, in some way to overcome its inherent limitations. Thus Aristotle showed that a science of first philosophy could be attained if it is begun on the basis of sound doctrine in the study of Nature. That this meant for him not only a study of the very general principles but also an analysis which would extend to the very elements of which things are composed, is well brought out by the commentator on the *Meteorology* of Aristotle.

It must be considered that the science of this book, and likewise of all natural science, should not be despised by man. In fact, he who despises it despises himself. And, although many say that natural science should not be prized because it has no utility in the study of divine things, in which the most blessed life and the happiness of man consists, as the Philosopher says in *X Ethics*, still these men deceive themselves. Not only the science of this book, but also the whole of natural science, where we consider both the common things and those particular and proper to each part, is ordered to the study of divine things, This is because we arrive at a knowledge of the causes through the manifest and natural things which are as effects. This is why the Philosopher in the *Metaphysics* begins with sensible substances and in the twelfth book proves the nature of separated substances through arguments drawn from astronomy.[5]

Thus, while the study of being is in some way above the capacities of man, it is this very difficulty which makes it appropriate as an ultimate end. In the Greek ideal, man's aspirations could only be satisfied in the contemplation of things which would in at least a limited way carry him beyond his changing, sensible existence. In the *Ethics* and *Politics*

---

[5] Anon. in *Opera Omnia* of St. Thomas, *In IV Meteor.*, lect. 1, n. 2.

Aristotle works out a *modus vivendi* by which man, or at least some men, could arrive at an end of this sort. In the last part of the *Politics* he speaks of a speculative life for the whole society whereby all citizens would participate in some way in this " divine " life. This life would be realized most completely in the philosophers. However, even these latter would attain only a participation in that more perfect life which exists in the separated intelligences. The other members of the society would in turn participate, to the extent possible for each, in the contemplative life through the philosophers. This would be achieved by ordering the whole social conversation to the intellectual life, including entertainment, education, law, and the arts. Aristotle conceived of music as playing a special role in the communication of this life. In this way, since the speculative life is itself something divine and thus beyond the ordinary powers of man, the ultimate happiness of man and of society itself would be found by bringing out that which is absolutely best in man's nature.

It would not be quite precise to say that such an idea of man's nature and his end is rejected today. Actually, for the most part it is not even considered. Most men today, including a great many who call themselves philosophers, would be scandalized by any analysis which seriously considers " separated intelligences " and which would attempt, in the purely natural order as opposed to the supernatural, to find a place for them in any discussion of the end of man. As far as finding man's end in the life of the intellect, many would probably admit that it is in some way desirable but not very practical.[6] Furthermore, if man must contemplate let the object be man. Such a complete rejection of the Greek ideal can be explained very well by carefully considering the concept of motionless motion and by studying the kind of philosophy or " world view " to which it gives rise when it is considered as the fundamental idea in the study of Nature. This is not to say that

---

[6] This would explain some of the modern confusion in discussions of the " liberal " arts.

such definitions used in modern science are invalid. Quite the contrary, they are indispensable if we are to have modern scientific research. Any attempt to require the modern mathematical physicist to use the idea of motion as *actus entis in potentia inquantum huiusmodi* would be ridiculous. It is equally ridiculous to expect that a philosopher can use the scientist's motionless motion and arrive at a world view which would satisfy the highest aspirations in man's nature. In fact, if the expectation would in any way be taken seriously the result could be catastrophic.

In the Whidden Lectures at McMaster University in 1959 [7] Dr. Charles De Koninck showed very clearly that speculation based on the definitions of modern mathematical physics does not lead us to a knowledge of " Nature and Nature's laws." Quite the contrary, we shall have a " hollow universe " devoid of Nature and intellect. At first glance this seems opposed to what was said earlier about the study of Nature being a necessary introduction to first philosophy. This is certainly knowledge about nature that the modern scientist is looking for. Many modern scientists are not even interested in the practical applications of their theories. Their aim is " pure " research into the laws of Nature. The use of mathematics in this endeavor would apparently even receive the sanction of Aristotle who himself used mathematics in his more particular analysis of natural phenomena. Thus, to speak of this speculation as producing a " hollow universe " would seem to be exaggerating differences which are only minor. That this is not the case can be seen by examining more closely the object and method of the modern scientist.

In the idea of motion given by Cassirer at the beginning, there is the term " place " and " change of place." It is a term which the modern scientist or philosopher seldom uses. Instead they often use the term " space " which does not mean the same thing at all. For Aristotle place is the innermost motionless

[7] Published as *The Hollow Universe* (Oxford University Press, 1960).

boundary of what contains.[8] For modern science, as Cassirer says, " Objective reality passes from *place* to *change of place*. . . ." This fundamental opposition shows up again in the analysis of the notion of " between." In *V Physics*, chapter 3, Aristotle defines the terms " together," " apart," " in contact," " between," " in succession," " contiguous," and " continuous." In all but one of these terms the definition given applies to mathematical objects as well as to things as they exist in Nature. The one exception is the term " between." " Between," he says, " is that which a changing thing, if it changes continuously in a natural manner, naturally reaches before it reaches that to which it changes last." The peculiar nature of this term is well recognized by the modern philosopher. Here is what Cassirer has to say about it:

The evolution of modern mathematics has approached the ideal, which Leibniz established for it, with growing consciousness and success. Within pure geometry, this is shown most clearly in the development of the general concept of space. The reduction of metrical relation to projective realizes the thought of Leibniz that, before space is defined as a *quantum*, it must be grasped in its original qualitative peculiarity as an ' order of coexistence ' (*ordre des coexistences possibles*). The chain of harmonic constructions, by which the points of projective space are generated, provides the structure of this order, which owes its value and intelligibility to the fact that it is not sensuously presented but is constructed by thought through a succession of relational structures. . . . In this sense, modern geometry seeks to free a relation, such as the general relation of ' between,' which at first seems to possess an irreducible sensuous existence, from this restriction and to raise it to free logical application. The meaning of this relation must be determined by definite axioms of connection in abstraction from the changing sensuous material of its presentation; for from these axioms alone is gained the meaning in which it enters into mathematical deduction.[9]

These opposed notions of " motion," " place," and " between " arise from a fundamental difference in the respective notions of Nature and the natural.

[8] *Physics IV*, ch. 4, 212a 20.   [9] *Substance and Function*, ed. cit., pp. 91-92.

Aristotle, while admitting that " Nature loves to hide " and recognizing that knowledge in any scientific way would be very difficult to attain here, nevertheless held to its objective reality. The modern approach to Nature is well brought out by Cassirer in another of his works. After pointing out that modern science has exercised a great influence in a practical way on the modern world, he says:

The real achievement of science lies elsewhere; it is not so much in the new objective content which science has made accessible to the human mind as in the new *function* which it attributes to the mind of man. The knowledge of nature does not simply lead us out into the world of objects; it serves rather as a medium in which the mind develops its own self-knowledge. . . . One world and one Being are replaced by an infinity of worlds constantly springing from the womb of becoming. . . . But the important aspect of the transformation does not lie in this boundless expansion, but in the fact that the mind now becomes aware of a new force within itself. . . . The highest energy and deepest truth of the mind do not consist in going out into the infinite, but in the mind's maintaining itself against the infinite and proving in its pure unity equal to the infinity of being.[10]

If all that is intended here is to show that man's intellect is capable of producing an infinity by which it can equal and thus in some way overcome the infinity in the processes of Nature, there could be no dispute about this. That this is going to be used to find out how things are in Nature is easily seen by following Cassirer's arguments in the remainder of his book. He holds that:

Both (nature and knowledge) must be understood in terms of their own essence, and this is no dark, mysterious ' something,' impenetrable to intellect; this essence consists rather in principles which are perfectly accessible to the mind since the mind is able to educe them from itself and to enunciate them systematically.[11]

Thus where Aristotle finds something " dark " and " mysterious " in Nature which escapes the power of man's intellect,

[10] *Philosophy of the Enlightenment* (Princeton: Univ. Press, 1951), p. 37.
[11] *Ibid.*, p. 45.

the modern philosophers and scientists who follow Cassirer will see Nature as " perfectly accessible to the mind."

In his study of Nature and Nature's ways Aristotle often uses the principle that " art imitates Nature." In this way he was able to discern, in an analogous way, some of the processes by which Nature achieves her end. In fact, even the notion that Nature operates for an end is arrived at by this reasoning in *II Physics*. Many moderns, if they are aware of this method in his works, often characterize it as " anthropomorphic " and reject it out of hand. This is indeed curious because if we compare the results obtained by the " anthropomorphic " method of Aristotle with those of the modern philosophers for whom Nature is an open book, we should expect that the former would find its end in man while the latter would have some extrinsic focus. That this is not the case, as least for Aristotle, was shown earlier when it was pointed out that for him man would have an end in something divine. Man's happiness was to be found in the contemplation of that divine principle which is the source of all being. When those for whom nature is " perfectly accessible to the mind " turn their attention to questions of ethics and politics they use notions indicating that man is supreme in his determination of his goal and that society exists only by some sort of a " social contact." With respect to this last notion Fr. Charles McCoy has said:

It may seem curious that the idea of contract be employed to express a natural relation. However, the secret of its appropriateness is to be found in the fact that the naturalism of this political philosophy demanded an innate social propensity which could be raised to the level of a sufficient explanation of social groupings in such a way as to leave no law to be observed which in any sense is imposed from without, but to leave only a ' natural law ' which the moral subject gives to itself. And nothing is better designed to express this kind of naturalness than the idea of contract.[12]

---

[12] " The Turning Point in Political Philosophy, *Am. Pol. Sc. Rev.*, XLIV (1950), 678 ff.

Thus where Aristotle arrived at a society where man is ordered to speculation of things which are above man, the moderns place man in a society or " social grouping " which has no law " which is in any sense imposed from without." The end of man in this latter society will be not the contemplation of the world, but will consist rather in remaking the world according to the finite capacity of his own intellect. Or, as someone has said, " The purpose of philosophy is not to explain the world but to change it."

It seems, therefore, that how we study Nature and how we define motion and the ideas used in that study will make an important difference in our conception of man and his role in the universe. The wordy and confused notion of motion which was used by Aristotle in his analysis enabled him to arrive at a universe which is open to something higher than man, while the clear concept of the motionless motion of modern science ends in a " hollow universe," closed about the small and finite intellect of man himself.

ROMAN A. KOCOUREK

College of St. Thomas,
        St. Paul, Minnesota.

TIME, THE NUMBER OF MOVEMENT

∽

I T has been suggested that for our age the particular riddle
the Sphinx has set is that of time. Many of the perennial problems which torment the mind of man are more
or less involved with time;—to cite but one example: the
problem of man's free will and God's knowledge of future contingent events. Though time is the measure of our duration and
of our activities, it is nevertheless far from clear. An object
is intelligible only in so far as it is in act. Upon investigation,
however, time seems to be more potential than actual. The
past is no longer, the future is not yet, and the only actuality,
the " now " is not time.

Modern emphasis on physics has again brought into prominence this problem of time, but mathematical physics, presumably concerned with time, actually deals with its measurement rather than with its nature. This neglect by physicists
of the nature of time goes back to Newton who wrote: " I
do not define time, space, place, and motion, as being well
known to all." [1]

The basic text for an understanding of the nature of time is
Aristotle's *Physics*, Book Four, Chapter Ten, and the commentary on it by Saint Thomas Aquinas. Yet even his study
bristles with difficulties. One of these I have chosen as the
subject of this paper. Aristotle defines time as " . . . the
number of movement according to a before and an after." [2]
Thus he seems to put the formality of time in number. Now,
if time is a number and number depends on some mind, it
would seem that if there were no mind there could be no numbering of motion and hence no time. Aristotle recognized this
problem as a valid one: " Whether if soul did not exist time

---

[1] Isaac Newton, *Mathematical Principles of Natural Philosophy*, Definitions:
Scholium, trans. by Florian Cajori (Univ. of California Press, 1947), p. 6.
[2] Aristotle, *Physics*, IV, c. 11, 219b1-2.

would exist or not is a question that may fairly be asked, for if there cannot be someone to count, there cannot be anything that can be counted, so that evidently there cannot be number; for number is either what has been or what can be counted." [3]

Would we, following the Aristotelian doctrine find ourselves forced to hold that prior to the creation of man (or at least of a higher animal with memory and hence a knowledge of time) there was no time and all things were instantaneous? We are cautioned against drawing too hasty a conclusion however by these words of Aristotle: " . . . it is evident that every change and everything that moves is in time." [4] Certainly prior to the creation of man things changed and moved, so in Aristotle's own words they were " in time." Such a conclusion however seems to contradict his position that if there were no soul there would be no time.

There is some doubt however that this is truly Aristotle's position. The above translation is based on a text of William of Moerbeke. Aristotle's own text is an uncertain guide because it is in such poor condition and because the critical study of it is rendered uncertain in that the introduction of a period or a comma, missing in the text, would change the meaning. After a brief survey of the history of the problem it will be the purpose of this paper to show that it is more in keeping with the thought of Aristotle to hold that time is formally a being of nature and not of reason. True, the greater number of philosophers think that time would not be if there were no soul. We shall try to show that it is the thought of Aristotle and of St. Thomas that time is an *ens naturae* and not an *ens rationis*, and to exist even if there were no soul; not indeed perfect in being, but rather imperfect, as in motion.

An investigation of the history of the question shows that without doubt Plato believed time to be real:

Now the nature of the ideal being was everlasting, but to bestow this attribute in its fulness upon a creature was impossible. Where-

---

[3] *Ibid.*, IV, c. 14, 223a21-25.
[4] *Ibid.*, IV, c. 14, 223a-14-15.

fore he resolved to have a moving image of eternity, and when he set in order the heaven, he made this image eternal but moving according to number, while eternity itself rests in unity; and this image we call time.[5]

Here Plato identifies time with the motion of the spheres, hence a being of nature. Even without an intelligence time would be a reality because it is nothing more than the actual movement of the spheres. It was precisely on this point, that is, the identification of time and movement, that Aristotle criticized Plato asking how, if time and movement were the same, we could speak of movement being fast or slow.

Aristotle denied their identity, yet admitted that time and movement were always found together. His conclusion was that time was the number of movement according to a before and after. It is the reality of this number that we are investigating. As mentioned above, Aristotle's position is doubtful and because of the uncertain condition of his text we cannot look to him for a satisfactory solution of the problem. His text quoted at the beginning, based on William of Moerbeke, would seem to put time in the mind and only movement in nature. The Latin version of the Arabic also tends to support this interpretation. Moreover the renaissance texts render this passage in the sense that if the soul is not, there is no time but only motion which is numerable.

In spite of these numerous indications that Aristotle meant that if there were no soul there would be no time, it seems that his thought is otherwise and in fact seems to require that time be in nature even without soul. In support of this thought we call attention to the fact that for Aristotle number in the definition of time is taken as "numbered" number, (not "numbering" number), and so a being of nature. Likewise Aristotle reduces time to quantity, and places "when" as an accident caused by time.

Among philosophers from Aristotle to Saint Thomas we find

[5] Plato, *Timaeus*, 37 D, trans. by Benjamin Jowett (New York, 1892), III, p. 456.

almost all holding time to be constituted in its formality by the mind.

Galen (129-199 A. D.) taught that time was the sucession of our perceptions as known. He then places time as a mental being which does not exist if there is no soul which perceives.[6] Plotinus (205-270 A. D.) defines time as the life of the soul in movement. It is not to be conceived as outside of soul.[7]

An obscure Boetius on the other hand, thinks nothing prevents number from being without that which numbers. Thus time can exist without soul. Perhaps his position is due to a strong Platonic influence.[8]

Themistius (c. 320-390 A. D.) finds fault with Boetius. What can be numbered and numbering are correlative; one cannot be without the other. If there is no one to number there is no numbering and so if there is no soul to number there is no time.[9]

Saint Augustine (354-430 A. D.) shows delightful humility in acknowledging his ignorance of time: " If no one asks me, I know; if I want to explain it to a questioner, I do not know." [10] Yet after much analysis he concludes that it is the mind which gives time: " It is in you, O my mind, that I measure time . . . what I measure is the impress produced in you by things as they pass and abiding in you when they have passed: and it is present." [11]

In the sixth century Simplicius expressed his disagreement with the thought of Boetius, holding that although the numerable can exist without soul as does movement, yet number and hence time can in no way exist without soul. Only movement exists in nature, for to consider the prior and posterior belongs

[6] Albertus Magnus, *Lib. IV Physicorum*, tr. III, cap. 3, ed. Borgnet, III, pp. 310b-311a.

[7] G. H. Turnbull, *The Essence of Plotinus* (New York, 1934), p. 107.

[8] For this point I am indebted to the unpublished notes of the Rev. J. A. Weisheipl, O. P.

[9] See note 8.

[10] St. Augustine, *Confessions*, Book XI, chap. 14 (New York, 1943), p. 271.

[11] *Ibid.*, Book XI, chap. 32, p. 283.

to mind numbering. He therefore concluded that time is a being of reason and not of nature.[12]

Averroes (1126-1198 A.D.), following the Arabic version of Aristotle referred to in the beginning of this article, considered that the prior and posterior in the definition of Aristotle exist only potentially if there is no soul. They are actual if there is a soul. If numbered in act there is time in act but, if there is no soul, time is only potential. Time has no " to be " in nature except in potency. Time is in act only in the operation of the mind numbering, whence there is no time formally except in so far as the mind numbers according to a prior and posterior. This distinction was followed by all the Averroists from the thirteenth to the sixteenth century as well as by Saint Thomas in his commentary on Book One and Two of the *Sentences*.[13]

In spite of the almost complete unanimity of his predecessors on this question Saint Albert showed his great originality, insisting that the nature of time was something real: ". . . *et ideo fluxus ille realis erit realiter tempus.*" [14] In developing his thought St. Albert said that, to number, three things were required: numbered matter, formal number, and the soul efficiently (not formally) counting. Even if there is no soul, yet there is number according to formal being and according to numbered number. Now that by which a thing is numbered is twofold: that by which it is numbered efficiently (the soul) and that by which it is numbered formally. As soon as we have multiplicity, discreteness, otherness, we have formal number and so ". . . if there is no soul number is not just potential, but it exists according to the habitual form of discreteness of numbered things." [15] Without a doubt St. Albert thought time, the number of motion according to a prior and posterior, existed formally in nature whether or no there was a soul.

---

[12] See note 8.

[13] St. Thomas, I *Sent.*, dist. 19, q. 2, a. 1; q. 5, a. 1; dist. 37, q. 4, a. 3; II *Sent.*, dist. 12, q. 5, a. 2.

[14] Albertus Magnus, *Lib. IV Physicorum*, tr. III, cap. 16, ed. Borgnet, III, p. 340a.

[15] *Ibid.*, pp. 339b-340a.

The young Thomas of the *Sentences* thought time dependent on the mind: ". . . the notion of time is in some way completed by the action of the soul counting . . ."[16] Yet in his commentary on the *Physics* he adopts a quite different position. Whether this change was due to the influence of St. Albert we do not know. In the commentary on Aristotle's treatment of this problem Saint Thomas says: ". . . it is necessary to say either that there is no time if there is no soul or to say more truly that without the soul time is a kind of being (*utcumque ens*)."[17] In explaining this St. Thomas says that if there is movement without a mind, so too is there time because the prior and the posterior in motion *are*, and this is just what time is, namely the prior and posterior in motion in so far as they are numerable. Realizing that it was this "numerable" which seemed to demand a soul St. Thomas clarifies its meaning: enumeration depends on a mind, but the "to be" of numbered things does not depend on mind (unless it be the cause of things, such as the divine intellect). As there can be sensibles without sense existing, so the numerable and number can exist without numbering.[18]

Moreover, Saint Thomas questions the validity of Aristotle's analogy comparing number and the sensible, i. e. that just as if there is no one to sense there is no sensible so if there is no one to number there is no number. Commenting on this he says that it is *forte conditionalis*:

For if there is a sensible, it can be sensed; and if it can be sensed there can be someone sensing. But it does not follow that if there is a sensible that there is someone sensing. It also follows that if there is something numerable there can be someone numbering . . . but it does not follow that if there is no one numbering that there is not anything numerable.[19]

To understand how Saint Thomas can hold there is a number

---

[16] St. Thomas, II *Sent.*, dist. 12, q. 5, a. 2.
[17] St. Thomas, *In IV Phys.*, lect. 23, n. 5.
[18] *Ibid.*
[19] *Ibid.*

without someone numbering we must look to the Aristotelian concept of number:

All plurality is a consequence of division. Now division is twofold: one is material, and is division of the continuous; from this results number, which is a species of quantity.[20]

Number is quantity resulting from division in matter; plurality, discreteness. The plurality in movement, which is time, is produced by the present instant actually dividing the movement according to a before and after—into the past and future which are its parts. This instant in dividing is always " other " according to the succession of time and movement.

Time is not number with which we count, but the number of things which are counted, and this according as it occurs before or after is always different, for the ' nows ' are different.[21]

From this otherness there results plurality which is time and this plurality is present whether or not there is soul to count it.

The *nunc*, the instant which divides, is something other than the *factum esse* of movement,—that successive actualization of potency which is movement; yet to each *factum esse* there is a corresponding *nunc*. Plato's error was to identify the two.

One might ask how, if time is continuous quantity it can be defined as number, which is discrete quantity.[22] In its formality it is discrete, it is the " now " dividing and in so far as it is dividing the " now " is always different. Yet the " now " is also a boundary—the termination of the past and the principle of the future and thus realizes the definition of a continuum. According to Aristotle: ". . . the now also is in one way a potential dividing of time, in another the termination of both parts, and their unity." [23]

Like movement, time has a fluid existence; only the instant, the division of time, actually exists. Thus Aristotle says of it

---

[20] St. Thomas, *Sum. Theol.*, I, q. 30, a. 3.
[21] Aristotle, *op. cit.*, IV, c. 12, 220b8-10.
[22] *Ibid.*
[23] *Ibid.*, IV, c. 12, 222a17-19.

that it exists "barely and in an obscure way" [24] and Saint Thomas speaks of it as an " *utcumque ens*," [25] a kind of being, an imperfect being.

Its perfection, the existence of its parts, past and future, is not realized without the operation of the soul. The power of retaining the past in memory and of looking ahead to the future requires an intellect. " . . . the totality itself of time is obtained through the ordination of the soul numbering the prior and posterior in motion . . ." [26]

It is this aspect which was viewed by the authors cited at the beginning of this article. What they failed to see was the claim time had to some real being in the actuality of the instant which continuously unites the past and future since it is the term of the past and principle of the future.

SISTER M. JOCELYN, O. P.

Rosary College
River Forest, Illinois

---

[24] *Ibid.*, IV, c. 10, 217b32-33.
[25] St. Thomas, *In IV Phys.*, lect. 23, n. 5.
[26] *Ibid.*

PART FOUR

SPECIAL PROBLEMS IN SCIENCE

EVOLUTION AND ENTROPY

ော

MOST biologists today would agree with George Gaylord
Simpson that, " the factual truth of evolution is taken
as established and the enquiry goes on from there." [1]
Yet as André Lalande has shown, there are paradoxes in our
commitment to the theory of evolution,[2] and one may face
them without necessarily opposing the theory itself. One of
these apparent antinomies is raised by the law of entropy, the
second law of thermodynamics. Since evolution, at least in
the living world, is regarded by probably all its advocates as
an uphill thrust, how can it co-exist with entropy, the so-called
downhill tendency of the cosmos? Many observers take the
view expressed by Norbert Wiener that evolution or entropy
is only a temporary phenomenon and that in the end entropy
will exert its universal dominion to end all life processes [3] in
our universe. But even within scientific cosmology, the solution
can hardly be so simple. For it has been customary to speak
of the past and continuing evolution even of the inorganic
world. Thus in a paper delivered at the University of Chicago's
Darwin Celebration and significantly entitled, " On the Evidences of Inorganic Evolution," Harlow Shapley intended " to
suggest that terrestrial biological evolution is but a rather small
affair, a complicated sideshow, in the large evolutionary operation that the astronomer glimpses." [4] Has the term " evolution," as though it were not already ambiguous enough, been
extended to cover all the events believed governed by the
second law of thermodynamics? If this is so and if evolution

---

[1] *The Meaning of Evolution* (New York, 1951) p. 11.

[2] *Les illusions évolutionnistes* (Paris, 1931).

[3] *The Human Use of Human Beings* (New York, 1954) pp. 40-47. L. Whyte
regards entropy in the title of his book as *The Unitary Principle in Biology and
Physics* (New York, 1949).

[4] *The Evolution of Life*, Vol. 1 of *Evolution after Darwin*, ed. S. Tax (Chicago,
1960) p. 23.

thus becomes a universal cosmic tendency, what becomes of entropy and of the opinion that " it is difficult to conceive of circumstances that would invalidate the statistical proof of the Second Law "? [5] Obviously, the paradox suggested by Lalande remains unresolved and probably exists in more pointed form than the cosmologies of his own day would have urged. If the apparent antimony between evolution and entropy is to be frankly faced, there is clear need for carefully tracing each of the two concepts to their empirical evidence.

Despite all of its obscurity, entropy is understood well enough to be embodied in mathematical equations. Yet evolution, even apart from the greater attention paid to it in the popular press, is probably easier to illustrate at a physical level. All natural change, e. g., the development of an oak from an acorn, a frog from a tadpole, and flesh and bone from food materials, is in a loose sense of the term an evolutionary process in which the better comes into existence.[6] Because progress is more intelligible in the physical world than the down-hill drive of entropy, evolution may be more profitably discussed first.

I

Like other leading ideas in modern science, e. g., the heliocentric theory in physics or the atomic theory in chemistry, the theory of evolution has analogues going back as far as the Greeks, for instance Anaxagoras,[7] and appearing in Christian writers like St. Augustine with his " seminal reasons." [8] Yet the theory of evolution, as we now know it, together with the empirical evidence adduced in its favor, is an original achievement of modern science. Collingwood, despite his frequent exaggerations, had an insight in taking the post-Newtonian conception of matter to be nature as history.[9] Even

[5] C. F. von Weizsäcker, *The History of Nature* (Chicago, 1949) p. 57.
[6] *Sum. cont. Gent.*, III, cc. 3, 4.
[7] Cf. Aristotle's report, *Phys.*, I, 4, 187a20 ff.; the best secondary source on Anaxagoras is F. Cleve's, *The Philosophy of Anaxagoras* (New York, 1949).
[8] Cf. for instance, L.-M. Otis, *La doctrine de l'évolution* (Montreal, 1950).
[9] *The Idea of Nature* (New York, 1960) pp. 9 ff.; 133 ff.

in this modern and history-minded period, it is a well known fact that the first evolutionist was not Darwin.[10] In the writings of Buffon, Kant, and Laplace there are theories of the evolution of the solar system. Buffon, in his monumental work, *Epochs of Nature* (1778)[11] theorized that the solar system originated from a collision between a comet and the sun, and he proposed a whole chronology concerning the cooling of the earth to its present temperature. Kant held to a nebular hypothesis in which an original cosmic dust, subjected to the forces of attraction and repulsion, gave rise to the solar system as we now know it.[12] In 1796, Laplace brought the weight of his authority to the nebular theory and reduced the distribution of momentum among the apparently evolving planets to Newtonian laws. In the spirit of Shapley's remarks, already quoted, the notion of biological evolution when it finally caught on through Darwin's research and writing, could already be set within a larger evolutionary framework. In our own century, the study of the galaxy and the discovery, through more powerful telescopes, that there are other galaxies besides our own— in fact, billions of them with the most distant believed to be six billion light years away—led to the theory that there are countless " island universes " and extended the problem of cosmology from a study of the solar system to a concern with the laws governing the " arrangement, past, present, and future of the galaxies in the universe." [13]

As we look at the cold facts, there is a whole array of evidence that our universe was not always as it now is. There is, for instance, radioactivity, the elongation of the moon, the apparent succession of living forms as shown by the geological record, slight but none the less real irregularities in planetary move-

[10] Cf. B. Glass, et al, eds., *Forerunners of Darwin 1745-1859* (Baltimore, 1959).

[11] *Des époques de la nature*, ed. L. Picard (Paris, 1894), first published in 1778.

[12] Cf. W. Hastie, *Kant's Cosmogony as in his Essay on the Retardation of the Rotation of the Earth and his Natural History and Theory of the Heavens* (Glasgow, 1900).

[13] H. Bondi, "Astronomy and Cosmology," in *What is Science?* ed. J. Newman (New York, 1955) p. 66.

ment [14] which would have an appreciable additive effect over a long period of time. But perhaps one of the most crucial, because the most cosmic, evidences in this regard is the phenomenon of the expanding universe.

To approach the evidence for an expanding universe, it might be initially observed that the distances of the nearer stars, with respect to a terrestrial observer, can be determined from the various angles at which their light strikes the earth in the course of the earth's annual movement about the sun. From the angles involved, distances can be computed by simple trigonometry. But for more distant objects this change of angle (parallax effect) is so small that a different method must be used, and fortunately another tool is at hand. This tool is furnished by the stars called Cepheid variables which undergo periodic changes in their visible radiation, rapidly increasing in luminosity and then fading back into their original brightness. A correlation exists between the brightness of a star and its period of pulsation; the longer the period the brighter the star. The phenomenon of Cepheid variables, named from the star Delta Cephei, the first known example of such a pulsating star, enables us to know the absolute luminosity of the star in question, and when this is compared with apparent brightness, the distance of a Cepheid variable can be determined.[15]

By invoking the periodic law for Cepheid variables, Edwin P. Hubble showed that distant nebulae, such as the Andromeda nebula, once believed to be part of the Milky Way, are actually distant galaxies [16]—in the case of Andromeda, two million light years away. Moreover, this challenge to the older conception of a nebula led to the view that the universe is expanding.

---

[14] Although this irregularity in perihelion is discernible in the case of Mercury and is explained by relativity mechanics, it is believed to exist, in a degree too small to be observed, in the case of the other planets.

[15] An explanation of Cepheid variables will be found in A. Eddington, *The Expanding Universe* (Ann Arbor, 1958) pp. 7-8.

[16] For Hubble's work, see his *The Realm of the Nebulae* (Oxford, 1936).

As in the case of measuring cosmic distances, it may be profitable to make a brief summary of the method employed to reach the verdict of an expanding universe. This method makes use of an analogy between light and sound. When, for instance, a fast moving train approaches a by-stander near the track there is a rise in the whistle's pitch and, as the train recedes, a noticeable lowering of pitch. The physical reason given for this phenomenon is the addition and subtraction of frequency or wave-length because of the moving sound-source. As the train approaches, its own motion is added to that of the sound thus making for a shorter wave-length and higher pitch of the whistle; as the train recedes, there is a net lengthening of the sound wave and hence a lower frequency or lower pitch.

Something similar is believed to happen in the case of light waves reaching the earth from distant galaxies. The wave-length is shifted toward the red or longer wave lengths of the visible spectrum, indicating in the italicized words of George Gamow [17] that " *the entire space of the universe populated by billions of galaxies, is in a state of rapid expansion, with all of its members flying from each other at high speeds.*"

The expansion of the universe was proposed as a principle of cosmogony by Abbé Georges Lemaître who postulated a " primeval atom " in which all the elementary particles of matter were densely packed together. Lemaître regards this Ur-atom as an isotope of a neutron.[18] Gamow, who is in sympathy with this type of theory, has written:

The nearest guess is that the overall density of the universe at the time was comparable to that of a nuclear fluid tiny droplets of which form the nuclei of various atoms. This would make the original pre-expansion density of the universe a hundred thousand billion times greater than the density of water; each cubic centimeter contained at that time a hundred million tons of matter.[19]

[17] *The Creation of the Universe* (New York, 1952), p. 23.
[18] *The Primeval Atom* (New York, 1950) p. 142.
[19] *Op. cit.*, p. 19.

VINCENT E. SMITH

Von Weizsäcker who closely resembles Lemaître and Gamow in their cosmologies, speaks of a compressed primeval gas.[20]

Lemaître, tracing out the history of his exploding primeval atom, has computed that if the

fragmentation occurred in equal pieces, two hundred and sixty generations would have been needed to reach the present pulverization of matter into our poor little atoms, almost too small to be broken again.[21]

Summing up his theory on how the primeval atom expanded into our present universe, Lemaître with a flair for the poetic says:

The evolution of the world can be compared to a display of fireworks that has just ended: some few red wisps, ashes, and smoke. Standing on a well-chilled cinder, we see the slow fading of the suns, and we try to recall the vanished brilliance of the origin of worlds.[22]

All of these theories, as the opening phrase in the preceding quotation reminds us, are evolutionary. Gamow speaks of the original Big Squeeze. Such a type of theory points to the hypothesis for a beginning of some sort in the history of the cosmos we now know.

The beginning theory is regarded by Sir Edmund Whittaker as an argument for Creation, even for Creation in time.[23] E. A. Milne spoke of a t = 0 and held likewise to a temporal beginning of our cosmos.[24] With such a conclusion, however, and as both of these experts would admit, we pass beyond the frontiers of science in the narrow modern sense of the term and enter a meta-scientific region.

The more scientifically orthodox supporters of a beginning theory usually do not range beyond the view that there was some primeval matrix—an atom, a nuclear fluid, a compressed gas—densely packed togther; from this original stuff our uni-

[20] *Op. cit.*, p. 81.
[21] *Op. cit.*, p. 78.
[22] *Ibid.*
[23] *Space and Spirit* (London, 1946) pp. 118-121.
[24] *Modern Cosmology and the Christian Idea of God* (Oxford, 1952) p. 58.

verse is said to have arisen by explosion or expansion. Using a law projected on theoretical grounds by Lemaître and confirmed by Hubble, that the recession velocity of a nebula is proportional to its distance away, the date of the Big Squeeze can be set at about 10^{10} years,[25] although, as Lemaître argues, the velocity of recession may not always have been uniform.[26]

Like the other current cosmological theory to be mentioned later, the advocates of a primeval matrix account for the known abundances of various elements and must render an account of the relative numbers of heavier and lighter elements in various places throughout the cosmos. The universe as a whole is estimated to be about 55 per cent hydrogen, 44 per cent helium, and one percent of the heavier elements.

In the language of Lyttleton:

Hydrogen is to be regarded as constituting the primitive material of the universe, from which all other elements are somehow formed. This conclusion has a highly important implication, because it means that in its present state neither the sun nor any similar star can produce the heavy elements that are essential for the formation of the planets, such as our Earth, in which as we have seen it is the heavy elements that are abundant and the hydrogen by comparison exceedingly rare.[27]

It will not be fruitful, for purposes of this paper, to outline the theories, such as supernovation,[28] designed to explain the formation and distribution of the heavier elements.[29] It is important only to note that this is termed an evolutionary process. Shapley writes that " the evolution of matter appears to be a synthesis inside the stars of the heavy elements out of hydrogen, which is accepted as the primordial, abundant, and simple No. 1 element." [30] Then too, the whole process [31]

[25] Shapley, *art. cit.*, p. 32.

[26] *Op. cit.*, p. 79.

[27] R. Lyttleton, *The Modern Universe* (New York, 1956) p. 137.

[28] Cf. H. Bondi, *The Universe at Large* (New York, 1960) pp. 52-55.

[29] E. Findlay-Freundlich, *Cosmology* (Chicago, 1951) p. 50.

[30] Shapley, *art. cit.*, p. 35.

[31] In all the discussions of evolution throughout this paper, it is to be understood

may be regarded as evolutionary for the additional reason that, as manifested by the constitution and history of our earth,[32] it leads to the appearance and survival of the self-replicating macromolecules which are living things. Surely this process is a build-up; it is progressive; it is an evolution, and according to biologists, it leads, after living things finally appear, to higher and higher species. It is proper to speak of the Big Bang theory,[33] held by Lemaître, Gamow, and von Weizsaecker, as an evolutionary account.

Before considering entropy, the down-hill drive in our universe, mention must be made of the so-called steady-state theory which has grown up in Great Britain and is held by such cosmologists as Gold,[34] Bondi,[35] Hoyle,[36] and Lyttleton.[37] According to this hypothesis, the universe never had a beginning and therefore did not have to undergo the differentiation from a primeval atom. The work done in the never-ending expansion of the universe is accounted for by a continuous creation. Hydrogen, the " No. 1 element " in the cosmos, is created at the rate of one atom per litre of volume every billion years. This is Bondi's figure.[38] From hydrogen, other and heavier elements are then built up. Bondi further states:

The expansion of the universe, which can be inferred either from thermodynamics or from astronomical observations, would seem to

that, by the laws of logic, we are dealing only with hypothesis— the best positive account we can so far give of how things come to be as they are. We are not dealing with fact, as in the proposition, " Man is a rational animal." Yielding to current conventions, we have simply used the term " evolution " without grammatically mentioning the logical qualification to be put upon it as only a very strong hypothesis.

[32] Cf. A. Holmes, *The Age of the Earth* (London, 1937); H. Jeffreys, *The Earth* (Cambridge, Eng., 1952); E. Bullard, *The Interior of the Earth* (Chicago, 1953).

[33] "After the full complement of the atomic species had been formed during the first hour of expansion, nothing of particular interest happened for the next 30 million years." Gamow, *op. cit.*, p. 74.

p. 142.

[34] Cf. E. Mascall, *Christian Theology and Natural Science* (New York, 1956)

[35] H. Bondi, *Cosmology* (Cambridge, Eng., 1952).

[36] F. Hoyle, *The Nature of the Universe* (New York, 1950).

[37] *Op. cit.*

[38] *Cosmology*, p. 143.

lead to a thinning out of material. By the perfect cosmological principle [by which Bondi means, roughly, the uniformity of nature] the average density of matter must not undergo a secular change. There is only one way in which a constant density can be compatible with a motion of expansion, and that is by the continual creation of matter.[39]

The continuous-creation theory must not be confused with pair-formation where an electron and a positron are " created," as the physicist says, from electric field.[40] And above all, the continuous-creation, in view of its proponents, must not be regarded as requiring a Creator. As Hoyle writes, " The most obvious question to ask about continuous creation is this: Where does the created material come from? It does not come from anywhere. Material simply appears—it is created." [41] Lyttleton affirms that the appearance of newly created hydrogen " is a property of space itself. . . ." [42]

By virtue of their theory of continuous creation, the steady-state theorists in a sense would have to deny the process of evolution we have described above or at least to qualify their interpretation of evolutionary cosmogony. For them, the universe always was and always will be. As old galaxies recede from view, new ones are formed. The work for these processes, demanded by the classic formulation of energy laws, is accounted for by the continuous creation of the " No. 1 element." In this manner, the steady-state theorists believe they can overcome the so-called " beginning " which appears so mysterious within the usual canons of scientific investigation. But as Milton Munitz has ably argued, the steady-state theory does not eradicate the apparently mysterious principles from cosmogony. It simply replaces one enigma with another.[43] For the continuous creation of new matter is just as mysterious

---

[39] *Ibid.*

[40] This is explained by Einstein's $E=mc^2$ and does not depart from the principle of conservation of mass-energy.

[41] *Op. cit.*, p. 123.

[42] *Op. cit.*, p. 201.

[43] " Creation and the ' New ' Cosmology," *British Journal of the Philosophy of Science*, V (1954), 32 ff.

to the logic usually employed by science as the hypothesis of a " beginning."

A third theory of the origin of the world, based upon the notion of a " pulsating universe," may be in the offing.[44] But the two leading cosmologies actually in vogue are the ones briefly sketched above, and our concern in this paper will be confined to them. Our interest, of course, is their bearing upon evolution.

Despite the comparison by Munitz, the steady-state theory has the ring of the gratuitous about it and seems to require *ad hoc* amendments to the usual formulation of the laws of thermodynamics. Gamow even believes that there is experimental argument against the steady-state theory in the evidence of Stebbins and Whitford [45] showing at least some of the galaxies to have such a long red shift that their color cannot be accounted for by the Doppler effect previously described. The reddening is so pronounced that it might seem necessary to explain it by inter-galactic dust which scatters light in much the same way that the sunset is reddened by our terrestrial atmosphere. But this hypothesis would require more dust than can be admitted on other grounds. A tenable hypothesis seems to be that observed galaxies, in their youth by comparison to their mature period, contained a greater abundance of a special type of star (Red Giants), and if this is the case, it is necessary either to accept a developmental view or to patch another *ad hoc* assumption on the steady-state theory to make it tenable.

But even if the steady-state cosmology be entertained as a possibility in the light of all the evidence which our unaided reason can marshal,[46] it still bears witness to evolution. The steady-state cosmologists accept the view that the universe is

[44] Finley-Freundlich, *op. cit.*, p. 56; Shapley, *art. cit.*, p. 33.

[45] Gamow, *op. cit.*, pp. 33-34.

[46] This conditional acceptance is made in the same spirit that St. Thomas attaches to Aristotle's view of an eternal world. As a starting point for the proof for a Prime Mover it is the " more difficult " assumption (*De Pot.*, q. III, a. 17), and if within it, the proof can stand up, it can certainly stand up on a beginning theory.

expanding. They hold to the formation of heavier elements out of hydrogen as one of the general principles for matter's development. They re-interpret the evolutionary movement so that it is endless in both directions and so that any deficit caused by " evolution " is continually being overcome. But they do recognize some kind of cosmic advance, and hence our later assessment of evolution will include the evolutionary aspect of the steady-state theory itself.

Our only point so far is that the two leading contemporary cosmologies are theories of evolution.

II

The concept of evolution, an up-hill tendency, forms one part of the paradox in modern cosmology; the other is the law of entropy, the second law of thermodynamics. This law was actually stated by Carnot in 1824 and hence it is also called the Carnot principle. Although still invoking the caloric theory, Carnot likened a heat engine to a hydraulic system, say a mill wheel. The gist of Carnot's argument did not become explicit until subsequently, and so his views will be here summarized in the later and more polished form taken from other pens.[47] In the case of the hydraulic engine, to restore a quantity of water to an earlier position at the top of the wheel, energy must be supplied to the wheel from some source besides the quantity of the water in question. Simplifying the analogy still further, let us imagine a source of water and a sink below it. To drive the water from the sink back to the source, the water and the sink are not enough; we have to supply energy from the outside, for instance with a pump or a heater. Were it possible, from within any closed mechanical system, to restore the system to its initial state after a disturbance of this original set of conditions, a perpetual motion machine could be constructed, and one of the ways of phrasing the Carnot principle

[47] Carnot's principle is discussed in P. Bridgman, *The Nature of Thermodynamics* (Cambridge, Mass., 1950) chap. 2.

is that it simply rules out a perpetual motion machine of this type.

Carnot likened the behavior of a water system to the flow of heat, but the full meaning of his achievement came only when Clausius [48] formulated the Carnot principle to read that heat, of itself, cannot pass from a cooler body to a hotter one— any more than the water in our analogy can flow " uphill." But what did Clausius mean by " entropy,"—the term he introduced to clarify and generalize the second law of thermo-dynamics which, in the reading he gave it, simply states: the entropy in any closed mechanical system always tends to increase to the maximum?

The strictly mathematical physicist will want to regard entropy as " a variable of state " as as " a function of state." But this definition, valid as it is within a strictly mathematical physics,[49] cannot supply the fundamental physical meaning we would like to find. Clausius himself wrote that if we want to assign to entropy a proper name, we can

say of it that it is the *transformation content* of the body, in the same way that we can say of the quantity U that is the *heat and work content* of the body. However, since I think it better to take the names of such quantities as these, which are important for science, from the ancient languages, so that they can be intro-duced without change into all the modern languages, I propose to name the magnitude S the *entropy* of the body, from the Greek word *e trope* a transformation. I have intentionally formed the word entropy so as to be as similar as possible to the work energy, since both these quantities which are to be known by these names are so nearly related to each other in their physical significance that a certain similarity in their names seemed to me advantageous.[50]

But what is the " physical significance " of " transformation content "? Perhaps we may take a cue from Lindsay and Margenau who write, " the quantity we are seeking will be

[48] Cf. W. Wilson, *A Hundred Years of Physics* (London, 1950) pp. 37-39.
[49] For the nature of mathematical physics, cf. *In II Phys.*, lect. 3 (passim).
[50] Cf. W. Magie, ed. *Source Book in Physics* (New York, 1935) p. 234.

meaningless unless it refers to equilibrium states." [51] Heat
tends of itself to flow from a hotter body to a cooler one—never
the reverse—and the flow ends, when the temperatures of the
two bodies are equal. Entropy is this tendency to equality,
to equilibrium, to uniformity.

It will be appropriate later on to spell out more carefully the
fine-print meaning of equilibrium or uniformity in order to
show how general this tendency must actually be and to
indicate that this entropic drive is a dedifferentiation by contrast to the differential structure in an evolutionary process.
But let us tighten our hold on the meaning of entropy so far
attained. Our second law of thermodynamics reads that the
entropy in any closed system always tends to increase to the
maximum. The augmentation of entropy is a measure of the
use of energy. In a steam engine, for example, some of the heat
is dissipated through the machinery and cannot be recovered
for use; more generally, in any closed system, energy exchange
always involves in the end a dissipation of heat throughout
the parts of the system, so that no machine is one hundred
per cent efficient.

The second law of thermodynamics thus records the degradation of energy and, if our cosmos is finite, the downhill drive
of the universe itself. [The law of the conservation of energy
expresses the constancy in quantity of the energy involved in
any closed process; but the law of entropy records the qualitative change in such energy.] Some of it passes into a state in
which it is no longer available for work. In any machine there
is a loss of available energy because of the dissipation of heat
through the machine itself.

Now the law of entropy, like all the laws of thermodynamics,
is not of merely local significance like an equation that applies
only to electricity or magnetism. All energy can be converted
to mechanical energy, and hence all energy transformations—
thus all the motions in our universe—involve a change of some
of the energy into unusable heat. In other words, since all

[51] R. Lindsay and H. Margenau, *Foundations of Physics* (New York, 1936) p. 215.

usable energy has a mechanical equivalent and hence can be reduced to mechanical energy which in turn, when passing from a potential to a kinetic stage, produces unrecoverable heat, the law of entropy, though arising out of a study of heat, really applies to all closed energy transformations and, if the universe is finite, to all cosmic motion.

This is why Eddington could call the law of entropy " time's arrow." [52] Entropy is a measure of the direction in cosmic processes as a whole. It reports that our universe, previously claimed to be in evolution, has in reality always been going downhill. Slowly it is moving toward uniformity and equilibrium where all heat will have have been transformed into an unusable state and where, as a result, all further motion will become impossible. This is what is meant by the heat-death of the universe.

The law of entropy was being formulated at a time when, despite the theory of Daniel Bernoulli and the experimental evidence of Count Rumford, the caloric theory of heat was still in vogue. About the middle of the nineteenth century the kinetic molecular theory of matter, thanks to Joule and Maxwell, finally became acceptable, and in this perspective, the much older idea that heat is a phenomenon of motion was finally given quantitative form. The temperature of a substance could be correlated to the average kinetic energy of the molecules, or more simply put, heat came to be considered as a random motion of particles. As such, it is a problem in statistics like the throwing of dice or the shuffling of cards.

Despite all the historical and philosophical interest which the study of heat can command, we are interested in the problem here only to round off our discussion of entropy. Against the background that heat is the random motion of molecules in material substances, or that " from the standpoint of the kinetic theory, heat is disorganized random mechanical energy, whereas mechanical energy proper is directed, ordered," [53] it is possible

---

[52] *The Nature of the Physical World* (New York, 1928) chap. 5.

[53] A. d'Abro, *The Rise of the New Physics* (New York, 1953) I, 398.

to gain a better possession of the meaning of entropy. Thus if entropy is a tendency to uniformity, uniformity itself is one synonym for a random aggregation of particles. As a statistical equilibrium, such particles have a uniformity of behavior. The ideal statistical aggregate is " the same all over."

Using a different language to reach eventually the same conclusion, it can be seen that if heat is a random motion and if there is a tendency of a hot body to lose heat to a cooler one until the temperature of both are equal, there is a tendency between the two bodies to form an undifferentiated or random state—in this sense a uniformity—with respect to each other. As acquiring more heat, a cooler body acquires more randomness; in other words, an increase of heat means an increase in randomness as microscopic particles move about. If there is a tendency in the cosmos toward an equality of temperature among and within all bodies, this may be described as a tendency from a less random or differentiated state to a more random and undifferentiated state—a tendency from the less probable to the more probable. This indeed is another way of interpreting the Carnot principle. The original constellation of things must have been one of lesser probability in the vocabulary of statistics, and as time has unfolded, there has been a movement from the less probable to the more and more probable. And so it will continue in the future. " Order," as von Weizsäcker has summed it up,

is a state which can only be realized in a very special way and which, therefore, in practice, never originates of itself. Disorder, on the other hand, is a generic name for the totality of all states in which no definite order is realized; it can thus be realized in a thousand different ways. When therefore any change not precisely determined takes place in nature, it is to be expected with overwhelming probability that it leads from order to disorder and not vice versa.[54]

The tendency in our world toward uniformity is thus a tendency to randomness, a tendency to disorder, a tendency

[54] *Op. cit.*, p. 168.

to statistical equilibrium. The common end-product of all energy reactions is the spread of heat or the increase in randomness. By contrast to the order, described by von Weizsäcker, which is differentiated and heterogeneous, the random or disordered, in the language of thermodynamics, is undifferentiated and homogeneous. If entropy reigned alone in nature, our world would gradually be undergoing a levelling influence where difference, or otherness, an essential in all motion, would slowly be disappearing.

There are several qualifications that would have to be put upon the law of entropy if the discussion were to become more precise than is intended here.

For one thing within the kinetic molecular theory itself, if the particles of a system are truly disorganized, there is a small statistical possibility that they may, in their aggregate, move "uphill" and this fact has led, as d'Abro suggests, to the downgrading of entropy to the status of an approximation.[55] Such a view, projected within the classical kinetic molecular theory, would be supported for different reasons by the statistical thermodynamics of quantum theory.[56] Moreover, Tolman suggested that a relativistic treatment of entropy might not require the irreversible march toward the "heat-death" of the universe.[57] Finally, the steady state theorists restrict entropy to local systems and permit the addition of hydrogen, in the quantity previously stated, so that the total entropy of the universe, far from declining, remains constant, i. e., in a steady state.[58] As they deny evolution in its orthodox sense, so the steady-state theorists see a universe where entropic losses are being overcome.

Nevertheless, with all of these qualifications, it may still be true that the law of entropy—and could we not argue in a similar vein concerning evolution?—is one of those approxima-

[55] *Op. cit.*, I, 399.

[56] But directionality is also indicated by the non-conservation of parity. See the article with this title by P. Blackett, *American Scientist*, XXVII (1959), 509-514.

[57] R. Tolman, *The Principles of Statistical Mechanics* (Oxford, 1938).

[58] H. Spencer Jones, "Continuous Creation," *Science News*, XXII (1954), 29.

tions, true for the most part as Aristotle [59] maintained but not invested with absolute certitude like the type which post-Cartesian physics has been seeking in the physical world. Moreover, and as Aristotle also showed in his dialectical evaluation of his predecessors, approximations can put one on the road to reality itself.[60] Thus, there is no intention here of using such highly derivative notions as entropy and evolution to decide the issue of the fundamental principles in nature; for this question is decided at a level far more general than that attained by modern science with its specialized techniques of experiment and its mathematical apparatus. But within this framework, both entropy and evolution may suggest some basic truths or reinforce some truths already recognized.

III

Several reservations will be useful in order to understand the spirit of the ensuing comparisons involving evolution and entropy.

1) However fruitful it might otherwise be to assess the methods for studying both evolution and entropy and thereby to gain a better hold on the meaning of the results, such an excursion into logic and epistemology will not be undertaken here.[61]

2) The leading cosmologies of our day are evolutionary. This we have seen in the very language of cosmologists themselves. It is apparent in the build-up, a qualitative differentiation, of the heavier elements from hydrogen [62] and in the final conditioning of the universe to support life in its higher

---

[59] *Phys.*, II, 5, 196b 10-11.

[60] *Ibid.*, I, 5, 188a 18-29.

[61] This issue has been raised by E. McMullin in " Realism in Modern Cosmology," *Proc. Amer. Cath. Phil. Assoc.*, XXIX (1955), 137-160.

[62] " What, then, does this steady-state universe look like? Although it is unchanging on a large scale, it is not unchanging in detail. Each individual galaxy ages owing to the way its resources of hydrogen are being depleted by its conversion into helium inside the stars, and for other reasons." H. Bondi, *The Universe at Large*, p. 43.

and higher forms. The gradual preparation of matter to sustain life would itself be evidence of the evolutionary direction in the history of nature. Teilhard has summed up the truly evolutionary trend, believed discernible throughout the whole cosmos, by his term " complexification." [63]

In this light evolution is irreducible to entropy, even though both may be universal and correlative; and the techniques to measure entropy may not in general be fitted to detect the qualitative and finalized character of genuine evolution. We may have here an analogue to Bohr's principle of complementarity. Nevertheless, evidence for both principles, for whatever conviction it may carry, has become embodied in the language of contemporary cosmologists, and is there to see even in the outline we have been sketching.

3) Whether evolution and entropy are absolute and necessary laws need cause us no scruples in our assessment of their meaning. The continued existence of apparently very old living forms that did not either evolve or become extinct may be an exception to evolution as a truly absolute universal, and there are arguments that entropy too is only approximation. But if evolution and entropy are true for the most part, they are, by such a status alone, entitled to a legal status in scientific explanations.

Will further research modify our current notions of evolution and entropy? Perhaps it will. But once more these two concepts must be taken seriously by the philosopher of nature. For the philosopher, even though not limited to current experimental evidence and theory, is bound to take account, to the extent that he can, of up-to-the minute scientific findings. If he waits until all such results are in, he will wait forever. But if he sifts through the reports of the science of his time, he may hit upon that element of truth to be found in every system of thought [64] and, in the case of modern physics, an element usually submitted to more or less careful checks.

[63] Teilhard de Chardin, *The Phenomenon of Man* (New York, 1959) p. 48.
[64] *Meta.*, II, 1, 993a 30-993b 7.

This tenuous hold on truth is all we can expect in exploring nature's details.

With all of these restrictions, what is the problem to be treated? It is the paradox mentioned by Lalande more than a generation ago and never fully faced, let alone resolved. The gist of the problem is that there are two conflicting laws reigning in our cosmos. One is the law of evolution leading from disorder to order or from uniformity to differentiation. The other is the law of entropy which finds the cosmos as a whole going from order to randomness and from differentiation to uniformity. How can these opposites co-exist? Are we not in a position like that of Parmenides who was led to deny motion because it seemed to involve irreconcilable opposites?

Yet, in addition to the undoubted evidence for motion, there may also be enough evidence for both evolution and entropy to bid us find a corresponding place for both of them in our cosmology. In Book I of his *Physics*, Aristotle found a place for the embryonic theory of evolution in Anaxagoras and for the quasi-entropy of Empedocles. For all of the early naturalists as serious students of nature saw dimly, Aristotle said, and they framed obscurely, some important truths about nature.[65] But they did not push their analysis to the fundamental principles in nature [66] which are two first contraries and their subject.

This is not Aristotle's positive argument for primary matter and its two first contraries of substantial form and privation, and we are applying a similar dialectic to approximate [67] what would be reached scientifically on other grounds. Let us go over the dialectic to see how it operates.

Evolution and entropy, the uphill and down-hill tendencies detected by modern cosmology, are contraries. They are opposites, and all motion, tends, from different points of view, to

[65] ". . . for all of them identify their elements, and what they call their principles, with the contraries, giving no reason indeed for the theory, but constrained as it were by the truth itself." *Phys.*, I, 5, 188b 28-30.

[66] St. Thomas, *In I Phys.*, lect. 10, n. 172 (ed. Angelo Pirotta).

[67] This is one reason why dialectic is called *tentativa*. *In IV Met.*, lect. 4, n. 574.

be characterized by them both. That is to say, there are no processes which tend to be governed by only one of these principles, say entropy, while other motions are ruled only by evolution. For entropy is generally regarded as universal,[68] and if modern cosmogony is a witness, equally universal is the principle of evolution. Hence, evolution and entropy must simultaneously characterize the same change and the same changing things. Therefore, the substratum of these two tendencies must be indifferent to both of them. If it inherently possessed one, it would expel the other; and vice versa.

Such a triadic structure seems to throw us back upon the three first principles of change discussed in perennial philosophy. Evolution is a sign of form; entropy, of privation; and the indfferent substratum, of primary matter. We are speaking here of signs—not of principles; of effects not of causes. For evolution and entropy, if they do signify form and privation, are derived and secondary contraries which must be traced back to their first principles. But this determination of signs and effects is all we are after, here. It is evidence of the kind of dualism which has been re-affirmed in recent physics in establishing new bridgeheads between modern science and traditional philosophy.

Teilhard, though not alluding to the substratum we have claimed as a necessity to bring evolution and entropy together, has reinforced the effort we have made above:

In every physico-chemical change, adds thermodynamics, a fraction of the available energy is irrecoverably 'entropised,' lost, that is to say, in the form of heat. Doubtless it is possible to retain this degraded fraction symbolically in equations, so as to express that in the operations of matter nothing is lost any more than anything is created, but that is merely a mathematical trick. As a matter of fact, from the real evolutionary standpoint, something is finally burned up in the course of every synthesis in order to pay for that synthesis.[69]

Entropy measures the loss factor, the privation, the exhaust

68 Von Weizsäcker, *op. cit.*, p. 57.   69 *Op. cit.*, p. 51.

of what is "burned up" in the movement toward form. But what loses and what gains? It must be a substratum indifferent to either process, the subject in which privation and form succeed one another.

IV

Though not concerned with the physical meaning of evolution and of entropy but more with logic and pedagogy, there is one final observation that may be in place here. For we have argued that the philosopher of nature is not dependent on the evidence of entropy and evolution to establish his three first principles of all change. He knows them because, in the order of learning, the analysis of nature on a general level precedes the specialized knowledge like that achieved in modern science; this pedagogical order is commanded by the very nature of human knowing.[70] Does our study of evolution and entropy lend any confirmatory weight to this order in our reasoned knowledge of nature?

Let us look at this matter closely, not because it is a physical problem but only because evolution and entropy have been in focus. Our question, to phrase it properly, concerns the level where our reasoned knowledge of nature should begin in order to be truly sure of itself. Should it begin with the microphysical, the astrophysical, or at some other level?

Our authentic science of nature, sure of where it is starting and of the principles it finds there, cannot begin with the microphysical. For there may be forces and factors operating in the universe at large which will not show up in microphysical analysis. Thus, there could be no entropy to a single particle, and for the same reason, the scientist could not speak of evolution at this atomistic level. Even the biological evolutionist cannot discuss evolution in the case of single individuals. He speaks of populations. "Complete knowledge of the individual events in the history of life," according to Simpson, "is absolutely unobtainable, even in principle."[71] By the same

---

[70] *Summa Theol.*, I, q. 85, a. 3.
[71] "The History of Life" in *The Evolution of Life, op. cit.*, p. 121.

token, the astronomer employs statistics to detect trends in his "billions of galaxies." [72] The point is that the over-atomization point of view, in terms of the familiar figures of the trees and the forest, may lead us to overlook some of the cosmic laws which a broader look would reveal. This is especially true when our analysis becomes microphysical.

Shall we begin, on the other hand, with the astrophysical? If we do, we will find another source of obscurity. For all our knowledge of distant times and places is dependent on what we know from things on earth, however this knowledge be refined and modified later on. If we leap, therefore, to astrophysical problems without a prior study of things and events within more direct experience, we will lack tested equipment to make a realistic sounding of the dark depths to which we have plunged.

Entropy and evolution thus make it relevant to inquire where our deliberate possession of natural science should begin. And there is no more logical beginning for a truly synthetic reading of the book of nature than reason's consideration of material things as they are first available in direct experience. Such knowledge any scientist must inevitably possess, in however uncritical and unobtrusive a fashion, before he resort to the special techniques of experiment and mathematics. Using knowledge of this type, we have claimed to make evolution and entropy not only more physically meaningful than perhaps they now are but also consistent with each other.

VINCENT E. SMITH

Philosophy of Science Institute,
St. John's University,
New York, N. Y.

---

[72] H. Shapley, *Galaxies* (Philadelphia, 1943)

FROM THE FACT OF EVOLUTION TO THE PHILOSOPHY OF EVOLUTIONISM

ᚙ

PART I: FROM THE FACT OF EVOLUTION

STATEMENTS made by serious students of contemporary evolutionary theory seem to be, even to this day, in open conflict about the " fact of evolution." At the Darwin Centennial Celebration held at the University of Chicago (November, 1959), the statement was constantly reiterated: " Biologists one hundred years after Darwin take the fact of evolution for granted, as a necessary basis for interpreting the phenomena of life." [1] Huxley repeated the point: " The evolution of life is no longer a theory; it is a fact and the basis of all our thinking." [2] Dr. Sol Tax, chairman of the Convention, summed up the panel discussions by extending the concept to all areas of scientific endeavor:

But perhaps most of our schools still teach evolution, not as a fact, but as only one alternative among explanations of how the world has come to be what it is. No matter what gets done about our religious beliefs, this particular phenomenon must now come to an end. We cannot deal with the difficult problems of the world unless our education takes account of *demonstrated empirical fact*. (Italics added.) [3]

However, in one of the most critical papers submitted at the Centennial, Dr. E. C. Olson suggests an underlying confusion involved in these statements. He writes:

It is certain that few negative responses would result from the simple question " Is the general concept of organic evolution valid? "

---

[1] *Evolution After Darwin*, edited by Sol Tax (Chicago, 1960) III, 107. This three-volume work contains the University of Chicago Centennial papers and discussions and will be used as a constant reference. Hereafter, the work will be signified by the initials *EAD*.

[2] *Ibid.*, p. 111.   [3] *Ibid.*, p. 247.

were it to be submitted to the biologists working the various disciplines today. If, however, a second question were asked, one requiring a definition of organic evolution, it is equally likely that a varied suite of answers would result, and, if the answers were honest, there would be a fair sprinkling to the effect "I don't know." [4]

After insisting that there is a silent segment of significant numbers among biologists and other scientists who feel that much of the fabric of evolutionary theory accepted by the majority today is actually undemonstrated or even false, Olson goes on:

The statement is frequently made that organic evolution is no longer to be regarded as a theory, but is a fact. This, it seems to me, reveals a curious situation that causes considerable difficulty in understanding evolution both among laymen and among biologists who are not intimately concerned with its study . . . If organic evolution can be defined simply and loosely as the changes of organisms through successive generations in time, then it can hardly be questioned that, within our understanding of the earth and its life, evolution has occurred. In this sense it must be considered a reality . . .[5]

If, however, the definition of evolution goes further and asserts that contemporary synthetic theory (neo-Darwinian, mutation-selection) is the theory of evolution, as was done many times during the Convention,[6] then, Dr. Olson points out, that "fact of evolution" must be rejected as unproved and invalid. The explanation of *how* the process of orderly change of successive generations through time has been accomplished must be dissociated from the statement *that* such an orderly succession has taken place. Only then will many scientists accept the proposition "evolution is a fact." [7]

Olson's critical series of observations in the midst of the Centennial discussion of the status of evolutionary theory today throws important light upon the confusion which has reigned for over a decade about this proposition: "evolution is a fact." In 1951, the eminent geneticist T. Dobzhansky wrote:

[4] *Op. cit.*, I, 525.   [5] *Ibid.*, p. 526.   [6] *Loc. cit.*   [7] *Ibid.*, p. 527.

Evolutionists of the nineteenth century were interested primarily in demonstrating that evolution has actually taken place. They succeeded eminently well. Evolution as an historical process is established as thoroughly and completely as science can establish facts of the past witnessed by no human eyes. At present, an informed and reasonable person can hardly doubt the validity of the evolution theory, in the sense that evolution has occurred.[8]

Just a few months before this statement was published, Pope Pius XII wrote the following statement in the encyclical *Humani Generis*, the Catholic Church's most important and explicit comment on the problems connected with evolutionary thought:

If anyone examines the state of affairs outside the Christian fold, he will easily discover the principal trends that not a few learned men are following. Some imprudently and indiscreetly hold that evolution, which has not been fully proved even in the domain of natural sciences (*nondum invicte probatum in ipso disciplinarum naturalium ambitu*), explains the origin of all things, and audaciously support the monistic and pantheistic opinion that the world is in continual evolution.[9]

Dobzhanski certainly meant to include the origin of the human species by this evolutionary process which he claimed to be an indubitable fact. But Pope Pius XII, when he expressed his mind on the question of the origin of man from some pre-existing living form, again reverted to an expression which seems contrary to the statement of the geneticist (and the majority of scientists speaking on the question). After making it clear that the Church by no means disfavors the evolutionary inquiry into the origins of man from living matter in keeping with the most careful research, he adds:

However, this must be done in such a way that reasons for both opinions, that is those favorable and unfavorable to evolution, be weighed and judged with the necessary seriousness, moderation and measure . . . Some, however, highly transgress this liberty of dis-

---

[8] *Genetics and the Origin of Species,* 3rd ed. (New York, 1951), p. 11.

[9] Cf. translation of the Encyclical Letter *Humani Generis* prepared by The Paulist Press, New York, 1950, p. 6.

cussion when they act as if the origin of the human body from pre-existing and living matter were already completely certain and proved by facts which have been discovered up to now and reasoning on those facts (*per indicia hucusque reperta ac per ratiocinia ex iisdem judiciis deducta, jam certa omnino sit ac demonstrata*) . . .[10]

On the face of things, there seems to be a fundamental disagreement between the statements concerning the " fact of evolution " made by most scientists today and those written in *Humani Generis*. But this apparent disagreement is one found not only in the dialogue between the theologian and the scientist, or the philosopher and the scientist. There is fundamental ambiguity and apparent disagreement about the significance and the validity of the proposition even among scientists, as Olson's paper reveals. There cannot be true disagreement in a dialogue, however, until there is fundamental agreement about the meaning of the terms used in the discussion. Minimal topical agreement must be had: men must agree to disagree.

The proposition " evolution is no longer a theory, it is a fact " is valid or invalid depending upon the significance assigned to two terms: " evolution " and " fact." If we disengage the series of events called evolution from any discussion about the *way* evolution might have taken place, we might begin with the definition of evolution set down by Panel Two at the Centennial Convention as our constant in the present discussion:

Evolution is definable in general terms as a one-way, irreversible process in time, which during its course generates novelty, diversity, and higher levels of organization. It operates in all sectors of the phenomenal universe but has been most fully described and analyzed in the biological sector.[11]

This definition was agreed upon by Huxley, Emerson, Axelrod, Dobzhansky, Ford, Mayr, Nicholson, Olson, Prosser, Stebbins, Wright, and, presumably, by all other members of the Con-

---

[10] *Ibid.*, p. 19. [11] *EAD*, III, 107.

vention.[12] Assuming, for the moment, the definition of evolution stated here, let us turn our attention to the other undefined element of the proposition, the term " fact."

What is a Fact?

Although the term is much used (and abused) in ordinary speech, the accepted meanings of the word " fact " are greatly varied. These variations fall into the following five categories: (1) a thing done; deed, specifically, an unlawful deed, crime; (2) that which has actual existence; an event; (3) the quality of being actual; actuality; as, the realm of fact as distinct from that of fancy; (4) the statement of a thing done or existing; as, his facts are false; loosely, the thing supposed (even though falsely) to be done or to exist; (5) Law: specifically, usually in the plural; any of the circumstances or matters of a case as alleged; also, that which is of actual occurrence; reality as an event.[13]

The range of meaning here indicates some ambiguity, but a fact is, for most people, some deed or event which is known to have actually taken place. Analogously and loosely the term is applied to events supposed or alleged to have taken place, even though the supposition may be unsupported, but in ordinary speech the usual meaning is clear. The term fact implies an element of certainty, or, at least, the removal of doubt about the actual existence of some event. Something is factual, or a fact, when it is known, either directly or indirectly, to exist or to have existed. One can attain the factual either by evidence or by inferences from evidence, but in any case, until one can ascribe actual existence to a deed or a thing, the term " fact " is not properly ascribed. To the ordinary person, fact is contrasted to fiction, fancy, mere supposition, hypothesis, guesswork, inconclusive evidence and uncertain or doubtful inferences.

When the student of language begins to investigate the

---

[12] *Loc. cit.*
[13] *Webster's New Collegiate Dictionary*, 2nd ed. (Springfield, Mass., 1953).

special and even technical usage of the term " fact " in the sciences and the arts, he finds the word taking on refined and special meanings, sometimes quite incomprehensible and seemingly contrary to popular usage. Metaphor, analogies and sometimes equivocation enter into the use of common terms in specialized fields. The term " fact " has not escaped analogous and even equivocal modification in its use by the sciences and the arts.[14]

For example, in legal cases, certainty is not required for adjudication. In the words of Hart and McNaughton:

In a criminal case, guilt need not be found beyond all doubt. The trier of the fact must be satisfied of the defendant's guilt only " beyond a reasonable doubt." In a civil case, the facts are ordinarily to be found on the basis of " a preponderance of evidence "; this phrase is generally defined as meaning simply " more likely than not." The question for the trial judge is whether a " reasonable jury " on the evidence submitted could find that the facts have been proved by a preponderance of the evidence . . .[15]

That compiling evidence and making inferences in criminal and civil law cases should have this quality of uncertainty about its " facts " is widely known and rather expected. We would expect something quite different, however, when we consider the evidence and inferences proper to the " exact sciences " of physics and chemistry. In the physical and natural sciences:

Observation is just opening one's eyes and looking. Facts are simply the things that happen; hard, sheer, plain and unvarnished.[16]

At one time in the not too distant past, the meaning of fact in the physical and natural sciences did seem to be quite " sheer, plain and unvarnished." The scientist discovered empirical facts, formulated laws generalizing the observed facts, and organized the laws into synthetic theories.[17] Without much ad-

---

[14] Cf. *Evidence and Inference*, ed. by D. Lerner (Glencoe, Ill., 1958).

[15] *Ibid.*, p. 53.

[16] E. Mach's words as quoted in N. R. Hanson, *Patterns of Discovery*, (Cambridge, 1958), p. 31.

[17] Cf. L. de Broglie, *Matter and Light* (New York, 1939) p. 18.

justment, this formula is found in the classical text-books on the methodology, not only of physics and chemistry, but of the biological, anthropological, psychological and sociological sciences as well. Whatever the technique of elaborating laws and theories—which might be proper to each discipline—one might suppose that a " scientific fact " would be an event, or thing, or deed which could be immediately and certainly observed, or inferred with certitude from technical observation. So the classical methodologies of the 19th and early 20th Centuries seemed to view the use of the term " fact."

But with the rapid revision in the methodology of particle physics (micro-physics) due to the indirect techniques necessary to handle the data, many remarkable changes have taken place in the canonized terms of classical macro-physics, biology, and the human sciences. Classical meanings attached to such terms as causality, fact, law, hypothesis, probability, etc. ceased to correspond simply with the concepts introduced by the micro-physicist. On his level of research, the observations of the facts themselves, because of the very indirect techniques of experiment he is forced to employ, cannot be disengaged from the concepts, assumptions, constructs, analogies and extrapolations used to set up the operation of discovery. The " thing " studied became a spatio-temporal measurement; its " properties " became a description of the processes by means of which these measurements are made.[18] Fact and inference, technique of observation and the event or thing observed, were so blended that the classical meanings were radically altered in the direction of subjective analogy. In the light of the methodology of micro-physics:

Observations, evidence, facts; these notions, if drawn from the " catalogue sciences " of school and undergraduate text-books, will ill prepare one for understanding the foundations of particle theory. So too with the ideas of theory, hypothesis, law, causality and principle. In a growing research discipline, inquiry is directed not to rearranging old facts and explanations into more elegant

---

[18] F. Renoirte, *Cosmology* (New York, 1950) p. 118.

formal patterns, but rather to the discovery of new patterns of explanation.[19]

This ambiguity which has entered into the language of science by the operational methods of micro-physics has not completely modified the usage of the term " fact " on the level of the macro- and the megalo-sciences. There are many scientific disciplines which still give the term " fact " the meaning of something known to have actual existence, something either observably or inferentially known to be certain. But the techniques, terminology and methods of physics have set the pace for theoretical scientific thinking for the past three centuries, and biologists, chemists, phychologists, anthropologists, sociologists and even historians have not remained unaffected by this change in the fundamental meanings of the basic concepts of physics. For our purposes here, it suffices merely to mention this increasing tendency for technical scientific language to depart from the common dictionary acceptation of such terms as " fact " and " observation."

The Facts of Prehistory

Returning to the issue of the " fact of evolution," we are confronted with another problem. If we accept, for purposes of discussion, the definition of evolution set down by the panelists at the Darwin Centennial Convention (quoted above), we find ourselves involved in a question which is essentially an historical one, or, more properly, a problem of *prehistory*. As T. Huxley wrote in 1907:

Primary and direct evidence in favour of evolution can be furnished only by paleontology . . . If evolution has taken place, there will be its mark left; if evolution has not taken place, there will lie its refutation.[20]

Huxley was speaking of organic evolution, but the problems of

[19] N. R. Hanson, *op. cit.*, pp. 1-2.
[20] Address on " The Coming of Age of The Origin of Species," in *Darwiniana* (London, 1907), p. 239.

the origin of life, of the elements, of the earth, the stars, the nebulae, etc. are, *a fortiori*, problems of prehistory. Consequently, the evidence and inferences brought forward in support of these " facts " unwitnessed by human eyes will be the kind proper to the disciplines which study historical process. Not that the neo-sciences (e. g. neo-biology) cannot offer buttressing arguments for some of the prehistorical inferences, but the kind of evidence and inference which constitute the principal argument of evolutionary process is determined and limited by the very nature of the problem of prehistory.

In matters concerning the sciences of prehistory (paleontology, archaeology, etc.), two extremes must be avoided: (1) expecting more from the kind of evidence and inference than is reasonable, and (2) attributing greater stability and reliability to the evidence and inferences than is reasonable. In order to avoid these excesses, it is necessary to assess properly what kind of problem the prehistorian poses, and the power and limits of his methodology in seeking solutions. The sciences of prehistory are similar to written history in one way, but quite dissimilar in another. Perhaps we can best understand the problem of discovering " facts " and making " inferences " in prehistory by comparing its methods to those of the professional historian.

Scientific history differs from other sciences and arts in its subject-matter, its facts, its primary aim, its language, its theories and interpretations, its methods and its meaning.[21] Its subject-matter is the recorded past, more or less dramatized or put into order. The recorded past is a series of individual events, actions, persons, non-recurring for the most part, seen in the context of a space-time continuum. The facts are individual, concrete, unrepeatable events made available by the witnesses who recorded them. The primary aim of history is to reconstruct the events in their individuality, thus resembling a literary narrative rather than a scientific treatise. The lan-

[21] Cf. *The Philosophy of History in our Time*, ed. by H. Meyerhoff (New York, 1959) pp. 18-22.

guage, then, is literary and not scientific. Fact, theory and interpretation form a closely knit complex in the historical narrative so that there are very few " simon-pure " historical facts without some interpretation.

Historical method is a combination of scientific evidence and inference with imagination, insight, and empathy. History employs causal and even teleological explanations, shows trends and illuminates events, but is not causal in the strict scientific sense. The meaning of the series of contingent events and their patterns depends upon the theological or philosophical assumptions of the historian. Upon most of these statements, contemporary historians agree.[22] Of course, the accent in mustering evidence and inference will differ with each philosophy of history, but we can easily perceive that the historian's " facts " are not the facts of common usage. His facts are affirmations on record, or inferences from records, that something has happened.[23]

We must pass over the debate among contemporary scientific historians about the knotty problem concerning the certainty or probability of historical evidence and inference.[24] This we know, that the laws of observation and logic obtain in history as in every science, and the degree of probability or the attainment of certitude depend upon the trustworthiness of the available witnesses. Obviously, since history cannot be repeated and therefore " tested out " like a scientific experiment, the element of conjecture mounts up in this discipline. " Historical facts " lie more in the realm of actual events which *probably happened*, than in the category of actual events which *certainly happened*. The reason is simply that the historical method depends so much upon indirect evidence, inferences which depend entirely upon the relative trustworthiness of the statements of the witnesses.

If the element of uncertainty prevails in securing evidence and making inferences in history, how much more is this the

[22] *Ibid.*
[23] *Ibid.*, p. 124.
[24] R. G. Collingwood, *The Idea of History* (New York, 1957) p. 261.

condition of scientific prehistory which must draw conclusions without the aid of the statements of witnesses. Piggott, in a very critical and illuminating paper at the Darwin Centennial Convention states:

What follows from this is, I think, of paramount importance and insufficiently recognized: the nature of the evidence dictates the nature of the inferences which can be properly drawn from it . . . I want to stress here that the past-as-known which is based on archaeological evidence is not, and cannot of its nature be, the same as the past-as-known based on evidence which involves the written record in lesser or greater degree.[25]

In human prehistory (e. g. archaeology), what must take the place of written records and preserved technological phenomena is the mental artifact called the *model*. This is a human construction based upon extrapolation, interpolation and rational analogies to things known to us more directly and immediately. Simpson stresses the point that the paleontological record of fossil remains of past eras of organic life must be read with two factors in mind: (1) the essential tool (in reading the record) is extrapolation from what we know in neo-biology and present geological formation, an extrapolation which has serious limitations and must be carefully regulated; and (2) the very nature of the materials makes it obvious that the record should not be read with a score of fundamental biases.[26]

A close reading of both Simpson and Piggott will reward the reader with an insight into the limits and the powers of prehistory. On the one hand, the warnings and misgivings about which Olson, Case and Zuckerman and many others have written concerning the conclusions of scientific prehistory are clearly borne out.[27] Yet, on the other hand, the reader will be struck

---

[25] *EAD*, II, 87.

[26] *EAD*, I, 129-34.

[27] Cf. Olson, *EAD*, I, 532-37; E. C. Case, " The Dilemma of the Paleontologist," in *Contributions from the Museum of Paleontology*, Vol. IX, No. 5 (University of Michigan, 1951) p. 180; Zuckerman's statements quoted in E. O. Dodson, *Evolution: Process and Product* (New York, 1960) p. 197.

by the value of the conclusions which are obtained by pains-
taking methods in this most inaccessible of scientific materials
—the events which took place millions of years ago, unwitnessed by any human being.[28] A patient study of the methods
of geology, archaeology and paleontology manifests two significant points: (1) " facts " based upon evidence and inference
proper to scientific prehistory are *sui generis*, and, in themselves, highly conjectural and logically tentative; and (2) the
convergence of prehistoric " facts " with the evidence and inferences drawn from neo-science (biology, anthropology, etc.)
yields an unexpected reasonable basis for a series of important
convictions about what happened during these past eons of
time. Scientific prehistory should neither be overstated, nor
underrated, in its ability to resolve some of the problems of
origins.[29]

Fact as a Reasonable Conviction

Remembering the distinctions made thus far about the way
the term " fact," whether from evidence or inference, is used
variously in the sciences depending upon the availability of
such evidence and inference, it becomes easier to understand
what is meant by the statement made by Olson, and repeated
at the Darwin Centennial Celebration:

Organic evolution—the process of orderly change of successive generations through time—does occur and apparently has occurred
for the total period of life on the earth. There can be many theories
of how it occurred, each of which may explain part or all of what
has been observed, and these theories may be in complete conflict
without invalidating the basic fact of evolution.[30]

In the first place, Olson recognizes, as do all those who take
the pains to qualify their conclusions with the appropriate

---

[28] Good introduction to the methods of prehistory can be found in G. G. Simpson,
Life of the Past (New Haven, 1953) and J. R. Beerbower, *Search for the Past*
(Englewood Cliffs, N. J., 1960).

[29] Tendency to underrate scientific prehistory is a limitation of works such as
G. H. Duggan, S. M., *Evolution and Philosophy* (Wellington, New Zealand, 1959).

[30] *EAD*, I, 527.

caution, that he is speaking of a " basic fact " of prehistory, not of history, not of physics, nor of chemistry, biology, etc. (except in the supplementary sense upon which we shall soon elaborate). Whence comes this general agreement about this prehistoric " fact "? Insofar as any conclusion can be drawn from the evidence and inference proper to prehistory, every reasonable objective doubt has been removed, and the evidence has converged with such consistency that a firm, reasonable conviction has been generated in the minds of those who have expertly explored the problem. Le Gros Clark puts it clearly this way:

> It is an interesting question, but one which is not easily answered—just at what point in the gradual accumulation of circumstantial evidence (as we have in evolution) can the latter be accepted as adequate for demonstrating the truth of a proposition? Perhaps the most we can say is that, in practice, this point is mainly determined by the multiplicity of independent sources from which this evidence is derived; if several lines of argument based upon apparently unrelated data converge on, and mutually support, the same general conclusion, the probability that this conclusion is correct may appear so high as to carry conviction to the mind of the unbiased observer.[31]

Let it be noted that Olson's " basic fact of evolution," like Dobzhansky's statement quoted earlier, is in the logical order of " probability so high as to carry conviction to the mind of the unbiased observer." Without disparaging the logical quality of the phrase " fact of evolution," it remains in the *order of probability, not in the order of certainty.* By its very nature, evolutionary theory relies on proof and demonstration, the inferences of which have all or most doubts removed, but do not claim the security that the case could not be otherwise. Indeed, for the scientific prehistorian, he might wonder that anyone would raise the question whether he meant by the " fact of evolution " that it was objectively certain and could not be otherwise. He would insist that his science produced proofs of

[31] " The Crucial Evidence for Human Evolution," in *American Scientist*, 47 (1959) 299-300.

the kind described by Le Gros Clark—so highly probable that the unbiased, objective observer must be convinced by the convergence of disparate but mutually supporting evidence. No more, no less. *This is what a prehistoric fact means to the prehistorian.*

In this sense, evolution is a " fact " as opposed to a mere hypothesis which has not the documentation sufficient to remove doubt and generate the conviction described. Evolution is a " fact " as opposed to a theory among theories of reputation, as the " steady-state " theory is opposed to the " pulsating universe " theory in cosmology.[32] Evolution, as defined by Olson, abstracting from the various hypotheses concerning how the process took place, enjoys the status of having no other reasonable natural explanation of the converging evidence to oppose it with sufficient evidential support to produce high probability or conviction. Evolution is a " fact " as opposed to a low degree of probability. On certain levels, e. g. on the level of organic evolution, the degree of probability is high. What the phrase " evolution is a fact " does *not* mean, however, is that it now enjoys the status of demonstration which generates the certitude of direct observation or inference which follows so necessarily from that observation that it could not be otherwise.

Thus it is readily seen how the statements of Dobzhansky, Olson, Simpson, Huxley and others at the Darwin Convention, who constantly used the phrase " fact of evolution," were not unequivocally in opposition to the statements made by some philosophers and theologians in their attempts at a dialogue upon common issues. The two quotations from *Humani Generis* above, for example, assert that evolution has not been fully proved even in the domain of natural sciences and that those transgress liberty of discussion who act as if the origin of the human body from pre-existing and living matter were already completely certain and proved by facts which have been discovered up to now and by reasoning on those facts. It is of capital importance to understand these statements of

[32] *EAD*, I, 32-33.

Pope Pius XII in the context, not of a biological treatise, but of a theological treatise. He was not concerned about biological or anthropological methodology; he was not writing a paper for the Darwin Centennial Celebration. He was writing a theological document, using the language proper to the readers to whom it was addressed, namely, the outstanding theologians and philosophers of the Catholic Church. He was writing primarily for those Catholics who were familiar with the logical distinctions between those arguments which generate certitude and those which conclude only to a degree of probability. The reason was evident. Theologians have to evaluate carefully the degree of probability of scientific propositions in order to place them properly in the context of another source of truth—Divine Revelation.

Pope Pius XII was not questioning the validity of the concepts of prehistory as synthetic models organizing much of organic or even cosmic science; he was not controverting the evolution of species or even the possible organic relationship of the human body to other primates. He was using traditional logical concepts of certitude, probability, rhetorical convictions, in order to show that many evolutionary propositions do not enjoy certitude but only a limited degree of probability and that there are many elements of evolutionary teaching which are still seriously controverted—a fact which Olson and others took great pains to point out to the Convention. For these reasons, therefore, the " fact of evolution " could not be placed in opposition to matters of Divine Faith as a truth known to be demonstrated with certitude.

It is manifest from the context of *Humani Generis* what Pope Pius XII wished to do, namely, to call seriously into question whether the " fact of evolution " explains the existence of all things and supports the monistic and pantheistic opinion that the world is in continual evolution.[33] He by no means contradicts the assertions of Dobzhansky, Le Gros Clark, Olson and others that the objective observer, looking without

[33] *Humani Generis, ed. cit.,* p. 6.

bias at the converging evidence, must be convinced of the very high probability that evolution has taken place. He does not address himself to that problem; he merely advises professional caution. The proposition he does controvert is that the " fact of evolution " applies equally and unequivocally to the origin of all cosmic entities; the universe, the nebulae, the stars, the elements, life, diversity of organisms, man's body, his mind, culture and society, morals, religion, language and art. In fact, *Humani Generis* controverts just what the Darwin Centennial Celebration controverted when it manifestly showed that the phrase " fact of evolution " applies equivocally to many scientific disciplines, and to some areas, not at all. Let us see what happened at the Darwin Centennial in its application of the concept " fact of evolution."

The Fact of Evolution

Whether there is presently sufficient converging evidence for the reasonable and unanimous (among scientists) conviction that monophyletic descent with modification accounts for the variety of organic species, including man, on the earth was not even discussed at the Darwin Centennial Convention. As Simpson wrote in his *The Meaning of Evolution* (1949), the evidence is in and the case has been fairly adjudicated. Assuming two essential propositions: (1) that a *natural* explanation, consonant with what we know now in neo-biology about organic development, is available; and, (2) that extrapolation, analogy and indirect convergent proof be allowed where direct proof is unavailable; then, the accumulation of arguments found in any good modern text-book on evolution suffice to convince the unbiased and objective observer that evolution has, in fact, taken place.[34]

Indeed, the case for the prehistoric fact of organic evolution is a very good one. Biologists no longer question it, that is to say, they have no reasonable doubts about the connected series of natural events distributing organic species in space and

---

[34] *The Meaning of Evolution* (New Haven, 1949) pp. 4-5.

time. They do debate the relative advantages of the mechanism of evolution proposed by the neo-Darwinian, the macro-mutation-saltation, or some form of Lamarckian theory. But, as Olson says, even if one or all of these explanations prove inadequate, no one would seriously doubt that the evolutionary series of organic events occurred.[35] What is the basis for this assurance?

There is not sufficient space here to give an adequate summary of the converging evidence for monophyletic descent with modification, and unless the reader realizes the full impact of each piece of converging evidence, he is quite likely to take a negative and dialectically critical view and reject the evidence as logically inconclusive. As a mere dialectician, he is prone to ask more of the evidence and the inference than possibly can be made available, and fail to appreciate how very convincing the evidence, taken together, really is. The following considerations constitute the essential elements of this converging evidence.

In the first place, the paleontological record needs a natural explanation consistent with neo-biology. Reject this proposition and you place the question of origins outside the domain of natural science, and must invoke catastrophic theories, preternatural influences, divine interventions by miracles, etc. which would be both bad science, bad natural philosophy and bad theology.[36] Scientific prehistory shows a series of origins and developments from the pre-Cambrian period over 500,000,000 years ago to the present which leaves no doubt among disinterested observers that there was a series of successive origins of plants and animals. Most of the species of plants and animals that we know today are quite recent in the fossil record,

[35] *EAD*, I, 527.

[36] The natural philosopher would abhor a jumbled, disorderly concourse of unrelated natural events as totally out of keeping with natural laws. *Natura non facit saltus.* The theologian would abhor the thought of God specially and immediately creating, for example, distinct species of finches for each of the several Galapagos Islands at different times (multiply this miraculous intervention by the hundreds of thousands!) for it goes directly contrary to the theological axiom that God ordinarily orders all things wisely through secondary causes.

and good phyletic sequences of origins have been established by scientific prehistory. This series includes the fossil evidence for some structural development of *homo sapiens*. The only available *natural* explanation which does not conflict with the natural processes which are manifest in geology and neo-biology is the evolutionary one, common descent with modification.

On the infra-specific level, Ford's field work on the moth and the selective forces at work in modifying the species supports the concept of natural modification in species and varieties; Dobzhansky's work (and others) on *Drosophila* give convergent support to the theory of common descent with modification from the standpoint of mutation of genes and the survival of such mutation within the population. On the generic level, the amazing series of freshwater molluscs *Pauludina* can be traced in a single 300 foot deposit: nine species with more and more complicated shells emerge from one smooth-shelled species. Equally significant is the same kind of evidence found in English chalk of the *Micraster* (sea urchin) series. On the Family level, the *Equidae* (horse) series elaborated by Marsh and Simpson is most striking. Twelve to fifteen genera of horses can be traced with convincing dialectic and fossil documentation from the Eocene period, 60 million years ago, to the present living genus, *Equus*. Similar studies, though not quite so convincing perhaps, have been made among the ammonites, camels, swine, crocodiles and fishes.[37]

Taken singly, any one series is established with the use of a scientific methodology which is vulnerable to the stringent rules of demonstrative logic. Yet, remembering the *singular nature* of the problem of origins and the only methods natural science has at its disposal, it is not *certain demonstrative proof* that we are after, but that *high degree of convergent probability* which produces conviction and removes all reasonable doubt.

---

[37] Cf. Dodson, *op. cit.*, and especially, the symposium *Genetics, Paleontology and Evolution,* ed. by Jepson, Mayr and Simpson (Princeton, 1949).

With the paleontological record objectively before us, and the series of simpler forms to the more complex appearing in distinct periods of space and time, let us see how all the disciplines of neo-organic science contribute buttressing, yet divergent, arguments in support of common descent with modification. Again, limited space allows only a schematic summary. In biogeography, the area which was so convincing to Darwin, we find biogeographical realms, discontinuous distribution and exological zones. Within the local areas, we find marvelous resemblance and adaptation to the particular environment. These singular conditions can best be explained by common descent with modification. How else can the distribution of distinct species of finches on the various islands of Galapagos be explained, species which so closely resemble the genera of finches on the South American mainland?

In taxonomy, the classification of plants and animals, a marvelously delicate hierarchical relationship is manifested, just what would be expected from common phylogenetic descent with modification. As Darwin had put it " the only known biological explanation for close similarity in nature (among organisms) is common descent." [38] This statement is not universally true, as more recent studies have shown,[39] but the argument is dialectically sound and weighty. Taxonomic relationship is best explained by common descent with modification.

A similar convergent argument is contributed from the morphological sciences, e. g. anatomy and physiology. A study of the organ systems of animals manifests a phyletic prototype which is varied from class to class, family to family, etc. These homologies and analogies are best explained by common descent with modification. In embryology, the student finds that individuals of different species (e. g. the hog, calf, rabbit and man) pass through embryological stages which are almost identical, a fact which is best explained by common decent

[38] *The Origin of Species*, Chapter XIV (6th ed.; Modern Library), p. 320.
[39] The trend called " parallel evolution " is described in Simpson's *Life of the Past*, pp. 127 ff.

with modification. From cytology and biochemistry, other arguments are advanced. For instance, protoplasm, blood, hormones and enzymes show properties which are remarkably similar in large groups of animals. This is best explained by descent with modification.[40]

These basic observations and generalizations from the several departments of biology could be multiplied and detailed with endless documentation, but this summary must suffice to give the uninitiated reader some sense of the convergence of argument and the buttressing strength of the contribution of neobiology to the general argument of organic prehistory. Again, close study of any fundamental textbook on evolution will guarantee two important insights: (1) the special kind of answer one must expect from a natural investigation of origins —its limits, if you will; and (2) within this context, the power of the argument, the high probability which the convergence of evidence generates among those who view the question of origins impartially.

As a member of the animal kingdom, the species *homo sapiens* is included in the general arguments above. Physical anthropology has used the scientific methods of prehistory with almost uncanny effectiveness to produce a series of hominoid descent with modification comparable to the best phylogenetic series among the other mammals. A classification of skulls (and other fossilized parts), based upon several fundamental characters, which, taken together, comprise a total morphological pattern distinguishing the anthropoid ape skull from the hominoid type skull, reveals a graduated series rivalling that of *Equidae*. From *Australopithecus* (500,000-1,000,000 years ago) through *Pithecanthropus* (200,000-500,000) represented by Java and Pekin man, *Pre-Mousterian* (100,000-200,000) represented by Steinheim, Fontechevade and Swanscombe, *Early Mousterian* (50,000-100,000) represented by Mt. Carmel in Palestine and others in Europe, to *Late Mousterian and Modern Man* (about 50,000) represented by the Neander-

---

[40] See Dodson, *op. cit.*, for full treatment of these arguments.

thals on one branch and modern European man on the other, we find surprising fossil documentation of descent with modification of the human body.[41] To the physical anthropologist, the weakness lies not so much in this series of developments, but rather in the lack of fossils connecting *Australopithecus* with the fossil hominoids (great apes) of the Pliocene and Miocene eras. Le Gros Clark admits that mere extrapolation backwards in the absence of concrete fossil evidence is not a satisfying procedure.[42] This hiatus is disturbing, but not of such proportions as to shake the general conviction that *homo sapiens* is biologically related to the rest of the animal kingdom in a natural continuum, even though much important evidence remains to be uncovered. What the paleoanthropologist does have by way of documentation of the " fact of physical evolution " of man is very good.

The Fact of Cosmic Evolution

In the Darwin Centennial Celebration papers, as has been stated, the question whether evolution is a fact was barely alluded to. It was taken for granted.[43] The issue of the Centennial was far more extensive in scope. The burden of the papers and the panel discussions was to show that the concept of evolution (and especially the neo-Darwinian interpretation) was valid in every major scientific discipline. The " fact of evolution," it was asserted, can and should be extended to the origin of mind, culture, life, the cosmos itself and all it contains. It was in this extension of evolutionary thought to the problem of origins in every field that the Centennial papers, *Evolution After Darwin*, provided expert commentaries of great value.

A careful analysis of the way the concept " fact of evolution " is used in the fields outside biology reveals *a fact of considerable importance*. The concept " fact of evolution," valid in the matter of organic origins and diversity as described

---

[41] W. E. Le Gros Clark, *The Fossil Evidence for Human Evolution* (Chicago, 1955).

[42] *Ibid.*, p. 163.   [43] *EAD*, III, 107.

above, becomes *equivocal* as it is applied to the origin of life, chemicals, stars, nebulae, mind, language, culture. Neither " fact " nor " evolution " retain the same meaning, and the evidence and inferences are of another kind, varying from discipline to discipline. In point of fact, there is great uncertainty that the concept " fact of evolution " is relevant in some areas of scientific study. This element of equivocation in terminology, in evidence and in inference, is often completely overlooked, and the degree of conviction generated in the biological sciences is by no means present to the same degree in some of the other areas of science.

This mutation in evolutionary concept as the observer goes from one field to the next is of greatest importance in evaluating the scientific dimensions of evolutionary theory. The problem is treated in detail elsewhere,[44] and can only be touched upon here by a few examples drawn from the Centennial papers. Applying the hypothesis of evolution to the origin of life, H. Gaffron compared the status of the " fact of evolution " in biology to that of biochemical biopoesis (the natural origin of life from the inorganic). After admitting the conviction generated by convergence of evidence in biology, he states:

The situation in respect to biopoesis is exactly the reverse. There is nice theory, but no shred of evidence, no single fact whatever, forces us to believe in it. What exists is only the scientists' wish not to admit a discontinuity in nature and not to assume a creative act forever beyond comprehension.[45]

The acceptance of the " fact of evolution " of life from non-life is based upon a conviction of an entirely different kind. The biologist and the biochemist look across a chasm which is filled only by a combination of imagination, extrapolation, human faith and a lively hope. This is not to disparage research in biopoesis, for out of this combination emerge working hypotheses with which the problem of biopoesis may one day be

---

[44] R. J. Nogar, O. P., " Evolution: Its Scientific and Philosophical Dimensions," *St. John's University Studies*, ed. Vincent E. Smith (Jamaica, N. Y., 1961) Series 3.
[45] *EAD*, I, 45.

solved. But today the concept " fact of evolution " cannot be applied to the origin of life except in this *equivocal* sense. Evidence and proper inference is lacking at the present stage of investigation.

When the concept " fact of evolution " is applied to the origin of chemical and physical elements, an even greater degree of *equivocation* on the terms " fact " and " evolution " is present. Smart,[46] Urey,[47] Fowler [48] and others are very guarded about the extremely hypothetical nature of the knowledge concerning the formation of the elements of our own system. Highly tentative backward extrapolation and reasoning from analogies with our present system of elements, coupled with many alternative theories, all enjoying some reputation, give another meaning to the phrase " fact of evolution " of the elements. As Shapley's paper on the evidence for inorganic evolution plainly manifests, the origin of the universe is hardly a scientific question at all, and the theories about the course of the universe's prehistory alternate between some one-way process and a cyclic process, a steady-state and an expanding universe depleting its energy.[49] The degree of conviction generated in these cosmic sciences is not so great as to rule out serious doubts and alternative explanations, and the meaning and status of the " fact of evolution " is equivocal.

Almost without exception, the Darwin Centennial panelists and those who submitted papers for *Evolution After Darwin* agreed that when the organic process introduced *homo sapiens* upon the cosmic scene, the concept of the " fact of evolution " radically changed. Man may be terminal to a somatic-germinal evolution determined in part at least by the forces and mechanisms of selection and mutation which were operative in all the other higher animals, but once the species *homo sapiens* evolved, his evolution was no longer to be manifested in human body

[46] *The Origin of the Earth*, Chapter 10 (Cambridge, Eng., 1951).

[47] *The Planets: Their Origin and Development* (New Haven, 1952) p. 11.

[48] See the analysis of scientific cosmology in M. K. Munitz, *Space, Time and Creation* (Glencoe, Ill., 1957).

[49] *EAD*, I, 33.

and gene complexes but rather in psychological potentialities.[50] Kroeber, Washburn, Howell, Hallowell, Critchley, Hilgard, Brosin, Piggott, Steward and Tax asserted in their professional contributions that the " fact of evolution " of man's mind, his language, his culture, his society, has a very limited and equi- vocal usage in comparison to its use in biology. Hallowell rejects, with Hilgard, the notion that there are no differences, except quantitative ones, betwen the learning of lower animals and man,[51] and Steward goes so far as to say:

This paper is largely an admission of the general uncertainty now surrounding the concept of cultural evolution . . . In the physical and biological universes, evolution implies change which can be formulated in principles that operate at all times and places, al- though the particular principles of biological evolution differ from those of the physical realm. Expectably, or at least by analogy, then, cultural evolution should contain its own distinctive prin- ciples, which also underlie cultural change. *By this criterion, no one has yet demonstrated cultural evolution.* (Italics added.)[52]

These papers on cultural anthropology, archaeology, psy- chology and language not only show this radical change in the concept of evolution as it is applied to man, but they even show a strong tendency to ignore the concept of man's prehistory and concentrate upon man as he is now known to be the fashioner of his own future. Scientifically, man is best known, not in what he was in his prehistory, but in what he presently is and does. The " fact of man's evolution " is a concept which is most equivocal; it is a concept which seems to be becoming obsolete in the sciences of human behavior and activity.[53]

The Fact of Evolution: A Summing Up

When we hear or read the statement that evolution is now no longer a theory but a fact, and should be taught as such, a healthy response to the statement should include neither the panic of complete and irrational skepticism or denial, nor the

---

[50] For example, Huxley, *EAD*, I, 19; Tax, *EAD*, III, 280.
[51] *EAD*, II, 360.   [52] *EAD*, II, 182-83.   [53] *EAD*, II, 16.

excessively uncritical naïveté of the statement made to science teachers attending the last session of the five day Panel at the Darwin Centennial Celebration:

Properly taught, the knowledge which our students gain should produce in them a sense of the universality of evolutionary processes, from the prebiological molecular level through the prehuman world to man with his physical, mental, and sociocultural development, thus integrating the physical, biological, and social sciences, and, through history, the humanities. This sense of change leads to the habit of "thinking of reality in terms of process" rather than in terms of static situations.[54]

Careful delineation of the wide varity of meaning attached to the concept "fact of evolution" gives us a well focused view of both the power and the limits of evolutionary theory. The theory is a very complicated combination of univocal, analogous and equivocal statements, especially when an attempt is made to apply it to every scientific area of study. Some of these statements are strongly supported by evidence and securely drawn inferences; others are hopeful hypotheses and arbitrary assertions. Perhaps Beckner's summary of evolution theory in biology is a fair evaluation of evolutionary thought in general:

My own view is that evolution theory consists of a family of related models; that most evolutionary explanations are based upon assumptions that, in the individual case, are not highly confirmed; but that the various models in the theory provide evidential support for their neighbors.[55]

PART II: TO THE PHILOSOPHY OF EVOLUTIONISM

As long as the "fact of evolution" is understood in its wide variety of equivocal senses, variously substantiated with that degree of probability presently afforded by the methodology used in each scientific discipline, the true value of the diachronic

---

[54] J. C. Mayfield, "Using Modern Knowledge to Teach Evolution in High Schools," Graduate School of Education Symposium of the Darwin Centennial Celebration. (Chicago, 1960) p. 7.

[55] M. Beckner, *The Biological Way of Thought* (New York, 1959) p. 160.

352 RAYMOND J. NOGAR

concept can be seen. Not only does a process of evolution add
a dynamic space-time dimension to our understanding of the
cosmos, but the evolutionary theory also provides a concept
of synthesis for many disparate scientific approaches. Beckner
observes:

Evolution theory is of philosophical interest because of the way it
integrates principles of the most diverse sorts, but, in addition, it is
of interest because here we find the most diverse patterns of concept
formation and explanation unified in a single theory.[56]

For many scientists and observers, this quality of unifying
the work of many sciences, of integrating the explanations and
approaches of diverse disciplines, is the outstanding contribution of evolutionary theory. It is commonly said that Darwin
did for biology and the life sciences what Newton did for
classical physics. The very crucial question is raised by Beckner, and others at the Darwin Convention, whether, in fact,
evolutionary theory provides an integration by way of a *constructural model* (or series of models) which is able to embrace
the research of many sciences, or whether it provides *universal
laws*, like Newton's laws of motion, the laws of conservation
of mass and energy, the laws of thermodynamics. Mental constructs are universalized only in the imagination; universal laws
are causal and necessitate the events of which they are causal.
If there is a universal cosmic law of evolution (or laws), then
it can be turned into an ultimate philosophical principle of
the origins of cosmic entities, as some assert. If there is no
universal cosmic law of evolution demonstrated by science,
then no such philosophical generalizations are valid and the
" fact of evolution," so far as a synthetic principle is concerned,
remains a very useful construct but is non-causal, as others
assert. The answer to this question is crucial, *for it determines
whether philosophies or ideologies* [57] *of evolutionism have bases
which are scientifically established in the laws of nature.*

[56] *Ibid.*, p. 160.
[57] For useful distinction between a true philosophy and an ideology, see W. O.
Martin, *Metaphysics and Ideology* (Milwaukee, 1959)

Are There Laws of Evolution?

If we can model our discussion of natural laws upon the methods of physics, the science which has for several centuries set the pace for methodological procedure, three closely inter-related tasks must be performed in establishing a body of knowledge (1) isolate the phenomena to be studied; (2) describe unambiguously what is happening; and (3) discern some specific permanence in the flux of events under observation. By this process, for example, the laws of conservation were formulated.[58]

We have seen how equivocity enters into the very texture of evolutionary theory at every level of the " fact." Consequently, in this difficult question of prehistory and origins, there is a special and sometimes insurmountable difficulty in knowing whether the first two conditions above are satisfied. Isolating facts of prehistory and describing them unambiguously is, by the very nature of the problem, a large order. Assuming the most complete and reliable analyses of phylogenies, however, can we discern some specific permanence in the flux of events under observation?

B. Rensch takes up the problem of the " laws of evolution " in his paper for the Centennial Convention, and the question of the direction of evolution was fully discussed.[59] At first sight, it seems that in the flow of evolutionary events many laws can be formulated: (1) the law of increasing complexity; (2) the law of progressive speciation of phyletic branches; (3) the law of increasing size; (4) the law of migrations; (5) the law of adaptive radiation; (6) the law of irreversibility (Dollo's law); (7) the law of evolutionary continuity, etc.[60] Rensch lists sixty different rules which seem to have the quality of regularity, and he admits that they can be multiplied indefinitely.[61] But

[58] G. Holton, *Introduction to Concepts and Theories in Physical Science* (Cambridge, 1952) p. 278.
[59] " The Laws of Evolution," *EAD*, I, 95-116.
[60] R. Collin, *Evolution* (New York, 1959) p. 55.
[61] *EAD*, I, 110.

the curious fact about these " laws of evolution " is that *they have no universal character*. They are verified in limited areas only and admit of many exceptions. For this reason, biologists prefer to call them " rules " and " trends " rather than laws.[62]

More importantly, *the rules or trends are not attributes of evolutionary process, but are restrictive limitations on the process imposed by the existing fundamental laws of neo-science*. As Rensch points out:

> The large number of general rules quoted above may be sufficient to show that, in spite of primary undirectedness, evolutionary alterations occur in forced directions to a large degree. *After all, every generalization in the field of biology means a restriction of evolutionary possibilities*. (Italics added.) [63]

Dobzhansky confirms this observation that evolutionary pattern, though showing trends, is historical only, and nothing in the known history of life on earth compels one to believe that the evolution of organisms is predetermined to change in one direction only.[64] All the discussants at the Convention agreed that evolutionary process is unique, non-recurrent and irreversible, even though " trends " can be detected which show that the process is non-random. The course of evolution shows, generally, three stages: diversification, transformation and stabilization. But the process itself cannot be predicted, is unique and contingent, cannot be reversed (by which laws of nature are formulated) and is, by its very nature, *historical*.[65]

The upshot of this analysis is of capital importance. The laws of nature, which are formulated in the neo-sciences about the universe as we now know it, are truly universalized; they are the laws of permanence, typical and verifiable by repetition and reversibility. The *rules* of evolutionary process, on the other hand, are contingent, non-reversible, unpredictable and bear the stamp of restriction based upon the natural laws of

[62] Simpson, *EAD*, I, 167; *Collin, loc. cit.*

[63] *EAD*, I, 111.

[64] *EAD*, I, 405.

[65] G. G. Simpson, *The Major Features of Evolution* (New York, 1953) p. 312.

neo-science, the laws of permanence. *Strictly speaking, then, there is no universal law of evolution: there is only historical (prehistorical) process.*

Enter: Philosophies of Evolutionism

The importance of this last point cannot be overestimated. It is precisely at this major point that evolutionary theory provides an illegitimate extrapolation, often quite surreptitious, from a partially documented and very useful model called the "fact of evolution" into the realm of philosophy or ideology based upon an undocumented and thoroughly controverted "law of evolution." *The supposition of a universal, causal, cosmic law of evolution is not a valid inference from any known series of natural facts or laws established by science.*

It is absolutely necessary to disengage the philosophies based upon this false supposition from the scientific evolution in order to clear the air of many ambiguities which impede not only the educated person's understanding of evolution, but also the discussions among science, philosophy and theology. It is often wrongly thought, for instance, that the theological document *Humani Generis* quoted above is an unenlightened veto of the biological "fact of evolution." A close reading, however, will show that Pope Pius XII was repudiating, rather, the philosophies of evolutionism, whether they be mechanistic and monistic, or dialectical materialism, or the life-philosophies of historicism and existentialism.[66] Without denying a single piece of scientific evidence or a single legitimate inference, and even encouraging the useful research into origins of all cosmic entities including man's body, he was denying that there is a shred of evidence from the natural sciences to prove that evolution is a cosmic law that explains the origin of all things, a law which repudiates all that is absolute, firm and immutable and gives value only to events and their history.[67]

Unfortunately, there are many scientists, as well as philoso-

---

[66] *Humani Generis*, pp. 6-7.
[67] *Ibid.*

phers and theologians, who fail to draw the line between their scientific foundations which are firmly supported by evidence and their philosophical, or, more generally, ideological speculations. At one moment, they speak about biological or anthropological or cosmic evolution, and suddenly, without warning—and perhaps without knowing it themselves—they universalize evolutionary theory into a causal cosmic law and begin to draw philosophical conclusions about the universe in which we live. To the observer untrained in the logical arts, evolutionism, historicism, existentialism, mechanistic or even dialectical materialism may seem to be the necessary consequences of contemporary " evolutionary fact."

A few examples taken from current scientific thinking on the subject of evolutionary theory will illustrate this unwarranted extrapolation from the " fact of evolution " to the " philosophy of evolutionism." Rensch, after enumerating scores of rules of evolution, says:

> It was necessary to enumerate these rules, in order to evaluate the degree by which the primary undirectedness *is changed into a forced evolution* . . . (Italics added.) [68]

He then infers that the evolutionary rules and laws are complex manifestations of the universal laws of causality, and that each epigenetic development of the process was necessarily determined and implicit in the former stages through the universal laws of causality.[69] His final conclusion follows:

> Summing up, we may assume that the whole evolution of the cosmos including the evolution of living beings, was pre-existing in consequence of the " eternal " cosmic laws of causality, parallelism and logic. However, up to now, such an assumption can be only a philosophical working hypothesis.[70]

In Rensch's statement there is some token of warning that this inference is really an assumption in the philosophical order. Other scientists, however, argue a more direct philosophy of evolutionism from the data of the " fact of evolution "

[68] *EAD*, I, 110.   [69] *EAD*, I, 113.   [70] *Loc. cit.*

as though, from the evidence of biological evolution, there is but one philosophical inference available: a monistic, mechanistic historical unfolding which is the cause and explanation of the origin and diversity of life and living things. Simpson, for example, after admitting that inorganic evolution is a special case, concludes:

> Evolution is, then, a completely general principle of life and is a fully natural process, inherent in the physical properties of the universe, by which life arose in the first place (biopoesis) and by which all living things, past or present, have since developed, divergently and progressively.[71]

The reader will note carefully that the prehistoric process of the origin and development of life, including man, *is generalized into a physical law* by which an immanent natural process necessitates the present order of living things. Simpson, after admitting that the " ultimate mystery," the origin of the universe and the source of the laws or physical properties of matter, energy, space and time are presently unknown to science, goes on:

> Nevertheless, once those properties are given, the theory demonstrates that the whole evolution of life could well have ensued, and probably did ensue, automatically, as a natural consequence of the immanent laws and successive configurations of the material cosmos. There is no need, at least, to postulate any non-natural or metaphysical intervention in the course of evolution.[72]

He everywhere insists that there are no universal laws of evolution [73] and that the process of evolution is a unique, irreversible and directionless historical sequence of events.[74] Yet here he insists that the " fact of evolution," as we know it for living things, even in their origin from the inorganic world, demonstrates a causal, automatic process resulting from " the immanent laws and successive configurations of the material cosmos." And with this " demonstration," he rules out *scientifically* the possibility of any vitalistic or finalistic explanation

---

[71] " The World Into Which Darwin Led Us," *Science*, 131 (Apr. 1, 1960), p. 969.
[72] *Ibid.*, p. 972.　　　　[73] E. g., *EAD*, I, 167.　　　　[74] *Ibid.*, p. 173.

of the evolutionary process. The fact that he goes so far as to label any opposition either "lower superstition" or "higher superstition" is of rhetorical importance, manifesting clearly the personal philosophical intensity of his views.[75]

It is crucial to evolutionary analysis to detect the steps which are taken in the mental process by which what is known about prehistory can be gradually universalized into a philosophical principle of cosmic development without even noticing the illegitimate inference. In a restricted sense, evolution can be called a fact, but we must have a care for equivocation. In no sense is evolution a law of the cosmos; it cannot be so generalized. Here the false step is taken:

For, where comparative anatomy offers only probability, paleontology brings certitude. Paleontology becomes, because of the breadth of its conclusions, a truly philosophical science.[76]

By some giant mutation of insight, science demonstrates that the historical process is immanently necessitated by the physical properties of the elements to produce increasing complexities, and that is simply all there is to the process. What began as scientific prehistory has suddenly become a life-philosophy of historicism, and its basis is " a necessary inference from science itself." A biological theory has become a monistic, mechanistic, historicist, life-philosophy of the cosmos by an illogical leap that remains to most observers completely undetected. Huxley finds it easy to draw this conclusion from the scientific findings of prehistory:

All reality is in a perfectly proper sense evolution, and its essential features are to be sought not in the analysis of static structures or reversible changes but through the study of the irrevocable patterns of evolutionary transformations.[77]

---

[75] " The World Into Which Darwin Led Us," ed. cit., p. 973.

[76] M. Vandel, quoted by Msgr. B. de Solages, "Christianity and Evolution," translated by H. Blair for Cross Currents from the Bulletin de Littérature Ecclésiastique, no. 4, 1947.

[77] Review of Life of the Past by G. G. Simpson, Scientific American, CLXXXIX (1953), 88.

Philosophies of evolutionism, and they are as old as Heraclitus, are distinct from scientific evolutionary theory, and they take various shapes and meanings depending upon their primary assumptions. After Darwin, however, the various ideologies began to be framed in the context of evolutionary science, and the names Spenser, Marx, James, Bergson, Le Roy, Dilthey and Jaspers come to mind as representing some expression of a philosophy of evolutionism.[78] It is, in a limited sense, true to say that evolutionism, historicism and existentialism are fundamentally identical expressions on different levels of being: cosmic evolution, evolutionism; mankind's evolution, historicism; personal evolution, existentialism. The emergence of ideological expressions of evolutionism from the scientific study of origins and prehistory, the outstanding feature of American evolutionary thought in the last decade (crowned by the Darwin Centennial in 1959), results from two dangerous tendencies in scientific thought.

Fundamental Errors

The first of these is the unrestricted and uncritical use of the *scientific device of extrapolation*. At the Convention, Olson warned against its dangers.[79] Simpson declared its limitations.[80] Piggott is severely critical of every form of extrapolation, whether it be interpolation, interpretation, analogy or any other form of filling in the gaps of our knowledge with " postulates which fulfill an emotional need." [81] Case, Le Gros Clark, Gaffron and many others have tried to make explicit the limits of this necessary device of scientific prehistory.[82] But there is no doubt that what often appears in text-books and the more popular expressions of current thought on origins is far from

[78] The interrelationship of these ideologies is clearly traced in I. M. Bochenski, *Contemporary European Philosophy* (Berkley, 1957).

[79] *EAD*, I, 532.

[80] *EAD*, I, 121.

[81] *EAD*, II, 92.

[82] E. C. Case, *op. cit.*; Le Gros Clark, *The Fossil Evidence For Human Evolution, loc. cit.*; Gaffron, *EAD*, I, pp. 44-50.

critical,[83] and the fanciful and unlimited use of extrapolation does much to gloss over the highly tentative nature of evolutionary trends, and, what is worse, seems to give a universal status to the "fact of evolution," whereas, in point of fact, there is no such cosmic law.

This first error, the illegitimate use of extrapolation, can be corrected by caution in applying the device and, above all, by explicating its use so that the basis for inferences can be seen clearly. The second error is more deep-seated, both theoretically and practically. It is what Maritain calls *the gnosticism of history*.[84] As the discussants at the Darwin Convention admitted, the prehistoric process which has been scientifically recorded and is called "the fact of evolution" is essentially *in the genus of history*. It is not science in the sense of the tested knowledge of reversible natural processes. As Simpson put it:

That evolution is irreversible is a special case of the fact that history does not repeat itself. The fossil record and the evolutionary sequences that it illustrates are historical in nature, and history does not repeat itself.[85]

Historians reproach the philosophy of history with four capital sins, accusations which throw a bright light upon the fallacious extension of authentic scientific evolution to a philosophy of evolutionism. H. Marrou expresses the indictment this way:

First, its almost inevitably oversimplified, arbitrary and wanton approach in regard to the choice of materials, the historical value of which is assumed for the sake of the cause; secondly, its self-deceptive ambition to get at an *a priori* explanation of the course of human history; thirdly, its self-deceptive ambition to get at an *all-inclusive* explanation of the meaning of human history; and fourthly, its self-deceptive ambition to get at a so-called *scientific* explanation of history, the word "scientific" being used here in

---

[83] Compare with the above, for example, the article "How Life Began," by E. A. Evans Jr. in *The Saturday Evening Post*, Nov. 26, 1960, pp. 25 ff.

[84] *On the Philosophy of History*, ed. J. W. Evans (New York, 1957) p. 31.

[85] *Major Features of Evolution*, p. 312.

this quite peculiar sense, which can be traced back to the sciences of nature, that with such an explanation our thought enjoys a kind of intellectual mastery over the subject-matter.[86]

This rather vehement reproach can, more quietly, be applied to the philosophies of evolutionism. Evolution is an historical process, and, as such, it can have no *a priori* explanation; to assume one and then arrange materials to document it would be false to good scientific method. Simpson admits that the record cannot be read without bias, but bias must be reduced to a reasonable and defensible minimum.[87] Since no true law of evolution is discernible, evolution cannot have an all-inclusive explanation written into its own process to be divined by analysis or arbitrary intuition. Evolution is an irreversible process and therefore cannot be reconstructed according to necessitating laws. Since evolutionary process can neither be its own explanation nor reconstructed according to necessitating laws, *scientific evolution cannot be the basis for any philosophy of evolutionism.*

Those who see evolution written into the " laws of nature " confuse two things: the *necessity of the laws of nature* and the *contingency of the historical events* which run their course quite naturally. The necessity proper to the laws do not make the events necessary. As Rensch observed, the laws of biology *restrict* evolutionary change; the laws of nature are preservative, stable, typical, and ever tend to permanence of structure and function to the most extraordinary degree.[88] The unique, irreversible, non-lawful, historical process which is the sequence of contingent events we call evolution is not a law unto itself, necessitating all things that it elaborates. Evolution, like any history, can be characterized, interpreted or deciphered in a certain measure so as to reveal limited general *trends*, to use Simpson's term. But the history does not cause, nor necessitate, nor explain the natures or their laws. The cosmos is not merely

[86] Quoted in Maritain, *op. cit.*, p. 30.
[87] *EAD*, I, 121.
[88] *EAD*, I, 101.

its history; mankind is not merely its history; a person is not merely his biography. The cosmos and its natures have histories; mankind has a history; a person has a biography.[89] Since the " fact of evolution " can never be more than a partially decipherable series of contingent events, it can never be universalized into a philosophical principle giving ultimate insight and interpretation of the cosmos in which we live or our personal being by which we live. Philosophies of evolutionism, or, better, ideologies of evolutionism, may *appear* to be valid inferences from scientific evolution, but, upon close inspection the appearance is an illusion.

Conclusion: The Rhetoric of Evolutionism

The evolution of life is no long a theory; it is a fact and *the basis of all our thinking.* (Italics added.) [90]

By its rhetorical excesses, false philosophy of evolutionism can readily be detected. In the statement just quoted, Huxley sounds the dominant note of the final phase of evolutionary thinking in America, especially prevalent during the past decade. Taking the " fact of evolution " beyond extrapolation and even beyond the mere philosophy of evolutionism, he gives a scientific theory the qualities of a faith with a prophetic *mystique.* This is no longer science or philosophy; it is a rhetorical formulation of evolutionism into an easily recognizable personal apologetic. Huxley proclaimed this " new evolutionary vision " in his Convocation address at the Darwin Centennial Celebration:

In the evolutionary pattern of thought there is no longer either need or room for the supernatural. The earth was not created; it evolved. So did all the animals and plants that inhabit it, including our human selves, mind and soul as well as brain and body. So did religion. Religions are organs of psychosocial man concerned with human destiny and with experiences of sacredness and transcen-

---

[89] C. De Koninck, " The Nature of Man and His Historical Being," *Laval Théologique et Philosophique,* V (1949), 271.

[90] Huxley, *EAD,* III, 111.

dence. In their evolution, some (but by no means all) have given birth to the concept of gods as supernatural beings . . . they are destined to disappear in competition with other, truer and more embracing thought organizations.[91]

To him, scientific evolution not only necessitates a new philosophy, it inaugurates a new prophetic vision, a new religious hypothesis to replace both the old hypotheses of supernaturalism and materialism (Marxian Communism). He develops his thought:

I submit that the discoveries of physiology, general biology and psychology not only make possible, but necessitate, a naturalistic hypothesis (for religion), in which there is no room for the supernatural, and the spiritual forces at work in the cosmos are seen as a part of nature just as much as the material forces. What is more, these spiritual forces are one particular product of mental activity in the broad sense, and mental activity in general is seen to have increased the intensity and importance during the course of cosmic time. Our basic hypothesis is thus not merely naturalistic as opposed to supernaturalist, but monistic as opposed to dualistic, and evolutionary as opposed to static.[92]

One cannot read the proposal of a new faith called " evolutionary humanism " in Huxley's *Religion Without Revelation* without sensing strongly the rhetorical attributes which have accrued to a once scientific dimension of the " fact of evolution." Huxley's extension of evolutionary thinking to the position of a vision of the meaning of all reality is serious because it is done in the name of science. Yet this highly ideological and personalized explanation of the universe by cosmic history is filled with obvious gloss of analogy, metaphor and equivocation. It is extremely subjective, and, in the religious sense, apologetical. Time is the synthetic factor and the whole burden of his evolutionary philosophy is rhetorically aimed at commanding the conviction of the reader in the name and by the authority of science.

It should not be thought that the rhetorical philosophies of

---

[91] *EAD*, III, 252-53.
[92] *Religion Without Revelation* (New York, 1957) p. 187.

evolutionism are confined to the exponents of atheistic humanism (Huxley) or atheistic materialism (Marxists). They take
many forms, one of which is found in the writings of those who
claim that the " fact of evolution " necessitates a diametrically
opposed religious hypothesis, namely, a revealed supernatural
religion (Fr. Teilhard de Chardin). The starting point for the
philosophy of evolutionism is ever the same:

> Is evolution a theory, a system or a hypothesis? It is much more:
> it is a general condition to which all theories, all hypotheses, all
> systems must bow and which they must satisfy henceforward if
> they are to be thinkable and true. Evolution is a light illuminating
> all facts, a curve that all lines must follow.[93]

The vision which follows in *The Phenomenon of Man* is quite
different in what it prophesies from that of Huxley, for, as the
assumptions are modified, the prehistory of the cosmos tells a
different story. One story ends with an immanent god, man
himself; the other ends with a transcendent God, the God of
the Christian revelation. But the basic rules according to which
both accounts are fashioned are identical.

Whether the suppositions be supernaturally revealed truths,
assumptions of monistic materialism, dialectical materialism
or humanism, the first step is the elevation of the " fact of
evolution " to the status of law, a necessary series of scientifically demonstrated events. The next step is to elevate the " law
of evolution " to the level of a narrative world-view to which
everything else must bow and in the light of which everything
else must be understood. The third step is to personalize this
new world view with a highly personalized rhetoric of conviction.

In its final stages, the philosophy of evolutionism is an essentially personalistic, unverifiable intuition, rhetorically involved
in ideological feeling and emotion, using a life-self-cosmos
narration as the key to the meaning of reality. The rhetoric
of evolutionism usually can be distinguished from mere phi-

---

[93] T. de Chardin, S. J., *The Phenomenon of Man* (New York, 1959) p. 218.

losophy of evolutionism by the visionary language of the synthesis. The philosophy of evolutionism can be distinguished from the scientific " fact of evolution " by its illegitimate extrapolation and claim to universalization. Thus disengaged, the fact of evolution can rightly be assessed as one of the most significant developments of modern science.

RAYMOND J. NOGAR, O. P.

Albertus Magnus Lyceum
Dominican House of Studies
River Forest, Illinois

THE RHYTHMIC UNIVERSE

∽

UNLESS a modern biologist, who tends to be concerned exclusively with the ultra-fine structure of genes and the feed-back mechanisms of hormones, has a broader outlook fostered by an acquaintance with the humanities and a sturdy philosophy, the world becomes a strange unreal universe, apparently far removed from the world he once knew. This broader view of the universe can have many rewarding moments, such as those experienced by this writer while visiting the laboratories of Dr. Frank A. Brown, Jr., at the Marine Biological Laboratory, Woods Hole, Massachusetts, in the summer of 1959. Immediately one felt the impact of a research that was as close to the sea as the laboratory itself. Other laboratories at the famed MBL had electron miscroscopes, television microscopes, radiation scalers, and unique and sophisticated apparatus of various sorts; but here in the Brown laboratory one found much simple, home-made equipment, with intact animals going through their paces before a group of trained observers.

Huge water baths regulated the temperature of glass respirometers which housed crabs with their whole oxygen supply contained in plastic bags. Their every breath was registered by automatic recording devices. In another room, snails glided over a marked course, all unaware that their meanderings were being suggested by the motion of magnets manipulated by researchers underneath their experimental platform. Fiddler crabs in a photographic darkroom regularly changed the color of their skin just as though they were still at home on their native beaches, becoming white at night and dark in the daytime, seeming to possess some sort of magic insight into an outer world from which they were completely isolated. Clams opened and closed their shells according to a set rhythm and made recordings of their activities on special devices, while

366

crabs ran to and fro or were quiet during regular intervals of time. This was the picture one got while visiting the laboratory of one of the outstanding biologists of our time.

When one questioned the biologists who were performing these experiments as to the type of data they were receiving, their answers brought many new and interesting facts to light. The large repository of accumulated and processed data which they possessed and a number of charts they had prepared, based on their observations of the behavior and metabolism of the plants and animals studied, had led the investigators to the conclusion that all these observed activities, despite every effort at isolation from the outside, were moving in rhythm with the motions of the cosmos. Although the organisms were being studied under conditions of temperature, light and other environmental factors artificially maintained at an unvarying constancy, the plants and animals participating remained some- conclusion how in perfect accord with major cosmic or geophysical conditions of the outside world.

A confirmation of this apparently indestructible harmony with the outer world, and even with outer space, arose from one summer's observation when the workers were at loss to account for the very eccentric results obtained from a certain set of experiments. When the meteorologic data corresponding to that particular period were consulted, it was discovered that the erratic behavior coincided exactly with a sudden and large outburst of sunspots! This correlation strengthened their suspicion that their organisms were somehow getting some type of " information " from the outside which was not being observed in the laboratory.

Dr. Brown and his associates have published extensively the results of their work, and it is very interesting to note the evolution of the hypotheses involved as the work progressed for a number of years. In particular one is struck by the great similarity between the conclusions and explanations arrived at by Dr. Brown from controlled observations, and the Aristotelian doctrine concerning the influence of the " heavenly bodies." The most recent and perhaps the most comprehensive review of this work was published by Dr. Brown in a recent issue of *Science*.[1]

Living organisms, Dr. Brown points out, inhabit a world of rhythms.[2] The whole physical world, from that of the orbiting electrons in the atom to that of our planetary system revolving about the sun, shows regular cycles, or periodic changes. There are solar, lunar, tidal, monthly and annual cycles, which greatly affect the animal and plants; but in spite of the ever-changing environment, the organisms maintain a very constant homeostasis.[3] To maintain this marvelous constancy, the organisms themselves have "built-in" rhythms that respond to the periodic changes in their physical surroundings. There exists an abundant literature describing observed rhythmicities of various sorts of animals. These rhythmicities appear to be inherent, for they persist not only when the animals are in their own habitats, but even when they are removed from the place where the particular periodicity seemed to constitute an advantage for individual survival and that of the species.[4]

Perhaps one of the most arresting examples of rhythms is

[1] Frank A. Brown, Jr., "Living Clocks," *Science*, CXX (1959), 1535-1544.

[2] Frank A. Brown, Jr., "The Rhythmic Nature of Animals and Plants," *Cycles*, XI (1960), 81-92.

[3] Walter B. Cannon, *The Wisdom of the Body* (New York: W. W. Norton, 1932), pp. 20-21; Frank A. Brown, Jr., "The Rhythmic Nature of Life," in *Recent Advances in Invertebrate Physiology: A Symposium* (Eugene, Oregon: University of Oregon, 1957), edited by Bradely T. Scheer.

[4] Frank A. Brown, Jr., J. Shriner and C. L. Ralph, "Solar and Lunar Rhythmicity in the Rat in 'Constant Conditions' and the Mechanisms of Physiological Time Measurement," *Am. Jour. Physiol.*, CLXXXIV (1956), 491-496; Frank A. Brown, Jr., M. F. Bennett and H. M. Webb, "Monthly Cycles in an Organism in Constant Conditions during 1956 and 1957," *Proc. Nat. Acad. Sci.*, XLIV (1958), 290-296; Frank A. Brown, Jr., R. A. Freeland and C. L. Ralph, "Persistent Rhythms in O_2 Consumption in Potatoes, Carrots and the Seaweed, Fucus," *Plant Physiol.*, XXX (1955), 280-296; Frank A. Brown, Jr., M. F. Bennett, H. M. Webb and C. L. Ralph, "Persistent Daily, Monthly and 27-day Cycles of Activity in the Oyster and Quahog," *Jour. Exp. Zool.*, CXXXI (1956), 235-262; Muriel I. Sandeen, Grover C. Stephens and Frank A. Brown, Jr., "Persistent Daily and Tidal Rhythms of Oxygen Consumption in Two Species of Marine Snails," *Physiol. Zool.*, XXVII (1954), 350-356.

furnished by studies made on the color change in the skin of the fiddler crab, *Uca pugnax*.[5] Near dawn on the beaches, the skin of this crab is observed to begin to darken, becoming darkest at noon, while near sunset it begins to blanch, becoming lightest at midnight. In its natural habitat the fiddler crab begins feeding at dawn, and it is believed that the darkening of the skin protects it from the radiant energy of the sun and makes it less conspicuous to its predators. When collected and taken to a photographic darkroom where light, temperature and other environmental factors are maintained constant, these crabs continue to change color as if they were still on their native beaches, although this color change has no longer any survival value. In the course of studying these changes, the observers detected not only a diurnal color change produced by a diurnal rhythm of melanin dispersion (causing darkening), but also a supplemental tidal color change accompanying a tidal rhythm of dispersion. This latter tidal rhythm of darkening and blanching was closely related to the feeding periodicity and was in phase with the times of high and low tide of the crab's natural habitat. So true was this, that crabs collected from beaches that had tide times different from those of the location of the laboratory where they were observed, maintained their rhythm of color dispersion in step with their former home.

Although these diurnal and tidal rhythms held constant in the laboratory, they could, nevertheless, be " re-set " out of phase with the external solar and tidal times by exposing the animals to very low temperatures or to continuous illumination over a period of several days. The crabs would then keep the regular twenty-four hour cycle and the twelve and one-quarter hour cycle, but with a six-hour lag. Thus, instead of beginning to darken at six o'clock in the morning, the crabs would begin to darken at noon, blanching not at six o'clock in the evening,

[5] Frank A. Brown, Jr., Milton Fingerman, Muriel I. Sandeen and H. M. Webb, " Persistent Dirunal and Tidal Rhythms of Color Change in the Fiddler Crab, *Uca pugnax*," *Jour. Exp. Zool.*, CXXIII (1953), 29-60.

but at midnight. This ability to be "re-set" constitutes an advantageous adaptive characteristic for the species, making it possible for the beginning time of the cycle to be varied in harmony with changing physical conditions depending, for example, on location.

Besides rhythms of pigment change, still others were observed correlated to the feeding habits of the fiddler crab. Among these were the change in rate of oxygen consumption and in running activities. With respect to the first, crabs and other organisms kept in sealed respirometers showed a daily variation in oxygen consumption which coincided with the crab's natural feeding times. With respect to the second, wires attached to the legs of crabs contained in vessels of seawater and connected to mechanical recording devices registered a daily fluctuation in activity which coincided with the diurnal and tidal running times of the free fiddler crabs on their native beaches.

Rhythms were likewise observed in such diverse organisms of the plant kingdom as potatoes, carrots and the seaweed, *Fucus*. Here, too, even when the humidity and barometric pressure were considered to be successfully maintained at a constant level by the experimenters, there continued to be observed a regular pattern of increase and diminution in the rate of oxygen consumption for a number of organisms. These observations, more than any others, led to the formulation of hypotheses indicating that some kind of "information," some kind of stimulus, undetected by the observers, was getting through to the isolated organisms. The possible roles of ionization of air and of various components of cosmic radiation as transmitters of this "information" are now under investigation. Recent work appears to offer something in the nature of substantiation of these explanations.

This shift of attention to outside "information," outside stimuli, marks an interesting new departure. In contrast to the tendency to consider each organism as an isolated entity, it suggests that outside stimuli, emanating (in the case of cosmic radiation) even from outer space, may possibly have a determining role in the rhythms of terrestrial organisms. The mechanism, or mode according to which these various rhythms function has been studied by a number of biologists and biochemists. Their results indicate that such rhythms as color change are due to the action of hormones on the chromatophores (pigment organs) in the skins of the crabs and other animals studied.[6] There is evidence in some cases to show that the hormones themselves are produced consequent to stimuli deriving from the central nervous system which has first been stimulated by light from without.[7] When the pigment, under the action of the hormones, is dispersed in the chromotophores, the skin has a dark color, depending on the color of the pigment; when it is undispersed and concentrated, the skin is paler. In addition, a kind of mid-way system, the neuroendocrine system, has been found to function in many activities which are rhythmic.[8]

The tendency to look for the basic answers as emanating from physico-chemical forces internal to the organism leads the biochemist and the dissecting endocrinologist closer and closer to the test tube and, it would seem, further and further from the actual organism as an entity. In keeping with this investigative approach, the persistent rhythms detected in organisms were first thought of as produced by purely internal processes, by " endogenous clocks." The organisms were postulated as possessing inherited mechanisms for the rhythmic behavior observed, these " clocks " being considered as running on their own frequencies, unaffected by outside environment.

[6] Muriel I. Sandeen, " Chromatophorotropins in the Central Nervous System of *Uca pugilator*, with Special Reference to their Origin and Action," *Physiol. Zool.*, XXIII (1950), 337-352.

[7] Frank A. Brown, Jr., H. Marguerite Webb and Muriel I. Sandeen, " Differential Production of Two Retinal Pigment Hormones in Palaemonetes by Light Flashes," *Jour. Cell and Comp. Physiol.*, XLI (1953), 123-144.

[8] Francis G. W. Knowles, " The Control of Pigmentary Effectors," in *Comparative Endocrinology* (New York: Wiley & Sons, 1959), ed. by Aubrey Garbman, pp. 223-232; Berta Scherrer, " The Role of Neurosecretion in Neuroendocrine Integration," *ibid.*, pp. 134-140.

It would now seem, however, that while it is true that organisms inherit regulatory apparatus, or "feed-back mechanisms" which affect the observed rhythmicity, nevertheless these potential mechanisms require first of all to be "set off" by some external environmental factor which is functionally in the normal environment of the animal or plant. This appears in Pfeffer's studies of the so-called "sleep movements" of a certain species of bean seedlings. He found that if the seeds were germinated in the dark, and if the seedlings were kept in the dark, they did not show the "sleep movements." In the natural habitat these "sleep movements" consist in the drooping of the leaves during the night. Pfeffer could, by exposing his "sleepless" plants to a brief period of illumination, cause them to assume the same "sleep movements" as the plants in nature. Even when returned to continuing darkness, the plants now persisted in a daily "sleep" rhythm, which consisted of a drooping of the leaves during a part of the twenty-four hour cycle.[9]

Dr. William Brett has demonstrated instances similar to that of the light-triggered "sleep movements" of the bean seedlings in the case of the emergence of flies from their pupal cases. If kept through their developmental period in total darkness, the flies, whose normal emergence during the twenty-four hour cycle is at daybreak, emerge at any and all hours of the day. But when such dark-adapted larvae were illuminated at a given time with a single flash of light for a period as brief as one minute, the flies then emerged for days after from their pupal cases at exactly that same time in the twenty-four hour cycle. This light-flash was evidently a daybreak-substitute which triggered off the rhythmic emergence of the flies at the twenty-four hour intervals.[10]

As long as purely "endogenous" clocks, located at a nervous

---

[9] W. Pfeffer, *Abhandl. sächs. Akad. Wiss. Leipzig.*, Math.-Phys. Kl., XXX (1907), 259, and XXXIV (1915), 3. Quoted by F. A. Brown, Jr., *Science*, CXXX, No. 3388 (1959), 1535.

[10] Frank A. Brown, Jr., "The Rhythmic Nature of Animals and Plants," *Cycles*, XI (1960), 87.

and endocrine center, are postulated, with their mechanism to be explained purely by physico-chemical means on the internal molecular level, the horizon for investigation holds no great promise. With the introduction of hitherto disregarded or unknown external geophysical forces as possible motivators in the periodic physiological processes of animals and plants, however, a whole new perspective of research is opened up. This new dimension of inquiry and its implications are thus presented by Dr. Brown:

The thesis supported by this article, namely, that during the timing of cycle-lengths of the rhythms in animals and plants in so-called " constant conditions " the organisms are still continuously receiving from the external environment information about the natural geophysical cycles, removes some of the romantic glamor inherent in the alternative view that all living things must possess within themselves uncannily accurate clocks capable of measuring, independently, periods ranging in length from the day to the year. On the other hand, its implications are tremendous with respect to the potentialities involved, through the demonstration that living things are sensitively responding to additional kinds of stimuli at energy levels so low that we have hitherto considered the living organisms completely oblivious to them. These latter potentialities may soon loom importantly in many areas of biology and medicine, especially in such problems as animal navigation and behavior.

The demonstration that the physical environment of living things is organized *temporally* in terms of still unknown subtle and highly pervasive forces which the living organisms can resolve encourages one to speculate that there may be some comparable subtle and pervasive *spatial* organization of the environment which is contributing at least in a small way towards accounting for geophysical distribution or periodic migrations of organisms.[11]

Dr. Brown was led to his conclusion concerning the continuing reception by organisms of unobserved or unknown " information " from the external environment by the failure of his findings to support currently accepted " laws " in physiology which did not take such a factor into account. The first such finding was the discovery that many of the so-called

---

[11] *Ibid.*, p. 92.

" persistent " rhythms in animals and plants were independent
of temperature over wide ranges.[12] If the rhythms in question
were purely chemical reactions, as many physiological processes
are, then there should have been proportionate increases and
decreases in the rates, for example, of color change, oxygen
consumption, and activity in the fiddler crab consequent upon
a raising or lowering of the temperature by ten degrees centi-
grade. Yet this did not prove to be the case. The rhythms
continued unaltered over several successive ten degree increases
in temperature. In addition to this, still another finding contradicted the concept of purely chemical reactions as the sole
explanation of observed periodicities, namely, the fact that
these rhythms appeared to be immune to the action of drugs
and poisons known to interfere with many different physiological reactions, especially those involving enzyme activity.
The mechanisms responsible for the rhythms, it would seem,
must be regarded as something decidedly more than purely
chemical reactions.

A second unassimilable finding seemed to contradict the
assumption of genuinely " controlled " conditions. Many investigators were led to postulate inherent, independent " clocks "
in organisms because the rhythms continued in their periodicity
under what were considered to be constantly controlled conditions of temperature, light, atmospheric pressure and other
environmental factors. They accepted this explanation in spite
of the fact that there were experimenters through the years
who reported data that contradicted the idea of inherent, independent " clocks." Examples of such data, quoted by Dr.
Brown, are the work of Stoppel in a basement in Iceland,
Cremer in a deep salt mine in Germany and the two Hempels
in Lapland. These experimenters showed that under very
constant conditions of this kind the regular observed rhythms
were in fact interfered with during the time of the mid-night

[12] Frank A. Brown, Jr., H. Marguerite Webb, Miriam F. Bennett and Muriel I.
Sandeen, " Temperature-Independence of the Frequency of the Endogenous Tidal
Rhythm of *Uca*," *Physiol. Zool.*, XXVII (1954), 345-9.

sun.[13] The investigators who discovered these very interesting exceptions claimed or implied that the rhythms in the bean seedlings or insects which they used, depended upon rhythmic changes in the environment which, in some manner, still pervade all ordinary so-called laboratory contant conditions.

Dr. Brown's own observations of an interference in the rhythms of oxygen consumption by organisms which correlated with changes in outside barometric pressure constituted for him the recognition that not only geophysical, but even cosmic forces have a governing external influence on the rhythms of terrestrial organisms. He states that it was the rhythm in oxygen consumption of organisms matching changes in barometric pressure which led him to consider cosmic radiation as a possible factor in the periodicities. Evidence has now been obtained to show a definite relationship between the metabolism cycles of several organisms and certain fluctuations in cosmic radiation.[14] Dr. Brown also showed that fiddler crabs exhibit a measurable response in the state of their pigmentary systems to alterations in the intensity of cosmic ray showers by shielding the animals with varying thicknesses of lead sheets.[15] Other possible factors suggested are the differences of potential between the earth and the ionosphere and the various magnetic fields:

There is good likelihood, judging from the known simultaneous influence of such forces as light, temperature and tactile stimuli, that if these organisms possess the capacity to respond to one type of these relatively low-energy, or diffuse, types of environmental stimuli such as are implied by these results [correlation between oxygen consumption in organisms and the barometric pressure],

---

[13] Frank A. Brown, Jr., " The Rhythmic Nature of Animals and Plants," *Cycles,* XI (1960). 87; and "An Exogenous Reference-Clock for Persistent Temperature-Independent, Labile, Biological Rhythms." *Biol. Bull.,* CXV (1958), 81-100.

[14] Frank A. Brown, Jr., H. M. Webb and M. F. Bennett, " Comparisons of Some Fluctuations in Cosmic Radiation and in Organismic Activity During 1954-1955 and 1956," *Am. Jour. Physiol.,* CXCV (1958), 237-243.

[15] Frank A. Brown, Jr., H. M. Webb, M. F. Bennett and M. I. Sandeen, " Evidence for an Exogenous Contribution to Persistent Diurnal and Lunar Rhythmicity under So-called Constant Conditions," *Biol. Bull.,* CIX (1955), 238-254

they also possess the capacity to respond to a complex of them. Supporting such a multiple-factor view is the fact that the forms of the rhythms and their monthly variations appear to correlate to some extent with the barometric pressure, but at the same time have large significant variation at some times of the day and month that show little indication of any correlation with pressure.[16]

It was, in effect, the irregular, unexplainable deviations of the rhythms that led the investigators, not to discard their data as being impossible, but to look for a more primary, or ultimate cause of the effects observed. By checking the available meteorological data, they concluded that living organisms are very sensitive to influences from outer space in the form of components of cosmic radiation. These conclusions led the scientists to more exciting and fruitful discoveries than had resulted previously from more than twenty years of research.

Dr. Brown's researches point, then, to outside, even extragalactic, influences in the behavior of living organisms, as noted, for example, in a periodicity in terrestrial organisms related to the occurrence of sun spots, with a variation in color change which is affected by the intensity of cosmic radiation.

One might ask what is so extraordinary about the perception that terrestrial organisms are influenced in their behavior by a heavenly body such as the sun, or even by cosmic rays emanating from some unknown source? The effect of the sun upon the growth and life cycle of living things is common knowledge. More than merely confirming the *fact* of extra-terrestrial influence, Dr. Brown's discoveries clearly demonstrate an *order*, and —in view of the factors studied—an order on a cosmic scale. Order is implicit in rhythm, for rhythm presupposes a combination of variation with constancy. In other words, for events to re-occur with a certain regular periodicity, there must be a certain fixed pattern beyond the reach of chance which is the " clock " for these events; this supplies the " programming."

The regular periodicity observed by Dr. Brown and his associates, a periodicity which, with continuing investigation,

[16] *Ibid.*, p. 253.

appears to be related to causal factors on a more and more cosmic scale, certainly suggests the presence of a real entity or entities moving in a constant manner in such a way as to cause periodic variation. The hypothesis of ultimate regular motions in the universe causing a regular periodicity is, as is known, that of Aristotle and St. Thomas Aquinas. This hypothesis attempted to explain the simultaneous effect of constancy and periodicity as derived from the perpetual, regular, apparent motion of the heavenly bodies such as the fixed stars and the planets; the periodicity in terrestrial organic life was thought to be caused by the apparent northerly and southerly variations of the sun and the planets in the zodiacal circle. It should be noted that this hypothesis, already in St. Thomas' day, had extended beyond the limit of the fixed stars in seeking to locate the ultimate corporeal source of cosmic motion, for the detection of the precession of the equinoxes required the positing of a further motion beyond that of the fixed stars.[17]

[17] "From the perpetuity of generation [Aristotle] concludes to the perpetuity of celestial motion. . . . He concludes that if something remains the same throughout the course of generation, it is necessary for something to remain numerically always the same, acting in the same way, in order to cause perpetuity. But nothing in the realm of generation and corruption could be a cause of the perpetuity which is found in generation and corruption, since none of these things exist always, nor could all of them taken together be such a cause, since they do not all exist at one time, as is shown in *Physics* VIII. It remains, therefore, that there must be some perpetual agent which acts continuously in a uniform way to bring about perpetuity. And this is the 'first heaven' which moves and resolves all things by a diurnal motion.

"But since that which continuously acts in the same way solely causes an effect which remains constant, while in those things which are generated and corrupted there appear effects which do not always remain constant since at one time they are generated and at another time corrupted, it is therefore necessary, if there is to be generation and corruption in the lower [i. e. terrestrial] beings, to posit some agent which varies in its activity. And this agent he states to be the body which moves in reference to the oblique circle called the Zodiac.

"Since this circle declines in both directions from the equinoxial circle, it is necessary that the body moving in a circle through the Zodiac be sometimes nearer and sometimes farther away, and for this reason it causes contrary effects by its nearness and farness. We indeed perceive that those things which are generated as the sun approaches are corrupted when the sun recedes, for example, the various herbages which come forth in the spring and dry up in the fall. The sun and the

Needless to say, in considering the suppositions of Aristotle as expounded by St. Thomas, it is not a question of urging their literal acceptance, since even their authors did not consider them to be demonstrated.[18] Rather it is a matter of considering them from the standpoint of their general intellectual approach, an approach which accords well, for example, with findings indicative of universal cosmic rhythms making themselves felt in the periodicity of terrestrial organisms, since it is an approach sensitive to the over-all rhythmicity of the universe felt even in the smallest details of earthly life. This

other planets move indeed through the zodiacal circle, but the fixed stars are said to move around the zodiacal poles, and not around the equinoxial poles, as Ptolemy shows. From the motion of these there is caused the generation and corruption of all things generated and corrupted, but this is more evident in the case of the motion of the sun." St. Thomas, *In XII Metaph.*, lect. 6, nn. 2510-11.

In another place St. Thomas explains: " One must consider that in the time of Aristotle there had not been detected the motion of the fixed stars, which Ptolemy sets down as moving from west to east around the poles of the Zodiac at the rate of one degree every hundred years, in such a way that a full revolution of the Zodiac is completed in thirty-six thousand years." (*In II De caelo et mundo*, lect. 17, n. 7) This is the precession of the equinoxes which today is computed as twenty-six thousand years. From the point of view of apparent motion, the fixed stars in the various constellations of the Zodiac are in the course of a precession from west to east in such a way that the vernal equinox, which several thousand years ago took place when the sun was in Aries, now takes place, due to this apparent motion of the signs from west to east, in the previous sign, that of Pisces. At the present computation the rate of precession would be about 1.4° per hundred years. St. Thomas then concludes: " Therefore the ancients laid down the sphere of the fixed stars to be the first moving body, and to have only one motion, which is the diurnal motion. But on the supposition that the fixed stars move, it is necessary for this sphere to move with two motions, namely its own proper motion, which is that of the fixed stars, and the diurnal motion, which is that of the supreme sphere which is without stars." (*Ibid.*) I wish to express my gratitude to Father Pierre Conway, O. P. for pointing out and translating these and subsequent passages from St. Thomas.

[18] " These matters into which we inquire are difficult since we are able to perceive little from their causes and the properties of these bodies are more remote from our knowledge than the bodies themselves are distant from us in a purely spatial way." (*Ibid.*, n. 8) Speaking of the number of planetary motions, St. Thomas says, " We shall state what the mathematicians have to say about this. . . . Whatever remains unstated, however, shall have to be investigated by ourselves or taken on the authority of those who investigate such things or developed later from the facts now stated by those who treat these matters." (*In XII Metaph.*, lect. 9, n. 2566)

point of view is aptly summarized in the celebrated statement of Aristotle, " Man is begotten by man and by the sun as well " (*Physics*, II, 194 b 10) .[19]

There is a further point of contact in which the observed results of natural rhythms and the conclusions of the *philosophia perennis* would seem to be in accord: the recognition of a basic *order* in the universe. One is not compelled, whatever the urgent extrapolations of the materialist, to accept the order observable in a single organism as the result of random combinations over a period of billions of years. There is even less cogency in the assertion of random events as the cause of order when that order involves not the internal mechanism of a single organisms, but a whole cosmic network in which the individual is seen as a single note pulsating in rhythm with a very real " harmony of the spheres." One might accept the possibility that a simple melody could result from the random spattering of ink on lined paper. Equivalently, by the assertion of randomness, one is asked to accept a completely orchestrated score of the *Jupiter* as the result of the same process.[20]

The detection and measurement by the experimenters cited of what might be called " cosmic rhythms " is an affirmation

[19] " It is necessary according to the Philosopher to lay down some active mobile principle which by its presence and absence would cause variability as to generation and corruption in the lower bodies—and such a principle is supplied by the heavenly bodies. And therefore whatever, in these lower bodies, generates and moves towards specific form acts as an instrument of the heavenly bodies, as in the statement that man is generated by man and by the sun as well." *Sum. Theol.*, I, q. 115, a. 3 ad 2.

[20] In the dry terms of formal logic, the argument for the chance origin of life from the inorganic by random events involves two cases of *petitio principii* and one of the *fallacy of consequence*. The question is begged first in the assumption that life *could* come from non-life, prescinding from time and any instrumentality. This remains to be proved experimentally. It is begged again in the assumption that this origin is from chance, and from chance alone. But, by definition, a chance event need never happen.

The fallacy of consequence (If p, then q; but q, therefore p) is involved in the argument: If a random event were possible and did take place, then we would have living organisms today; but we have living organisms today: therefore. . . . Such an inference would be vaild only if it were the *only possible* inference, but this is clearly not the case.

of order, for rhythm is a species of order. Taking order as "the sequence of one thing upon another according to some principle," the solar, lunar, tidal (and possibly extra-galatic) rhythms of organisms are instances of order. Events in these organisms are observed to repeat themselves at certain intervals: these rhythmic intervals express the principle involved.

What is the source of this order? There is no theoretical reason, nor any experimental data, to hint that the cosmic order implied by the rhythms must be the result of random events. Rather there is implied what sound science implies in all its searchings: the presence of an intelligent and intelligible pattern in the universe.[21]

The discovery of order as in the rhythmicity of fiddler crabs and other organisms, far from granting any substantiation to the theory of random beginnings, militates strongly against it. The tendency of these findings is to suggest, not that the observed order is the result of chance, but rather that what was thought to be chance is seen to be more likely an aspect of order. Thus the interruption of periodicity in fiddler crabs, at first considered a random event, later seemed more likely to be, when a simultaneous variation of sunspots was learned of, an instance of the influence of a certain rhythmicity hitherto not considered by the researchers. This is scarcely astonishing, for events which may appear to be random to one considering only particular causes in a limited range, may be seen to be co-ordinated when one becomes conscious of a broader picture.[22]

---

[21] Writers as diverse as Einstein and Aquinas are agreed on this. The familiar " Der Herr Gott ist raffiniert, aber boshaft ist er nicht " can be compared with St. Thomas' commentary on the Aristotelian dictum, "Art imitates nature." (*Phys.*, II, 194a20) " The reason why art imitates nature" say St. Thomas, " is that the principle in the activity of art is knowledge. But all our knowledge is received through the senses from sensible and natural things; whence we operate in artifacts according to the likeness of natural things. But the reason why natural things are imitable by art is that the whole of nature is ordered by some intellective principle to its end, in such a way that the work of nature is perceived to be the work of an intelligence, as it proceeds through determinate means to certain ends, which process art indeed imitates in its operation." *In II Phys.*, lect. 4, n. 6.

[22] " It is plain that effects as related to some lower cause appear to have no order to each other, but to coincide accidentally, which, if they are referred to a higher

The experimental determination of rhythmicity indicates a more cosmic and universal, rather than a particular base. Such indications point away from theories of a random origin of organized life, and towards the conviction of a cosmic order in which random events have their part simply as normal deviations from the rule in a lesser number of cases. Order is not known to be the *per se* product of chance, and need *never* occur from it. Order does occur from intelligence, as the products of human intelligence show. Sound science may well suppose a supreme intelligence behind the events of nature. Such an intelligence can be demonstrated (though not experimentally) to be necessarily immaterial, infinite and personal.

But, the cautious inquirer may ask, could not one suppose even the final cosmic, supreme order to be possibly the result of chance? No, for chance cannot be conceived as anything other than an exception to order. The supposed supreme chance configuration presupposes a more extensive order of which it is an exception of lesser degree. Whoever speaks of chance implies, whether he acknowledges it or not, an even more primordial " order."

The fascinating researches and challenging results of talented

common cause, are found to be ordered to each other, and not conjoined accidentally, but simultaneously produced by one *per se* cause. If the flowering of this herb or that, for example, is referred to a particular force which is in this plant or the other, there appears to be no order of one to the other; rather it appears to be accidental that when this plant blooms, the other blooms also. And this is because the cause of the power of this particular plant extends to the flowering of itself, and not to that of another; whence it is indeed the cause that this plant should bloom, but not that it should bloom simultaneously with the other. But if reference is had to the power of the heavenly body, which is a common cause, the event is found to be not accidental, namely that when this flower blooms, the other should bloom also, but to be ordered by some first cause ordaining this, which simultaneously moves both herbs to florition." St. Thomas, *In VI Metaph.*, lect. 3, nn. 1205-6.

The consideration of angelic knowledge throws light on this conclusion: " The angels know all natural causes. Whence certain things which appear contingent and to be accidental when some of their causes have been considered are recognized to be necessary by the angels, since they know all the causes involved." St. Thomas, *De verit.*, q. 8, a. 12.

scientists such as Dr. Brown confirm one's opinion of the profound insights of the perennial philosophy of nature. One becomes convinced that a thorough familiarity with the Aristotelian-Thomistic synthesis does not remove one from the scientific world of today. It serves rather to put one in tune with its most fruitful explorations, as indicated by the direction of the findings of Dr. Brown and his colleagues. Far from erecting mental blocks, a knowledge of Aristotle and St. Thomas can serve only to provide the Catholic scientist with thrilling and stimulating perspectives which, while awakening a researcher's curiosity, point and beckon towards the First Cause.

SISTER MARGARET ANN, O. P.

College of St. Mary of the Springs,
Columbus, Ohio.

MIND, BRAIN AND BIOCHEMISTRY

෩

M AN lives in a fascinating, kaleidoscopic world, and the microcosm that is man is itself a wonderful complex of the changing and the abiding. There is constant change at every level of his physical and psychological make-up. Yet behind this ever-changing phenomenon there is a permanent substratum, a human *person* who undergoes these changes.

Careful studies have shown that there is a constant turnover of much of the body's chemical components. On the neuro-physiological level the pulsating brain has been called "an enchanted loom where millions of flashing shuttles weave a dissolving pattern, always a meaningful pattern, though never an abiding one; a shifting harmony of sub-patterns." [1] On the chemical level the unending array of mobile patterns is well known to biochemists. On the level of man's conscious life the constant flux is even more evident: sensory images, ideas, desires and emotions tumble over one another in rapid succession. The facts of change are so constant and obvious as to lead many to doubt the reality of anything permanent. Some scientists wonder whether there really is such a thing as a *person*, for they point out that even the so-called person seems to undergo marked changes, sometimes to the point of developing a psychosis. Schizophrenia, for example, suggests a split of personality. The schizophrenic reveals himself as one having a dual personality, at one time revealing the behavioral pattern of one personality, and at other times manifesting an entirely different personality. But, we may ask, is this a true split of the *person*?

[1] C. S. Sherrington, *Man on His Nature*, 2nd ed. (Garden City: Doubleday, 1953), p. 184.

It is clear that the psychologist and the ontologist do not mean the same thing when they employ the words " person " and " personality." The psychologist, on the one hand, looks for thought, emotion and habit patterns which lead to a consistent and predictable behavior. These for him constitute the " psychological person." The ontologist, on the other hand, perceives the ontological oneness, even the uniqueness, of an existing reality which remains unchanged ontologically throughout the constant physical and psychological variations. This existential reality, the ontological person, under certain conditions is capable of manifesting itself differently, not because of any radical change in its being, but because of modifications in its bodily or mental life. The " person " ontologically understood is the *subject* in which the changes occur. It remains identically itself throughout aberrations of mind and body. The ontological person, therefore, is the fundamental reality which originates with conception (or shortly thereafter) and remains unchanged until death. Obviously the behavioral changes associated with mental illness occur *in* the ontological person, but they are changes *of* the psychological person. Hence, a schizophrenic is one being, one rational, existent being, manifesting more than one emotional and behavioral pattern.

The ontological person is an autonomous totality composed of numerous interdependent functional parts. All the parts live by the same life, the unique life of the person, and yet each part has its distinctive vital function. Certain functional parts are so thoroughly dependent upon others that the distinctiveness of specific functions and parts is not infrequently called into question.

One important problem much discussed today and in the past concerns the relation of the mind to the brain. Is the mind, as some insist, nothing more than the brain in its functional capacity? If so, is an injured brain the same as an injured mind? Or is the mind a reality distinct from the brain? If so, how do they interact in normal thought, and where is the failure causing mental disease? These and other related questions are acute issues today.[2] In particular, the question of the relation of biochemistry to behavior has special relevance to the basic issue. If the mind is a reality distinct from the brain, how does a chemical compound interact with it? And if mental illness is nothing but a malfunctioning of the brain (whose function is ultimately dependent upon molecular activity), how can psychotherapy, that is, a non-chemical treatment, be effective in reversing an abnormal brain biochemistry?

THE MIND-BODY PROBLEM

Since man first began to philosophize, the precise relation between his thinking mind and his tangible body has been considered an important problem. Sage, savant and poet, have offered explanations, sometimes fundamentally opposed, sometimes only differently expressed. Plato has left us the metaphor of the soul as a charioteer to the body's chariot; Descartes' dichotomy of matter and spirit leads to an angelism and a division even wider than Plato's. The biologically based solution of the Aristotelian tradition has been poetically expressed in Gerard Manley Hopkins' " man's spirit is flesh-bound when found at best." The materialist solution of dialectical materialism eliminates the problem by calling mind a manifestation of matter in motion. We will examine in a subsequent section some of the contemporary data and hypotheses concerning the relation of biochemical disturbances to abnormal mental behavior. Reflection on the data to be presented may help to shed some light on the important problem of the mind-body relationship. Physiological principles can be introduced as needed.

Descartes' attempt to establish a philosophy on his *Cogito ergo sum* has made the mind-body problem an insoluble one.

[2] S. Kety, "A Biologist Examines the Mind and Behavior," *Science*, CXXXII (1960), 1861-70; H. W. Magoun, " Early Development of Ideas Relating the Mind and the Brain," in CIBA Foundation Symposium, *Neurological Basis of Behavior* (London: Churchill, 1958), pp. 4-27; W. G. Walter, "Adolf Meyer Research Lecture: Where Vital Things Happen," *American Journal of Psychiatry*, CXVI (1960), 673-694.

By starting with a subjective foundation for his philosophy, René Descartes was never able, nor was anyone else able, to leave the subjective domain. The objective world of sense was forever beyond the reach of mind, and mind beyond the reach of sense. His conception of the human soul as something so distinct and separate from the living body as to be independent leaves the body and soul two *complete* entities. It is no wonder that physiology and mechanistic psychology soon found no place for the ghostly, angelic Cartesian ' soul.'

A certain parallelism between mental thoughts and physical mechanics was taught by Descartes, and a limited influence of the mind on body was allowed through the pineal gland. Leibniz, however, could see no reason for this limited influence of mind on matter, since the two entities were completely diverse in nature. Consequently the only parallelism open to Leibniz was a harmony between these two, pre-established by God. This parallelism was put into a scientific context by the psychologists Fechner and Wundt.

Among modern neurophysiologists, J. C. Eccles, a professed Cartesian, has given much thought to the mind-brain problem.[3] Eccles, following the lead of other investigators,[4] develops the notion that brain and mind liaison takes place primarily in the cerebral cortex. According to him this liaison is possible only when there is a high level of activity in cerebral tissue. To avoid possible misunderstanding Eccles distinguishes the action of the mind, or will on the brain from the reverse action of the brain on the mind (perception). He conceives the mind as acting on the brain by virtue of the latter's " critically poised neurones " which act as hypersensitive detectors of " minute spatio-temporal fields of influence " emanating from the will. The brain-to-mind action is explained by assuming that the spatio-temporal patterned activity of the cerebral cortex can

---

[3] J. C. Eccles, *The Neurophysiological Basis of Mind* (Oxford: Clarendon, 1953), pp. 261-86.

[4] E. D. Adrian, *The Physical Background of Perception* (Oxford: Clarendon, 1947); C. S. Sherrington, *op. cit.*

act on the spatio-temporal patterning of the mind. There is, so to speak, a two-way street: the cerebral *detectors* can also act as *transmitters* so that the mind can both influence and be influenced.

Eccles' philosophy of mind and brain has not been widely accepted. In the first place, it is still a mechanical explanation. The mind is assumed to operate on the brain in the same way as the brain operates on the mind. In other words, his view ascribes to the mind a mode of activity which is proper to material things. Descartes at least admitted a real difference between thought and mechanics. In the second place, even as a physical type of ghost the ' mind ' in Eccles' view is still too remote from cerebral activities. There is only one life by which the mind and brain function. The realistic explanation must somehow account for the real unity of life as well as for the apparent difference between thought and cerebral physiology. Descartes' dichotomy between spirit and matter has at least some grounds of intelligibility, but Eccles' dichotomy between a materialistic mind and neurophysiological activity is devoid of all intelligibility. Finally, an adequate resolution of the mind-body problem must allow the mind to act according to its non-material nature, explaining simultaneously the ontological unity of the person and the diversity of thought and physiological changes.

To date the only adequate solution to the mind-body problem is the one suggested by Aristotle and Galen, and developed throughout the centuries even to our own day. The solution can be called adequate because it does in fact explain the ontological unity of the living being and at the same time accounts for the immaterial nature of thought and the effect of biochemical changes on the psychological person. The Aristotelian view, commonly called the hylomorphic theory, can easily be misunderstood. If it is misunderstood, the hylomorphic theory offers no real solution at all; in fact, it might even be an obstacle to a real solution.

First it is important to note that according to the Aristotelian view the soul and body are *not two distinct entities*, that is, they are not two actual wholes. Two distinct entities could never make up one ontological person. There would have to be the Cartesian dichotomy of a navigator in a ship, a driver in an auto, a prisoner in his cell. It was Descartes' failure to appreciate the potential nature of the body with respect to the living principle that led to the dichotomy. The converse is likewise true: it was Descartes' failure to appreciate the activating nature of the soul that led him to conceive the soul as an isolated reality. Although the words " soul " and " body " suggest two distinct existents, they are not to be so understood, if a solution to the problem is to be reached.

Reflection on this point can be developed in two ways. First, the word " body " is really not the same when applied to a living body and to a corpse. The living body not only functions differently from a corpse, but it *is* different; it is living. One might admit a remote similarity between a living body and its corpse; it is indeed a commonly understood manner of speaking to call both " bodies." But it would be absurd to identify the living body with the mass of matter which remains after death. It might be objected, however, that nothing is discoverable in the living body which is not also in the inert mass of the corpse. It is true that if a chemical analysis were made *immediately* after death or with some means guaranteeing preservation from corruption, the same chemical compounds would be found, with the possible exception of extremely labile compounds such as adenosine triphosphate (ATP) or creatine phosphate. But a physical or chemical similarity is not the same as biological similarity. Biologically a living organism functions; a dead one does not. This should suggest that life cannot be identified with chemical activity. Furthermore, even chemical similarity will gradually diminish as the analysis is made further removed in time from the instant of death. This seems to indicate clearly that the principle of life, whatever one calls it, is responsible for the unity and identity of the living organism.

A second line of reflection leads to the relationship between body and the principle of life. If organic activity is possible only when life is present, then the principle of life is not separate from a living organism. In fact, it is by reason of the life-principle that the body is living and biologically organic. In other words, the life-principle *activates* the matter in giving it organic life and unity of being. In this context, the material mass of the body and the chemical compounds are *recipients* of activation; they are capacities, potentialities for actual life. When Aristotle designated this ' matter ' as a passive capacity, it was in relation to the activizing principle of ' form.' Just as human life cannot be understood except in relation to an organism, so an organic body cannot be understood without reference to the life-principle, commonly called a soul. It would be absurd to think that the soul is some kind of unknown chemical substance. Rather the soul is that by which every chemical compound in an organism is living. Hence it is futile to search for a ' soul ' through chemical analysis.

Second, it is important to note that there are important differences between a human soul and a purely animal soul, even though both are life-principles informing a highly complex organism. The principle of human life performs functions, such as thinking, willing, idealizing and reflecting, which are not limited to space-time patterns. This is not to say that thinking and willing are activities performed outside of space and time, but only that they are not limited as sensations and emotions are. In the Aristotelian tradition this transcendence of thinking and willing shows the spiritual nature of mind and will. The non-limited behavior of mind and will is, of course, derived from the same life-principle which animates the human body. Consequently the single life-principle in man is the unique source of both organic life in the body and of mental life transcending the limitations of space-time patterns. There can be no doubt that man's soul is an extraordinary type of reality: it animates an organic body, yet its nature and functions are not entirely limited to the biochemistry of the body.

Now, how does this relate to the mind-body problem? Simply that the human life-principle is the source of both cerebral activity and mental activity, inasmuch as none of these activities is manifest in a corpse. Granting the essential difference between cerebral activity and mental activity, it would be a serious misconception to conceive their interaction after the manner of two physical beings, e. g., as two chemical compounds, or as an electromagnetic wave reacts with an appropriate detector. The reciprocal influence of mind and brain is altogether unique and any attempt to understand its nature must take cognizance of this fact.

Limiting these reflections further, we may ask, how then does this bear on the problem of mental health and disease? There is no doubt that the living body has an important role in these matters, since injury to the physical organ, the brain, results in some aberrations of mental and emotional activity of the living person. Obviously the brain does not and cannot function in the absence of the life-principle. It is true that chemical reactions, electrical currents and enzyme activity, precisely as such are not living, for they can be produced outside a living body. However, in a living body they are concurrent, concomitant with the activity of the life principle and are directed to the functional integrity of the whole organism. The mind in its operation needs the brain. Every thought not only has some echo in the brain tissue, but in the present condition the mind is dependent on the brain as on an instrument. Clearly if something is awry in the physical apparatus, the instrument, the mind is to that degree impeded in its normal function.

The brain is not simple in its structure or function. Although the brain is spoken of as a single organ, and sometimes even thought of as having a single function in much the same way as the heart is said to pump blood, in actuality it is extremely complex.[5] This complexity is due not simply to the ten thousand million or more neurons which are part of its composition,

---

[5] J. Papez, " Neuroanatomy," in *American Handbook of Psychiatry*, ed. Silvano Arieti (New York: Basic Books, 1959), pp. 1585-1619.

but also to the nerve cells which happen to be arranged in certain groups or patterns. Anatomically these patterns are regions such as the cerebral cortices, the cerebellum and a number of sub-cortical structures. Refined observation reveals that the neurons are often grouped in smaller functional areas, or units called " nuclei." Chemical studies of the brain reveal regional differences both qualitative and quantitative that may be reflective of functional heterogeneity.

Even if direct experimental evidence were not available, one could conclude on other grounds that the brain displays some localization of function. The functions of the brain are numerous, as evidenced by the sensory functions of the mind; and a multiplicity of simultaneous functions requires a multiplicity of parts. Increasing complexity of activity requires a corresponding increase of material parts, though not necessarily in a one-to-one relationship of part to function. Now, since there is a multiplicity of organic parts, these parts must occupy different places in the brain. In other words, there must be a spatial organization of parts, not haphazardly disposed, but according to the operational dependence obtaining among them. It follows, then that a multiplicity of functions, requiring a plurality of parts, will require a localization of these functions. By this is meant that particular functions will be associated with certain anatomical areas and perhaps even with biochemical topography. Nevertheless, there is at times considerable overlapping.

Over the years, our knowledge of localization of functions has become more precise.[6] (Yet this is not to deny that in certain activities the whole brain apparently is involved.) The mass of material which has accumulated has been authoritatively and comprehensively reviewed in three volumes of a recent publication.[7] The various projection areas for motor or

[6] R. W. Gerard, " Neurophysiology, Brain and Behavior," in S. Arieti, *op. cit.*, pp. 1620-38.

[7] J. Field, *Handbook of Physiology*, Sect. I, *Neurophysiology* (Washington: Am. Physiological Soc., 1959-60).

sensory activities have been known for some time. But the corresponding secondary areas are a more recent discovery. Much of our earlier knowledge regarding localization of brain function was derived from accidental injuries to the human brain. Thus, for example, cerebral vascular accidents ("strokes") may lead to paralysis of limb or speech. Recent experimentation with animals has sought to determine functional centers in the brain by electrodes. These are permanently implanted in specific areas of the brain, mild electrical stimulation is applied, and the behavior pattern of the animal is observed.[8] An alternative procedure is to allow the animal to determine whether or not it is to be so electrically stimulated.[9] From such experiments it has been concluded that certain areas are " rewarding centers " since the animal would repeatedly stimulate itself in a seeming orgy of "pleasure" until it became physically exhausted several hours later. Similarly in the same general areas but at different specific points there have been discovered centers which mediated punishing effects since the animal would refrain from restimulation.[10] Other studies involving experimental destruction of specific nuclei of the hypothalamus revealed centers which were apparently concerned with hunger, anger and the sex drive.[11] These and other data have now established the existence of functional centers in the brain for drives and emotions as well as for motor and sensory activities.

Electrical stimulation of exposed temporal lobes of conscious human subjects during neurological procedures has contributed

[8] W. R. Hess, *Diencephalon: Autonomic and Extrapyramidal Functions* (New York: Grune & Stratton, 1954). This work is a comprehensive English résumé of his original contributions which were reported in detail in *Das Zwischenhirn* (Basel: Schwabe, 1949) and in *Die funktionelle organization des vegetativen Nervensysteme* (Basel: Schwabe, 1948).

[9] J. Olds and P. Milner, "Positive Reinforcement Produced by Electrical Stimulation of Septal Area and Other Regions of the Rat Brain," *Journal of Comparative and Physiological Psychology*, XLVII (1954), 419; J. Olds, "Self-Stimulation of the Brain," *Science*, CXXVII (1958), 315-324.

[10] J. Olds, *op. cit.*, pp. 317-324.

[11] W. R. Hess, *Hypothalamus und Thalamus* (Stuttgart: Thieme, 1956); W. R. Ingram, "The Hypothalamus," *Clinical Symposia*, VIII (1956), 117-56.

greatly to our knowledge of such centers.[12] We know that definite areas of the temporal cortex when stimulated by a mild electrical current has evoked in certain subjects a detailed record of some past experience. Under certain conditions even present experience can somehow be evaluated in the light of a related past experience. It is possible, too, to evoke an emotion, most frequently fear, but sometimes loneliness or sorrow. The exact significance of these observations must still be determined before further light can be shed on normal and abnormal behavior.

The philosophical vocabulary of Aristotle and Aquinas has no term corresponding to the modern expression " behavior." Indeed even in current usage the precise meaning of the term must often be determined from the context. In reference to human behavior it is ordinarily conceived as including those operations or actions of men which are considered to proceed from the whole organism or individual. Thus the term is applied not only to deliberate, consciously motivated actions, which may be considered rational acts, but also to those which follow on emotions, or are influenced by infra-conscious factors. Normal behavior, then, is that which fits into a system of public logic and is presumably in contact with the real world. Abnormal behavior, in this context, in some ways offends public logic, although the private logic of the individual may be rigorously observed. As a consequence, the individual, at one or more points, fails to contact the real world.

The term behavior in the present context, consequently, does not directly connote such isolated phenomena of the autonomic nervous system as heart rate, blood pressure, respiratory rate, perspiration, and so forth. Nevertheless, behavior has physiological and biochemical correlates of which any one parameter may precede, accompany, or follow the individual's total response to a particular environmental situation. A person's

[12] W. Penfield, " The Interpretative Cortex," *Science,* CXXIX (1959), 1719-25; W. Penfield and L. Roberts, *Speech and Brain Mechanisms* (Princeton: Univ. Press, 1959).

behavior may be influenced by his internal milieu, but it is not fully determined by it. For example, ingestion of various drugs can accelerate or decrease reactions of the autonomic nervous system even to the extent of inducing intense emotional activity. The individual's behavior is clearly influenced, but the ultimate determination of this behavior depends upon intellect and will, unless the activity of these immaterial faculties is completely inhibited. The dependence of rational activities on the sensory functions imposes a kind of limitation upon the intellect and will. If the operation of the pertinent sensory faculties is impeded, then to some degree the function of the intellect and will is also impaired. It is difficult to determine the exact point at which the activities of intellect and will may be completely inhibited.

The biochemical substrata of the emotions have, of late, received considerable experimental attention.[13] Although emotion, like sensation, is itself non-chemical, there are numerous physiological and biochemical changes associated with an emotion, just as there are numerous changes associated with cognitive sensation. The physiological component of vision, for example, includes a variety of biochemical changes. Light impinging on the rods and cones in the retina is absorbed by the photosensitive pigment and produces a series of transformations leading to nervous excitation.[14] The nerve impulses sent along the optic tract are dependent on biochemical activities for their propagation inasmuch as restoration of the ion gradient, for example, requires energy. Additional biochemical changes are further associated with whatever neuronal activity takes place at the central receptors after receiving the nerve impulses. Finally, in the formation of the integrated sensory image associations are made with past experience, and all of

---

[13] H. F. Harlow and C. M. Wollsey, ed., *Biological and Biochemical Basis of Behavior* (Madison: Univ. of Wis., 1958); L. J. West and M. Greenblatt, *Explorations in the Physiology of Emotions: Psychiatric Research Reports*, 12 (January), 1960.

[14] G. Wald, "The Photoreceptor Process in Vision," in *Handbook of Physiology*, ed. cit., Sect. I, vol. I, pp. 671-92.

this involves considerable biochemical activity. At this point the cogitative sense (or the intellect) may apprehend the object or event perceived as good or harmful to the individual.

The judgment estimating the perception to be good or harmful evokes an emotional response toward or away from the object. Hand in hand with this affective, or emotional response, there is a purely physiological and biochemical response which may involve a host of chemical changes in the body. Norepinephrine and epinephrine, for example, are liberated from nerve endings and from adrenal medulla in various proportions, depending on whether fear and anxiety, or anger and daring are the primary emotional components. Concerning human subjects, it has been reliably reported that normal urinary excretion of norepinephrine with increased secretion of epinephrine is associated with anxious and passive emotional reactions.[15] Active and aggressive emotional displays were found to be associated with an increased secretion of norepinephrine. Other investigators have suggested that anxiety is mediated by epinephrine, and anger by norepinephrine.[16] Much research still needs to be done before any definite associations can be made with various emotions. One item, however, does stand out: the biochemical changes can sometimes be induced without thereby producing the true emotion. It has been noticed, for example, that continuous infusion of epinephrine can produce subjective feelings very similar to those found during anxiety, and yet it would not be sufficient to produce the emotional anxiety state.[17] On the other hand, norepinephrine cannot produce comparable subjective experiences so as to be related to the emotion of anger.[18] All of these inves-

[15] F. Elmadjian, " Excretion and Metabolism of Epinephrine and Norepinephrine in Man," in F. A. Gibbs, ed., *Molecules and Mental Health* (Philadelphia: Lippincott, 1959), pp. 77-99.

[16] D. H. Funkenstein, S. H. King and M. E. Drolette, *Mastery of Stress* (Cambridge: Harvard, 1957), pp. 19-25.

[17] D. R. Hawkins, J. T. Monroe, M. G. Sandifer and C. R. Vernon, " Psychological and Physiological Responses to the Continuous Epinephrine Infusion—An Approach to the Study of the Affect, Anxiety," in West and Greenblatt, *op. cit.*, pp. 40-52.

[18] *Ibid.*, p. 48.

tigations confirm the traditional view of the emotions as immanent activities consequent upon an estimative judgment, distinct from biochemical changes, yet associated with them.

Another factor which tends to modify the operation of the mind and will is temperament. In the absence of any extensive analysis of this area, it might be said that a considerable component of temperament is physiological in origin.[19] This in turn may reflect a genetic influence on the biochemical constitution of the individual. The four basic temperaments furnished by classic authors classify men according to the kind of response made to a given stimuli: the quick and slow, the lasting and ephemeral. Each of the basic temperaments is characterized by the possible pairs made up from one in each set. This suggests an actual connection with the central nervous system geared to respond in a certain manner to stimuli. Differences in temperament are apparently associated with differences in the responsiveness of the nervous system. Whatever an individual's temperament might be, it must be taken into consideration when evaluating normal and abnormal behavior. At present too little is known about the correlation of temperament and abnormal behavior to draw any conclusions.

The endocrine pattern of an individual, however, is clearly associated in some way with temperament. It is tempting to suggest that the hormonal factors may actually constitute the primary biochemical substratum of temperament. It is well known now that the hypothalamus influences the activity of the pituitary gland, probably through the release of neurohormones.[20] The pituitary gland, in turn, governs the activity of several other glands, the adrenals, thyroid and gonads, whose products influence the activity of other organs in the body and the brain itself. While the sexual behavior of animals is primarily determined by the hormones liberated by the gonads, there are other influences in man which modify the basic

[19] L. M. Bond, *The Effect of Bodily Temperament on Psychical Characteristics* (River Forest: Aquinas Library, 1948).

[20] W. S. Fields, ed., *Hypothalamic-Hypophysial Interrelationships* (Springfield: Thomas, 1956).

gonadal effect. Nevertheless the great influence of various hormones on human behavior cannot be overlooked. Administration of thyroxin to a hypothyroid individual can convert a sluggish, perpetually tired individual to a bright, active person. Out of such observations has grown the entirely new field of psychoendocrinology.[21]

BIOCHEMICAL DISTURBANCES AND ABNORMAL BEHAVIOR

In classifying biochemical disturbances and abnormal behavior, it is best to begin with the class of congenital mental deficiencies which result from what is frequently called a " metabolic error." In its essential form this concept was first proposed by Sir Archibald Garrod when he suggested that certain diseases, e. g., alkaptonuria and albinism, could be explained by the absence of certain specific enzymes.[22] However, it has not yet been directly established that a particular enzyme is absent. All that one can conclude is that the enzyme in question is not *functioning* properly. The failure of an enzyme to function normally can be due to at least one of several causes: (1) the enzyme may truly be absent, (2) it may have a relatively slight structural abnormality, or (3) though normal, it may not be able to function because of some obstructive alteration in the cell or organism.[23] Furthermore, in some instances the enzyme defect can be further traced to the apparent absence or failure of a particular gene.[24] The resulting condition can involve a variety of physiological disturbances, some of greater consequence than others. In some cases the full development of the illness can be forestalled by eliminating from the diet those substances which cannot be metabolized because of the enzyme defect.

---

[21] M. Reiss, " Psychoendocrinology," in M. Reiss, ed., *Psychoendocrinology* (New York: Grune & Stratton, 1958), pp. 1-40.

[22] D. Y-y. Hsia, *Inborn Errors of Metabolism* (Chicago: Year Book, 1959), p. 105.

[23] *Ibid.*

[24] R. W. Lippman, T. L. Perry and S. W. Wright, " The Biochemical Basis of Mental Dysfunction. II: Mental Deficiency (Amentia)," *Metabolism*, VII (1958), 274. Cf. L. S. Penrose, *The Biology of Mental Defect* (New York: Grune and Stratton, 1949).

One type of congenital mental deficiency is exemplified by the condition known as phenylpyruvic oligophrenia or as phenylketonuria.[25] The first term emphasizes the impairment of the brain or mental function; the second refers to the relatively high concentration of phenylpyruvic acid found in the urine of the affected individual. Careful study of many cases has revealed that it is an hereditary disorder of protein metabolism mediated by a non-sex-linked recessive gene.[26] As a result of this genetic defect, there is a defect of the enzyme system, phenylalanine hydroxylase. Without the proper functioning of phenylalanine hydroxylase, there is an excessive accumulation of phenylalanine in the blood and cerebrospinal fluid. The precise manner in which the deleterious effect is brought about is not known. Apparently it is the excess of phenylalanine (or one of its products) which interferes with the proper development of the central nervous system and leads to a consequent mental retardation. If this condition is discovered very early in the infant's life, the development of mental deficiency can be largely prevented by administering a diet free of the offending amino acid.[27]

Another type of mental deficiency resulting from a congenital metabolic defect is cretinism.[28] It should be noted, however, that a primary deficiency in the synthesis of the thyroid hormone is not the only cause of cretinism. It can also arise from other causes of thyroid hypofunction, e. g., from abnormal embryonic development of the thyroid gland or from deficient dietary

[25] For a general review of this disease see the following: G. A. Jervis, " Phenylpyruvic Oligophrenia," in *Genetics and the Inheritance of Integrated Neurological and Psychiatric Patterns* (Baltimore: Williams & Wilkins, 1954), 259-282; W. E. Knox and D. Y-y. Hsia, " Pathogenic Problems in Phenylketonuria," *American Journal of Medicine*, XXII (1957), 687 ff.

[26] Lippman, *op. cit.*, p. 276; C. Mitoma, R. M. Auld and S. Undenfriend, " The Enzymatic Defect in Phenylpyruvic Oliogophrenia," *Proceedings of the Society for Experimental Biology and Medicine*, XCIV (1957), 634.

[27] M. D. Armstrong and F. H. Tyler, " Studies on Phenylketonuria. I: Restricted Phenylalanine Intake in Phenylketonuria," *Journal of Clinical Investigation*, XXXIV (1955), 565.

[28] Cf. J. B. Stanbury and E. M. McGirr, " Sporadic or Non-Endemic Familial Cretinism with Goiter," *American Journal of Medicine*, XXII (1957), 712.

iodine. A few weeks after birth the characteristic physical stigmata appear, accompanied by signs of involvement of the central nervous system.[29] Decreased acuity of the special senses is evident; speech and socialization are retarded; muscular coordination is impeded, and unless the condition is treated the mental status of the individual is no more than that of an idiot.

The second large class of biochemical disturbances giving rise to abnormal behavior consists of *acquired* metabolic malfunctions. This class can be broken down into diseases arising from some nutritional deficiency and those arising from a toxic substance either *exogenous* or presumptively *endogenous*. The latter type, indeed, may be due in whole or part to a congenital defect, but in the present state of our knowledge it remains an open question. Diseases arising from nutritional deficiency are of many types, but only one need be mentioned because of its striking mental involvement: pellagra.

Pellagra has a variety of symptoms which, in the more advanced stages, include a considerable mental dysfunction characterized by a clouding of consciousness, hallucinations and confusion, frequently terminating in a psychosis if adequate treatment is not instituted.[30] It has been determined that this condition is due to the absence of one of the B vitamins, nicotinic acid (or its amide), or its precursor, tryptophan.[31]. In 1937 it was discovered that pellagra could be relieved by administering nicotinic acid (not to be confused with the alkaloid nicotine).[32] The importance of this vitamin is that it is an integral part of one of the coenzymes, known as diphos-

[29] H. P. Rome and D. B. Robinson, "Psychiatric Conditions Associated with Metabolic, Endocrine and Nutritional Disorders," in *American Handbook of Psychiatry, ed. cit.,* II, p. 1274.

[30] R. L. Cecil and R. F. Loeb, ed., *A Textbook of Medicine* (Philadelphia: Saunders, 1959), p. 547.

[31] J. Gregory, "The Role of Nicotinic Acid (Niacin) in Mental Health and Disease," *Journal of Mental Science,* CI (1955), 85.

[32] D. T. Smith, J. M. Ruffin and S. G. Smith, "Pellagra Successfully Treated with Nicotinic Acid: A Case Report," *Journal of the American Medical Association,* CIX (1937), 2054.

phopyridine nucleotide (DPN). It is essential to the metabolism of carbohydrates, and its absence can seriously impair energy production. Since almost the sole source of energy for the brain is glucose, it is obvious that anything which interferes with the proper metabolism of this carbohydrate will also reduce brain function considerably.

The most interesting group of acquired biochemical disturbances causing abnormal mental behavior is that arising from the ingestion of a toxic substance. Obviously a great variety of chemical substances can produce toxic symptoms when taken in excessive quantities or by an individual with an idiosyncrasy for a particular compound. Among the inorganic substances must be listed lead,[33] manganese,[34] mercury [35] and bromides.[36] Of these, the bromides are perhaps the best understood.[37] For example, an excess of bromide ion in the blood, generally resulting from an excessive use of bromide salts to " quiet the nerves," replaces an equivalent amount of chloride ion in the body fluids. When the concentration of bromide ion reaches 150 mg. per cent,[38] toxic symptoms are likely to appear. These symptoms may range from simple sluggishness and forgetfulness to delirium and hallucinations. In certain predisposed cases, a pattern of transitory schizophrenia has been known to appear.[39]

Among organic compounds known to produce behavioral abnormalities are such items as amphetamine, cortisone, ACTH

[33] W. T. Haverfield, P. C. Bucy and A. S. Elonen, " The Surgical Treatment of Lead Encephalopathy," Journal of the American Medical Association, CXIV (1940), 2432; R. K. Byers and E. E. Lord, " Late Effects of Lead Poisoning on Mental Development," American Journal of Diseases of Children, LXVI (1943), 329.

[34] G. C. Cotzias, " Manganese in Health and Disease," Physiological Reviews, XXXVIII (1958), 503-531.

[35] L. T. Fairhall, " Inorganic Industrial Hazards," Physiological Reviews, XXV (1945), 182.

[36] M. Levin, " Bromide Psychoses: Four Varieties," American Journal of Psychiatry, CIV (1948), 798.

[37] M. Levin, " Toxic Psychoses," in S. Arieti, op. cit., p. 1222 ff.

[38] Ibid., p. 1224.

[39] M. Levin, " Transitory Schizophrenias Produced by Bromide Intoxication," American Journal of Psychiatry, CIII (1946), 229-237.

and barbiturates.[40] Ethyl alcohol, as everyone knows, affects normal behavior in varying degrees. In extreme alcoholism, as for example in delirium tremens and acute alcohol hallucinosis, optic and auditory hallucinations, respectively, are common.[41]

A very interesting group recently brought to the attention of the psychiatric profession is known as psychomimetic drugs. A descriptive definition of these drugs presented a few years ago is still adequate: " Psychomimetic agents are substances that produce changes in thought, perception, mood, and, sometimes, in posture, occurring alone or in concert, without causing either major disturbances of the autonomic nervous system or addictive craving, and, although with overdosage, disorientation, memory disturbance, stupor and even narcosis may occur, these reactions are not characteristic." [42] In some respects the behavioral changes brought about by these drugs resemble the mental and emotional symptoms associated with one or other of the psychoses. Most of these drugs in current experimental use are naturally occurring compounds, or compounds obtained from them by slight chemical change. Among the better known of these interesting drugs are lysergic acid diethylamide (LSD-25), mescaline (from the Peyote cactus), and psilocybin (from the mushroom, Psilocybe mexicana Heim).

The first of these drugs, LSD-25, is apparently unique in the truly minute amount which will produce the typical mental changes. These changes usually begin in an half hour and reach a peak at one and one-half hours. Among the outstanding symptoms are visual hallucinations, often fantastic in structure. While auditory hallucinations are rare, taste disturbances are quite frequent. Consciousness itself, however, is never markedly affected, and orientation in place remains intact, but there is rather a profound change in the perception of time. After about

[40] M. Levin, " Toxic Psychoses," *ed. cit.*, p. 1225 ff.

[41] G. N. Thompson, "Acute and Chronic Alcoholic Conditions," in S. Arieti, *op. cit.*, pp. 1208-1210.

[42] H. Osmond, "A Review of the Clinical Effects of Psychomimetic Agents," *Annals of the New York Academy of Science,* LXVI (1957), 418.

eight hours the symptoms ordinarily disappear.[43] No claim is made here that a true psychosis can be duplicated by the use of this drug. In fact, schizophrenic patients who have taken LSD state that the experiences induced by the drug are different from their own schizophrenia. To date, many experimental attempts have been made to isolate particular biochemical changes which induce the observed effects. However, no certain conclusion has yet been reached.[44]

The third and final category of metabolic disorders leading to abnormal behavior is a miscellany. In the other classes, the disorder was traced either (1) to a congenital defect involving an absence or a malfunction of an enzyme or hormone, or (2) to what was called, for want of a better term, " an acquired mteabolic disorder " resulting from a nutritional deficiency or from ingestion of a chemical substance. Although these first two classes can account for some of the emotional and mental diseases, they cannot, at present, account for the psychopathological conditions known as " functional psychoses." It has been suggested in the past and again more recently that schizophrenia, for example, is the result of an abnormal metabolism producing a toxic (neuro- or psychotoxic) substance.[45] Presumably in such an explanation, the *symptomology* of the disease would be traced to the action of the endogenous toxic compound, whereas the metabolic error producing the " psychopoison " would be the disease itself.

[43] A. Wikler, *The Relation of Psychiaty to Pharmacology* (Baltimore: Williams & Wilkins, 1957), pp. 69-70.

[44] H. Hoagland, "A Review of Biochemical Changes Induced *In Vivo* by Lysergic Acid Diethylamide and Similar Drugs," *Annals of the New York Academy of Science*, LXVI (1957), 445-458; J. A. Bain, "A Review of the Biochemical Effects In Vitro of Certain Psychomimetic Agents," *Annals of the New York Academy of Sciences*, LXVI (1957), 459-467.

[45] H. Osmond, " Chemical Concepts of Psychosis (Historical Contributions)," in M. Rinkel and H. C. B. Denber, ed., *Chemical Concepts of Psychosis* (New York: McDowell & Obolensky, 1958), pp. 3-26; R. G. Heath, " Physiological and Biochemical Studies in Schizophrenia with Particular Emphasis on Mind-Brain Relationships," in C. C. Pfeiffer and J. R. Smythies, *International Review of Neurobiology* (New York: Academic Press, 1959), I, 299-331.

Probably the most extensive biochemical study of mental illness has been of that large amorphous group, the schizophrenias. A recently published review of the field makes it clear that biochemists are still very far from giving a biochemical account of schizophrenia.[46] The more thorough biochemical approach to the problem has been to explore biochemical parameters of the whole body, rather than to restrict investigations to the chemistry of the brain.[47]

First of all with regard to schizophrenia, there is little doubt that no single factor will account for it. Schizophrenia, after all, is a generic name and not a specific disease. Further, it is most probable that there are predisposing factors as well as " triggering " events which must be considered. While there is suggestive evidence for some genetic factor in the development of schizophrenia, this is not certain. A further difficulty is that too little is known of the brain's biochemical topology. There is a real probability that the biochemical changes in question take place in very restricted areas of the brain. It is even possible that chemical systems operative in these areas are unknown in others. Consequently, any abnormality in such unique systems would be extremely difficult to detect, since the existence and nature of the system itself would hardly be suspected. One attractive hypothesis, though as yet unproved, is the possibility of an abnormal metabolism of commonly occurring substances, such as epinephrine yielding adrenochrome, adrenolutin or similar compounds.[48]

The isolation of serotonin (5-hydroxytryptamine), a substance found in the brain in relatively high concentrations (although also present in other tissues of the body), has raised the hopes of some that this substance might be implicated in

[46] S. S. Kety, " Biochemical Theories of Schizophrenia," *Science*, CXXIX (1959), 1528-1532 and 1590-1596.

[47] D. Richter, " Biochemical Aspects of Schizophrenia," in Derek Richter, ed., *Schizophrenia: Somatic Aspects* (New York: MacMillan, 1957), pp. 53-75.

[48] A. Hoffer, "Adrenaline Metabolites and Schizophrenia," *Diseases of the Nervous System*, Monograph Supplement, XXI (1960), No. 2, pp. 1-8.

the etiology of schizophrenia.[49] It has been suggested that a metabolic disorder which alters the concentration of serotonin in the brain would result in a psychosis.[50] Notwithstanding the amount of evidence to show that serotonin as well as several other compounds (e. g., norepinephrine, acetylcholine, gamma aminobutyric acid) have important roles in the proper functioning of the brain, no definite conclusion can yet be drawn with regard to their causality in mental illness. Another substance which has been suggested as a causative agent in schizophrenia is taraxein.[51] This compound, isolated from the blood of schizophrenic patients, has been known to produce bizarre behavior in animals and in volunteer human subjects.[52] The chemical nature of taraxein has not yet been determined precisely. Unfortunately, not all the evidence supports the view that taraxein is a psychotoxic substance produced by schizophrenic patients.[53] Consequently, no single substance has yet been found which conclusively induces this particular mental condition.

* * *

There remains the task of correlating relevant material already discussed with certain observations. First, too little is known at present for an adequate biochemical specification of the exact nature of mental health; it is not even possible to associate a particular disease with a specific biochemical change or with a pattern of changes (with the possible exception of

[49] Kety, op. cit., pp. 1592-3.
[50] D. W. Wooley and E. Shaw, Science, CXIX (1954), 587; J. H. Gaddum, " Drugs Antagonistic to 5-Hydroxytryptamine," in CIBA Foundation Symposium on Hypertension (Boston: Little, Brown and Co., 1954), pp. 75-77.
[51] R. G. Heath, S. Marten, B. E. Leach, M. Cohen and C. Angels, " Effect on Behavior in Humans with the Administration of Taraxein," American Journal of Psychiatry, CXIV (1957), 14-24.
[52] R. G. Heath, S. Marten, B. E. Leach, M. Cohen and C. A. Feigley, " Behavioral Changes in Nonpsychotic Volunteers Following the Administration of Taraxein, The Substance Obtained from Serum of Schizophrenic Patients," American Journal of Psychiatry, CXIV (1958), 917-20; R. G. Heath, B. E. Leach and M. Cohen, " Mode of Action of Taraxein: Follow up Studies," in Gibbs, op. cit., pp. 17-43.
[53] Kety, op. cit., pp. 1590-91.

certain mental deficiencies as mentioned above) . Further, it is extremely hazardous at present to say whether the observed biochemical abnormality is the cause or the effect of a mental illness. They might even be concomitant, the result of a common cause. While the tendency in research at present has been to search for a gross and manifest biochemical abnormality, it is entirely possible that small changes in one anatomical area may be *accumulative* with similar small changes in other areas. Further, the deviation from the normal range in the activity of one biochemical system, though relatively insignificant in itself, may be highly important when coupled with changes in other chemical systems that serve the same ultimate behavioral expression. Notwithstanding certain reversals met with in current research, we may say summarily that the experimental determination of some kind of disturbance in the biochemistry of the central nervous system, at least, is confidently expected. It might further be noted that mental health might be dependent, in the chemical order, on the proper concentrations of certain compounds and on activities of particular enzymes in specific areas of the brain, whereas mental illness may result from an imbalance of these very same substances.[54] The fact that chemical compounds, e. g., LSD, mescaline, amphetamine, can bring about symptoms of mentol illness suggests the brain's chemistry has been disturbed.

On the other hand, it is possible that mental health and disease involve the chemistry of the entire body and not merely that of the brain. It is generally recognized that the body under stress responds with a change in the endocrine balance.[55] The basic hormonal and biochemical patterns of the body, which may represent the physiological component of temperament, could act as a dispositive cause for certain behavioral

[54] L. G. Abood, " Some Chemical Concepts of Mental Health and Disease," in *The Effect of Pharmacologic Agents on the Nervous System* (Baltimore: Williams & Wilkins, 1959), p. 393.

[55] J. S. L. Browne, " The Interplay Between Endocrine Disturbance and Psychological Aberrations," CIBA Foundation Colloquia on *Endocrinology*, vol. III, *Hormones, Psychology and Behavior* (Philadelphia: Blakiston, 1952), pp. 112-19.

disturbances, whereas the actual disturbance itself might have as its proximate biochemical cause the altered chemistry of the brain.

Nevertheless, there is no basis for the claim put forward by some, that *all* mental illnesses will some day prove to have their origin in such chemical changes. It is well known that a persistent emotional reaction with its attendant chemical changes can bring about changes of a more permanent kind, which in turn produce the variety of pathological behavior. Even a moral stress can be the primary factor in the etiology of an individual's mental aberrations. Some moral stresses could conceivably be successfully countered in the shelter of the mind for a time. But sooner or later such stresses would bring in their wake emotional involvements with the consequent alteration in the normal biochemistry of the individual. More commonly, moral problems arise from patterns of activity and emotional behavior at variance with a person's moral code. Consequently, a daily involvement in such biochemical storms could rightly be expected to result in more permanent chemical changes. These changes would then be the molecular roots for the abnormal mental symptoms.

How then can a mental disease be reversed by psychotherapy, if biochemical changes are the substrata of the disease? One likely answer is that psychotherapy removes, gradually perhaps, the state of moral or emotional stress. Once these stresses have been removed, the attendant biochemical changes should reverse, unless relatively irreversible structural changes have taken place, and general homeostatic mechanisms will tend to restore normal biochemical functioning.

It should be remembered that pharmacological treatment of mental illness is more symptomatic than curative, unless the primary cause of the illness happened to be a truly biochemical disturbance. In this case a compound which will restore the normal biochemical pattern will also remove the psychological symptoms due to the abnormal chemistry. The use of pharmacological agents in the immediate treatment of abnormal behavior has been almost purely empirical. Yet, not only have such agents alleviated the disturbing symptoms, but they have often permitted other means of therapy to be more effective. Patients, otherwise unapproachable, can be made amenable to psychotherapy in this way. Then, too, a number of drugs are extremely useful in exploring the chemical foundations of normal and abnormal behavior.[56] Once again the sensitivity of man's emotional and mental makeup to his chemical environment is clearly indicated.

Fear has been expressed by some that the elucidation of the biochemical factors of behavior might compromise man's freedom and his moral responsibility. This would be true if his mind were no more than the functioning brain. In the last analysis man's freedom and moral responsibility are guaranteed by the spiritual, the immaterial nature of his mind. The mind does indeed depend upon the brain for the raw material of its thought, and the will is influenced by emotions and feelings. But the mind and will, transcending neurons, chemical and all matter, function with a certain independence from material limitations, and consequently cannot be forced by anything material. Only the hylomorphic interpretation of man's peculiar nature can explain satisfactorily his existential unity and his dependence upon as well as his transcendence over biochemical composition.

ALBERT S. MORACZEWSKI, O. P.

Houston State Psychiatric Institute,
Texas Medical Center,
Houston, Texas.

[56] M. Sidman, " Behavioral Pharmacology," *Psychopharmacologia,* I (1959), 1-19; R. M. Featherstone and A. Simon, *A Pharmacologic Approach to the Study of the Mind* (Springfield: Thomas, 1959).

CONSCIENCE AND SUPEREGO

&

T HEOLOGIANS and philosophers have rightly stigmatized Freud's concept of moral conscience as a caricature of the real thing. The psychological phenomenon which Freud called the superego, and which he equivalated with the traditional notion of conscience, in fact lacks the essential note of conscience. Nevertheless, since Freud was a gifted investigator, the presumption is that the superego is a reality and, since Freud credited it with a significant note in human activity, it would seem to be something important. The following paper attempts to analyze Freud's conception of the superego in terms of Thomistic thought, comparing it with more valid notions of conscience, and defining the area in human activity, especially in moral activity, into which the functioning of the superego enters as something significant.

I. THE NOTION OF THE SUPEREGO

(1) *The Fundaments of Human Nature According to Freud.*

Speaking broadly, the superego is the part in a man which tells him that he ought to do something or ought not to do it. In Freud's conception, a mature human personality comprises three basic structures: the id, the ego and the superego. If a rough description is permissible at the beginning, the id may be called the pool of instinctual drives, repressed complexes images and thoughts—a wholly unconscious area of the mind. The ego is the agency of all sense perceptions and conscious thought, and the initiator of deliberate activities. The superego is the source of moral incitement and constraint, and is largely unconscious.

Of these three, the primitive part and only native part is the id. In the id, instinctual impulses arise, and indeed arise by a natural and uncontrollable necessity, welling up continuously, as it were, as the psychological manifestations of more basic vital processes. When an impulse—the raw material of psychological life—arises, it is credited with creating a psychological tension; when it is discharged through some appropriate motor activity (as, for example, the infantile impulse to suck may be satisfied by the breast), the tension is dissolved. This relief of tension is pleasure; the law of the id is to seek it. Once an instinct has found an appropriate means of satisfaction, it becomes attached to the activity, and to the images and ideas of that activity, and henceforth is oriented towards obtaining satisfaction continuously through the same activity.

It happens, however, in the course of his development, that a child finds certain satisfactions prohibited, restricted, or prevented—he is not allowed to take the breast, or not allowed to keep it as long as he likes. He becomes more aware then of the impingement of the outside world; he is forced to take reality into account. Thus the ego begins to develop. The ego comprises the perceptions of the outer world, the coherent central processes of the individual, and the processes by which conscious motor activities are carried out. The principle that rules in the ego is reality; it relates man to the self he finds himself to be and to his environment. Fundamentally, of course, the ego is at the service of the id. Although it is attuned to reality, its main function even in this regard is to locate in reality the most appropriate means of satisfying instinctual impulses for the id, while avoiding the disagreeable results this satisfaction might sometimes entail.

To obtain its proper results, the ego must ' censor ' the instinctual movements of the id, that is, when the id demands some satisfaction which the ego has learned is actually productive of disagreeable results—pain, punishment, parental disapproval—the ego must negate the id's demands. A conflict ensues when the ego refuses to execute the action sought by the id. Eventually the ego refuses even to allow the idea to remain in consciousness; it suppresses the idea. But the idea with its instinctual drive does not die; it vanishes into the unconsiousness of the id, where it remains, still dynamic, still restless, still seeking some new outlet. How it can get past the censorship of the ego, and accomplish its purpose is a long and involved story; it is sufficient here to note that sometimes the instinctual drives successfully accomplish their aim; sometimes they are deflected from a minor object without severe psychological injury resulting; sometimes they are deflected at some cost to psychological balance.[1]

Within the ego, the superego is formed. Freud's earliest works did not mention this mental agency, but after long investigation, he found himself constrained to postulate some institution in the mind distinct from the ego and the id.[2] He found that much of the censoring process—the ' do this ' and ' do not do that,' in the sense of moral obligation—was accomplished not consciously, as the ego works, but unconsciously; and not on the basis of reality as the ego perceives it and consciously evaluates it, but on some other basis more

[1] Cf. Freud, " *Neurosis and Psychosis*," *Coll. Papers*, Vol. 2, pp. 250 seq. (Hogarth Press, London, 1956)

[2] Perhaps it would be useful here to note two of Freud's methodological canons, as an aid to following his reasoning on these subjects. First of all, he tried always to proceed on a strictly empirical basis. He would examine the psychological manifestations—thoughts, images, feelings, urges—as they were conscious or latent or dreamed, whether they seemed meaningful or not, whether they were competent or apparently disorganized and defective—and from the material gathered proceed to the postulation of the mental structures to explain them. This is, of course, the classic mode of procedure in establishing a faculty psychology; Freud, however, totally disavowed faculty psychology. To distinguish faculties by their acts and objects, and, more to the point, from their activities and objects, seemed to him a display of sterile theorizing. He was content in determining manifest activities in their concrete complexity, and the hidden activities, especially buried complexes, they seemed to postulate, but he did not attempt to define a structure of faculties which might underlie the variety of activities. His result would most resemble, in Thomistic terms, a description of actual habits or dispositions. Secondly, Freud tried to conceive the elements of his psychological structure in mechanistic and physical terms, in consonance with a basically anti-vitalist and materialist outlook. For this reason, many of his conceptions and the terms he uses to express them, seem mere metaphors, and not particularly apt metaphors, for the world of machines does not do justice to the subtleties of the mind. Once however these biases are taken into account, the real meaning of the things he is discussing is more apparent.

or less divorced from reality; and that this mysterious censor-ship's function was often effected with a psychological force considerably greater than that which usually accompanies reality-oriented activities. He formulated therefore the notion of the superego. The superego is a largely acquired but uncon-scious agency of censorship, formed within the ego, which forbids and commands and punishes disobedience by generating painful feelings of guilt.[3]

(2) *Arguments for the existence of the superego.*

What are the evidences for such a mental institution? First of all, there is the argument from the psychology of child development. Infants even at an early age are subject to a certain amount of ' training,' a matter of parental prohibitions or demands, reinforced with smiles and rewards or with frowns and punishments. In the beginning, the child must be con-stantly prompted to do what he has been told; the enforcing agency is part of the reality external to himself. Eventually, however, he will begin to do what he has been told even when his parents are absent. Evidently he has made their exhor-tations and prohibitions part of his own mental equipment. He has absorbed, not only what they have told him should be done or not done, but has also absorbed, or developed, the impulse to follow these directions. This, in a superficial way, is a description of the forming of the superego.[4]

Another argument for the superego is drawn from a situation common in psychoanalysis, the occurrence of ' resistance.' When analyzing a patient, Freud would endeavor to have him relate all the thoughts and images that came to his mind by the process of relaxed, free association. In this way he hoped to uncover the more or less hidden mental complexes which lay at the source of the patient's troubles. But he frequently

---

[3] Freud, *loc. cit.*

[4] Cf. Freud, " On Narcissism: An Introduction," *Coll. Papers*, vol. 4, pp. 50-53; Joseph Nuttin, *Psychoanalysis and Personality*, pp. 19-20. (Sheed and Ward, New York, 1953).

found that the patient would offer 'resistance' to the flow of thoughts—his memory would 'fail,' he would be unable to make a connection, he would dismiss a line of thought as meaningless and irrelevant. Often these breaks in the mental flow were accompanied by fairly distinct feelings of emotional distress. Or again, sometimes, when a sound explanation of some of the patient's thoughts or feelings was offered by the analyst, the patient would firmly or even violently reject them, for no manifestly good reason and with a great show of emotion. Freud concluded that the mental force which originally censored and repressed certain ideas (which were generally shameful or painful or humilating or in some way highly disagreeable) must be still operative in the psychism, and that, moreover, its present activity was itself largely unconscious. Therefore, besides the conscious censorship of the ego function, it was necessary to postulate another unconscious censoring agency.[5]

Another factor which enlarged and confirmed the concept of the superego was the sense of moral obligation manifested by many neurotics. Many patients who came for psychoanalytic treatment exhibited an intense need to measure up to moral standards often impossibly high and rigid. They seemed to be driven to achieve perfection according to self-imposed goals, and unable moreover to make allowances for any personal weaknesses or external circumstances which might make the goals unattainable. Ruled by these interior compulsions, they were unable to find satisfaction in the reasonable goals most people are contented with, unable to find peace in anything other than the achievement of their standards. Failure was always attributable to some fault on their part, and failure was followed by an acute sense of guilt. (This was also regarded as a weakness to be stamped out, and failure to overcome it produced further guilt feelings.) The standards by which they lived seemed beyond their own judgment, modification and control—they were unquestioned and unquestionable—and in fact, they seemed to be largely unconscious. Such a phe-

[5] Cf. Freud, *The Ego and the Id*, pp. 15-18. (Hogarth Press, London, 1957)

nomenon contrary to the best interests of the patient and seemingly imposed by some hostile and alien, and yet internal agency, seemed to Freud to demand a special mental structure to account for it.[6]

To these main arguments, Freud added others, not always as plausible. He seemed to think, for instance, that the presence of the superego was betrayed by ordinary phraseology in everyday speech. Thus the exprssion: " I feel inclined to do this but my conscience says ' no '," led him to infer the existence of a power in man separate and contrary to the primary personality, the " I." As has been pointed out, however, the same situation can be expressed: " I will not do this, although I am tempted to." Now this would indicate that the primary personality is separate from and contrary to the inclination. All, in fact, that can be deduced from such expressions is the presence of a duality; nothing can be concluded about the primacy of the factors involved.[7]

But leaving aside the debatable proofs, what can be deduced from the admissible evidence? Certainly many of Freud's observations as cited above are psychologically meaningful. Before we deduce any final conclusions, however, about the superego, we must go into a more thorough account of its actual formation, and this brings up the question of the Oedipus complex. For Freud, the superego—this inner sense of compulsion to do or not do—is formed out of the resolution of the Oedipus complex, and cannot be understood on any other basis.[8]

(3) *The origin of the superego.*

The Oedipus complex may be described briefly as follows. In infancy a male child develops first of all a strong instinctual attraction towards his mother, based on the warmth and affec-

---

[6] Freud, " On Narcissism: An Introduction," *Coll. Papers*, vol. 4, pp. 50-59. Cf. Karen Horney, *New Ways in Psychoanalysis*, pp. 207-210; Freud, " The Economic Problem in Masochism," *Coll. Papers*, vol. 2, pp. 265-66.

[7] Cf. Nuttin, *Psychoanalysis and Personality*, p. 178.

[8] Freud, *The Ego and the Id*, pp. 40-46.

tion she shows, and the satisfaction of his hunger by nursing, etc. At the same time he is identifying himself with his father, that is to say, he begins to mold himself on the pattern of his father.[9] He does this, not only because he is like his father, male, but also because he wants to share in the affection his mother has for her husband. In a few years, as the child passes through the ages of four and five, the increasing intensity of affection (which Freud conceived as basically sexual) for the mother, puts the father more and more in the light of a rival and an obstacle to the exclusive enjoyment of the mother's favors. Jealous and hostile feelings arise toward the father; the wish to get rid of him and replace him in the mother's affections becomes more manifest. This combination of identifying-hostile feelings (ambivalent feelings) towards the father and affection for the mother constitutes what Freud called the *simple* positive Oedipus complex. If this description in more or less Freudian terms seems hard to accept, perhaps the reality underlying the description can be more readily seen in the formulation of another psychoanalyst: In a child, love is extraordinarily wholehearted and jealous.[10]

In a girl child, the normal development of the complex is like that of a boy, but with the roles of each parent reversed; her ambivalent feelings develop with regard to her mother, with whom she identifies and whom she wants to supplant in her father's affections.

In either girl or boy, the situation can become much more complicated, and, according to Freud, usually does. The boy

[9] The concept of identification is a key concept in depth psychology. It signifies a psychological reaction something like imitation but much more profound. When a child identifies himself with another, he does not merely take up his patterns of behavior, he absorbs into himself wholeheartedly the ways of thinking, feeling, acting of the other person, and not only consciously but, so deep is the sense of unity with the other person, even consciously. The two principal motives behind identification are lost love and emulation. When one who is loved must be renounced, a compensation may be made in the form of identification, or when one meets a rival, identification can be motivated by the desire for equality with him. See Baudouin, *The Mind of the Child*, pp. 245-46. (Dodd, Mead & Co., New York, 1933)

[10] Baudouin, *op. cit.*, p. 51.

may not only have ambivalent feelings towards his father and simple affection for his mother, but he may display an affectionate, feminine attitude towards the father, and a corresponding identification and jealousy towards his mother, for in Freud's opinion, each individual is basically bi-sexual. In this case there is a two-fold Oedipus complex, also called the complete complex. Its parallel, with the proper substitutions, can be found in girls. Generally this secondary or inverted complex is subordinate to the primary complex as described respectively for a boy or a girl; it is possible, however, that it be the dominant complex in the child, in which case the basic instinctual orientation is reversed. In actual practice, the whole range of possibilities is found realized, from simple positive complexes to complete inverted ones.

However, in the complete Oedipus complex, there are only four instinctual trends to account for, regardless of their organization. For the sake of simplicity, we will limit ourselves to the case of the boy: his primary affection is for his mother, with a sense of identification with his father and a sense of hostility towards him as well. Secondarily, he has affection for the father with identification and jealous reactions towards his mother.

The next step is the dissolution of this complex. It is evident that the child cannot long endure the tensions aroused by the Oedipus complex. He cannot tolerate feelings of hostility towards his parents on whom he depends for all his love, affection, approval, protection, parents who are so much stronger than he is. He must suppress his hostility and its cause—the Oedipus complex.

The first step in this dissolution involves giving up the mother as an object of affections, and principally for fear of the father's punishing power. But it is not easy to give up an object one loves—something must take its place. In this dilemma, the boy can respond with either of two alternatives: he can either identify with his mother (we can give up a love object if we take it into ourselves, into imagination and

emotion, and there cherish it) or he can intensify his identification with his father (we can evade aggressors by identifying
with them).[11] This latter alternative is termed the more
normal, for it confirms the masculinity of the boy, and allows
him to retain a certain affection for his mother, i. e. after the
pattern of his father's with whom he has now identified himself. The relative strength of the masculine-feminine dispositions in the child determines, in Freud's early opinion, which
identification will preponderate.

Insofar as the boy identifies with his father, not only does
he preserve his relationship to his mother as love object, but
his relationship to his father as love object (the inverted
element in the complete Oedipus complex) is dropped. Similarly, in renouncing his mother as primary object of love, and
in overcoming his jealousy towards her, he will achieve by
identification an affection for the father, patterned on the
mother's. The Oedipus complex is now wholly resolved, as
the boy is strongly identified with his father and mildly with his
mother, and affectionate towards both, hostile towards neither.[12]

(4) The superego is born.

*The identification with the two parents is the beginning of
the superego*, the origin of the sense of right and wrong, the
starting point for ' morality,' religion and culture. In virtue
of the identification of himself with his parents, into which he
has been pressed by the need of overcomnig the Oedipus
complex and the conflict which ensued from it, the child
unconsciously and unreservedly makes his own the attitudes
towards right and wrong which have been expressed by his
parents, for *his very sense of rightness and wrongness is the
introjected image of parental approval or disapproval.* Henceforth he feels inwardly that he must do the things dictated
by parental images he has absorbed, and this is the sufficient

---

[11] Cf. Anna Fred, *The Ego and Mechanisms of Defense*, pp. 117 seq. (Hogarth
Press, London, 1954)

[12] Freud, *The Ego and the Id*, pp. 40-46.

reason for his sense of obligation; similarly, he must avoid what the inwardly adopted images forbid, and if he does not, he feels guilty.

For Freud, this is the sole source of moral ideas; there is no place in this scheme for intelligent insight into the natural order of things or of values as a possible principle of the sense of morality.[13] Deliberate consideration and judgment play no part in morality; the moral norms for any individual are the parental images, with all their imaged laws, commands, power and authority, which first exist for the child in external reality and are then automatically introjected by the attempt to be free from the Oedipal conflict. Thus Freud terms the moral sense a precipitate in the ego of the parental figures, deriving its compelling force from the sexual urges which have been inhibited and re-channelled, deflected from their primal aims and objects precisely by means of the formation of parental images. By the force of these mental identifications, the child is determined in his sense of morality—all that he will do and say, think and like, is now established for him through parental identification.[14] Morality then, is essentially infantile, on a level with the mental development of the child absorbing it, and hence uncritical. It is, moreover, unconscious, perhaps because it was formed at an unreflective stage of life, perhaps because the crisis by which it was formed and with which it is associated was a painful crisis, and thus subject to repression; these points are not clear in Freud.

[13] Some of Freud's disciples hold that the sense of morality has origin in elements which are prior to the dissolution of the Oedipus complex (cf. Ferenczi, Melanie Klein, Erikson), and others give some weight to the function of reason (the reality related ego) in forming the moral sense, but it seems safe to say that all orthodox Freudians make the effects of the dissolution of the Oedipus complex the major component in the production of a sense of right and wrong. In Freud's own writings there is mention of pre-oedipal elements, e. g. instinctual movements and formations, which presumably would have some effect in the development of a sense of morality, but it does not seem that Freud himself made the deduction explicit. See, for example, " Instincts and Their Vicissitudes," *Coll. Papers*, vol. 4, pp. 75-79.

[14] Freud, " The Economic Problem in Masochism," *Coll. Papers*, vol. 2, pp. 263-266; *The Ego and the Id*, pp. 46-51.

In actual fact, of course, the identifications mentioned above may not take place so easily. If the Oedipus complex itself is not normal, or if it cannot be completely resolved normally, the stage is set for later psychological difficulties. These considerations, however, are irrelevant to our present point. Here we wish only to inquire further into what this mode of formation tells us about the superego itself—what character is imparted to the superego from the resolution of the instinctual forces which comprised the Oedipus complex.

Obviously, insofar as the superego is formed by the process of identification, it serves as a norm or ideal for the ego, as a pattern to which the child must conform. A boy wants to be like his father, and feels that he does wrong if in any way he fails to live up to this ideal. This is the simple ego-ideal aspect of the superego, the basis for the urge to strive for perfection. But along with this ideal-pattern aspect, there are certain prohibitions set up in the child's mind: he must not do certain things that his father does. This aspect—the taboo-aspect— is understandable when we recollect the original motive for forming the ego-ideal—the child wishing to escape from the tensions aroused by feeling rivalry for the father. He escaped by avoiding any further competition with his father, with regard to his mother's affections; he left the field to his rival and contented himself with emulating him. Inextricably bound up with the image of his father are his father's prerogatives: his special place in the mother's affections. The child then has abandoned his former role of rivalry; he is careful now not to trespass, he formulates a series of prohibitions whose fundamental enforcement agency is, subjectively, the forbidding image of his father. This is the basis of the prohibitory sense in people. The superego then is twofold: to be like the father, and not to do everything he does.[15]

To a lesser degree, in the resolution of the normal complete complex, the child also wants to be like his mother, and yet not like her, i. e. not to take her place in his father's affections.

[15] Freud, *The Ego and the Id*, pp. 44-45.

With these deep desires as their roots, all the prohibitions, exhortations, expressed or implied wishes, ideals, goals, opinions, and attitudes, etc. of his parents take on added force and meaning—they begin to constitute for the child the code by which he regulates his life; the code which, if he obeys it, produces a sense of contentment like the contentment he felt when his parents approved of him; the code which, when broken, gives him a sense of guilt or wrongdoing like the guilt he felt when he experienced a threat in his relationships with his parents.

The force of the superego depends on many factors. The stronger the original Oedipus complex, the stronger the identifications necessary to resolve it, and therefore the stronger the ego-ideal which results from it. The more rigid and harsh the parents were, the more rigid and harsh is the image developed from them, and the more urgent the need of resolving the complex—both factors producing a more exacting superego.[16]

Other factors may also account for the strength of a superego. In every person there is a certain narcissistic element—self-love—which varies inversely with the strength of his object loves. (It is a matter of common experience that love of self impedes love of others, love of others leads to a certain self-forgetfulness.) Now a child has an enormous narcissistic love, almost a megalomania. He can be pictured as thinking that the whole world revolves around him, that he should have every satisfaction, and he becomes enraged when thwarted. Freud asks: Where does this narcissistic love go in the adult, for obviously it is much diminished in normal adults. His conclusion is that, since this love must be directed somewhere, it must have been absorbed in the love of the ego-ideal. This accounts for much of the force the ideal exerts on the ego, (e. g. it has the force of the displaced narcissistic impulse) and manifestly the greater the degree of narsissistic love, the stronger is the resulting superego.[17]

[16] Freud, " The Economic Problem in Masochism," *Coll. Papers* , Vol. 2, pp. 263-66.

[17] Freud. " On Narcissism: An Introduction," *Coll. Papers,* vol. 4, p. 50.

In a similar fashion, the drives of other basic instinctual impulses are found expressing themselves through the superego. The masochistic element, which finds pleasure in being hurt, turns up in the superego as ' obedience ' and submission, or as self-deprecatory or self-accusing impulses.[18] The exhibitionist urge is displaced into the desire for approval. Sadistic impulses, which find pleasure in hurting, turn up as moral domineering, as contempt for others because of their ' moral ' inferiority. In general, the fundamental libidinal impulses are deflected from their sexual orientation to the parents (infantile objects) to de-sexualized social relationships, to institutions of law, religion, politics and all forms of public and community activity, for which one now has respect, love, devotion, etc., as the super-ego pattern dictates.[19]

In Freud's formulation these evolutions of instinctual movements to new aims and objects must be understood as simple mechanical transfers of psychic energy from one mode of discharge to an alternative mode more acceptable to the ego. New objects were demanded by the ego when infantile objects were found to bring punishment; the id is satisfied as long as they can substitute for the primitive objects. Essentially, however, the id always retains its primal orientation; hence a person who is later loved because he resembles the parent, is loved by the same instinctual urge that originally found satisfaction in the parent. The psychic energy has been canalized to another but basically (psychologically) identical object.[20]

The result of this acceptation is that, for Freud, there is no real development of the superego after infancy, only a kind of re-structuralization of the primitive elements. The norms

---

[18] Freud, *op. cit.*, pp. 52-55; see Dalbiez, *Psychoanalytic Method and the Doctrine of Freud*, vol. I, p. 408-409. (Longmans Green & Co., New York, 1948).

[19] Cf. Nuttin, *Psychoanalysis and Personality*, pp. 44-45.

[20] Cf. Nuttin, *loc. cit.*, quoting Ernest Jones on this point. " The shift from the original sexual object to a secondary social object is not only a substitution of the one for the other, but rather a canalization of the primitive sexual energy in a new direction. To state it exactly, one should speak about displacement and not about substitution or replacement."

of moral conduct having once been established in early childhood, do not mature thereafter. The do's and don'ts of the
infantile period are basically the do's and don'ts of a whole
life span. As other factors make their influence felt on the
growing child—teachers, other members of the family, civil
authorities—and other ideals attract him—heroes, leaders—as
new goals and new prohibitions are incorporated into the superego, they are automatically associated with the old solely in
virtue of their identifiability with the original and basic parental
images. The latter, moreover, always remain the strongest and
most decisive elements in the individual's sense of right and
wrong.

(5) The Superego after Freud.

Psychoanalysis, following Freud, has been more or less faithful to his formulation of the notion of the superego, although
it has assiduously worked to clarify and enrich the concept,
Freud himself admitting that there was much yet to be explained. Ernest Jones, an orthodox disciple, introduced a
distinction into the superego, setting off a conscious sense of
morality which corresponds to adult moral valuation against
the unconscious moral norms derived from infantile reactions.
This distinction certainly goes a long way towards aligning
the superego with the moral sense as it is generally conceived.[21]

An instance of another approach, aiming at clarifying and
stabilizing the relationship of the superego to infantile mental
formations, shows the varieties of infantile thinking often
manifested in superego activity. Children, for example, exhibit
a species of magical thinking, not clearly distinguishing fact
from fancy, and wish from deed. There is also a childish sense
of justice—the child thinks he must be punished for wishes as
well as deeds, and that punishment is inevitable and poetically
proportioned to the crime. He also thinks he can propitiate an
offended authority by ritualistic acts, by undoing in an imaginative way the wrong he has done. This kind of thinking is

---

[21] Cf. Dalbiez, op. cit., p. 409.

apparent in adults, as part of their moral outlook, especially in some cases of neuroses.[22]

Since religion and morality are so closely bound together, some authors examine religious phenomena to detect the evidence of superego characteristics. Freud himself originally interpreted the role of God as an evidence of the father identification reaction in the formation of the superego. Others see in the combination of exhortation to an ideal and prohibition of evil acts found in sacred writings the reflection of the two fundamental aspects of the superego, ideal and taboo.[23]

These authors, as well as many others, accept Freud's basic configurations, and develop and apply them, with the purpose of explaining all (or perhaps only some) ethical or moral and religious conduct on the basis of deep and early instinctual movements, and the reactions to them. Others however pick and choose among the elements of the superego, accepting some and rejecting others as insufficiently proved, or simply erroneous. Dr. Horney, for instance, does not accept the superego as a special mental agency, but rather as a special need—as a need to be perfect and infallible, and a need which must be maintained by pretense wherever reality denies it. Like Freud, she sees the genesis of this need in parental authority, not, however, as the resolution of untenable sexual orientations. When a child has been forced to conform too rigidly to parental standards, he loses his own initiative, goals and judgments. He takes the easy way out, abandons his sense of self-reliance, and relies solely on the approval of others, becoming finally the victim of alien norms of conduct. These norms then do not constitute a valid moral standard for the individual; they are not responses to true values rightly apprehended and appreciated. They are nothing but a sham of morality, which has taken the place of true standards and effec-

---

[22] Cf. Vincent P. Mahoney, M. D., "Scrupulosity from the Psychoanalytic Viewpoint," *Bulletin of the Guild of Catholic Psychiatrists*, vol. V, #2.

[23] Mortimer Ostow, "Religion and Psychiatry," *American Handbook of Psychiatry*, pp. 1789 sqq.

tively prevents true standards from developing. In two ways this formulation of superego activity is a radical departure from Freud's. In the first place, it allows for a twofold form of moral standards in individuals—a true moral code based on verified and voluntarily adopted standards, and a false moral code, based on parental dominance. Freud would have all moral codes to be of the second type. Secondly, the latter type of moral codes does not necessarily have to appear in a child— the Oedipus complex is not universal, hence not universally resolved by the introjection of parental images. Hence a purely superego-type moral standard may not always appear, and even when it does appear, it may be resolved and supplanted by a reasonable and conscious form of morality. What is involved in this latter form of moral sense (and rejected in Freud's formulation) is an enduring capacity in the individual to grow morally, from infant morality to mature morality, by a qualitatively differentiated development of moral insights. Hence the effects of infantile experiences and the modes of infantile reaction, however profound, are not the decisive determinants of mature character.[24]

Other psychoanalysts have followed these same general paths, deriving many fundamental ideas from Freud, but developing them less mechanistically, and with more appreciation of the intelligent and free aspects of human psychology, and more optimism about its plasticity in response to these more human influences. Fr. Joseph Nuttin accepts the notion of the deep influence of parental authority on the mind of children, but insists on the positive and creative elements in the child's reaction. For him, identification is not merely a passive adoption of alien standards consequent on the repression of sexual urges, but more a drive towards self-realization, which in the child is admittedly in the direction of being like his father, but even here is not wholly devoid of some kind of appreciation of the values adopted. And as the child grows older, there is more and more the aspect of reasonable discernment and willing

[24] Karen Horney, *New Ways in Psychoanalysis,* Chap. XII.

cooperation in the discovery and acceptance of ideals and prohibitions, which, so long as they are objectively valid, serve
not to stultify the character but to enlarge and enrich it.
There is moral growth through widening awareness and revision
of old standards in the light of new ones. This is not to say
that such a conscious drive towards self-realization operates
equally well in everyone, or entirely in anyone, but it is in
evidence frequently enough to demand some explanation beyond Freud's. Nuttin therefore rejects the idea that the original
identification of a child is purely the result of the failure of
sexual possession, and that subsequent identifications are really
the infantile identifications repeated in new instances, and
finally that real moral development is arrested at the infantile
stage. Finally he rejects the ubiquity of the Oedipus complex,
and, consequently, the doctrine that the resolution of this
complex results in the formation of what is man's sole agency
of normative or moral conduct, a superego.[25] This also seems
to be the position taken by Roland Dalbiez in his critique of
Freudian doctrine.[26]

(b) *Conclusions about the superego.*

What therefore can be concluded? Certainly it can be granted
that there is an internal but acquired norm for judging right
and wrong, and that in its formation it is closely connected
with parental training, deriving indeed much of its efficacy
from the deep emotional ties with parents, which in infants
constitute almost the whole of affective life. The first and
natural impulses of a child would be to be like his parents.
It can also be seen that excessive harshness in discipline can
cause excessive rigor in the norms adopted by children, and
excessive sensitiveness to the demands of these norms, and that
obedience to the norms can generate a sense of satisfaction,
disobedience a painful sense of guilt, quite dissociated from real

---

[25] Joseph Nuttin, *Psychoanalysis and Personality*, pp. 63, 178-183.
[26] Roland Dalbiez, *Psychoanalytic Method and the Doctrine of Freud*, vol. I,
pp. 407 seq.; vol. II, pp. 280-327.

right and wrong. These norms could, moreover, be so restrictive that they would prevent or inhibit normal growth to moral and emotional maturity. They could operate practically unconsciously in virtue of their early and unquestioned acceptance; they constitute *the way* to do things, the way things have always been done, and the factor of unconscious influence could be increased if the norms themselves form parts of painful emotional complexes. These norms can become involved with elements of self-love, of self-deprecation, of childish dependence on others, of aggressive or spiteful attitudes. Their character can invade and color all the moral and religious life of an individual, and, no doubt, of a society too.

That moral codes are formed simply and universally as the result of the repression and resolution of some sexually oriented instinctual complex directed towards the parents is an unwarranted generalization, however useful the concept might be in understanding particular cases of abnormal mental development. That a moral norm is nothing but an engulfed parental image, unsusceptible of real growth and qualitative development is also untenable, along with its corollary, that there is no objective validity to moral, social and religious standards.

But leaving aside these exaggerations, it must be admitted that the concept of the superego has deepened our insight into the actual workings of the human psychism, and has proved its value in the solution of some difficult psychological problems.

II. The Notion of Conscience

Our purpose now, however, is to try to apply some of the conclusions taken from the study of the superego to the traditional understanding of the notion of conscience among moralists. Before making this application, however, some ambiguities in the use of the word ' conscience ' should be cleared up. In its strictest sense, the term ' conscience ' is used to designate an act of the practical intellect, expressing the moral quality of some concrete action either to be done or already done. It is an act of conscious knowledge, and a comparative act, measuring concrete conduct against some pre-established norm; hence it presupposes the existence of some kind of moral knowledge acting as the rule of its judgment. Then, in a secondary and derived sense the word ' conscience ' is used to designate this normative knowledge itself; for example, in the expressions: a strict conscience, a delicate conscience. Conscience may be taken therefore either as the act of judging the morality of some concrete action, or as the norms (more or less abstract) according to which this judgment is formed.[27]

Freud also uses this distinction. Sometimes he speaks of conscience as an act of consciousness bearing on the qualities of obligation attaching to certain forms of conduct, or on the sense of satisfaction or guilt attaching to them. " It would not surprise us if we were to find a special institution in the mind which performs the task of seeing that narcissistic gratification is secured from the ego-ideal and that, with this end in view, it constantly watches the real ego and measures it by that ideal. If such an institution does exist, it cannot possibly be something which we have not yet discovered; we only need to recognize it, and we may say that what we call our *conscience* (Freud's italics) has the required characteristics . . . a power of this kind, watching, discovering and criticizing all our intentions, does really exist; indeed, it exists with every one of us in normal life." [28] At other times however, Freud speaks more broadly, and conscience is the superego itself, i. e. the norm by which conduct is judged. " We have ascribed to the super-ego the function of the conscience and have recognized the consciousness of guilt as an expression of a tension between ego and super-ego. The ego reacts with feelings of anxiety (pangs of conscience) to the perception that it has failed to perform the behest of its ideal, the super-ego." [29]

[27] Cf. D. Prümmer, O. P., *Manuale Theologiae Moralis*, pp. 195-199, where certain other acceptations of the word " conscience " are also given.

[28] Freud, " On Narcissism: An Introduction," *Coll. Papers*, vol. 4, pp. 52-53. See also: *The Ego and the Id*, p. 73.

[29] Freud, " The Economic Problem in Masochism," *Coll. Papers*, vol. 2, p. 263. See also: *The Ego and the Id*, p. 49.

In the first sense of conscience, i. e. as an act of consciousness, there seems to be no notable difference between Freud's meaning of the term and the traditional meaning. In the derived sense, in which conscience is taken as the norm of conduct, there is considerable difference. We have seen above what Freud believed about the formation of the norms of conscience and about their nature. Let us briefly recount now a more traditional idea.

(1) Conscience and the norms of conscience following St. Thomas

According to St. Thomas, conscience is neither a faculty nor a habit, nor any kind of inner voice which infallibly announces the right or wrong. For him conscience is nothing more nor less than an application of ordinary reason or intelligence, not in the realm of philosophy nor of science nor of art, but to particular, concrete actions or conduct, judging whether these be right or wrong. Conduct here is taken in the broadest sense, to include all deliberate thoughts, desires, words, deeds and omissions thereof, and they fall under the judgment of conscience whether they are actions already accomplished or only proposed. In the latter case, if they are proposed, conscience obliges, or induces and instigates, or perhaps merely permits, or, finally, forbids. In the former case, concerning past actions, conscience approves or disapproves, excuses and defends or " bites." Conscience is called the dictate of reason in these practical instances because it is the function of reason to pass the judgment of right and wrong; it is called the natural judge, because it is based on the native power of intelligence knowing that right should be done and wrong avoided; it is called the instinct of the human spirit because the spirit instinctively looks for the truth in moral issues.[30]

All of this refers to the act of conscience, that is, to the judgment passed by reason. To follow this judgment is the

---

[30] St. Thomas, in De veritate, q. 17, a. 1.

basic law of *subjective* morality; whoever departs from this law sins. It follows then, that if a man never departs from the judgment of his conscience, he does not sin. Even if his norms are wrong through no fault of his own, he is guiltless if he follows his conscience; but he is guilty if he departs from it, even if by chance what he chooses to do be objectively right. If a man's norms of conduct are objectively right, and he always follows them, he not only does not sin, but he also makes no mistakes. If his norms are objectively wrong, he will not sin in following them, but he may make great mistakes and tragic ones. He would belong to the ranks of those who mean well but blunder. From this point of view it is of evident moment to know how objectively true norms of conscience are discovered, or, as moralist say, how to form a ' right conscience.'

(2) *The norms of conscience.*

We have said above that the act of conscience is a judgment of reason passed on concrete actions; the norms of conscience are the standards discovered and formulated by man's reason, by which he can distinguish right from wrong. Reason in short sets up the rules by which it judges.

According to St. Thomas, it is within the power of man's reason to discover, at least in broad outline, the rules by which he ought to live. The power of reason bears upon not merely the superficial appearances of things, but their meaning or significance, the essential characteristics of things and the essential relations of things to each other, not equally well in all men nor perfectly in any man, but as always tending to a deeper, clearer and fuller understanding of the nature of things. The knowledge of the essences of things is not a formalistic knowledge, like a diagram of a basic structure, for to know things essentially not only must their nature be grasped but also their strivings, their natural potentialities and their natural appetites to fulfillment, and the ends or purposes which do in fact fulfill them. Moreover, in discovering the moral order, the power of reason must also work reflexively; man must be conscious of himself, and of what he is and of what he needs and wants, realizing his potentialities and the things that fulfill them and the power he has over the means of attaining these things in which knowledge he is not only led by his own appetites, both animal and rational, but also by the pleasures and satisfactions that one action or another in fact obtains for him. This knowledge of himself and of the world around him cannot remain merely scientific and abstract. To live and to live rightly it must be applied to the concrete situation in which he finds himself, and to the person he actually is; for this he must be able to read signs and apply his knowledge to the case at hand. At the heart of all this conscious activity, ruling and informing all his conduct is the basic insight that he is responsible to some degree for his actions and his life, and accountable to greater or lesser extent for good and evil.

The fact of experience is that men know this, and by this power of reason, do grasp and understand the purposes and ways of life, and formulate what they have understood into intelligent rules by which they guide themselves. Reason so informed and instructed in the matter of conduct is the norm of conscience.[31]

[31] In making reason the essential agent in the formulation of the norms of conscience, there is a real danger of hyper-intellectualism. For our present purposes, it is necessary to underline the rational function, but the profound influence of other psychological factors must not be overlooked. In formulating their standards of conduct, men are deeply influenced by their 'feelings,' by the impulses, appetites, desires, urges, etc. which move them to action; what 'feels' right is often taken to be right. And this is not a wholly false principle for moral guidance; essentially man's appetites move him towards what is good for him. This is especially true if sufficient weight is given to his rational appetites, his appetites for truth and certainty, for justice and peace with others and for himself, for human community, etc.

Moreover, since appetite is not a force simply extraneous to reason, but more a co-principle of action, appetite is naturally apt to be moved by reason, and can in fact become impregnated with the force of reason; in St. Thomas' words, it can participate in reason. Men are psychologically plastic, subject to being molded by their own activities. If then a man habitually follows reason, his appetites become reasonably formed, prone to what is reasonable, and in this way the appetitive

(3) *St. Thomas on natural law.*

All men concur in the broadest outlines of the norms of conscience; in St. Thomas' words: all men know the primary principles of the natural law. That his life is good, that he must have food, drink, clothing and shelter to preserve it comfortably, that he must grow and mature in mind and body are laws of life evident to all men. How he might accomplish these ends may differ widely from man to man and nation to nation, but that they must be accomplished is accepted by all. That he needs a wife and family, companionship and society, and the life of the community, is also evident—" the solitary man is either a beast or a god "—and that he needs whatever is necessary to preserve peace, justice and cooperation in the community is equally evident. That knowledge and the arts, and the power these afford are good; all men know these things in a general way as the laws of their nature. These are the things that make for happiness, and all men desire happiness, at least enough to make the privations of life worthwhile. All these things can be understood by the native power of reason interpreting and formulating all human needs of mind or body in terms of what men ought to do. Ultimately all men would like perfect and flawless happiness, to know whence

force and the whole man become reasonable, i. e. virtuous. Then since reason tends to follow appetite, appetite which is reasonable tends to conform to right reason.

However, it is also obvious from all experience that appetite can guide man falsely, urging what is in fact wrong. In essence, the urging of appetite is never wrong; it is only moved by its proper object, and it is right that it be so moved. The wrongness of an appetitive movement arises because some circumstance of time or place or opportunity is lacking, or because the degree is too great or too little, or for some other reason to which appetite itself is blind. It is the work of reason to weigh all the conditions of an action, and judge its suitability in the whole context; hence it is sometimes the work of reason to resist or postpone the satisfaction of an appetite. And if reason consistently fails in this work, appetite may develop into a hindrance to right reason.

In discussing the formation of norms of morality, these, and indeed many other, considerations would have to be taken into account. It is not the place here for that discussion, but it should at least be noted that there is more to morality than syllogizing, and with that in mind, we can safely enlarge on the role of reason in making moral standards.

they came and where they are going and why. Should they conceive an ultimate happiness as possible, they also seek out the laws which govern its attainment.

Moreover, since the generalities of natural law do not prescribe specific remedies for every concrete situation, men elaborate applications of the law, either as more or less reasonably evident deductions from the natural law, or as simple arrangements of convenience. These are the various positive human laws, more or less detailed, more or less conformed to the natural law, which, with the natural law, comprise the customs of the community. This structure of law, prescribed by reason and more or less reasonably expanded, is, as far as it is grasped by each man's native ingenuity, the norm of his conscience.

How does any individual actually come to a knowledge of these laws? Obviously he begins by learning what his parents teach him, and goes on learning the laws of his community, especially from those members who are commissioned to uphold and instruct in the laws. Not only is his mind instructed; the whole man is informed, molded not only by words but by the pattern of approval and disapproval reigning in the community. Ideally, however, the role and function of reason or intelligence should never be compromised in the educative process; ideally the essence of the individual's growth to maturity is a growth in the understanding of the truth underlying the formulas of the law. Education should not be a merely passive reception, nor a repressive operation; if it is well done, the words and examples of the community and the patterns of their aproval and disapproval underline and clarify the truths basic to the law, quickening, broadening and substantiating what the experience of the growing individual is continually teaching him.

III. COMPARISON OF CONSCIENCE AND SUPEREGO.

Is this not the superego, the acceptance first of parental norms of conduct, and later of community norms, and is it not even a weaker explanation insofar as it neglects to account for the deeper motives of acceptance, namely the introjection of parental images and the instinctual bases of these introjections? Superficially there seems to be a resemblance, and perhaps that is the reason why Freud so easily equated the superego with what was traditionally termed the norms of conscience, but there is also an obvious difference. In the traditional account, the role of intelligence is decisive, in Freud's account, the role of intelligence is practically negligible.[32]

(1) *Intelligence in conscience and superego.*

In the formation of the superego, standards of conduct are absorbed by the child without reference to their reasonableness; they in no sense make an appeal to his intelligence and in no sense constitute a guide and instructor of intelligence. They are adopted by an automatic process of imitation-introjection, for the sole purpose of resolving an instinctual conflict. They are engulfed uncritically by an infantile mind incapable of judgment, and in themselves are incapable of forming the power of judgment. For St. Thomas, on the other hand, it is essentially good and reasonable for the child to accept parental judgments, and these judgments as expressed by the parents are pedagogues for the infantile mind. Even at an early age the child begins to find some sense in them and as he matures, he ideally gains more and more insight, and precisely because he was taught.[33] For St. Thomas, then, the norms of conscience

---

[32] It would in fact have been strange if this were otherwise, for Freud nowhere in his psychology gave adequate weight to the factor of reason in human conduct. The reasons for this might be historical and methodological, for Freud was continually breaking new ground in psychology with his techniques of psychoanalysis, and even in his long and productive career did not come to the end of the trails of discoveries in the inferior parts of the human psyche, the areas of sense and instinct. If he had lived longer, he might have eventually satisfied himself with what was found in these levels and turned to the phenomena of intelligence and will; but this can now be only hypothesis. The fact remains that the function of reason has not yet been satisfactorily established in psychoanalysis.

[33] This might seem, offhand, to be an unreasonably optimistic estimate of a child's intelligence, but if we do not demand more than the bare essentials of intelligent

are planted early, even before they can be fully understood, but by their nature they invite understanding, and ideally, this understanding is eventually achieved. For Freud, the norms of conscience have no particular reference to reason, are accepted without judgment by the child, and becoming unconscious are hardly ever afterwards susceptible to critical evaluation. Throughout life man carries with him his basically infantile standards of right and wrong, as a static precipitate in the mind from the resolved Oedipus complex.[34]

Another consequence of Freud's interpretation is that the superego tends to be a wholly repressive function. It is not necessarily so, but tends to be, for it is only by chance that an instinctual impulse will escape the censor of the superego. Since the superego is formed on a non-reasoned and non-purposive basis, it haphazardly may or may not be a good agency for guiding instinctual activities into profitable channels. (As a result, the happiest people are those who grow up in the least developed society; neurosis is a characteristic of civilization.) For St. Thomas, since reason is ideally the ultimate guide of standards of conduct, it will always tend to profit human

activity, we can find manifestations of the rational mind at a surprisingly early age, much earlier than the age of five. We do not expect, at that age, to find intelligence well developed and capable of sustained reasoning, but we can find definite signs of intelligent perceptions. At the age of seven months, the average child can imitate simple syllables, respond to and imitate gestures, heed a simple prohibition. At fifteen months language is beginning, at two years he can himself use language, and understand a surprising amount of what is said to him—clear signs of properly human intelligence. He can cooperate at feeding and dressing himself, enjoy being the center of attention, understand a variety of verbal commands, and make up his mind whether or not he will obey. At the age of three, he is well in control of language, at the age of four his imagination has become inventive, his sense of independence marked, (although not too genuine; it is conditioned on his basic dependence). At four and a half, he can reason, likes long discussions, shows a surprising wealth of material and experience to draw on, and seems to be prompted by an intellectual, philosophizing sort of interest. At five, he likes to be taught, and wants to be good. (See *Child Behavior*, Ilg and Ames, Chapter 2.) Certainly the roots of rational morality can be planted at this age.

[34] Some of the post-Freudians have modified this severe position, making the superergo a more pliable and reasonable mental structure, as has been noted above, but Freud himself held largely to his original formulation.

growth, moderating excesses without repressing instincts, and guiding energies purposively into the surest and most rewarding paths of development; if it fails to do this, it is the failure of application, not of principle.

Social custom, then, for St. Thomas, does not make individual standards; it preserves and transmits them. The work of making them is ultimately the work of reason, of which custom itself is the product. Moreover custom is always subject to revision by reason, to clarification and modification, and, ideally, the constant re-working of custom by reason brings custom continually closer and closer to a true ideal for man's conduct.[35]

The heart of the difference, however, between Freud's super-ego and St. Thomas' conscience rests ultimately in their opposing views about the essence of the sense of obligation. For Freud, the sense of obligation, and its consequent, the sense of guilt for obligations unfulfilled, are generated primarily by unconscious images. It is the introjected image of the parents, threatening punishment or the withdrawal of affection, which in a sense haunts a man all his life, as a vestige of his childhood life, and throughout his life supplies the motivation for adherence to his standards. The pressures of the fears and favors which once dominated his real environment, and which were absorbed from it, interiorized and soon lost to consciousness, are the real, ultimate and adequate explanation of all actions which are motivated by the sense of right and wrong. For St. Thomas, the essence of the sense of obligation is intelligent insight. As soon as a man perceives, early in life and howsoever dimly, that he is an ' unfinished product,' potential and plastic, and able to grow and urged inwardly towards growth and

[35] Since for Freud the customs of the family and community were the standards the child introjected, upon which he formed his ego-ideal, a problem arose, naturally, regarding the original formation of the customs. Denying reason the function of first perceiving and formulating the norms of right and wrong, Freud was obliged to turn to other explanations and these were not, by his own admission, entirely satisfactory. For a fuller account of this point, see Dalbiez, *Psychoanalytic Method and the Doctrine of Freud*, vol. II, pp. 300-312.

development and some eventual perfection, and that there are ways of acting that profit him and ways that damage him, and that he (at least apparently) can choose one or the other freely —as soon as this is perceived, even in a general and more or less indefinite way, man responds with the sense of obligation, i.e. with the sense of responsibility for his own actions. In the broadest sense, he perceives without any further instruction that he should do what is ' right ' and avoid what is ' wrong.' These two, however, might be more precisely defined.

To sum all this up and perhaps clarify some points, something might be said of that correlative of law, namely obedience. Against the not uncommon opinion that all obedience is, at best, a temporary expedient, and not entirely in harmony with human dignity, and an unwarranted imposition of one man's will on another's—as a form of oppression, Catholic morality has always held for the essential nobility of obedience as a virtue for those who are subordinate. In essence, the Catholic position is that, a man's strength and virtue should be easily responsive to authority, if he is in a subordinate position. Lest this position be misunderstood, a distinction must be made immediately. There are two forms of obedience, the servile obedience of slaves and the filial obedience of children, or the civil obedience of citizens, and the like. In servile obedience, the command is given and the service exacted, not for the sake of the slave, but for the use and profit of the master. There is no dignity in this. Filial obedience is radically different. Ideally, the command is given and obedience is required, not for the benefit of the parents, but precisely for the benefit of the child. This presupposes, of course, something more fundamental, namely, that in the natural order of things, children are in a position to benefit from their parents' knowledge, love, power and care, and will further benefit the more thoroughly they respond to the expressions of these qualities. Ideally, their growth will be quickest, surest and richest, if they respond perfectly to parental guidance. Ideally, if the parental norms are set up as prompted by love and guided by intelligence, the child will most rapidly attain the full and balanced use of his own powers, and precisely under the influence of obedience. In the moral order, obedience leads to the knowledge and acceptance of the right reason which is actually right, and that is the ideal norm of conscience.

(2) *A superego-like conscience.*

In the account given above of the function of reason in the formation of the norms of conscience, and of the role of insight and obedience, the words ' ideal ' and ' ideally " have been carefully inserted at strategic points, for, undeniably, the descriptions have been more idealistic than realistic. In the world we live in, the ideal is never achieved; if a family or community tends to approach it, we say it is good, and where they more or less fail, we have a more or less corrupt or degenerating society. But wherever there is failure to attain to the ideal development of the norms of conscience, the alternative is not a lack of norms, for people do not live without any standards of right and wrong. When reasonable norms do not develop, distorted norms take their place, and if reason has not produced the norms, they have their origin in other psychological processes. The investigation of these distorted norms, the uncovering of their roots and the tracing the paths of their development have been Freud's helpful contribution in the total picture of conscience and morality, and a contribution which is of no small import. For while Freud did not come to a sound notion of the nature of real conscience, he did come to a deep understanding of the psychological processes that often pass for conscience, and in fact the purpose, nature and conditions of his work would bring him most in contact with these aberrations. His work was mostly with those who were mentally or emotionally troubled, and he took advantage of the unusual opportunities presented to him to open up to investigation by means of the technique he had invented, whole new realms of psychological activity. He realized that factors which operate almost imperceptibly in normally functioning minds would be exposed by the stresses imposed on the psychism, and more available to analysis.[36] He did not perhaps, however, realize sufficiently the limits of his method and material: that the patients he was examining were being moved more by feeling and imagery than by reason. This may be the reason he passed over the role of intelligence, in his analysis of human activity in general, and in the study of conscience in particular. It is also, however, the reason he may have contributed much to the understanding of the nature of defective consciences, for the defects arise at the level of instinct, imagery and passion.

The study of the origin of a defective conscience (i. e. a conscience formed non-reasonably), must take into consideration both the individual in whom the conscience is formed and the agencies forming it. The individual may have native defects of intelligence and of emotional strength and balance which account for the formation of non-reasonable standards; on the other hand, all else being equal, the imparting of the standards by parents or community may preclude reasoned acceptance. The child is born with no innate ideas about morality or anything else, and throughout his life, but especially when he is younger, will be swayed in the formation of judgments by his imagination and memory, by his capacity to correlate concrete experiences, by his emotional responses, by his attitudes and interests, and so on. He is plastic regarding moral ideals, but the form they take within him will be markedly conditioned by the mode of his active acceptance of them. On the other hand, the agent forming him will function more or less reasonably. So far as the norms proposed and imposed may not be reasonable, they may more baffle intelligence than enlighten it; they may impede or distort the growth to emotional maturity. If the norms themselves are ill-proportioned to human nature,

---

[36] St. Thomas also considered certain psychological problems only in terms of conditions of mental stress, e. g. of rapture and prophecy, and did not fail to mention the analogies with mental disease. See *Summa theologiae*, II-II, qq. 171-175; *De veritate*, qq. 12-13.

or badly proposed, they necessarily become upon adoption repressive and destructive. Herein is evidence of some of the qualities Freud found in the superego.

The defect of the norms of conscience as proposed by parents can arise in a number of ways. The rules themselves can be too demanding, compelling an adherence to stricter standards of self-discipline or self-denial than is reasonable, forbidding things which in themselves are legitimate and useful. The classic in this field is the Puritan code of standards, which eventually outlawed all normal human satisfactions and pleasures.[37]

Even if the standards imposed are not in themselves unreasonable, they may be unreasonably imposed. They may demand too much from the child too quickly, from ignorance of the relative weakness of the young mind; there may be too much punishment, too strict an adherence to the letter of the law, too little legitimate indulgence, no allowance for circumstances, no sense of the patience needed to train chidlren. Or they might be too laxly proposed, or too confusedly, sometimes strictly, sometimes laxly. The child will learn what to do, but not how to do it; he will not know what to expect of himself, and later, what to expect of others. All the norms proposed might be reasonable except one—how to respond to norms.

The corruption of moral standards can also come about when parents over-extend the legitimate scope of their action, giving direction where they cannot actually benefit their children, exercising authority in matters which are no more than matters of taste, keeping the reins of authority over the growing children too long, or even invading the legitimate areas of self-

---

[37] Why anyone would come to adopt such strict standards is a complicated question. It may come from ignorance, from a misinterpretation of human nature, or it may come from weakness, as an overcompensation for an unadmitted (perhaps inadmissible) personal weakness, or there may be elements of malice in it, as the desire to use power to dominate rather than to serve. In any case, the defects of those who are charged with forming the consciences of the young are not under judgment here, nor in the cases mentioned below; they may be wholly involuntary and free of personal guilt. Their effect nevertheless will be the same.

determination for all men, e. g., decisions in marriages and careers, with the result that the same children as adults will rebel against norms as such, and this in virtue of the natural law!

Finally the corruption can occur when the norms themselves are wrong, and this can be taught both by word and example. If, for example, children are shown that lying and cheating are useful, that revenge is a family matter, that kindness is weakness, that race prejudice is an acceptable attitude, the norms themselves which they imbibe will sooner or later, to a greater or lesser degree, conflict with what experience teaches them, and lead them into personal conflicts.[38]

But an inquiry into the reasons why a man fails to develop a mature and reasonable sense of morality must consider the individual too. Defects, as has been said, originate from the individual's own psychological make-up, under the best of training. Some, for example, are by temperament more timid and diffident, inviting protection and submitting to it; others are more agressive, looking for weaknesses and taking advantage of them. Some are by temperament more placid; some are more restless and invite restraint. Some might, even as infants, need more food, and, if not satisfied, develop a disposition to 'greed.' Some might be friendlier, inviting gentle treatment. In infancy, dispositions might be present to all kinds of attitudes, to greed, spite, hostility, diffidence, distrust submissiveness, friendliness, arrogance, and these dispositions and their ramifications and the reactions to them may explain in many cases the form of a deficient sense of morality.

How can all this be applied to understanding the formation of conscience, and what has Freud contributed to this understanding? Whether the formation of conscience norms is adversely affected because of some deficiency on the part of the child in whom the conscience is formed, or because of a defect on the part of the parents, the essence of the trouble will be the failure of reason to form reasonable dispositions in the

---

[38] Cf. *Summa theologiae*, II-II, q. 104, a. 5.

mind and heart (i. e., in the psychological operations and their principles) of the growing child. St. Thomas, speaking of the universality and immutability of the natural law in men's hearts, summarizes briefly the reasons which may make it fail. " Some have a mind depraved by passion, or by bad customs, or by bad natural dispositions, for example, robbery was not reputed evil among the Germans formerly, although it is expressly against the natural law." [39] " In regard to other secondary precepts, the natural law can be wiped out of the hearts of men, either on account of bad persuasions, . . . or even because of depraved customs and corrupt habits." [40] Freud, with the methods he developed, brought forth an amazing wealth of detail which up to that time had only been suspected or more or less generally intuited concerning the actual conditions of the genesis and development of a " mind depraved by passions," of " bad natural dispositions," and " corrupt habits." He laid the foundations of a science treating of the instinctual movements in man and of their vicissitudes when they are blocked, of the formations of complexes and of psychological conflicts, of the formations of attitudes more or less unrealistic, of the breakdown of the mind and emotional balance under the stresses of these aberrations, of the force of these factors and of their unconscious mode of operating. He emphasized in a striking manner what was known before him but not perhaps sufficiently evaluated—the importance of the emotional factor in the child-parent relation, not only by the way it may take the place of reason in the adoption of norms of conscience, but also how it reinforces the power of reason in the development of a true conscience. It was not perhaps realized before Freud the depths to which the child was formed and conditioned purely on the basis of his own emotional response to the dominant figures in his environment, especially by the motives of love and fear. It gave many explanation of the roots of actions and attitudes, not only from

[39] *Summa theologiae*, I-II, q. 94, a. 4.
[40] *Ibid.*, a. 6.

the primary instinctive movements, but also from the processes of identification, reaction formation, and the other mechanisms which can be adopted to cope with difficulties. Finally, he underlined the extent to which these movements and developments, being unconscious, are, once formed, not susceptible to easy reformation.

All this is of major import in problems of judging, guiding and reforming consciences. Until the factors are understood which have gone into the formation of norms of conduct, the conduct itself cannot be fully evaluated—how many evil dispositions which puzzle, perplex and depress their possessors would be easier to bear with and perhaps master, if their origins were known, and the importance of their presence not so much exaggerated. Until the process of formation of psychological dispositions is understood, how can the ground be prepared for effecting a change? Freud's work underlines the fact that consciences cannot be reformed by simple instruction, the re-educative process must go deeper, into the reformation of attitudes and emotional patterns, and sometimes therapy is necessary, and sometimes, perhaps, the only solution is to tolerate the situation. In short, an examination of superego functions can give some idea of the elements in man's sense of obligation which are not an outgrowth of true moral sense, as certain feelings of guilt are not representative of true guilt, and of the origins of these elements in the depths of feeling and instinct, of their validity, therefore, if there is any, and of their invalidity, and finally of their curability if they are curable. Certainly, this would lead to the formation of a more balanced conscience.

(3) Some practical applications.

The insights opened up by depth psychology have not been overlooked by moralists studying the various shapes which consciences actually assume in ordinary life. The most explicit applications to date have been made in reference to the scrupulous conscience, which exhibits the classic pattern of compulsive, obsessional neurosis. The conclusion is now fairly widely accepted that scruples are nothing more than a particular form of this neurosis, and can and should be treated accordingly. Since scruples had previously been considered a form of conscience defect often almost wholly unamenable to correction, the usages of psychoanalysis can be credited with opening up what was a practical impasse.[41]

It would seem, moreover, that there is much room for further profitable study in this area. The timidity of the timorous conscience, the harshness of the rigid conscience, the stubborness of some erroneous consciences, are characteristics on which psychoanalysis has been able to throw much incidental light. Some of these qualities—any one of which is at least unfortunate for the individual and for his associates—can be understood only in the light of basic instinctual or affective demands, or as reactions to such demands. Moreover, although they ordinarily resist even the most vigorous deliberate and direct attempts to eradicate them, even with all the good will in the world, sometimes they respond with surprising ease to the kind of indirect insight which depth psychology is prepared to offer.[42] In most of these cases, simple instruction is not enough to change efficaciously the basic attitudes from which these qualities flow. There must first be a deeper reorganization, a reversal of some more or less unconsciously adopted

[41] See: "Scrupulosity," Rev. John R. McCall, S. J.; "Scrupulosity from the psychoanalytic viewpoint," Vincent P. Mahoney, M. D.; "The Problem of scrupulosity," Joseph D. Sullivan, M. D. in *The Bulletin of the Guild of Catholic Psychiatrists*, December, 1957. Also: "La théologie du scruple," L. B. Geiger, O. P., and "La pastorale, et les scruples," N. Mailloux, O. P., *La Vie Spirituelle, Supplément*, n. 39, 1956, 400-439.

[42] "Bodily attitudes such as stiffness and rigidity, personal peculiarities such as a fixed smile, contemptuous, ironical and arrogant behavior—all these are residues of very vigorous defensive processes in the past, which have become dissociated from their original situations (conflicts with instincts or affects) and have developed into permanent character-traits, the 'armour-plating of character.' . . . When in analysis we succeed in tracing these residues to their historical source, they recover their mobility and cease to block by their fixation our access to the defensive operations upon which the ego is at the moment actively engaged." Anna Freud, *The Ego and Mechanisms of Defence*, p. 35.

pattern of behavior, on which the defective qualities are based, before the qualities themselves will suffer reformation. This is not to say that formal psychoanalysis is required for every character defect; the point is that in the psychological and moral process of acquiring self-knowledge, the insights of depth psychology are often the decisive ones. Therefore, spiritual directors, counsellors, confessors and all those concerned with the interpretation of character should be familiar with at least the major psychological formations known to depth psychology.

To consider the multitude of specific moral problems on which depth psychology has thrown some illumination would be to carry this study too far beyond its original purpose. The work of synthesis has been started and will continue, for its practical value is already widely recognized. Eventually the traditional expositions of morality and its defects should incorporate and be enriched by all that is sound in psychoanalysis, as it has in the past absorbed and organized into itself whatever was true and useful. This is its genius and we need have no fear that it will forget it.

MICHAEL E. STOCK, O. P.

Dominican House of Studies,
Dover, Massachusetts.

PART FIVE

SOCIOLOGICAL ASPECTS

THE CONTEMPORARY CHALLENGE TO THE
TRADITIONAL IDEAL OF SCIENCE

∾

THE ideal of scientific knowledge which was traditional in Western Europe until modern times reflects the mentality of the Greeks of the classical period of philosophy by whom it was first formulated. The Greek of classical times was whole-minded; he saw things primarily as a whole, and his outlook was organic. Human life and culture for him was not something partial and one-sided, but a complete and unified whole engaging the whole man in all his activities. The universe itself was regarded, fundamentally, as a whole, as profoundly one and simple beneath all the variety and multiplicity of life and nature, in so far as the inner essence of reality is simple and common to all. This implied a basic unity of action in the universe, made evident in the reign of law; chance events led beyond themselves to a thorough-going teleology which reveals that the universe is logical, in so far as its structure and activity are based on design. On the surface there is unending change and variety; below all this flux there are permanent elements, and the flux itself is guided by eternal and unchanging laws, so that it is a rational process. The world was regarded as a system of rational law, with unity of structure, as is most evident in man himself, who is a part of nature; but it may also be seen from the structure of crystals, flowers, musical sounds and the movements of the celestial spheres. The universe is not just a conglomeration of disparate entities, but a cosmos, a harmonious and symmetrical whole, hierarchical in disposition.

If the universe is logical and rational, and man gifted with reason, then he can understand the universe. It is possible and necessary that he should enquire into the reasons of things and events to seek the inner reality, the essence, and to discover the laws of nature. Convinced of this, the Greek was given to leaping from the individual event to the general law or hidden essence. He did not neglect the individual or contingent aspects of reality, but he saw beyond this to the universal which they revealed, and of which they were instances. The principles and procedures guiding the mind in its search into the realm of essences and causes could be stated and codified as a strictly scientific process leading to the knowledge of the essence of things and of the causes of events.[1]

Three main assumptions thus came to determine the ideal of scientific knowledge which was taken over by the great Scholastics: 1) scientific knowledge is a body of doctrine, of systematically connected truths about a determinate subject, founded on experience, and reduced to principles from which they could be deduced, and which refer to the proper causes of that subject; 2) the universe is a cosmos, an ordered hierarchy of essences, between which there are intelligible relations, as also between essence and properties; 3) the human intellect is able to know such essences and to perceive such relations.

These assumptions were fully accepted by the great Scholastics who also worked out the implications of the Aristotelian ideal of science. They stressed the fact that the notion of science is analogical, being differently realised on the various levels of abstraction, and capable of being predicated even of God. The distinction of levels of abstraction, together with the distinction of subject-matters and of kinds of causality, and therefore of explanation, made it possible to elaborate a systematic doctrine of scientific knowledge and method remarkable for its clarity and comprehensiveness. In the natural order, all the sciences were seen as dependent on the supreme science of metaphysics, which was also the vital link which made possible the grandiose synthesis of Christian thought placing reason at the service of faith in the divine science of theology.

---

[1] Cf. H. D. Kitto, *The Greeks* (London: Pelican Books, 1952), chap. 10; E. A. Burtt, *The Metaphysical Foundations of Modern Science* (Garden City: Doubleday, 1954), pp. 15-35. To avoid exaggeration of this aspect, see E. I. R. Dodds, *The Greeks and the Irrational* (Los Angeles: University of California, 1951).

The Modern Drift from the Old Ideal

Hardly had this sublime synthesis been attained, in the golden age of scholasticism, than forces began to show themselves which began the work of undermining it. Principal among these was Nominalism, which was, in essence, an attack upon metaphysics, in the name of the individual, regarded as the sole reality, to the detriment of intellectual knowledge by way of universal concepts. If such concepts are merely subjective means of ordering acquired knowledge, without any objective reference beyond that which is present in intuitive knowledge of individuals, then such concepts as being, cause, substance, essence, are little more than words. In that case, theology is deprived of its scientific character, and as a consequence we find a movement towards either positive theology or towards pietism. Philosophy, thus left to its own resources, and cut off from being, turned either inward, in an endeavor to guarantee its validity from within, thus becoming critical and subjectivist; or turned to the natural sciences for support, the Rationalists trusting above all in mathematics, and the Empiricists taking physical science as their ideal. With Bacon and Descartes, the break-up of the medieval synthesis, begun by Ockham, is, in essentials, complete; the two main paths to be followed by later thinkers, the inductive and the deductive, the way of analysis and the way of synthesis, have been traced out; and philosophy, formerly the queen of the natural sciences, though the handmaid of theology, came to be more and more dependent on, and subordinate to, natural science.

Empiricism obviously continues the revolt of the Nominalists against metaphysics; rejecting universal concepts, and reducing the activity of intellect to the ordering and correlating of phenomena made known by the senses, it restricts scientific knowledge to one only, and that a lower form, of the kinds recognised by those of a more metaphysical frame of mind. But Descartes was perhaps even more drastic, mutilating thought at both extremes of the central process of abstraction, its source in sense-experience, and the supreme term into which all concepts must be resolved, being. Obsessed by his desire for what is absolutely clear and evident, he ruled out sense-knowledge as unworthy to form part of science, and the notion of being as vague and empty. If the idea of being into which alone all other ideas may be resolved, and from which they ultimately derive their intelligibility, is discarded, the only unity possible for human knowledge is that of method; and the method which immediately presents itself, as eminently clear and certain, is that of mathematics. Science must have a starting-point; and if being is rejected, its place must be taken, not by one central radiant source of light, but by several independent ultimate units of intelligibility, regarded as clear and distinct in themselves, and objects of so many intuitions. Scientific thinking is thus reduced to one of its modes, intuition, playing upon " simple natures," such as thought and extension; and scientific method is whittled down to a few simple rules which, in effect, impose the mathematical type of procedure upon all the sciences. Basically, this is the error of univocation; if the analogy of being has not been grasped, neither can the analogy of science. The vital unity of knowledge, growing out from the basic intuition of being, gives way to a dead uniformity of isolated compartments of thought, all upon the same level of intelligibility, so that the richness and limitless variety of experience and reality are lost sight of, even the soul itself being treated, in Gilbert Ryle's words, as the " ghost in the machine." [2]

M. Maritain has described this Cartesian revolution in terms which I cannot hope to better:

Unqualified in principle to comprehend the analogy of beings, and so from the first closing to itself approach to divine things, the Cartesian analysis, cutting up and levelling down, can only break the internal unity of beings, destroy alike the originality and diversity of natures, and violently bring everything back to the univocal elements which it has been pleased to select as simple principles. Henceforth, to understand is to separate; to be intelligible is to be capable of mathematical reconstruction. To take a machine to pieces and put it together again, that is the high work

---

[2] *The Concept of Mind* (London: Hutchinson, 1951), pp. 15 and 16.

of the intelligence. The mechanical explanation becomes the only conceivable type of scientific explanation.[3]

Descartes' generic notion of science does, however, retain many of the traditional elements, although deduction is regarded rather as a string of intuitions, and induction as a kind of careful inventory of simple elements; the universe is still regarded as a cosmos, but not in virtue of his philosophical appreciation of order and diversity. The direct object of science is presented as the ideas of the mind, and their correlation with external reality can be assured only by illegitimate appeals to the veracity of God as author of nature, and to the principle of causality. Once such appeals were shown to be illogical, and Hume was to show how easily this could be done, if it were granted that the direct object of knowledge is an idea, not only could it no longer be maintained that the universe is a cosmos, but it would follow that the mind could not know reality as it is in itself. The full fruits of the revolution started by Descartes would become apparent only in the critiques of Kant.

In his preface to a well-known work by G. Gurvitch,[4] Leon Brunschvicg makes some interesting reflections on the relation between Descartes and Kant. He maintains that Kant, and after him, German philosophy generally, did not perceive the import of the classical rationalism of Descartes, which provided a system of reference for placing problems about reason, by clearly formulating the methodology of modern science, as based upon the new mathematical physics. The mental process employed in the new science, he argues, has nothing in common with Aristotelian deduction or Euclidian intuition; it is not a movement from universal to particular, or from concrete to abstract, but from the simple to the complex. It seeks to equate problems, and to solve them by algebraic composition. Basing itself on an elementary equation, it attains to a vision of cosmic phenomena as a unified whole. Thus the realism of the intelligible world gives way to the dynamism of the intel-

---

[3] *Three Reformers* (London: Scribner, 1929), p. 73.
[4] *Les Tendances Actuelles de la philosophie Allemande* (Paris, 1949), pp. 3-8.

lectual process; the intelligible is separated from intelligence, and ontology from idealism. Descartes was able to co-ordinate science and philosophy by thus simultaneously eliminating Euclidian imagination and Aristotelean reasoning. This was a complete break with the medieval tradition, a revolution which based scientific thinking upon the creative force of analysis, and was made possible by detaching mathematics from the apparatus of Euclidean deduction and from the necessity of spatial representation. He could thus establish a rigorously mechanistic cosmology, which determines the equation on which the conservation of the universe rests.

Kant, though he discovered this separation of intellect from intelligence in his Analytic of Pure Reason, yet retained both the Euclidian and the Aristotelian procedures as valid. This led him to regard dialectical reason as supreme, and, since it is " incurably sophistical," to look for a speculative metaphysics which would aim at a subjective " imaginary focal-point." This, however, is to insulate philosophy against the methodology of science, and to consecrate the distinction between intellect and reason. This distinction, implying two forms of thought and truth, inspired the romantic movement culminating in Hegel, who sought to make this very opposition the main-spring of the process of reason.

Once reason sets itself above intelligence, which is essentially the power of judging, and spurns the clear and sure methods of positive verification of judgments, it inevitably demands that the world it knows should show forth its own image. Intelligence does not demand this; it is content to judge, to accept things as they are. Hegel's influence, continuing that of Kant, meant that speculation after him should be taken-up with the problem of the irrationality of the world. And if reason demands such rationality, and yet this cannot be shown, the problem of the absurdity of reason itself is forcibly raised.

The univocizing of the concept of science, present as we have seen in Descartes, is carried a step forward by Kant, who not only regards physics and mathematics as prototypes of scientific thinking, but replaces the correlation assumed by Descartes to exist between ideas and reality by a subjective co-ordinating of sense-impressions by means of innate forms and functions, and for the unifying role of the idea of being substitutes an imaginary point of reference in " consciousness in general." The concept of the universe as a cosmos, however, was held, both by Hume and by Kant, to be unfounded. The unity of the universe, and its order, are primarily those of law, and especially causal law. Hume claimed to show that causal laws are nothing more than subjective associations of perceived facts; and Kant concluded that the universe in itself is unknowable, and that what we call the order of nature is in fact only the correlation of phenomena in our own subjective world of experience. The intellect must abandon its pretence of knowing the nature of reality; the order and unity on which it feeds are found only in the mental world, and are its own production. This implies, however, that intellect must be regarded as essentially a logical faculty, and paves the way for the glorification of logical reason in the system of Hegel. Here the notion of science is patterned above all on logic, with stress on the deductive phases of thought, but to the neglect of the sources of knowledge in concrete experience. The Positivists were logical enough in repudiating such a purely logical ideal, and could claim the authority of Kant for regarding natural science as the only real science, so that philosophy, in so far as it is a science, must be identified with some general aspect of natural science.

Although the main trend of European thought from Descartes to the nineteenth century considered man primarily as one who is capable of scientific thought, especially mathematics and natural science, yet from the start of this period voices were raised in protest against this tendency, as being one-sided, and in fact a depersonalization of the real man. Hardly had Descartes put forward his mathematical angelicism, than Pascal pointed out the insufficiency of philosophy, and claimed that truth is grasped rather by the heart, by an affective intuition rising up from the soul of man, than by logical or scientific reason. The rationalism of Leibniz was offset by the humanism of Vico, for whom imagination was as important as reason, and art and history more human and real sciences than mathematics or physics; and the Enlightenment, centered on the glorification of reason, brought forth Rousseau to champion the claims of feeling and of the instinctive following of nature. The skeptical movement, which provided the background to Descartes' efforts to reform philosophy, contributed no little to undermining the confidence in reason; nor should one neglect the influence of Protestantism, whether Lutheran or Calvinist, separating, and even opposing, faith and reason, which was regarded as intrinsically corrupt. Bayle provides a telling example of the union of skepticism with Calvinist anti-rationalism, and shows us how far the break-up of the medieval synthesis had been carried by the beginning of the eighteenth century.[5]

If Kant may be regarded as the culmination of rationalism, he must also be seen as one of the main sources of the movement away from reason, by making practical reason superior to theoretical reason, in so far as morality alone can lead us back to contact with reality. Fichte would develop this aspect of the Kantian critique, using morality to explain the evolution of all things from a primitive consciousness urged towards self-perfection; whereas Schelling would conceive this primitive Ego as primarily aesthetic, and regard the evolution of the universe as an artistic creation, the work of imagination rather than of reason. Such idealistic systems, and particularly the logical monism of Hegel, did indeed continue the tradition of viewing the universe as a cosmos, which is fully intelligible to the human mind; but the universe so considered is not the world of everyday experience, of resistant reality, but one subjectively constructed within the consciousness of the individual, through a process whose inner spring and source is irrational.

The nineteenth century, although dominated at first by Idealism and later by Positivism, witnessed vigorous reactions against both these trends, against Idealism in the name of

[5] Cf. J. Collins, *God in Modern Philosophy* (Chicago: Regnery, 1959), pp. 127-133.

freedom, personality and responsibility which it effectively denied, and against positivism for identifying reason as such with the causal and deterministic instrument it had become in the hands of the scientists. Reason has other uses besides that of the cold calculations of the mathematicians or the correlating of physical facts. More emphasis was being placed on the cultural sciences, on art, morality, religion; and the recent rise of two new sciences was to have a profound effect on subsequent thought. History, now cultivated as a fundamental science, was to teach men to see things against a background of temporal process, as relative to it, and as conditioned by circumstances of time and place. Biology was to lead men to interpret reality in terms of life, especially when scientific evolutionism would show how both history and biology could combine to present an over-all picture of a dynamic universe. Evolutionism taught men to regard the universe no longer as a hierarchy built of essentially different levels of being, but as a process, in which there is a continuity of forms, evolving one from the other, and as a flux in which one can no longer distinguish immutable essences. Even thought is subject to similar changes, and systems of thought are seen as necessarily relative to the particular conditions of the mind in which they are born and of the civilization within which they are developed. It was but natural that Historicism should make its appearance, with Dilthey, denying any absolute truth, and seeing philosophies as expressions of historical periods and of recurring types of mentalities; and that the various philosophies of life—Nietzsche, Bergson, James—should reject the claims of the speculative intellect in favor of those of life, or movement, or action. With such authors, Irrationalism, at least in the sense of antirationalism, takes its place as a philosophy in our modern world.

The new attitude found a premature voice in Kierkegaard, in whom we find the revolt against Hegelianism, against the domination of human life by science, and against the notion of philosophy as a system of truths. Instead, he sought to introduce once more the individual, the real existent thing, as a category into thinking. He expressly rejected the Greek notion of science and philosophy, the Greek heritage which he condemned as dominated by mathematics, and the typically Greek notion of the universe as a cosmos. It is blasphemous, he held, to attempt to unite faith and reason; the medieval synthesis succeeded only in degrading faith. Ethics, cultivated as a science, is but self-deception, an excuse to avoid having to make decisions; the only reliable conclusions are those of passion. Philosophy, to be worthy of the name, cannot be the abstract and purely academic speculation of the university professor, but a personal thinking that is also a commitment. Man must learn to see himself, not as a substance, but as a series of possibilities, a chain of acts, a succession of decisions, which keep one on the dizzy heights of freedom. The way to truth is not that of science, or of airy speculation, but the way of subjectivity, which involves grasping oneself as a unique individual, with a unique situation and destiny, and arriving at one's own truth, which is truth for the whole man who, far more than intellect, is affectivity and will.[6]

One may not, of course, take Kierkegaard as representative of nineteenth century thinking, although he undoubtedly brought clearly to light many of the motives which, perhaps unconsciously, did influence the thought of many people. His protest against the subjection of man to mechanism, implying the degradation of the human person to the status of a mere function in a society more and more dominated by science, was to become a leading theme in the writings of the later Existentialists. This revolt against scientism was soon to be strengthened by a crisis within science itself, beginning with the French school of the critique of science—Cournot, Meyerson, Poincaré —which tended to show that scientific knowledge is largely conventional, with a validity that is mainly statistical, so that it cannot claim more than probability. The rise of the new mathematics, such as the non-Euclidian geometries of Riemann and Lobachevsky, together with the studies of Frege and

[6] Cf. W. Kaufmann, *Existentialism from Dostoevsky to Sartre* (New York: Meridian, 1958), pp. 14-18.

Cantor on the foundations of mathematics, tended to show that mathematics could no longer be regarded as the ideal type of absolute knowledge, but was based upon axioms and theorems freely chosen and adopted by convention. Such studies led naturally to an investigation of logical processes, and the subsequent renovation of logic stressed the dominance of hypothetical over categorical judgments, that is, of the relative over the absolute. In mathematical physics, the theories of relativity, and the formulation of the principle of indeterminacy, emphasized the part played by the scientist in building up his theories, which were thus seen to be more subjectivist than was formerly imagined. Relativism, already widely diffused by Historicism and Evolutionism, seemed now to gather new force from such studies on the nature of the sciences that had hitherto been generally accepted as prototypes of universal and absolute knowledge. In the new climate of such far-reaching changes in the mental outlook of modern science, the Greek notion of science, if at all retained, could at best be viewed as an unattainable ideal, or, more usually, as a technique or clarification rather than of discovery.

The Contemporary Scene

Among the main currents, outside of Catholic circles, which are significant in philosophy to-day, and pertinent to our problem, we may mention, first of all, *Physicalism*, which is usually associated with some form of Naturalism, and carries on the tradition of Positivism and Scientism. The only form of knowledge admitted as scientific by Physicalists is that delivered by the natural sciences, which seek to formulate laws " based exclusively on spatio-temporal coincidence and counting," [7] and deal only with the local movement of bodies. Various theories of intelligence have been proposed in line with this tendency, such as P. W. Bridgman's Operationalism, which states that the concept of any physical quantity must be defined by the

[7] J. Russell, S. J., *Science and Metaphysics* (London & New York: Sheed & Ward, Newman Philosophy of Science series, n. 1, 1958), p. 21.

description of the mental operations as well as the physical ones by which the values of that quantity may be determined. The meaning of propositions is to be sought, not by reference to some shadow-world of ideas, but to a series of operations which can be carried out empirically. All metaphysical thinking, of the traditional type, is, of course, ruled out of court by this standard as meaningless.

Scientists themselves, not infrequently, seem to adopt a similar outlook, at least in practice. The changes which, in our century, have revolutionized the scientific outlook, have gradually led scientists to seek, instead of the clear evidence which Descartes dreamt of, only the more simple among many possible hypotheses (the Axiom of Choice), and to regard nature, not as ruled by objective necessity, or as fully knowable in itself (Principle of Indeterminacy), but as attainable only under certain of its contingent aspects. Thought is no longer regarded as subjectively necessary, so that absolute certainty should not be sought (Law of Probability); human thought is admitted to be very imperfect, more probable than certain, more obscure than clear and distinct, at least concerning astronomic and intra-atomic entities. Such relativism, however, is not that of the Skeptics, but rather expresses a docile attitude of scrupulous attention to facts. Science to-day stresses objectivity, precision, rigid adherence to scientific method, and indifference to the " human equation," since it is regarded as a purely cerebral activity, which engages only the rational part of man.[8]

The actual school of *Analysis*, particularly at Oxford, may be said to continue the tradition of Empiricism, though in a new key, due to the influence of symbolic logic and of recent developments in mathematics and science, in semiotics, and the example and teaching of Wittgenstein. The tendency is to affirm the conventional nature of knowledge, to see it as a system for co-ordinating and interpreting facts rather than for explaining reality. Philosophy is considered to deal with lan-

---

[8] Cf. L.-M. Régis, O. P., *Epistemology* (New York: Macmillan, 1959), pp. 61-73.

guage, and to be, not a body of truths, but an activity, the analysis of linguistic forms, in order to uncover confusions that have their source in our manner of speaking, and to reveal that the traditional problems of philosophy are in fact pseudo-problems. Some kind of Behaviorism is frequently assumed in connection with such theories, and the prevailing atmosphere is nominalistic, although this is not so anti-metaphysical as it is with the Logical Positivists who work out a semiotic theory consistent with an assumed physicalism.

For Physicalists and Analysts, the subject-matter of science seems to be restricted either to facts, whether physical or physiological, and to the language in which such facts are stated. The influence of multi-valued logical systems contributes to undermine the conviction of an absolute truth, and logic itself has been, to a great extent, not only symbolized, but also conventionalised. The difficulties presented by a seemingly *a priori* and absolute mathematics were conveniently disposed of by Wittgenstein, who showed how mathematical propositions could be treated as tautologies.

Recent studies on the foundations of mathematics point mainly in the direction of *Formalism*, and the axiomatic approach, again influenced by the new logic, tends towards Conventionalism. The mathematical sciences are generally regarded as hypothetico-deductive systems, purely formal in themselves, without any direct reference to reality, whose elementary notions are left undefined, and whose axioms and theorems are established by convention. Klein may be taken as representative of the new approach to geometry, which is said to treat, not of real space, but of relations of position in any ordered multiplicity, in so far as these can be expressed in a coherent system, where the only principles allowed are those that determine such relations, and the fundamental concept is that of " group," applying to a series of operations, rather than quantity or number. Most theorists however regard arithmetic as more fundamental than geometry, and stress its affinity with logic. The Logicists—Cantor, Frege, Dedekind, Russell—reduce mathematics to logic, and try to construct a mathematical system without any reference whatsoever to reality, on the basis of mental operations, and of notions and axioms freely chosen in view of a determinate system. Hilbert would push this formalising tendency even further, basing both logic and mathematics on pre-logical and pre-mathematical symbols, and treating mathematics as sheer calculus without any regard to interpretation. Gödel, however, claims to have shown that the non-contradictory character of a purely formal mathematics cannot be shown, so that no system would be possible even in pure mathematics.

Signs of a welcome swing away from this conventionalism and towards realism are apparent in the views of the *Intuitionists*—Brouwer, Weyl, Heyting—who maintain that mathematics may not be reduced to logic, and is not a purely formal science, but based upon relations with experience. By intuition is meant the ability of the mind to grasp the structure of complex situations, and of the process of thought, anterior to all determinate forms of thought, whether philosophical, logical or mathematical. For mathematics, the basic intuition is of the pure relationship of serial order, from which the primary notions may be derived by a process of construction.

In philosophy proper, the most decisive influence today is that of *Phenomenology*, and it is noteworthy that Husserl was led to philosophy from his study of the foundations of arithmetic, in an attempt to combat psychologism. His notion of science is far closer to the traditional one than that of most of his contemporaries, although it remains to some extent formalistic; but an essential difference is that, for him, science must abstract completely from the real world, and be grounded upon an immediate intuition of ideal essences within our own subjective consciousness, and the method, in philosophy at least, must be descriptive and analytic. Undue emphasis on the constructive activity of the mind in determining the signification of the contents of consciousness led Husserl towards idealism; but Scheler opened up new vistas for a realistic phenomenology by upholding an affective intuition which reveals the world of values. Hartmann, while developing the realism of

Scheler, strongly affirmed the aporetic character of reality. Thought points beyond the known to the transintelligible, to the irrational; we have no right to regard the universe as a cosmos, rational in its essence, but, on the contrary, it must be admitted to be, for us at least, deeply irrational.

Among many of the *Existentialists* we find, although for different motives, this theme of the irrationality of the universe, presented in its extreme form—Sartre, Camus—as a nauseating absurdity; a dramatic expression of such sentiments may be found not only in the plays of Sartre, but in Beckett's *Waiting for Godot*. Not all Existentialists would deny that the universe is a cosmos, but they are at one in their opposition to abstract types of thought, and in rejecting the traditional notion of science as altogether unfitted for philosophy. Instead of the cold intellectual approach to reality, they favor the way of inner, lived experience, as much affective as cognitive, for this alone can grasp the individual in his reality and uniqueness; and they see philosophy as obliging him who engages in it to commit himself by his free choice and fully responsible decision to a genuine and authentic form of existence, by which he can create his own essential being. Although this philosophy is centered on man, yet many of the Existentialists see the human consciousness as open towards being, and thus prepare the way for a return to metaphysics; this is particularly true of Heidegger, Marcel, and Lavelle, who cannot be fully characterised as an existentialist.

Within the Catholic world, there are indications that several philosophers no longer regard the traditional notion of philosophy as adequate, or suited to the needs of modern man. This is most evident in such Catholic Existentialists as Marcel and Lavelle; but before them, Blondel envisaged a philosophy of the concrete, concerned with the individual, and centered on the notion of action. Following the lead of Gratry and Ollé-Laprune, he conceived philosophy in the Platonic fashion as the response of the whole man, who should philosophize with his whole soul, to his actual situation, of which his faith is an essential element. Gilson agrees with his notion of philosophy as being intrinsically incomplete and insufficient, unless perfected by faith as Christian philosophy. Others, especially in Italy and France, turn for inspiration to the Augustinian and Platonic tradition of Christian antiquity, and are somewhat skeptical of the dialectical and scientific approach of the Aristotelian mind as continued, for instance, in Thomism. A rather similar mentality seems to show itself in those who advocate the removal of logic and metaphysics from the academic course of philosophy, on the ground that the students' natural logic and rudimentary metaphysics are sufficient to enable them to devote themselves to the study of ethics and theology.

Summing up the results of this scanty survey of some of the more recent trends of thought, in their relation to the problem of scientific knowledge, it appears that for the Physicalists and Analysts, the only knowledge worthy to be called scientific is either physical science, or logic, as including the analysis of linguistic forms. This is, of course, to deny that philosophy, as traditionally conceived, is a science, and to identify science as such, univocally with one of its particular forms. More moderate positions, however, are now finding favor among some of the Analysts, who admit the relevance of metaphysical and ethical investigations.

The phenomenological school would seem, at first, to be a form of rigid intellectualism, and to defend the traditional idea of scientific knowledge; but the more significant Phenomenologists today have been concerned to employ the method given them by Husserl to investigate the world of existence, of values, of common human experience, or of the subconscious. In such regions, intuitive rather than scientific knowledge is sought, especially since it deals with what is so very contingent and individual.

Other philosophical trends, such as Existentialism, Historicism, Vitalism and the like, evidence a general devaluation of intellect at the expense of the other faculties, and a rejection of the greco-mathematical ideal of knowledge as not adapted to life and as remote from actuality. The world of nature is abandoned to the scientist; metaphysics, when not confused with idealism, is regarded as hollow abstractism; and philosophy is centered on man, being given the name and character of humanism. What draws the attention of these philosophers in man is not the relatively clear life of reason, but the irrational, subconscious, instinctive and primitive life, the lived experience of man as he actually is situated in a universe that appears to be brutal and incoherent. The highest form of philosophy, metaphysics, is not to be thought of as an objective and impersonal investigation into the nature of being as such, but as an intimate and personal reflection welling up from the depths of one's individual experience, in the face of one's real situation in the world, about such problems as death, freedom, responsibility, and such states as dread and failure.

Generally speaking, philosophers today seem to be preoccupied with the pre-rational, the pre-conscious, the antepredicative aspects of immediate experience. Principles hitherto regarded as self-evident are no longer conceded to be such; reason cannot be assumed to be self-transparent, for thought is not pure, abstract, self-sufficient, but conditioned by the human structure and by lived experience. One must note, however, that the pre-rational is not the same as the irrational, the world of blind emotion and ignorance. It is the *Lebenswelt*, that which is lived before all reflection; it is not opposed to reflection, but is its source and foundation. It comprises the whole man, his affectivity and impressions as well as his thought, his stored-up experiences and instinctive drives; for this is the pre-rational soil of all mental growth. Philosophy today reduces thought to this domain; psychoanalysis reduces activity to it; and much of the art of today traces its inspiration to it, and seeks to express it. In effect, we witness the general discredit of rationalism, the questioning of all received norms, the challenging of all received traditions, and the objecting to all that purports to be self-evident.

Modern man seems to be in search of a new type of philosophy, which will be essentially a humanism, with a new object: the individual, in his actual life, in its pre-rational roots; with new powers: the whole soul of man, with all its powers as engaged in lived experience; with a new method: a form of description that will invite to reflection and awaken experience; and a new aim: to bring man to a decisive option, by which he may freely and with full responsibility accept himself and his situation, and so begin to exist.

If, as may appear to many, it is an exaggeration to claim that this attitude is representative of modern man, one might take as typical, between the extremes of Analysis and Existentialism, of Physicalism and Phenomenology, the position of Bergson, for whom the knowledge characteristic of the intellect is deterministic science, whereas reality, as creative becoming, can be grasped only by intuition. He sees the history of philosophy as a conflict between the Greek conception, which would subordinate the flux of reality to the immobility of rigid ideas, and the more human and vital attempts to pierce by way of intuition to that duration which is the inner reality of things. And we should not forget that in Heidegger Existentialism and Phenomenology meet in an attempt to rejoin the insights of the pre-Socratics in a doctrine of being which rests on an intuition whose term is existence precisely as temporal. If philosophy is still a science, it is, for such authors as these, a quite different form of knowledge from that which Aristotle and his followers have regarded as scientific.

Tasks for Thomists

It might seem, at first sight, that there is little in common between the traditional notion of science and philosophy and these modern conceptions; yet we can indicate several points of contact between modern theories and the *philosophia perennis*. If the attention of many philosophers today is drawn towards the sphere of the pre-rational, this does not imply irrationalism, for their aim is, particularly in the case of the Phenomenologists, to discover meaning and rationality in that neglected field of research. The notion of intentionality has been re-introduced into the realm of consciousness, and normally this is recognised to imply that consciousness is open towards being, thus freeing philosophy from the subjectivism that has so long held it captive, and inspiring a revival of meta-physical thinking. This applied even to those who profess the way of subjectivity, since the reflective grasp of oneself ex-tends to one's situation, which includes others, both persons and things, and leads to the affirmation of inter-subjectivity and of a real pluralism. The more significant trends in recent philosophy are notable for their insistence on the distinction of philosophy, and especially metaphysics, from scientific modes of thought, and on its autonomy as the most radical discipline; and these same philosophical movements devote themselves untiringly to the defense of values, particularly such basic human values as personality, freedom, responsibility, and fre-quently also of art, religion and morality. In general, one may say that today there is an intellectual climate more favorable to the renewal of metaphysics than at any time during the last hundred years.

This situation is encouraging for the Thomist, but it implies a responsibility on his part to be aware of these significant developments, and to see the possible points of contact between his and outside schools of thought, as well as to discern the sources of confusion and misunderstanding that prevent a proper appreciation of his own position.

With regard to modern criticisms of his notion of philosophy as a science, he can point out that much is now expected of philosophy that properly pertains to religion, since religion has ceased for so many to be a vital force. What many now seek, in the name of philosophy, is really rather a *Weltanschauung*, a general, all-embracing outlook on life, in which philosophy, faith, convictions, traditions, affective leanings are fused to-gether in a vital whole that is only partly rational. There is a Christian *Weltanschhuung*, which includes a philosophy which may therefore be called Christian without in any way denying its intrinsic autonomy, and which can accept the new insights and modes of investigation of other philosophies. Seen in this way, much of what is valuable in modern philosophy appears to be complementary rather than opposed to the Thomistic synthesis, whose material object is extended to cover regions that have been neglected, and for which new methods of investigation are necessary. The rational nucleus of this global and vital vision of reality is philosophy, seen as a strict science. Philosophy is indeed insufficient for man to live by, but that means that it is imperfect, not as science, but as human. As a science, philosophy must be abstract, speculative, and to some extent impersonal; and it is above all by means of metaphysics that religion and faith can enter as vital and coherent elements into the Christian *Weltanschauung*. The way of subjectivity can be accepted as an excellent propedeutic to our ontology, and the phenomenological method finds ample scope for application in the new fields opened up by such reflexive self-consciousness, while Analysis shows how we need to demand greater rigour in our modes of thought and expression.

As the intellect is under fire from so many sides, one must stress its power to know the singular, distinguishing between abstract knowledge, and knowledge of the abstract, and to grasp existence, thus insisting on the role of judgment as distinct from merely conceptual thought. And far greater attention should be paid to pre-conceptual, or at least pre-logical, modes of thought such as are at work in the various forms of connatural knowledge, for instance, in art and morality. If we rightly insist on the analogical nature of science, we must resist the attempt to identify intellect as such with any one form of its activity; this has been perhaps the most fruitful source of misunderstandings in modern philosophy. The pernicious process of univocation is active when Descartes identifies intellect with mathematical reason, when Idealism identifies it with logical reason, when Bergson conceives it as the instrument of *homo faber*, or when Husserl conceives it as essentially the faculty of intuition. It is the same tendency which leads so many to identify science as such with one of its particular forms.

The analogical character of science depends, fundamentally, on the analogy of being, just as the doctrine of science, or epistemology, pertains to the critical function of metaphysics. Without a sane and solid metaphysics, no satisfactory and coherent doctrine of science is possible; and metaphysics is, in essence, a scientific elaboration of our natural insight into the nature and properties of being. If we wish to further the restoration of metaphysics, and by the aid of that supreme science to defend the proper hierarchy of the sciences and to indicate their nature and extent, we must emphasize the difference between the process of generalization, by which the logical concept of being is obtained, and the genuinely metaphysical process, quite distinct from ordinary abstraction, by which the full and rich ontological content of being is grasped. To see being, grasped in this way, as the primary object of all our thought, and the source of the intelligibility of all that we can know, allows us to distinguish and to order the various forms of knowing of which we are capable, while preserving their specifically distinct natures and procedures, all realising, in different ways, the common analogical notion of science.

The contemporary Thomist should be attentive to trends in modern science that recall the traditional notion, and to those movements in modern philosophy that defend the autonomy and necessity of metaphysics. He can find much in such tendencies that may aid him in his efforts to re-build and make acceptable the grandiose medieval synthesis; and he is admirably equipped to perceive where so many theories fail, or adverse criticisms miss the mark. With regard to the problem of science, he notes that the traditional notion is attached both on the side of its principles and of its factual basis. The existence of universally valid principles is questioned both by the Formalists and the Relativists; on the factual side we find a reluctance to grant more than statistic probability. Formalism and relativism can be adequately met only by showing how all our knowledge and all principles are grounded on the knowledge of being, and share in the objectivity and certainty of such knowledge. In this connection one might use to great advantage the concrete approaches to being characteristic of the Existentialists, the eidetic intuition of the Phenomenologists, and join hands with the mathematical Intuitionists who seek to trace out the order in which our primitive mathematical concepts are developed. In general, the radical investigations into the foundations of the sciences, so widely pursued today, suffer from the fact that they are more scientific than metaphysical, and their completion, by integration into a metaphysical exposition of the genesis of fundamental concepts and principles, in relation both to the concept of being and to the origins of knowledge in sensible experience, would both benefit the sciences, and perhaps lead the scientist to appreciate the peculiar and fundamental function of metaphysics. If the power of the intellect to see things as beings is granted, and the radical value of such knowledge admitted, it would not be too difficult to drive home the distinction, on the factual side of scientific knowledge, between the level of sense perception, or phenomena, ruled by change, and the level of essential natures and relationships, which provide a stable basis for the interpretation of change.

Metaphysics was the vital link which made possible the great medieval synthesis between philosophy and theology; the modern attempt to effect a similar synthesis between philosophy and science by means of mathematics has led to the dissolution of mathematics into a conventional axiomatics, and to the lamentable divorce between philosophy and science. Only the restoration of a metaphysics securely centered on being, and fully aware of its existential implications, can finally heal this unfortunate breach. And for the modern scientist, the way back to such an integrated synthesis may well be through a philosophy of nature which interprets the phenomena of change, with which the special sciences deal, in the light of the principles it has received from metaphysics. The philosophy of nature is the means by which the insights of the metaphysician can be deepened and extended, by attention to the ever new aspects constantly being revealed by the striking progress of the natural sciences in a universe that more and more takes on the appearance of a cosmos, and by which the certainty and objectivity which metaphysics alone can guarantee may be shared and communicated to the sciences.

AMBROSE J. McNICHOLL, O. P.

Angelicum, Rome.

A SOCIAL SCIENCE FOUNDED ON A UNIFIED
NATURAL SCIENCE

ᕲᕲ

The Social Sciences are Founded on Natural Science

IT is common enough to compare the social sciences un-
favorably with natural science. Sometimes it is the social
conservative who disparages the " claims of the social sciences," because he believes that social scientists tend to be too
liberal. Sometimes it is the natural scientist who is appalled
that the vague and tenuous theories, the sketchy statistics,
the public opinion polls of social sciences should be compared
with his beautiful equations so exactly verified in the neat
precincts of his laboratory. Sometimes it is the man-in-the-
street who contrasts the marvelous inventions given us by
natural science with the feeble attempts of social scientists to
predict or ameliorate our social crises.

What these critics do not realize is that historically the social
sciences arose precisely because man's knowledge of society
contrasted so painfully with his increasing exact knowledge of
nature.[1]

The social sciences, however, depend on natural science for
much more than an inspiration or an example of method. The
study of human behavior in society presupposes a sound understanding of the nature of man. This is the work of psychology.
Psychology in turn makes use of all the achievements of
physics, chemistry and biology both to understand man's own
structure and the environment in which he lives.

To be sure, this dependence of the social sciences on natural

---

[1] See Simon Deploige, *The Conflict between Ethics and Sociology*, trans. by
C. C. Miltner C. S. C. (St. Louis: Herder, 1938). Alvin Boskoff, " From Social
Thought to Sociological Theory," in Howard Becker and Alvin Boskoff, eds.,
Modern Sociological Theory in Continuity and Change (New York: Dryden Press,
1957), pp. 3-34 and J. Leclercq, *Introduction à la Sociologie* (Louvain: Nau-
welaerts ed. nouv., 1959), Chap. III-IV, pp. 39-74.

science ought not to be exaggerated. Ordinarily the social scientist cannot himself be an expert in natural science, nor does he have to sit idly waiting for a perfect account of man before he can begin to collect his own data, or develop his own conceptual systems. At any given moment there may be psychological information of which the social sciences do not yet have use, and there may be sociological findings which psychologists cannot yet explain.

Are the social sciences a branch of psychology?

Since this partial dependence of the social sciences upon biology and psychology is so obvious, we might well inquire whether the social sciences ought not to be regarded simply as a branch of natural science, namely as one of the fields of psychology. Comte long ago thought of sociology as the culminating natural science, including physics, chemistry, and biology as its elements. Today more and more the term " behavioral sciences " is becoming popular.

Indeed psychologists in attempting to define their own field commonly state that social psychology is an intermediate discipline connecting psychology and sociology. Klineberg says: "Psychology has been defined as the scientific study of the activities of the individual. Social psychology may be defined as the scientific study of the activities of the individual as influenced by other individuals." [2] I am afraid, however, that definitions of this type hardly satisfy the requirements of logic or of a rigorous philosophy of science.

---

[2] O. Klineberg, *Social Psychology* (New York: Henry Holt, 2nd ed. 1954) p. 3. The difficulty is stated by Kimball Young and Linton Freeman, "The conception of interaction has always been regarded as central to social psychology as well as sociology. From birth on, the survival of the human being depends on the intercession of another individual, normally his mother or mother-surrogate. As he grows up, he lives in social interaction with other members of his family and later with individuals in other primary associations; finally, he moves into the world of specialized secondary and segmentalized groups. Thus from birth on he is part and parcel of a series of interconnected, interactional units, the model of which is the dyadic parent-child, child-child, or adult relationship " ("Social Psychology and Sociology," in Becker and Boskoff, *op. cit.*, p. 550).

Is it safe to say that psychology studies the individual, social science studies society, and social psychology studies the individual in society? Of the many epistemological difficulties in modern science which had their origin in the dualism of Descartes, not the least is the notion that psychology deals only with the individual as a conscious self. What psychologist today would accept such a definition of his field? How can there possibly be a psychology of the individual in isolation from his social behavior and environment? Man lives and develops psychologically only as a social animal, in family and society. Psychology, therefore, must be a social psychology to be a science at all.

A second difficulty of a more technical but very fundamental character is raised by definitions of this type. It is a common error to classify sciences merely according to their subject matter. By such a procedure every field can be divided and subdivided into countless new disciplines merely by the advance of science from general to detailed questions. To proceed in this way is to make the number of sciences equal to the number of objects in the universe—a sort of classification which may serve the purpose of indexing, but which does not show the formal or axiomatic structure of sciences. Is organic chemistry in any significant sense a different science from inorganic chemistry? If so, then must the chemistry of proteins be considered a different science from that of carbohydrates and so on?

The classification of the sciences to be meaningful must not be based on a mere difference of subject matter, or levels of generality and particularity, but on a difference of point-of-view, of basic principles, and of the methodology consequent on point-of-view and principles. There must be, as the logicians say, a difference of *formal* object.[3]

To mark off the social sciences, therefore, as dealing with the more social aspects of human behavior does not separate it in any formal sense from psychology, nor from the rest of

[3] See W. H. Kane, "Abstraction and the Distinction of the Sciences," *The Thomist*, XVII (1954), 43-68.

natural science of which psychology itself is only a material part. Some social scientists do in fact consider their discipline simply a branch of psychology, and their position is at least clear and consistent.

Those who do not like to go this far, nevertheless find it difficult to defend their hesitation. Thus the distinguished social psychologist, Gordon W. Allport writes:

> No sharp boundaries demarcate social psychology from other social sciences. It overlaps political and economic science, cultural anthropology, and in many respects is indistinguishable from general psychology. . . . In spite of this apparent lack of autonomy, social psychology has its own core of theory and data and its own special viewpoint. Its focus of interest is upon the social nature of the individual person. By contrast, political science, sociology, and cultural anthropology take as their starting points the political, social, or cultural systems in which an individual person lives. It is obvious that a complete science of social relations, as Parson and Shils point out, will embrace both the personality system and the many-sided social systems.
>
> With few exceptions, social psychologists regard their discipline as *an attempt to understand and explain how the thought, feeling and behaviour of individuals are influenced by the actual, imagined, or implied presence of other human beings.*[4]

It is certainly very difficult to see why a study of the ways in which human behavior is influenced by the presence of other human beings is not the task of the science of pure psychology.

The Orientation of Social Theory

Before we accept this clear but rather radical conclusion, let us ask ourselves what would happen to the actual practice of social research if sociology were to be treated rigorously as a branch of psychology.

Formerly there was a marked rift between European and American sociology over the question of the relative importance of theory and of empirical research. Today this rift has opened

[4] In *Handbook of Social Psychology*, Gardiner Lindzey, ed., (Reading, Mass.: Addison-Wesley, 1954), p. 3.

wide within American social thought itself. Of course all social scientists admit that both elements are important, but some anxiously emphasize the building of conceptual systems at a high level of abstraction, others an intense application to empirical description and analysis. In practice this turns out not merely to be a difference in emphasis, but even one of *direction*, of fundamental orientation.[5]

It is significant that for the most part those who are especially interested in psychology tend to favor a theory-oriented social science. While the other group (still probably the majority in American sociology) are much more concerned with *social problems*, with the analysis and diagnosis of concrete historical situations, leading to the definition of alternatives for decision by policy-makers.[6]

If we are to accept the notion that the social sciences are a

[5] See the discussion in A. Rose, *Theory and Method in Social Science* (University of Minnesota Press, 1954) pp. 245-255.

[6] Thus Robert K. Merton in his introduction to *Sociology Today: Problems and Prospects*, ed. by himself, Leonard Broom, and Leonard S. Cottrell, Jr. for the American Sociological Society (New York: Basic Books, 1959) says: "Practically all the contributors to this book take note of how the division of sociology into a growing number of specialties has affected the flow of problems needing inquiry. In one form, a speciality is seen as affording a strategic site for investigating problems of general import for sociological theory. In another, and perhaps more frequent, form, general theory is seen as a source of problems that require solution to advance special fields, such as the sociology of law, cities, race and ethnic relations, criminology, and mass communications." p. xxix. Charles H. Page in the same volume discussing the motives which lead students into the field of sociology shows that for many it is the idea that social sciences aim at social reform. "This view, fairly widespread in academic faculties and among college students, draws many of the latter to classes in sociology, where it functions, moreover, to induce disenchantment when students confront extreme advocacy of a *disinterested* science of social life. Here is a problem for teachers, especially for those who fail to make clear that many sociological scholars of stature conceive of their discipline as scientific, certainly, but nevertheless directly involved in human betterment." p. 586. An odd fact is that the most militant positivists among sociologists are also the most explicit in their assertion of the practical character of sociology, thus G. A. Lundberg writes, "Positivists do not admit the assumed dichotomy between the pursuit of science on the one hand and social action on the other. We contend, on the contrary, that the pursuit of science is the most fundamental of all social actions." "Contemporary Positivism in Sociology," *American Sociological Review*, IV (1939), 42-55, quoted in Becker and Boskoff, *op. cit.*, p. 195.

part of psychology, social research must take the same direction as does natural science of which psychology is a part. Natural science has for its ultimate goal the proposal and verification of an embracing theory of the structure and development of the universe, man included. Natural science begins with concrete, empirical data. It returns to the concrete for verification. It has important technological application to concrete problems. Nevertheless natural science as such is not interested in the concrete or particular which it treats only as specimens. It is essentially oriented to pure theory, to universal laws and typical definitions which apply to natural things considered in abstraction from historical circumstances. For the scientist water is H_2O, not a sample taken from a particular river on a particular date.

If we apply a point-of-view to the social sciences, then we must treat the detailed analysis and description of particular social institutions and their historical development as mere material for induction, not as the proper object of our study.

Does this correspond to the real interests of social scientists? They do make inductions and generalizations, they do build general theories and verify them; but does social science stop there? Is not the real orientation of social science to use these generalizations as guides in analyzing particular, concrete, historical situations? Is not social science interested not only in what is universal, general and fixed in man as a social animal, but much more in the institutions which man has created and the modifications he undergoes through and in these institutions? Natural science sees theory as the ultimate goal. Social science sees theory rather as a guide better to understand the concrete and variable.

A sign of this is to be found in the discomfort which many experienced social scientists feel at all the current talk about the building of social theories. They are accused of being intellectually lazy, but is it not rather that they instinctively feel the theory-makers are leaving behind the very thing which makes social science interesting in its own right?[7] Another sign is the notorious fact that the most heroic efforts to arrive at a theoretical structure in the social sciences have yielded nothing comparable to that of natural science.

If we grant that the point-of-view of psychology and sociology are essentially different, since they have a different orientation with regard to theory and with regard to the historical and concrete, then we can easily defend the autonomy of the social sciences, since they will have their own formal object.

Psychology regards man and his behavior as they are determined by man's inborn biological structure and by his relation to his natural environment. The social sciences on the other hand study this same human being and his behavior not as innately determined or naturally environed, but as they are modified through the institutions, customs and artificial environment which man has himself created. To be brief, psychology deals with man as God and natural forces have made him, the social sciences deal with man as he has made himself.

Since those patterns of behavior which fall under human control are ever shifting, since they are strictly historical and contingent entities, the social sciences are ultimately concerned not with a universal theory, but with the analysis of what is essentially historical and existential. They are, as it were, the scientific refinement and elaboration of human *experience*, that gradually accumulated ability to face our own unique situation in the light of all our previous situations.

The Social Sciences and Value

The perennial problem of whether social science must be " value-free " takes on a new aspect once it is seen that the conceptual schemes of social science are not the goal but the guides by which it is able to penetrate and understand con-

---

[7] Significant in this respect have been the very diverse attitudes of American sociologists to the social action theory proposed by Talcott Parsons which had European origins. See Preston Valien and Bonita Valien, " General Sociological Theories of Current Reference," in Becker and Boskoff, *op. cit.*, pp. 78-92.

crete historical situations. If we select from among the various
notions of " value " which philosophers have proposed, the common view that " value " concerns the relation of means to end,
then it becomes at once apparent that there is no difficulty
whatsoever in the idea of a scientific study of means.[8] Certainly it is possible in an objective and rational fashion to
determine empirically whether or not a proposed means will
probably lead to a stated goal or not. If this were not possible
then the application of natural science to technology would fail.

The real difficulty concerns not the means, but the determination of the end. In the case of technology this question is
easily answered, the end is the thing or effect to be produced,
and this is a matter of choice lying outside the technology itself.
The doctor does not debate whether the patient should be
healed; that has already been decided by the patient. The
designer of weapons does not decide whether a war is to be
fought; that is the decision of the government. Some, therefore,
regard social science as " social engineering " and argue that it
studies means that would be productive of this or that social
effect, but is not at all concerned with which end is to be
chosen, since this pertains only to policy-makers.

Such a view, however, also threatens the autonomy of social
science, since it would reduce it to a technology. The obvious
fact is that social scientists, no matter how often admonished
by value-free purists, have never been able just to take ends
for granted. They are everlastingly fascinated by the different
ends which individuals, groups and societies seek, and with the
effect such goal-seeking has upon the whole society. Indeed
in countless different ways we find that contemporary social
science is very much concerned to point out that it is the goal
of a society which integrates its culture and behavior, and it
is a disunity of goal that leads to social disintegration.

Some believe that the sociologist has done his part when he
has uncovered the actual goals of social groups and assayed

---

[8] See the discussion of the history of this queston in Leo Strauss, *Natural Right
and History*, New York, 1953.

the effectiveness of the means which they have chosen in view of these goals. The choice of goals is simply an historical phenomenon to be explained, but not to be evaluated. Such a position ignores one great social fact which has stood the test of many attacks, namely that certain selected goals tend to persist through time and space. The infinite historical and geographical variety of social groups is not without pattern. Rather there are certain stable goals which a society must achieve or cease to develop or exist. A society which does not nourish its members, help provide for the family, help with protection from destruction, or supply an organized pattern of activity and a vision of the goal to be socially achieved, or which does this ineffectively cannot long survive. In recent years sociologists have argued that a society which does not respect the dignity and inherent rights of the human person will become socially rigid, unadaptable and eventually irrational in its policy.[9]

Thus an examination of the goals actually sought by social groups reveals that some have about them a stability and harmony with the preservation and rational development of groups and individuals, while others are shifting or socially disruptive. Goals which are variable can be considered as intermediate goals, and hence can be measured like means according to whether they are compatible with more fundamental goals or not.

It is the more stable and permanent goals which have value for society in themselves, and not merely as means. What is their origin, and how can they be accurately determined? I think that confronted with this question we should not hesitate to affirm that these fundamental goals are not determined

---

[9] Cf. William L. Kolb, "The Changing Prominence of Values in Modern Sociological Theory," Becker and Boskoff, *op. cit.* pp. 93-132; David Bidny, "The Philosophical Presuppositions of Cultural Relativism and Cultural Absolutism," in Leo R. Ward, *Ethics and the Social Sciences* (Notre Dame, 1959), pp. 51-76; Clyde Kluckhohn, "Values and Value Orientation in the Theory of Action," in Talcott Parsons and E. A. Shils, *Toward a General Theory of Action* (Cambridge, Mass.: Harvard U. Press, 1952), pp. 388-433.

by custom, or historical and social circumstances, but by the psychological and biological structure of man and his relation to the great natural factors of his environment. Thus our need for the family is rooted in the biological and psychological character of the child, and again the need of each individual for a certain freedom of life is rooted in his individual characteristics and personal power of deliberate choice.

Thus two facts emerge: First, the psychological foundation of the social sciences provides them with certain stable goals of human behavior which are valuable in themselves and which cannot be eradicated or fundamentally altered by social institutions or circumstances. They are stable values which can be objectively established by the ordinary methods of biology and psychology. The social scientist in this way has criteria by which to evaluate other variable intermediate goals and means. " Democracy," " prosperity," " peace " can be evaluated in a given society by finding out whether such intermediate goals really contribute to the attainment of the more stable ones. " Democracy " may serve to promote ultimate biological and psychological values in one society at one period of history, but not in another society or at a different time. Thus both subordinate ends and means in social life can be scientifically evaluated by the social scientist if he accepts from natural science certain fixed values as criteria.

Two difficulties can be raised against this contention, although both appear somewhat outmoded in light of developments in contemporary natural science. Indeed they are survivals in the social sciences of influences from the nineteenth century views of natural scientists.

The first difficulty is that a science of social values is impossible because it implies that human beings can make free choices of means to ends, and free choice destroys the determinism required for any scientific theory.[10] Surely it is realized

[10] Sociologists today, however, speak very modestly about their actual ability to predict. Cf. for example the discussion in Robert F. Bales, " Small-Group Theory and Research," Merton, Broom, Cottrell, op. cit., pp. 293-305. After admitting that " The nearest thing to this kind of publicly exposed, practical, naturalistic

today that indeterminism does not make a science impossible as long as it is not absolute. In physics we get along very well admitting that the universe is permeated by chance, as long as we admit that not all of its events are pure chance. Similarly social science does not have to insist that all human behavior is rigidly determined in order to scrutinize it scientifically. It suffices that human behavior exhibit some regularity and pattern. This relative determinism is sufficiently guaranteed by the stability of the human biological and psychological structure and its fixed goals. In practice both psychologist and social scientist actually observe a distinction between two kinds of human behavior. One is unconscious and automatic, or conscious but compulsive and instinctual, or explicable by custom and habit. Another is deliberate, conscious, creative, personal and responsible. The latter is peculiarly human, the former common to animals. It is this second type of human behavior which is most interesting to the social scientist since from it originate the major social institutions and the major social changes. It is *free* activity. To explain how it is possible is a psychological, not a sociological problem, but there is no need to explain it away in order to save the possibility of a science of society.

The second difficulty is that if we say natural science is able to determine goals and values, then we are making science " teleological," a consequence which many scientists would deplore. An adequate reply to this would have to be an extensive one. Suffice it here to point out that " teleology " is an ambiguous term. If for " teleology " we read " functionalism,"

---

prediction (i. e. " prediction about the course of natural events," not about a highly controlled laboratory event) I can think of in the social sciences is the prediction of elections by poll," Bales goes on to argue that nevertheless naturalistic prediction remains the goal of social science. " Of course, the goal that I have here called naturalistic prediction is a very ambitious and idealistic one. But we need a vantage point from which we can successfully put into perspective the problems of theory and research of a whole scientific field. The goal we need to visualize should serve not only as an immediately appealing stimulus to the beginning of work but also as an exacting criterion of scientific progress and an indicator of critical problems for further work. To my mind, nothing less than the goal of naturalistic prediction really answers these needs." p. 295, and p. 305.

and mean by it that biology can and must analyse the functional relation between the parts of the organism and the whole and the integration of their activity in the preservation and development of the organism, who can deny that functionalism is accepted in contemporary science and has proved extremely successful? It is only such functional analysis which is required for a biologist or psychologist to consider the stable goals of man.[11]

A psychology adequate to serve as the basis for the social sciences cannot be, however, a study of man based on a narrow methodology. The picture of man given by behavioristic, psychoanalytic, or purely phenomenological methods is too incomplete. Nor will a merely eclectic methodology serve the purpose. What is required is a psychology which makes use of all known methods of obtaining and analyzing evidence under the control of basic principles so rooted in the broad facts of experience that they can withstand searching philosophical criticism. There must be a unified psychology of man in which the dichotomy between the philosophical-humanistic and the scientific view of man is overcome.[12]

Since man is not a mere mind nor a Platonic soul but an organism forming a unit in the system of natural bodies, such a unified psychology presupposes a unified physical science of the sort which other contributors to this volume are proposing.

The Problems to be Studied by a Social Science Founded on Natural Science

What would be the outline of a social science oriented in this manner and founded on a unified psychology? It would

---

[11] See my paper "Research into the intrinsic final causes of physical things," *Proceedings of the American Catholic Philosophical Association*, XXVI (1952), 185-194 in which I attempted to show that final causality is just as empirically observable as efficient causality, since they are correlative to each other. Those who reject teleology in the Aristotelian sense must also accept a purely positivistic view of all causality.

[12] See the views of psychologists who are working in this direction in Magda B. Arnold and John A. Gasson, *The Human Person: An Approach to an Integral Theory of Personality* (New York: Ronald Press, 1954).

begin by gathering from psychology and the rest of natural science a sound description of man as he is a stable organism in a generally stable environment striving after certain general goals, not neglecting, however, data on individual and racial differences and possible evolutionary processes.

On this borrowed foundation it would then pursue its own researches, oriented not only to general theory, but toward application of this theory to concrete societies and events. Its first proper task would be to determine and classify intermediate goals and to evaluate them in terms of the stable goals established by psychology and biology. Also it would study the general types of habit and behavior which function as means to such intermediate and ultimate goals. At this point the existence of certain universal social forms would become evident and intelligible. In particular it would become apparent that the study of human behavior must give special consideration to the way in which the individual as an organic unit has a certain control over his own behavior, how the family is required by the interdependence of such units and how it has its own type of social control, and finally how the limitations of the family make necessary some larger total society with its own social control and with the power to supply the needs of all its members.

Thus besides a general study of the roots of human behavior there must be a three-fold sociology of the individual, the family, and the total society as each has a different natural origin and each its own mode of control. These are independent of each other in some measure and yet also interrelated so that the individual must be seen in his familial role, and the family in its social role.

The sociology of the total society would deal with the sociology of knowledge, of religion and of professional groups, the sociology of government (political science), and the sociology of economic groups. These sets of problems would not be separate disciplines but would be unified by the fact that all deal with the choice of diverse types of means to one common end, the good life of the total society.

Economics would be instrumental to this three-fold sociology. Economics is not the same thing as a sociology of economic life, since it deals not with human behavior as such, but with an essentially technological problem, the most efficient employment of the material resources of a society.

The general theory or conceptual schemes of the social science rests quite directly on those of natural science, since they are rooted in the description of abstract man. Since, however, the orientation of the social sciences is to the concrete, all this constitutes only the guiding principles of social analysis. These schemes of ends and means must be applied to the study of actual institutions and experiences.

Here it is that social science has needed to develop its own tool-kit. The infinity of historical facts and descriptions has to be reduced to manageable order. The general principles or conceptual schemes are guides in this process, but the concrete can never be deduced from the general, it must be directly observed in its unique character.

A multitude of concrete experiences must by a variety of devices be reduced to an ordered experience, a unified and formalized premise with which we can reason. Before modern times the chief failure of social thought was its dependence on merely fortuitous experiences, on impressions and stereotypes. The great achievement of modern social science is that it has developed techniques of critical history and description. Generalizations based on such critically analyzed data are not, however, to be compared with those of natural science. Since the social sciences refuse to abstract from the concrete historical circumstances they never can arrive at the certitude of clarity possible in the purely theoretical sciences. The fair test of their success is rather to ask if these techniques provide us with a better and more objective experience than is furnished by mere common sense.

Relation of social science to other disciplines

If we conceive social science in the manner just outlined we maintain its autonomy and unique point-of-view, we thoroughly justify both its tendency to seek a theoretical foundation and its innate orientation to the analysis of concrete historical institutions, and we command its search to develop its own special techniques. What is even more interesting is that by giving it a clearly defined autonomy we remove the tensions which have arisen between it and other disciplines.

First of all, as has been emphasized, the social sciences are seen to have a vital relation to natural science, yet are not a mere part of natural science, nor to be judged by the same standards. Next we can close the great gap which separates modern social thought from the ancient social thought still so influential in our culture. Until recent times social thinkers spoke of the " moral sciences." Commonly they distinguished three, the ethics of the individual, the ethics of the family, and politics or the ethics of society. These were called " special ethics," and the theoretical foundation which all three rested was called " general ethics." These sciences were evaluative, considering the relation of ends to means. Furthermore they were founded on the concept of natural law, that is, that certain goals are determined for human conduct by human nature itself, while others are instituted by human choice and are to be evaluated by their conformity as means to these fixed goals. Our analysis shows that this conception is essentially the same as that toward which the social sciences as we now know them tend to gravitate as they gain their independence from natural science.

The break between the older and newer conception was due to the fact that the ancient social thinkers had not developed the techniques necessary to bring their general theory into contact with historical description and experience.[13] It is signifi-

---

[13] The various attempts of Catholic sociologists to distinguish the social sciences from the moral sciences (for which see P. H. Furfey, *The Scope and Method of Sociology* (New York 1953). Sister Miriam Lynch, O. S. U., " Communication be-

cant that the Greeks developed considerable historical and sociological research which if it had been carried on would have closed the gap. In medieval and Renaissance times the transitional social situation led moral *casuists* to initiate similar researches.

Once we have grasped the special character of the social sciences, their relation to metaphysics and theology also becomes clearer. A sound metaphysics recognizes about itself that although it may serve to clarify the nature of social science and some of its basic concepts, such as that of value, it can never replace the study of concrete social institutions carried on by social science. Metaphysical methods are not adequate for the study of the concrete, and it was precisely the error of the Hegelians and of Marx to make this illegitimate leap from metaphysics to history.

Theology, on the other hand, does concern itself with the same problems as the social sciences even down to the historical particular, but it views them from a wholly different perspective. The theologian accepts from social science all its established conclusions and uses them as tools in his own exploration of reality, with the conviction that well-established scientific truth will be entirely compatible with supernatural truth. On the other hand both in social science and in theology there are many views which are only probable and provisional. As regards these the sociologist and the theologian can engage in fruitful discussion, each casting light on the phenomena from his own point-of-view. This discussion stimulates research in both fields, and the expert in either field is not obliged to

tween Philosophers and Sociologists," *American Catholic Sociological Review*, XIX (1958), 290-309 and Herbert Johnston, " The Social and Moral Sciences," in Ward, *op. cit.*, pp. 452-463 are parallel to the attempts to distinguish the philosophy of nature from modern natural science. The earlier writers tried to make the distinction in terms of " ultimate " and " secondary causes." More recently it is in terms of " philosophical " and " empiriological " or " constructural " modes of knowing. But neither of these criteria can form the basis for an essential division of the sciences. Only metaphysics deals with ultimate causes, and *every* science employs both " philosophical " i. e., demonstrative knowledge and constructural or empiriological knowledge.

incorporate into his own science what is not established by its own methods.

Sociology can be of great service to theology. According to theology the ultimate work of God in the universe is the Church, a society which is a spiritual body having Christ Himself as its head. History, viewed theologically, is the drama of the institution of this society by Christ and of its struggle to complete His mission. The Church as it now exists is a society developing in concrete circumstances. We as Christians and members of that society have to play our role in this present moment amidst these present conditions. Revelation shows us the nature of the Church and its history in outline, but to fill out this outline in thought and in action requires a profound analysis of our times, its forces and institutions, its social trends. From the life of the single parish to the life of the Church throughout the world we must see the life of the Church as it really is, studying it through the eyes both of faith and of science, with a vision that humbly accepts the facts, unafraid, since ultimate victory is assured.

This realistic Christian vision is possible today only if we make full use of the social sciences and of the natural science on which they are securely founded.

BENEDICT M. ASHLEY, O. P.

Dominican House of Studies
River Forest, Illinois

THE ROLE OF SCIENCE IN LIBERAL EDUCATION

 caro

THE dominance of scientific progress in our age of satellites and space ships is forcing modern educators to reconsider some of their basic tenets. Modern school children grow up in a world whose headlines, literature and even toys are couched in the technicalities of this advance. It is clear that science must become a more integral part of our educational system. While federal legislation and scientific organizations are providing the impetus for this change, educators, in particular liberal educators, are questioning the consequence. Progress would seem to demand a highly specialized science curriculum, but history warns against an inbreeding that would lead to barren technology. Modern society certainly requires engineers, technologists and specialists, but we must not forget that the primary end of education is to enable the individual to lead a full life as a human being.

Considering the modern trend, educators are asking, What will the curriculum of the future be like? Will it lead to a greater disparity between the humanities and scientific studies? Many fear the potential of this present trend to divide all human knowledge into ' science ' and ' non-science,' pitting the objective and real against the subjective and imaginary. In particular, what will be the consequences for Catholic Education? Here the traditional strain between the arts and sciences has always been more intensely felt. In Catholic Education science has been somewhat of a step-child, constantly upsetting the schedule by demanding additional time, and the budget by insisting on additional equipment. Perhaps—to express one attitude, science is too expensive in time and equipment, and consequently, ought to be deleted from our program at least at the level of higher education.

Can Catholic Education be truly Catholic and at the same time non-scientific? Or must a curriculum based on Catholic philosophy make the natural sciences an integral part of the curriculum, and not just an appendage attached because everyone else has them? In an allocution to scientists, philosophers and educators, Pope Pius XII expressed his conviction that a knowledge of science is fundamental to education. Speaking to the Fourth International Thomistic Congress, he said:

You know how advantageous and necessary it is for a philosopher to deepen his own understanding of scientific progress. . . . Each of the branches of knowledge has its own characteristics and must operate independently of the others, but that does not mean that they should be ignorant of one another. It is only by means of mutual understanding and cooperation that there can arise a great edifice of human knowledge that will be in harmony with the higher light of divine wisdom. (Sept. 14, 1955)

Addressing the Pontifical Academy of Sciences that same year, Pius XII pointed to the dangers which have arisen from the separation of science and philosophy, and he insisted that science itself has need of a sound philosophy.

Science is Liberal Education

A solution to the problem is found within the tradition of Thomistic realism. An educational system orientated to the thought of St. Thomas Aquinas places natural science in its proper context and revitalizes its integral connections with all other intellectual disciplines. The Angelic Doctor never feared man's fascination for the three-dimensional world of physical reality. Instead he realized that investigation of this world was the beginning of all knowledge. Within such a frame of reference, natural science is not another branch of learning whose present expansion may cause it to replace the trunk. It is rather the root. It is the means of transporting experiences, facts and first principles from the physically sensible world to all other fields of knowledge. And a tree's growth is not impaired but is enhanced by a vigorous expansion of its root system.

If development of the intellectual life is the essential objective of the school, then the acquisition of the habit of *science* becomes the epitome of this growth. Man is most human when he is the reasoning animal; and science taken in a general sense, including theology, social science, mathematics and natural science, is that habit which allows him to operate in this unique human way, that is, reasoning from first principles. The most liberalizing power we possess is this intrinsic habit of taking principles gleaned by direct experience with the physical world and forging ahead to a certitude that is *ours*, not the book's or some good authority.

Moreover, in view of the philosophical dictum, " All knowledge comes through the senses," it becomes obvious that all sciences find their roots in the sensible world and, consequently, in natural science. The perennial philosophy, therefore, assigns to natural science a unique role among the sciences. It is the source, or origin of human knowledge and intellectual principles. Since its proper object is the sensible world, it is the fountain head for the other sciences. Since its development requires a rigid application of the liberal arts, it becomes the battlefield for logic and mathematics and the proving ground for the arts of communication. From this point of view, natural science becomes the very foundation of a liberal education, and, conversely, a liberal or humanistic education becomes a necessity for a comprehensive scientific approach.

Is This Science?

Objections may be raised that natural science so conceived is really the philosophy of nature and not the positive sciences of modern civilization. There is, however, a growing group of Thomists who hold that there is but one study of nature, whether it be called the science of nature or the philosophy of nature. A comprehensive analysis of the writings of St. Thomas concerning the division of the sciences and an evaluation of various schools of interpretation can be found in a scholarly article by Fr. Benedict Ashley, O. P.[1] In opposition to positions that would divorce philosophy and science, Father Ashley distinguishes between metaphysics and the philosphy of nature, and maintains that there is a single science of nature which includes philosophical and positive aspects. This point of view necessarily assigns to natural science the key position within the educational curriculum and determines the expanse, the order and the orientation of the entire program. A science curriculum so conceived goes beyond the mere listing and explaining of discoveries and accomplishments; it goes beyond a facility to apply logically particular data to the theory of another. It is conceived to lead the student to a habit of mind capable of penetrating animate and inanimate phenomena in the light of true unifying principles. This habit of mind, however, is not innate intuition, for its acquisition requires vast experience with the facts of nature, great acumen with the tools of thinking and expression, and a systematic consideration of the fundamental theoretical systems of science. Each portion of the science continuum, consequently, has a specific role to play appropriate to the academic level of instruction and related to other subjects in the curriculum. Elementary science cannot be diluted general high school science, and secondary science must not be an enthusiastic caricature of the college science courses. Moreover, to be successful, there must be a constant interplay between science and the student's other subjects, and a continuous orientation of the science class toward the ultimate goal of education: true wisdom.

AN EXPERIMENT IN SCIENCE EDUCATION

Saint Xavier College of Chicago has attempted to realize a program based on these philosophical principles and, consequently, is receiving nationwide attention from educators. The

[1] B. M. Ashley, O. P., " The Role of the Philosophy of Nature in Catholic Liberal Education," *Proceedings of the American Catholic Philosophical Association*, XXX (1956), 62-85.

Saint Xavier Plan is a total program; it courageously includes all levels of education, elementary, secondary and collegiate. The history of Catholic education in Chicago finds Saint Xavier College a pioneer not only in its historic foundation, but also in its modern curriculum planning. Students of the '80's and '90's enjoyed the advantages of a non-graded school, while the advanced placement program of today operated in embryonic form between the college and high school as early as 1934.

General education became the pattern of the college curriculum in 1932, but continuous self-study for the purpose of revision and revitalization led the faculty toward a growing conviction that this reordering could not be limited to the collegiate level but must permeate the total educational system. Reform, to be effective, must embrace the school system in its entirety and it must envision the education of the individual as an organic whole, not as a fragmented trinity of grade school, high school and college.

Fortunately Saint Xavier College, conducted by the Sisters of Mercy, is part of a school system that consists of over 60 elementary and secondary schools, and includes over 800 teachers. The college, therefore, could elaborate a program embracing education from first grade through college, and carry it out in practice with all desirable control and jurisdiction. The initial endeavor soon found financial support from the Ford Foundation for the Advancement of Education and from the Carnegie Corporation of New York.

Members of the Albertus Magnus Lyceum under the able direction of Father William H. Kane, O. P., collaborated with the faculty of the college and its associated schools in the initial investigation. First grade teachers, college professors and theologians all had a role to play in the preliminary theoretical step: the formulation of a coherent and concise set of theological, philosophical and psychological principles as guides for the ideal education of a Christian person. The pattern set at that time was the " vertical approach "—an attempt to see each specific educational problem in the context of the entire continuum of formal education. As a result of these discussions, a clear notion of our goal emerged: to construct an education program in which the principles of Thomism are deliberately and determinedly followed. The detailed development of the entire curriculum may be found in several publications.[2] This article will be limited to the application of the general principles of the Saint Xavier Plan to one facet only, the natural sciences.

The science curriculum of the Saint Xavier Plan conforms to certain basic principles that are the guiding factors for the total program. Schooling at the elementary level is restricted to the pre-liberal arts and pre-scientific studies. Natural science requires extensive experience, keen application of the arts of logic and mathematics as well as mature judgment. Grade school children have none of these. Consequently, the nature study of the elementary school must concentrate on the acquisition of factual knowledge. This preparation for science must continue until the child has a proficiency in the pre-liberal arts of communication and arithmetic and an introduction to the liberal arts, the tools for making order within the mind by means of mental relationships. Mastery of these liberal arts, properly so called, is the proper work of the secondary school. Logic taught within the framework of English, and in the study of algebra and geometry, is perhaps the most distinctive feature of our secondary program. A student graduating from high school is prepared with the habits of logic and mathematics, trained to observe carefully, and equipped with a rich natural history. He is then ready to begin science, which is considered the proper work of the college.

A science curriculum that is oriented toward wisdom and acknowledges the guiding powers of both philosophy and the-

---

[2] " The Liberal Education of the Christian Person," The Saint Xavier College Self-Study: A Progress Report (Chicago: Saint Xavier College, 1953); Sister M. Muriel, R. S. M., " The Role of Natural Science in the Saint Xavier Plan," The Catholic Educational Review, LVI (1958), 397-404; O. W. Perlmutter, " A Program for Liberal Education," Commonweal, LIX (1954), 423-426; Sister M. Olivia Barrett, R. S. M., " Challenge Accepted," Transactions of the Illinois State Academy of Science (February, 1957).

ology, will also be unique with respect to content and methodology at each point along the continuum of formal education. The content of natural science encompasses most of the experiences of man, but the content must be ordered for the sake of teaching. The subject matter for each of the teachers must be ordered to the ultimate goal of the teaching program. It is not sufficient for the college faculty alone to be concerned with the philosophical dimensions of science. To maintain a continuum, each step forward in the knowledge of science must be directed toward the final goal. A point may partake of the continuum of a straight line only if it is related to the limiting positions of the two end points. So, too, the work of the individual teacher becomes part of the entire curriculum when he is properly oriented within the whole and recognizes the unique contribution that his teaching alone can make. Consequently each teacher must realize the goal that has been set and the means at each level of moving forward toward the goal.

Methodology of Each School

At the elementary level, the course in nature study provides the child with a rich fund of facts about the physical and biological world. The approach, however, is through the beautiful, the wonderful, the awe-inspiring. This aesthetic presentation does not hinder the essential requisite of order. In fact, it fosters a closer interrelation between science and man's cultural history. Emphasis is placed on the facts of nature and not on the theories of explanation. Consequently, we readily acknowledge that the elementary curriculum does not attempt to teach " science," but brings the child to observe nature, to question its regularity and to puzzle over its drive and purposefulness. These personal experiences of the early grades are gradually augmented by reading about or repeating many of the experimental findings of modern science, but the teacher is careful to distinguish between the facts and the hypotheses suggested to explain them. Moreover, the teacher is expected to be aware of the important philosophical facts revealed by these simple contacts with reality. Elementary science teachers are not making philosophers or scientists of their students, but in teaching nature study certain elementary philosophical truths, such as the existence of order and the difference between living and non-living, will arise. In respecting these fundamental philosophical truths in their work, teachers are being good pedagogues—they are introducing their young students to the world of ideas.

Science in the secondary school has two primary objectives: to expand the general knowledge of the sensible world initiated in elementary school and to develop in context the tools of science, particularly observation and the liberal arts of logic and mathematics. In completing natural history, great emphasis on logical order provides ample opportunity of forming sharp mental relationships. Moreover, the teacher carefully employs every opportunity for deepening the student's awareness by continually seeking out the philosophical truth revealed beneath the actual facts. Numerous principles are clarified by the teacher and consistently applied throughout the course. The experiential foundations for a clear comprehension of such concepts as nature, causality and purpose are laid. This constant concern for first principles proper to the subject prepares the student for the beginnings of true science.

At the college level the student is properly prepared to begin the study of science, that is, science in the precise sense suggested at the beginning of this article. To develop this intellectual habit with its own proper principles and methodology presupposes varied experiences concerning nature, considerable skill in the liberal arts, and a certain intellectual maturity. As previously mentioned these are the obligations of the pre-college curriculum. The college teacher is expected to guide the student through dialectical argumentation and strict scientific demonstrations to an initial grasp of those fundamental certitudes that are the fruit of man's genius in seeking knowledge of the physical world. The student slowly develops a relatively clear understanding of his powers and limitations in the continued search for truth. A comprehensive investigation of the few fundamental problems that have confronted natural scientists of all ages forces the student to become more critical in his thinking, and provides for both the science major and the non-scientist a frame of reference in which to compare and evaluate systems of thought resulting from particular solutions to these problems.

THE THEORY IN PRACTICE:

Elementary Curriculum

Success in curriculum building is found in the practice. Practice involves the education of a unity, a Christian person; and therefore, the process itself must be one of unification and not division. The unity will first be found within the subject matter taught, then within its interrelation with other subjects of the curriculum, and finally within the methodology of the teacher.

The specific objectives of elementary science, as previously stated, do not necessitate an autonomous position for nature study at the primary level. The child's rich background of actual experiences with the things of nature must begin with everyday situations in which he perceives by handling, tasting, smelling, listening, looking and then reflecting. Christian Doctrine provides the integrating force for both the natural and social sciences. The child quickly comes to a realization of plants and animals. In Christian Doctrine the story of Genesis adds the important realization that a loving Father provided this order. In social studies an application of this is made to the family unit.

Then the child's comprehension of law both divine and human, as well as its necessity, is enhanced by investigating natural law as it is found in living and non-living phenomena. At the third level, the need to use these gifts of creation properly is emphasized as the student begins to see how man can control and conserve the powers of nature.

At the fourth level natural science becomes autonomous, but the content of this science is determined by the history of man considered in the classes devoted to social science and Christian

Doctrine. Early in his education the student recognizes science as a human achievement and realizes that man's cultural history strongly influences his scientific progress. Astronomy and other facets of ancient science are studied in connection with the history of Greece and the Mediterranean world. Conservation is correlated with a study of the medieval ideal, so evident in monasticism, of an intelligent and reverent use of God's natural gifts in a harmonious social life. The study of the American way of life as it developed from colonial to modern times provides ample opportunity for the student to become familiar with modern scientific methods, either by actual experiments or by vicarious means, and to become aware of its successful application in modern technology.

The elementary science teacher has the additional responsibility of providing a proper attitude and orientation. Consequently, facts must always be distinguished from hypotheses; intuitive principles that will later form the basis of science must be recognized when met; nature must not be confused with mechanics. Understanding and meanings are more important than methods, and each step in the curriculum must be ordered to the level of the ability and experience of the child, thus assuring the development of an intelligent person capable of critical thinking.

Secondary Curriculum

Does high school science have a unique function distinct from that of the corresponding college courses? Within the Saint Xavier Plan the high school accepts the responsibility of presenting and developing the liberal arts. Therefore, the science courses are committed to this general directive as it applies to the study of the world of nature. Three distinct methods are used in the teaching of science at the secondary level: (i) the observational technique providing exercises in classification, generalization and differentiation, (ii) the experimental technique employing logical principles of both dialectical and demonstrative argumentation, and (iii) the mathematical technique requiring presentation of new mathematical processes for correlation of experimental data.

The first two years of high school science complete the natural history begun in the elementary grades. By this time, however, order has become an essential characteristic of science and its teaching. The subject matter, indeed, is basically that of the conventional general science and biology courses, but it has taken on a " new look " as a result of a radical relocation of topics. The freshman course, *Man in His World*, makes use of the natural concern of teenagers with self to stress the pivotal position of man and to study all other biological and physical phenomena in terms of their relationship to man. A systematic review of man's systems begins with the skeletal system, which provides man with his unique physical position among the animals, and ends with a consideration of his intellectual powers, placing him at the peak of material creation. General science topics are correlated with each of these systems.

The general organization of the science courses in high school is determined by our specific objectives for secondary science linked with the fundamental principles of pedagogy. Learning must begin with that which is best known. Consequently, the student should begin with himself as a whole being, and then proceed to the less known, the microscopic cells of which he is composed. Many high-school biology courses begin with cell theory, and go on to the study of systems. The Saint Xavier Plan, in which logical order rather than evolutionary theory is the criterion, reverses this order. Within each system a general consideration precedes a study of the particular organs. This is in accord with the philosophical principle of good pedagogy: from general knowledge to particular.

Each step forward must be intelligible to the student. Consequently, the student under the guidance of the teacher continuously seeks causal relationships that illuminate the relevance of each factor. Thus, in addition to learning facts, the student also develops his power of analysis as he proceeds from study to study. In studying the muscular system, the student discovers how the skeletal system achieves its end; and then the digestive, circulatory, respiratory, and excretory systems are easily seen as the means of providing the energy necessary for this movement. Correlation between this study of man and general science topics invariably arouses considerable interest. Most machine types, for example, can be found in the structure of the human skeleton and its interrelation with the muscles. The study of work, energy, and machines is fascinating when one's ordinary movement becomes the example of a simple machine in operation. The digestive system provides an opportunity to consider nutrition, which in turn requires some understanding of basic chemistry. The physical and chemical properties of air and the topics of weather and climate are taught after the respiratory system. Thus the essential general science topics, with the exception of heat, power, electricity, and conservation, are incorporated into the first year course. The study of the nervous system includes a consideration of the internal senses and a brief but enlightening introduction to some elementary principles of psychology. The student ultimately realizes that man's powers are not limited to vegetative and sentient functions. This simple presentation of the theory of knowledge as the culminating subject of the first year reveals why rational man is capable of controlling himself and his surroundings.

Man's Mastery of His World, the second year course, provides a comparable investigation of other creatures. The general science topics are again presented in conjunction with relevant zoological, botanical, and ecological subjects. The aim of these in second year is to show that man can use his rational powers to know, conserve, and control his environment. The interrelation of this course with religion, English and mathematics is noteworthy. The principles of definition and the concept of demonstrative reasoning are presented in the English and mathematics courses of the second year; these elements of logic find ample application in the natural science course. Similarly the understanding of man's emotional and intellectual life, emphasized in the natural science course, is an excellent prepara-

tion for the study of virtues and moral law in the religion
course.

Up to this point in the Saint Xavier Plan, science has been
limited almost entirely to *experience*. Therefore, it is called *pre-
science*. By the beginning of the junior year, however, the
student should be ready to approach the physical world under
a new aspect, one which can be called scientific in a qualified
sense. For the most part the student is not yet able to carry
out the logical steps necessary to unlock the mysteries of
natural science because, unlike geometry wherein the demonstrative pattern is relatively simple, the physical universe presents a complexity which requires a proficiency in logical techniques. Nevertheless, he is ready to follow the footsteps of
the great discoverers of the past—to think, to search, to find
with them the fundamental concepts of natural science. This
new approach can give him an appreciation of the part that
individual human endeavor plays in the development of science.
He can recognize the place of modern science within the total
accomplishments of the human race.

In the junior year the student considers the nature and
methodology of science, coming to the realization that science
is more than a collection of statements, formulas and information found in a book, a journal or in other peoples' heads.
Facts become scientific when their regularity suggests a common cause. Scientific knowledge is achieved when we can
demonstrate, or prove a fact by means of the universal cause
of that fact.

Emphasis on the causal nature of science, beginning already
in the junior year, is perhaps characteristic of the Saint Xavier
Plan; one might almost say that it is uniquely characteristic of
it. The causal nature of scientific explanations is not generally admitted. The modern revolution in physics brought with
it transformations that went far beyond the prevalence of integral signs and *psi* functions. Many eminent scientists now
believe that scientific theory is an artistic creation, that the
goal of scientific investigation is not to discover the nature of
the real world but merely to devise some fruitful guide to

further study. They believe that scientific theories of the future will be entirely statistical, eliminating every vestige of causal determinism. This, they say, is indicated by the present status of quantum mechanics and the principle of uncertainty. Against this background of doubt and disagreement, it is essential to train young minds how to find certitude and how to distinguish it from hypothesis. From the very beginning of scientific studies, the student must recognize when the subject matter is capable of true demonstration, and when the limits of science are so close that the available evidence can give us only great probability. If the student can sense in his studies the healthy security of " knowing what he knows," there is less likelihood of his succumbing to the universal skepticism of many modern scientists.

Within the chemistry and physics courses much of the usual material is deleted or reordered. Organization and selection depend on two specific objectives of the secondary physical science courses:

1. Students must see the need and actually apply the liberal arts of mathematics and logic within the framework of physical science.

2. The important facts, basic principles and fundamental theories of physical science must be studied in a sequence that will necessarily demonstrate the interrelation of these ideas into a unified whole.

A chemistry course based on three fundamental theories of matter—atomic, kinetic molecular and electronic—provides the necessary logical order, penetration and basic interrelation so often missed in the typical descriptive course. The history of science is used throughout the physical science courses, but merely as a tool for learning and not as an ordering principle. An adaptation of the Physical Science Study Committee Course provides the student with those basic concepts of kinematics and dynamics necessary for an understanding of modern physics and a vivid realization of the power of mathematics as a tool for measurement, for generalization and for speculation.

College Curriculum

A two year sequel in natural science at the college level completes the student's general education in science, preparing him to pursue specialized scientific studies with creativity and penetration or to advance within other disciplines while possessing a clear concept of the powers and limitations of modern science. Our conviction is that the fundamentals of natural science are basic for a liberal education. Consequently, the policy at Saint Xavier College is that all students, even those following a professional education, must complete the basic two years of college science. Usually general science courses at the college level employ either the survey or the great books approach. The Saint Xavier Plan offers a third alternative by accepting as its responsibility the need to seek principles, evaluate these and apply them to the detailed problems of local motion, chemical alteration, vital activity and psychic behavior.

The freshman is asked to carry out a dialectical search for the basic principles of changeable being after a consideration of the nature of scientific knowledge reveals the need for beginning with first principles. Various options are carefully considered, and the Aristotelian insight is chosen for further analysis. The Saint Xavier approach is not to be confused with the philosophical cosmology course often required by our Catholic colleges. Rather it is structured to provide a frame of reference for comparisons with modern systems of science and it is taught within the natural science division by specialists in that field. Changeable being, nature, motion, the infinite, time, place and space are analyzed as concepts fundamental to all scientific explanations and not as metaphysical intrusions on nature. The necessity of an "unmoved Mover" within this realm of the three-dimensional world of experience provides the student with a rational conviction independent of faith, which is a powerful tool in the apologetics of everyday life.

The three succeeding courses explore the means of using the fundamental principles developed during the first semester in an analysis of modern physical science, biological science, and psychology. No facile solution of concrete, individual problems is offered the student. The detailed facts of modern science were quite unknown to Aristotle and to St. Thomas, and most of those facts have been interpreted by philosophical principles alien or actually opposed to the sound principles of perennial philosophy. These courses attempt no ready-made syntheses of modern data with Aristotelian principles. Rather they alert the student to the constant need of examining principles which underlie scientific investigations and interpretations, and which periodically produce revolutions in scientific thought.

An exhaustive survey of modern developments is not our objective; hence, only selected problems are considered within each field. In the field of physical science, the structure of the macrocosm and microcosm requires serious consideration of Newtonian and relativity physics as well as mechanistic and statistical particle theory. The nature, origin and evolution of life are biological problems providing excellent opportunities for examining the validity of Aristotelian principles, while the consideration of the " mind-body problem " in psychology readily exemplifies the importance and perennial value of Aristotelian principles in the development of psychology.

If students coming to college are sufficiently familiar with facts and techniques of natural science, the major portion of these courses can be devoted to examining the principles basic to the various theories proposed for the solution of problems. This examination of diverse principles reveals the nature of the problem proposed, the precise aspect of relevant material under consideration, the limitations of the explanation, and the influence of these principles on other disciplines. Such an examination brings out clearly wherein diverse scientific views are similar, and wherein they are fundamentally opposed.

The impact of this four semester sequence in natural science can hardly be overestimated. It inculcates an awareness of the potential within human thought, an appreciation of the powers of science beyond gadgetry and technology; and it provides a means for philosophical tenets to permeate our analysis of modern science, thus initiating the unity of philosophy and science so frequently urged by the late Pope Pius XII:

There is one basic and current question which claims your special attention. We mean the relationship between scientific experimentation and philosophy. It is a point on which numerous problems have been raised by recent discoveries and studies. Let Us say at once that, in general, the honest and profound study of scientific problems not only does not tend to contradict the certain principles of the 'perennial philosophy' but rather receives from it a light which the philosophers themselves probably did not foresee and which in any case they could not have hoped would be so lasting and intense. (Opening session of the Fourth International Thomistic Congress, September 14, 1955.)

SISTER M. OLIVIA, R. S. M.

Saint Xavier College,
Chicago, Illinois.

AMERICAN CATHOLICS AND SCIENCE

ᐁᔑ

S INCE the time of Voltaire and the French encyclopedists
there has been a constant effort to discredit religion in
general, and the Catholic Church in particular, for its
alleged antagonism to natural science. The accusation is without foundation, for religion and science have entirely different
goals and deal with different subject matters. Religion is concerned primarily with the supernatural, while the experimental
and observational sciences are interested only in the natural.

It happens that religion and science are practised by men,
often the same men. Their successes or failures in the realm
of either religion or science are sometimes falsely attributed
to religion or to science itself. In 1931 Lehman and Witty [1]
made a study of church affiliation, or the lack of it, among
American scientists who were considered " outstanding." " Outstanding " was defined as inclusion in *Who's Who* and being
starred in *American Men of Science*. They reported:

1. " Only about 25% of the outstanding scientists in America
report church affiliation in their biographical sketches in *Who's
Who*," whereas " about 50% of all individuals whose names
appear in *Who's Who* provide this information."

2. " The 25% who give information regarding church affiliation are associated in most instances with the relatively liberal
denominations," such as the Unitarians and Congregationalists.

3. "Noticeable indeed is the small frequency of Roman
Catholics among the starred names in *American Men of Science*." Among 1189 outstanding scientists, three only report
membership in the Catholic Church."

4. From this they come to the unwarranted conclusion:
" The conspicuous dearth of scientists among Catholics sug-

---

[1] Harvey C. Lehman and Paul A. Witty, "Scientific Eminence and Church
Membership," *Scientific Monthly*, XXIII (1931), 544.

gests that the tenets of that church are not consonant with scientific endeavor."

In spite of the evident *non sequitur* of the conclusion, and of the questionable method by which it was reached, the article of Lehman and Witty stimulated a great deal of soul-searching among American Catholics in the sciences. Many Catholics realized the shortcomings as much as, if not more than, the authors of the article. Indeed, some had anticipated the writers by several years, and had taken steps to improve the quantity and quality of scientific teaching and research in Catholic institutions by organizing what was called the " Catholic Round Table of Science."

The prime movers of this activity were the late Monsignor Cooper, anthropologist of the Catholic University, and Father Anselm Keefe, O. Praem., of St. Norbert College, who acted as secretary throughout most of the organization's existence. The group met annually at the meeting of the American Association for the Advancement of Science, and a small publication, *The Tabloid Scientist*, was issued. Both in the meetings and in the pages of the paper the Catholic's inadequacies in the sciences were incisively singled out, and remedies were suggested.

Unfortunately, the organization began to hold meetings apart from the AAAS and other scientific societies at which technical papers were presented. While the motive—the stimulating of research among Catholic scientists—was good, such a program was inevitably divisive. If pursued, it would wall the Catholic scientist off from his colleagues and tend to the development of a " Catholic " science. This was directly contrary to the intention of the founders of the Round Table, and met with the marked displeasure of many of the members. Attendance at the national meetings fell off to such an extent that they were discontinued. The Catholic Round Table ceased to exist as a national organization. During its life, it had improved the status of science among Catholics. It inspired many to undertake research programs. They appeared in greater numbers at meetings of scientific societies and became more active in their affairs. Best of all, perhaps, it brought a healthy discontent to Catholic scientists. Dissatisfied with the accomplishments of Catholic institutions, they demanded more men and money for science.

In spite of these demands and their partial satisfaction, Catholic institutions were still lagging. A more exhaustive survey of " The Origins of U. S. Scientists " made by Goodrich, Knapp and Boehm[2] in 1951 showed that Catholic institutions had an index of only 2.8, as compared with 17.8 for other liberal arts colleges, in the preparation of graduates who went on for the doctorate in science. Far from dissenting from these findings, many Catholic scientists added data of their own to show that Catholic schools were not " pulling their weight " in scientific endeavor. Thus, in 1953, the second year of the National Science Foundation fellowship program, the present writer[3] called attention to the fact that, of 577 fellowships awarded, only 7 (1.2%) went to students in Catholic institutions; whereas, as Father Joseph Mulligan, of Fordham University pointed out, the student population was 6% of the undergraduate population of the country. Since then achievement in the NSF program has improved, but even in 1960 only to the point of 3% of the fellowships awarded. Father Mulligan has indicated some extenuating factors for these low percentages, but even so, Catholics are still not doing as much as they should.

Catholic scientists have made some notable contributions to the advancement of science in the United States, such as the work of the Jesuit Seismological Association, but these have been fewer than our numerical strength would call for. Few Catholics, for instance, have been elected to the National Academy of Sciences and, strangest of all, fewer still, from the United States, to the Pontifical Academy of Science. No Catholic has ever been president of the AAAS and very few have held offices in the other scientific organizations.

[2] H. B. Goodrich, R. H. Knapp and George A. W. Boehm, " The Origins of U. S. Scientists," *Scientific American*, CLXXXV (1951), 15.

[3] *Catholic Science Notes*, May 14, 1953.

These facts are accepted by all who have investigated the matter, but there is no agreement as to the explanation of the phenomenon. The reason assigned by Lehman and Witty, that the "tenets of (the Catholic) Church are not consonant with scientific endeavor," is patently false. There is nothing in the teaching of the Catholic Church which prohibits or discourages its members from engaging in the pursuit of science. Indeed, the popes, especially in recent times, have encouraged Catholics by word and example to devote themselves to scientific work. While the primary purpose of the Church is to lead men to salvation, it has always been a patron of the arts and sciences. Historians are agreed that were it not for the Catholic Church civilization might well have been destroyed during the barbarian invasions of Europe.

While divinely founded for a spiritual purpose, the Church is composed of men, and she might well paraphrase Terence to point a paradox: "*Divina sum: humani nihil a me alienum puto.*" Following the example of her Divine Founder, she makes use of natural as well as supernatural means in achieving her ends. Nothing is more "consonant" with the primary purpose of the Church than to encourage the discovery of truth in the natural realm. As St. Paul wrote the Romans (1:20) "The invisible things of Him from the creation of the world are clearly seen, *being understood by the things that are made.*" The Church from the very beginning, therefore, not only demanded learning of the clergy but also promoted it among the laity, first in the schools that developed around the cathedrals, and then in the universities which are her pride and glory.

The popes, in particular, have been outstanding patrons of science. This is shown by the numerous scientific works which they have promoted, and by the founding of the famous *Accademia dei Lincei* under papal patronage. One of the oldest science academies in the world, it is now succeeded by the *Pontifical Academy of Science*, whose membership includes the world's outstanding scientists, regardless of their religious beliefs.

It should be abundantly clear that there is nothing in the

tenets of the Catholic Church not consonant with scientific endeavor. It might rather be concluded that Catholics are not following the teaching of their church when they neglect the pursuit of truth in the natural sciences, as well as in the divine. How, then, are we to explain the deficiency in scientific achievement among Catholics?

First of all, such a deficiency is not true of Catholics as such. The leaders of the scientific renaissance in the 16th and 17th centuries, such as Copernicus, Cardinal Nicholas of Cusa, and even Galileo himself, were Catholics and some of them priests, as Conant points out.[4]

Catholic missionaries, like the Italian Jesuit Ricci, introduced modern science to China and other newly discovered lands. Others, like Father Marquette and his brethren in Canada, the United States and other American countries, were doing fundamental scientific research in geography and natural history. Members of the Society of Jesus, and of other religious orders, established colleges and universities where these subjects were taught long before Harvard and Yale were founded. Even today Catholics in Europe compare favorably with their non-Catholic colleagues in scientific achievement. Why should there be so marked a difference in the United States of the present? It is suggested that this is not a religious but a social phenomenon.

Catholics in this country are not only in a minority but also labor under handicaps not found among the rest of the population. Most American Catholics are comparative newcomers to this country. The majority are only first or second generation Americans, and as such have not had time to acquire a tradition of scholarship. Most of the original immigrants came from the lower strata of European society which had had few educational opportunities. This was particularly true of the Irish who constituted the first wave of Catholic immigration to this country. Partly because of the deliberate deprivation of

[4] James B. Conant, *Science and Common Sense* (New Haven: Yale University Press, 1951), p. 78.

adequate educational facilities by their British masters, the Irish immigrants to America were largely uneducated. Even the educated Irish in the past had been more interested in the arts and humanities than in the natural sciences, and this bent carried over to their descendants in America. Since the beginnings of Catholicism in this country are due chiefly to the Irish it is not surprising that scientific achievement was not high on the list of their attainments. This was recognized by Lehman and Witty, who show that Catholics are much more in evidence in such fields as drama and politics.

Whatever may be said of national background, the children of immigrants usually received no adequate education of any kind, due to the poverty of their parents. Those who did succeed in going to college generally selected careers of prestige, such as law or medicine, rather than that of scholarship. It should also be said that many of the best minds among these first generation Americans elected to follow the Master in a priestly or religious vocation, and thus were lost to science.

Another factor which operated adversely on the development of scientists in the Catholic population was the distrust and even fear on the part of many, especially among the clergy, of science as atheistic and dangerous to faith and morals. This was due largely to the controversy aroused by the publication of Darwin's *The Origin of Species*. Since Darwin was an Englishman and not a Catholic the theory of evolution somehow came to be looked on as anti-Catholic. The truth of the matter is that long before Darwin, the Catholic Lamarck had proposed evolution to account for our present species of plants and animals. It is interesting to note that the chief opponent of evolution at that time, and probably the one who did most to put off its acceptance until after Darwin's publication, was the Protestant, Cuvier. Some of Darwin's followers, notably Huxley and Spenser in England and Häckel in Germany, made unwarranted extensions of the theory into fields of philosophy and ethics. In the words of Wheeler, " Evolution, only a scientific theory for Darwin's ' modest mind,' itself became a philosophy, to some almost a creed." [5]

As a by-product of this controversy, there arose a school of science popularizers, like H. G. Wells, who took occasion to attack religion as the enemy of science. The most infamous of these was Andrew White, whose *Warfare of Science and Theology* was popular in the last century. Many pastors intent on protecting their flocks, especially the young, against this poison warned them of the dangers to faith and morals lurking in the field of science, especially when pursued in non-Catholic institutions. The last condition was usually present, for Catholics did not have the facilities of large universities in those days. The young person of ability and scholarly bent was urged to follow a safe career. No doubt many a potential Catholic scientist was lost in this way or, sadder still, some became scientists but gave up their faith because of opposition and because of lack of guidance. When such a student brought to a priest for solution the usual difficulties against the faith presented to him by his non-Catholic colleagues, he was told in some cases either that there was no problem involved, or that he should abandon science lest he lose his soul.

Another cause of the poor showing of Catholics in scientific accomplishment, was the lack, or the low quality, of science instruction in Catholic educational institutions. The recent furor so widely discussed in the public press showed that this condition was not confined to Catholic schools, but was more or less universal. As we shall see, however, it was aggravated in their case.

The Church through the centuries has fostered the pursuit of learning, even secular learning, as an aid to her mission. With the foundation of the United States a new factor entered education. The Constitution of the new nation guaranteed freedom of teaching, but at the same time left unchecked the development of a completely secular spirit in the public schools.

[5] L. Richmond Wheeler, *Vitalism: Its History and Validity* (London: Witherby, 1939), p. 164.

The Church engaged in the operation of a full-scale educational system from kindergarten to university. This system under the aegis of the National Catholic Educational Association has become a potent force for education, as well as for the preservation and spread of the faith in this country. It has won the admiration of Catholics throughout the world. There are, however, certain disadvantages in such an education, especially with respect to the development of scientists.

In the early days when Catholics were few and mostly poor, the schools also tended to be poor. The curriculum of the primary schools was held to a minimum—mostly the four R's—and science was not even thought of. High schools were fewer still, and concerned chiefly with the humanities with little, if any, science included. When science courses were offered, they were not infrequently taught by instructors themselves untrained in science. The same inadequacies obtained in the colleges. As a matter of fact, there was no clear distinction between high school and college. The early Catholic " colleges," following the European system, embraced everything from first grade to philosophy. The last three or four years corresponded roughly with the American college, at least with the junior college. Apart from the commercial curriculum, which was a catch-all for those who lacked the ability or taste for the Arts or Science program, the education was of the classical type with very little science. The " science " curriculum was distinguished from the arts curriculum not by the amount of science taught, but by the substitution of modern languages for Greek and Latin. This in itself is an indication of the low esteem in which science was held.

The science that was taught consisted of a general course called natural philosophy, largely physics. In some cases this was taught by a man well trained and really interested in the subject, though the field was so vast that he could scarcely do it justice. Often an individual teacher would take some part of the field as a hobby, such as astronomy or seismology, and develop an observatory where serious scientific research was conducted. The ordinary student, however, did not benefit from this. Little laboratory work was given, in part because of lack of funds, in part because it was not regarded as important. Students in early American Catholic colleges were not exposed to a scientific atmosphere, and, consequently, few of them ever thought of science as a career.

With the increasing standardization in education and the coming of the accrediting associations, the Catholic educational system had to be reorganized and regular science courses introduced into high schools and colleges. The quality of the high school teaching left much to be desired, but it was not worse than in the majority of American high schools.

The colleges, although now offering distinct courses in departments of biology, chemistry and physics, were often poorly equipped and under-staffed, sometimes with second-rate teachers. The reason for the first was lack of funds, for the second, the failure to produce scientists. Some members of religious teaching orders were sent to secular universities for special studies in the sciences and many of them were outstanding students. Great hopes were held out that they would return to their own institutions and build up strong departments for the training of Catholic youth. But in most cases they were made administrators and lost to science. Those who were not immersed in administration were given so much teaching and extracurricular work that they could do no research themselves, far less interest their students in it.

As for the few Catholic lay scientists available, the salaries offered were so low that they could not make a decent living for their families. Those who made sacrifices to stay encountered the same difficulties as the religious: too much teaching, too little money for equipment, and lack of interest on the part of students.

The lack of interest is an important factor. A study of the winners of the annual Science Talent Search among high school students has shown that most of them became interested in science at about the sixth grade. This would not have occurred unless they were reared in homes in which science was held in high esteem, or unless they had been introduced to it in grammar school. A parallel exists in the case of the college student. Unless he enters college with a scientific career in mind he will rarely develop a desire for one. As we have seen, most Catholic college students in the past have had neither the home environment nor a proper education in science at the grade school and high school levels. They come to college, therefore, seeking a general education or, at most, preparation for entrance to a professional school. Most high school students are left with the impression that biology is useful only for studying dentistry, medicine or medical technology; and that chemistry and physics are but the indispensable propaedeutics of an engineering or industrial career. No one has inspired them with the zest of study in science for its own sake, of wrestling with a problem because, as in the mountain climber's justification of his sport, " It's there." More prosaically, they do not appreciate the value and necessity of basic research in the sciences.

After the second world war when we, as a nation, finally realized our weakness in science, the Government began subsidizing both the training of scientists and their research. The writer, together with Professor James A. Reyniers, then of the University of Notre Dame, was appointed by President Truman to the Board of the new National Science foundation. From this vantage-point, the response of Catholic colleges and universities to this new opportunity could be observed. The statistics already cited on graduate fellowships show that in the beginning this response was poor. Today an increasing number of institutions are qualifying for research grants, and capable scientists are coming to the fore. More and more high school and college teachers are working to improve their teaching by taking faculty fellowships, and by attending summer and other institutes in science.

American Catholics have advanced notably in the improvement of instruction in the sciences, and this at all levels of education. Why do they still lag in the production of scientists? Some have suggested the economic reason: Catholic laymen need a larger income than can be obtained by teaching in a Catholic institution. But men will gladly sacrifice financial reward for the sake of a burning intellectual interest. With few exceptions, the great scientists have not been rich; most of them were comparatively poor. Rich or poor, they were so intent on the pursuit of knowledge that they refused to be diverted from it, even by the promise of greater material gain in other fields. What sparks that burning interest? Where has Catholic education failed?

It can not be argued that the intent single-mindedness of the devoted scientist indicates a higher level of intelligence than is required in other fields. Intellectual capacity (and dedication) must lie at the foundation of eminence in any pursuit, whether the great man be doctor, lawyer or merchant chief. The touch-stone of excellence in the study of the natural sciences is an insatiable curiosity. This thirst for knowledge of the causes of things is a natural human endowment, as any one can testify who has been subjected to the relentless series of " Why's " of a young child. The child's queries are not directed to motivation alone, but, as the scholastic would put it, to the four causes of natural things. All too often this initial curiosity is stifled, put off with " It's so because I say it's so " or " That is the nature of the thing." Most deadly of all responses to the burgeoning spirit of inquiry is the chilly rebuke for having raised the question at all. Is there an inherent factor, in content or method, in Catholic education that stifles pre-scientific curiosity?

Revealed religion is based on the word of God, with mysteries not explicable by human reason. Man comes to a knowledge of the supernatural only by faith. The primary purpose of a Catholic education is to teach these truths of faith. We do employ logic, philosophy, the resources of history and archaeology to show that there is no contradiction between these truths and reason, but in the final analysis their proof rests on the authority of God and his Church. This being the case, it is easy for those untrained in the relationship of faith and reason to allow an authoritarian approach undue influence in the teaching of non-religious subjects. Such confusion of the two orders, however, is not inevitable. Certainly, it was not the case with the great scholastics, nor is it today with the serious student of traditional scholasticism.

The faith of St. Albert the Great neither impeded nor unduly influenced his interest in nature and his scientific method in the investigation of it. His scientific methodology and his knowledge of nature did not vitiate his faith but provided the basis for the science of theology. The wisdom of Albertus Magnus, " a man so superior in every science that he can fittingly be called the wonder and the miracle of our time," [6] " was readily accepted by his most gifted disciple, St. Thomas Aquinas, who made it an integral part of his entire thought." [7] St. Thomas, as a physical theorist, has been overshadowed by his reputation as a theologian, in fact, " one could say that his valuable contributions to the development of physical science have been lost in the great mass of his writing on theology and philosophy." [8] The physical theory of St. Thomas, however, does not allow an authoritarian approach, nor even a general approach satisfied with easy answers. " A science which regards things only in general is not science complete in its ultimate act. . . . Hence it is evident that science, to be complete, must not be content with general knowledge, but must proceed to a knowledge of the species." [9]

Recent studies by members of the Albertus Magnus Lyceum [10] have clearly shown that the scientific methodology of

[6] Ulrich of Strasbourg, *Summa de Bono*, IV, tr. 3, c. 9, cited by J. A. Weisheipl, O. P., *The Development of Physical Theory in the Middle Ages* (New York: Sheed & Ward, 1959), p. 27.

[7] J. A. Weisheipl, O. P., *op. cit.*, p. 29.

[8] W. A. Wallace, O. P., " St. Thomas Aquinas, Galileo, and Einstein," *The Thomist*, XXIV (1961), 1.

[9] St. Thomas, *In I Meteor.*, lect. 1, n. 1.

[10] See W. A. Wallace, O. P., *The Scientific Methodology of Theodoric of Freiberg* (Fribourg: University Press, 1959); J. A. Weisheipl, O. P., *op. cit.*, and " Albertus Magnus and the Oxford Platonists," *Proc. Am. Cath. Phil. Assoc.*, XXXII (1958), 124-139; W. H. Kane, O. P., *et al.*, *Science in Synthesis* (River Forest, 1953); B. M. Ashley, O. P., *Aristotle's Sluggish Earth: The Problematics of the De Caelo* (River Forest, 1958); J. R. Nogar, O. P., *An Analysis of Contemporary Theory of Physical Science* (River Forest, 1952); M. A. Glutz, C. P., *The Manner of Demonstrating in Natural Philosophy* (River Forest, 1956).

the scholastics has traditionally refused to be weakened by extrinsic influences. If the contemporary failure of Catholic instruction in the sciences is a result of an authoritarian approach, that approach, in turn, is the result either of ignorance of the value of the traditional methodology or the putting aside of the difficult and demanding methodology of true science to which the tradition adheres. In either case, it is not the theoretical problem of the relationship of philosophy, science and religion which, in principle, was solved long ago, but the practical problem of Catholic educators, perhaps too busy to attend to and apply the principles themselves, or perhaps too poorly trained to appreciate the solution even when offered.

The practical problem is compounded in the classroom when the young mind is confronted with the distinction between revealed truth and empirical knowledge. The former is usually taught in short catechetical form which ignores the distinction. Thus the catechism asks, " Who made you? " and answers, " God made me." This is correct, but it does not explain how this was accomplished through secondary causes. The explanation perhaps will come later but, in the meantime, the child's mind is satisfied and, unless he is given a further stimulus later to investigate the natural phenomena of creation, he may go through life with a very truncated understanding of his existence.

An aggravating factor in the stifling of interest in science has been the unsatisfactory handling of scientific matters in the press. The Catholic press in the United States has been apathetic, if not actively inimical, to science. Granted that the primary purpose of a Catholic periodical is to inform Catholics about matters of the faith, they should deal with everything that affects Catholics. Our Catholic periodicals do cover almost everything from mystical theology to comics, and the sections on sports often boast the dignity of a special editor, but one finds little on science, and that little often badly done. Most of the articles on science are " refutations " of some scientific theory, generally by writers incompetent to judge the value of the theory they are attacking. Heavy-handed humor supplies for knowledge. The most embarrassing of these outpourings are the vitriolic attacks on scientists in which the epithets " godless " and " atheistic " are cast with irresponsible abandon. Catholic scientists are embarrassed and humiliated by them, and are hard put to it to explain to their non-Catholic colleagues that such effusions represent editorial opinion, and not the official stand of the Church.

It would be most advantageous if every Catholic periodical were to have one or more competent Catholic scientists on its editorial staff, or available as consultants. Nothing on science would be published without their approval and, more positively, they would write, or commission, timely, popular articles on scientific subjects. A program such as this would make the Catholic reader more aware of the importance of science in his life, and would put in proper perspective the relations between science and religion.

The News Service of the National Catholic Welfare Conference might do well to establish a panel of scientists as consultants on whom it could call for advice on its releases concerning scientific matters. Catholics would, on the one hand, be spared the embarrassment of ill-advised attacks on science and scientists, and, on the other, accept with confidence news of science appearing in the Catholic press.

The regrettable demise of the Catholic Round Table of Science has already been mentioned. Although its dissolution had been inevitable, many of the members missed the annual exchange of views at the convention of the AAAS. Some of them had approached the present writer regarding the possibility of reviving it. The notion had little initial appeal in view of the difficulties involved. Encouragement came with the forwarding of an enquiry from Mr. Kenneth Kelleher, a research physicist then with the Naval Research Laboratory in Washington. Mr. Kelleher asked Monsignor Hochwalt, executive secretary of the National Catholic Educational Association, whether there existed an organization of Catholic scientists and suggested, if there did not, that one be formed for the purpose of discussing problems concerning religion, philosophy and science. Monsignor Hochwalt himself was much in favor of such a program and urged the writer to undertake either the revival of the Catholic Round Table, or the organization of a new group. He offered the services of the NCEA in publishing a periodical in which such questions would be discussed and news of the activities of Catholic scientists would be chronicled. The writer undertook the editorship of the new publication, *Catholic Science Notes.* This was sent several times a year to all former members of the Round Table whose mailing list was made available by its last presiding officer, the Reverend John Cortelyou, C. M., head of the Biology Department of DePaul Universty.

Also at Monsignor Hochwalt's suggestion, a meeting of Catholics attending the AAAS convention at St. Louis in 1952 was called to determine whether there was sufficient interest in forming a new organization of Catholic scientists. The response was unanimously favorable. A call was sent out for an organizational meeting at the next AAAS convention in Boston in 1953, with Boston College serving as host.

The distinguished chemist and dean of the Graduate School of Princeton University, Sir Hugh Taylor, was asked to preside. After considerable discussion it was voted to form a new organization to be called the *Albertus Magnus Guild.* The Guild's Constitution states its purposes:

   i.) to serve as a means of contact among Catholic scientists;
   ii.) to promote productive scholarship and a greater participation in scientific activities by Catholic scientists;
   iii.) to assist Catholic scientists in relating the Church's teachings to the findings of science.

Sir Hugh Taylor was elected first president of the Guild. Later His Eminence Cardinal Stritch, Archbishop of Chicago, accepted the title of Honorary President and until his untimely death gave the Guild his whole-hearted support. His successor, the Most Reverend John J. Wright, Bishop of Pittsburgh, has continued such support. The publication of *Catholic Science Notes* was assumed by the Guild under the title of *Bulletin of*

the Albertus Magnus Guild. The annual meeting of the Guild
has been held every year during Christmas Week in connection
with the AAAS convention, since this organization embraces all
the sciences. Luncheon or dinner meetings are held at the
conventions of other learned societies, such as the American
Chemical Society, American Physical Society and the American
Institute of the Biological Sciences. Since 1956 the Guild has
sponsored, at each meeting, a " Science Sunday." A Solemn
Mass is celebrated at the Cathedral to which all attending
the convention are invited, and at which a sermon is given on
the relations between science and religion. This has been very
well received, and similar programs are now sponsored by
other faiths.

Local chapters of the Guild have been organized with great
success in many cities. The smaller groups hold more frequent
meetings, and devote themselves to special projects: lectures,
the promotion of scientific careers among students in Catholic
schools, the study of the handling by textbooks of matters
relating to faith and morals.

Even before the founding of the Guild, the writer had
attended the World Congress of *Pax Romana*, the international
movement of Catholic intellectuals, at Bonn in 1953. This
organization of Catholic professors and students has as its
purpose the bringing of Catholic influence into intellectual and
social movements, such as UNESCO, throughout the world.
It is organized by both national (the United States member is
the Catholic Committee for Intellectual and Cultural Affairs)
and professional groups and meets every year in a different
country.

Impressed by the work of the organization, the writer sought
the advantages of affiliation with it for the Guild. The Guild
voted to apply for membership in 1954, and this was done at
the 1955 meeting of *Pax Romana* in Nottingham, England.
Due to the good offices of Sir Hugh Taylor, then president of
Pax Romana as well, the Guild was admitted as a Corresponding Member. In 1958 the Scientific Secretariat of *Pax
Romana* in a conference at Louvain decided to organize the

Secretariat formally on a world-wide scale, a decision put into effect at the Vienna Congress of *Pax Romana*. The Executive Secretary-Treasurer of the Guild was elected a member of the Council. Thus the Guild now has international connections and works with Catholic scientists throughout the world for a better understanding between science and religion.

The Guild has grown in stature and membership, but many Catholic scientists remain apart. Some object to it, as we have seen, on the grounds that such an organization would tend to separate Catholic scientists from their colleagues. Such divisiveness is diametrically opposed to the purposes of the Guild. In that case, then, why any Catholic professional organization? Why a guild of Catholic physicians, of Catholic attorneys? In each instance the answer is the same: Facets of these disciplines reflect philosophical and theological problems. If the lamentable mistakes of the past are to be avoided, Catholic physicians, lawyers and scientists must meet with philosophers and theologians, perhaps even in harmonious dispute. The time of the omnicompetent man of the Renaissance is past. No present-day Pico would set out calmly to write *de omni re scibili et quibusdam aliis*. The syntheses of the great scholastics, embodying the positive knowledge of their own time, retain their value, but the flood of discovery since then demands evaluation—and the guidance—of their thought. European scientists have engaged in this effort, and have considerable influence on their contemporaries. In France the *Union Française des Scientifiques Catholiques*, and in Great Britain the *Philosophy of Science Group* of the Newman Association hold regular meetings at which philosophical and theological questions raised by science are discussed. The annual Spode House Conference of the latter group is especially stimulating.

Catholic scientists in the United States tend to avoid the philosophical aspects of science, and one finds few of them in organizations like the Philosophy of Science Association, where they should be active in relating the findings of modern science to scholastic philosophy.

One notable exception to the inactivity of Catholic scientists in this regard is the *Albertus Magnus Lyceum*, at the Dominican House of Studies, River Forest, Illinois. This is the life work of Father William H. Kane, O. P., in whose honor this volume is published. Father Kane and his associates have worked tirelessly at the synthesis of philosophy and natural science. The steady output of publications shows a vitality that augurs well for the progress of science among Catholics in the United States. May he have many more years of work in his chosen field.

PATRICK H. YANCEY, S. J.

Spring Hill College
Mobile, Alabama

NOTES ON OUR CONTRIBUTORS

JAMES A. WEISHEIPL, O. P., S. T. Lr., Ph. D. (Angelicum) in natural philosophy, D. PHIL. (Oxford) in medieval history, is Professor of Medieval Philosophy in the Pontifical Faculty of Philosophy at the Dominican House of Studies, River Forest, Illinois. Formerly Lecturer in Natural Philosophy at Hawkesyard Priory, England, he is Bursar-Archivist of the Albertus Magnus Lyceum.

EDWARD D. SIMMONS, Ph. D. (Notre Dame) in philosophy, is Associate Professor of Philosophy at Marquette University, Milwaukee. A frequent contributor to THE THOMIST, he has recently published *The Scientific Art of Logic* (Bruce, 1961).

JOHN A. OESTERLE, Ph. D. (Laval), former Fulbright Research Scholar at the University of Louvain, is Associate Professor of Philosophy at the University of Notre Dame. Among his publications are *Logic: Art of Defining and Reasoning* (Prentice-Hall, 1952), and *Ethics: The Introduction to Moral Science* (Prentice-Hall, 1957).

HERBERT RATNER, M. D. (Michigan) with graduate work in bacteriology, public health and nutrition, is Associate Clinical Professor of Public Health and Preventive Medicine at the Loyola University School of Medicine, Chicago. Formerly associated with the Great Books in Biology, he is now Director of the Oak Park Department of Public Health.

RICHARD P. McKEON, Ph. D. (Columbia), formerly Dean of the Division of Humanities at the University of Chicago, member of the U. S. delegation to UNESCO, and U. S. counselor of UNESCO affairs at the American Embassy in Paris, is Distinguished Service Professor of Greek and Philosophy at the University of Chicago. On leave of absence from the university, he is at the Center for Advanced Study in the Behavioral Sciences in Stanford, California.

DANIEL A. CALLUS, O. P., S. T. M., M. A. (Oxford), D. Phil. (Oxford) in medieval history, Fellow of the Royal Historical Society, Professor Emeritus of the University of Malta, is Regent of Studies at Blackfriars, Oxford, and Lecturer in Medieval Thought at the University of Oxford. He is widely known in Europe as an authority on thirteenth century Oxford and Paris.

WILLIAM A. WALLACE, O. P., S. T. Lr., M. Sc. (Catholic Univ. of America) in physics, Ph. D. (Fribourg) in philosophy, S. T. D. (Fribourg) in moral theology, has research experience in magnetic and acoustic field theory, and in ultrasonics. Author of *The Scientific Methodology*

521

of Theodoric of Freiberg, he is Professor of Natural Philosophy and Philosophy of Science at the Dominican House of Studies, Dover, Mass.

MICHAEL A. HOSKIN, M. A., Ph. D. (Cambridge) in mathematics, former Fellow of Peterhouse, is Lecturer in the History of Science at the University of Cambridge, England, and at Leicester. He has recently become General Editor of the Newman Association History and Philosophy of Science Series (Sheed & Ward), to which he contributed *William Herschel, Pioneer of Sidereal Astronomy.*

CHARLES DE KONINCK, Ph. D. (Louvain) in philosophy, formerly Dean of the Faculty of Philosophy and editor of *Laval Théologique et Philosophique,* is Professor of Natural Philosophy and Lecturer in Theology at Laval University, Québec, Canada. Widely known for his publications in the philosophy of science, he is visiting Professor of Philosophy at the University of Notre Dame.

SHEILAH O'FLYNN BRENNAN, Ph. D. (Laval) in philosophy, former Woodrow Wilson Scholar at the University of Oxford, is Professor and Chairman of the Department of Philosophy at St. Mary's College, Notre Dame.

MELVIN GLUTZ, C. P., Ph. D. (Pont. Fac., River Forest) is Professor of Philosophy and Student Master at the Passionist Monastery in Chicago. He is author of various studies in psychology and *The Manner of Demonstration in Natural Philosophy.*

ROMAN A. KOCOUREK, M. A. (Minnesota) in history, Ph. D. (Laval) in philosophy, is Associate Professor of Philosophy at the College of St. Thomas, and lecturer at St. Paul Seminary, St. Paul, Minnesota. He is author of *An Introduction to the Philosophy of Nature* (St. Paul, 1948).

SISTER M. JOCEYLN GAREY, O. P., Ph. Lic. (Fribourg), Ph. D. (Laval) in philosophy, is Professor of Philosophy at Rosary College, River Forest, Ill.

VINCENT E. SMITH, M. A., Ph. D. (Catholic Univ.) in philosophy with additional studies at Fribourg, Harvard, M. I. T. and Institutum Divi Thomae, is editor of *The New Scholasticism.* Former President of the American Catholic Philosophical Association, and widely known for his books, he is Professor and Director of the Philosophy of Science Institute at St. John's University, Jamaica, N. Y.

RAYMOND J. NOGAR, O. P., S. T. Lr., Ph. D. (Pont. Fac., River Forest), formerly lecturer in natural philosophy at the Pontifical Athenaeum Angelicum, Rome, is Associate Professor of Philosophy and Lecturer in Theoretical Biology at the Pontifical Faculty of Philosophy, River

Forest. He is Executive Secretary of the Albertus Magnus Lyceum.

SISTER MARGARET ANN McDOWELL, O. P., M. A. (Ohio) in plant physiology, M. S. (Institutum Divi Thomae) in bacteriology, Ph. D. (Institutum Divi Thomae) in medical research, is Professor and Chairman of the Department of Biology at the College of St. Mary of the Springs, Columbus. She has written many scientific papers, and at present she is engaged in cancer research.

ALBERT S. MORACZEWSKI, O. P., S. T. Lr., Ph. D. (Chicago) in pharmacology, has been specializing in the pharmacological differences of mitochondria from selected areas of the brain, carrying out his researches in the Department of Psychiatry of Baylor University College of Medicine at the Texas Medical Center in Houston. He is now Research Specialist on the staff of the Houston State Psychiatric Institute.

MICHAEL E. STOCK, O. P., S. T. Lr., (Washington), Ph. D. (Angelicum) in psychology, whose studies frequently appear in THE THOMIST, is lecturer in psychology at the Dominican House of Studies, Dover, Massachusetts.

AMBROSE McNICHOLL, O. P., S. T. Lr., S. T. Lic. (Rome), Ph. D. Fribourg), is Professor of the History of Modern and Contemporary Philosophy at the Pontifical Athenaeum Angelicum, Rome. He also lectures on aesthetics at the Graduate School of Fine Art at Villa Schiffanoia, Florence, and has contributed many articles to philosophical journals.

BENEDICT M. ASHLEY, O. P., S. T. Lr., Ph. D. (Notre Dame) in sociology, Ph. D. (Pont. Fac., River Forest), is Professor of Philosophy in the Pontifical Faculty of Philosophy at the Dominican House of Studies, River Forest, and Dean of the Department of Philosophy at St. Xavier College, Chicago.

SISTER M. OLIVIA BARRETT, R. S. M., M. S., Ph. D. (Notre Dame) in chemistry, is Assistant Professor of Chemistry at Saint Xavier College, Chicago. She has given much attention to the science program in the Saint Xavier plan.

PATRICK H. YANCEY, S. J., M. A. (Gonzaga), Ph. D. (St. Louis) in biology, is Professor and Chairman of the Department of Biology at Spring Hill College, Mobile. Formerly Member of the National Science Foundation, he is on the editorial committee (for science) of the *New Catholic Encyclopedia*, and Executive Secretary-Treasurer of the Albertus Magnus Guild, which he founded.

THE WRITINGS OF FR. W. H. KANE, O. P.
(1929-1960)

1929

" The Cause of Blessed Albert the Great," *The Torch*, XIV (Nov. 1929), 20-23; (Dec. 1929), 10-11.

1935

" Hylemorphism and the Recent Views of the Constitution of Matter," *Proceedings Am. Cath. Phil. Assoc.*, XI (1935), 61-74.

1939

" Introduction to Philosophy," *The Thomist*, I (1939), 193-212.

1944

" The Nature and Extent of Philosophy of Nature," *The Thomist*, VII (1944), 204-232.

1945

" The First Principles of Changeable Being," *The Thomist*, VIII (1945), 27-67.

1948

" The Nature of Sacred Doctrine," in Benziger Bros. edition of St. Thomas Aquinas, *Summa Theologica* (New York, 1948), vol. III, pp. 3085-93.

1949

" Ideals of Religious Life," *Cross and Crown*, I (1949), 421-447.

1952

" Unification of the Natural Sciences," *Main Currents in Modern Thought*, IX (1952), 115-117.

Comments on Fr. Leo A. Foley's " The Interplay of Art and Nature in Physical Theory," *Proceedings Am. Cath. Phil. Assoc.*, XXVI (1952), 140-146.

1953

Science in Synthesis. A Dialectical Approach to the Integration of the Physical and Natural Sciences. With J. D. Corcoran, B. M. Ashley and R. J. Nogar (River Forest: Dominican College of St. Thomas, 1953), 289 pp.

Review of Jacques Maritain's *Philosophy of Nature, The Thomist,* XVI (1953), 127-131.

Review of Werner Heisenberg's *Philosophic Problems of Natural Science, The Thomist,* XVI (1953), 425-8.

Comments on Jude R. Nogar's " Nature, Deterministic or Indeterministic? " *Proceedings Am. Cath. Phil. Assoc.,* XXVII (1953), 104-9.

1954

" Abstraction and the Distinction of the Sciences," *The Thomist,* XVII (1954), 43-68.

Comments on Fr. James A. McWilliam's " The Finality of Prime Matter," *Proceedings Am. Cath. Phil. Assoc.,* XXVIII (1954), 170-75.

" St. Albert's Portrait of Mary," *Cross and Crown,* VI (1954), 293-306.

1955

" The Subject of Metaphysics," *The Thomist,* XVIII (1955), 503-521.

" Religious Obedience," *Cross and Crown,* VII (1955), 39-59.

1956

" The Naturalistic Approach to Natural Science," *The Thomist,* XIX (1959), 219-231.

" Outline of a Thomistic Critique of Knowledge," *The New Scholasticism,* XXX (1956), 181-197.

" Philosophy and Science," *Bulletin of the Albertus Magnus Guild,* 3 Dec. 1956.

Review of Fr. Henry J. Koren's *Introduction to the Philosophy of Animate Nature, Cross and Crown,* VIII (1956), 117-8.

1957

" The Extent of Natural Philosophy," *The New Scholasticism,* XXXI (1957), 85-97.

" Introduction to Metaphysics," *The Thomist,* XX (1957), 121-142.

Review of S. Sambursky's *Physical World of the Greeks* and M. D. Philippe's *Initiation à la Philosophie d'Aristote, The Thomist,* XX (1957), 370-74.

1958

" La Causa Finale nella Scienza: Il Methodo Scientifico nella Biologia secondo Alberto Magno," *Sapienza,* II (1958), 376-389.

" Aristotle's Proof of the Unmoved Mover," *Fundamental Science* (Chicago: St. Xavier College, 1958).

" The Assumption," *Ave Maria,* Aug. 2, 1958.

1959

" The Virtue of Obedience," *Proceedings of the XII Annual Convention, The Catholic Theological Society of America,* (1959), 142-3.

Review of Fr. Herman Reith's *The Metaphysics of St. Thomas Aquinas, The New Scholasticism,* XXXIII (1959), 252-4.

Review of Fr. Louis Rasolo's *Le Dilemme du Concours Divin, The Thomist,* XXII (1959), 556-62.

1960

" Reasons for the Facts of Organic Life," *Philosophy of Science,* I (Jamaica: St. John's University, 1960), pp. 51-67.

" Evolution and Modern Man," *Science,* CXXXI (1960), 1820-21.

" Science and Philosophy," *Bulletin of the Albertus Magnus Guild,* VIII (1960), 3-5.

Review of Arthur Koestler's *The Sleepwalkers, The New Scholasticism,* XXXIV (1960), 380-82.

" May, the Month of Joseph and Mary," *Triune,* VII (1960), 14-15.

THE DIGNITY OF SCIENCE

edited by
James A. Weisheipl, O.P.

Scientific ideas, like diamonds, must be cut to precision and polished to perfection. This is not an easy task, and it requires the efforts of many thinkers. It requires the data and theories discovered by specialists in the various branches of science; it also requires the serious efforts of philosophers and scholars familiar with that data.

The Dignity of Science is a major contribution to the cooperative effort of scientists, educators, philosophers, and historians of science. The importance of this volume lies not only in the eminence of its contributors, but also in the unity of perspective. This unity stems from the conviction that the perennial philosophy of nature, formed by Aristotle and developed by Albertus Magnus and Thomas Aquinas, can give modern scientific thought a sound basis consistent with the dignity of man.

Divided into five parts — *Scientific Methodology, History of Science, Philosophy of Science, Special Problems in*

(continued on back flap)